C000172075

Late Cenozoic Environments and Hominid Evolution: a tribute to Bill Bishop

Late Cenozoic Environments and Hominid Evolution: a tribute to Bill Bishop

EDITED BY

PETER ANDREWS
Department of Palaeontology
Natural History Museum
Cromwell Road
London
SW7 5BD

AND

PETER BANHAM
Department of Geology
Royal Holloway
University of London
Egham
Surrey
TW20 0EX

1999

Published by

The Geological Society

London

THE GEOLOGICAL SOCIETY

The Society of London was founded in 1807 and is the oldest geological society in the world. It received its Royal Charter in 1825 for the purpose of 'investigating the mineral structure of the Earth' and is now Britain's national society for geology.

Both a learned society and a professional body, the Geological Society is recognized by the Department of Trade and Industry (DTI) as the chartering authority for geoscience, able to award Chartered Geologist status upon appropriately qualified Fellows. The Society has a membership of 8600, of whom about 1500 live outside the UK.

Fellowship of the Society is open to persons holding a recognized honours degree in geology or a cognate subject and who have at least two years' relevant postgraduate experience, or not less than six years' relevant experience in geology or a cognate subject. A Fellow with a minimum of five years' relevant postgraduate experience in the practice of geology may apply for chartered status. Successful applicants are entitled to use the designatory postnominal CGeol (Chartered Geologist). Fellows of the Society may use the letters FGS. Other grades of membership are available to members not yet qualifying for Fellowship.

The Society has its own Publishing House based in Bath, UK. It produces the Society's international journals, books and maps, and is the European distributor for publications of the American Association of Petroleum Geologists (AAPG), the Society for Sedimentary Geology (SEPM) and the Geological Society of America (GSA). Members of the Society can buy books at considerable discounts. The Publishing House has an online bookshop (*http://bookshop.geolsoc.org.uk*).

Further information on Society membership may be obtained from the Membership Services Manager, The Geological Society, Burlington House, Piccadilly, London W1V 0JU (Email: *enquiries@geolsoc.org.uk*; tel: +44 (0)171 434 9944).

The Society's Web Site can be found at *http:/www.geolsoc.org.uk/*. The Society is a Registered Charity, number 210161.

Published by The Geological Society from:
The Geological Society Publishing House
Unit 7, Brassmill Enterprise Centre
Brassmill Lane
Bath BA1 3JN
UK

(*Orders*: Tel. +44 (0)1225 445046
        Fax +44 (0)1225 442836)
Online bookshop: *http://bookshop.geolsoc.org.uk*

First published 1999

British Library Cataloguing in Publication Data
A catalogue record for this book is available from the British Library.

ISBN 1-86239-036-3

Typeset by Aarontype Ltd, Bristol, UK

Printed by Cambridge University Press, Cambridge, UK

Distributors
USA
  AAPG Bookstore
  PO Box 979
  Tulsa
  OK 74101-0979
  USA
Orders: Tel. +1 918 584-2555
        Fax +1 918 560-2652
        Email bookstore@aapg.org

Australia
  Australian Mineral Foundation Bookshop
  63 Conyngham Street
  Glenside
  South Australia 5065
  Australia
Orders: Tel. +61 88 379-0444
        Fax +61 88 379-4634
        Email bookshop@amf.com.au

India
  Affiliated East-West Press PVT Ltd
  G-1/16 Ansari Road, Daryaganj,
  New Delhi 110 002
  India
Orders: Tel. +91 11 327-9113
        Fax +91 11 326-0538

Japan
  Kanda Book Trading Co.
  Cityhouse Tama 204
  Tsurumaki 1-3-10
  Tama-shi
  Tokyo 206-0034
  Japan
Orders: Tel. +81 (0)423 57-7650
        Fax +81 (0)423 57-7651

Contents

Editors' Preface

The influence of Bill Bishop is reflected throughout this volume, even although his sudden death stopped a brilliant research career in full flow. Most of the authors are connected with Bill as research collaborators and students, or as the next generation of students of these supervisors, and much of the research reported here has been aided by grants from the fund that bears Bill's name.

This book arose naturally from a most successful commemorative research symposium entitled 'Recognizing Responses to Environmental Change' which, in November 1997, marked the 20th anniversary of Bill's death at the age of only 45. Most fittingly, the symposium was held in the Burlington House apartments of the Geological Society of London which Bill served so notably, first as Editor and then as General Secretary. The volume begins with an appreciation of Bill's life and work; the research contributions that then follow are arranged in three thematic sections, each with a scene-setting editorial introduction. The scope of the book gives some idea of the breadth and depth of Bill's influence, ranging as it does from the Pleistocene stratigraphy and geomorphology of England and Scotland to hominid evolution and adaptive radiation in the Neogene of Kenya and Uganda.

The editors wish to express their thanks to all those who have made this volume possible: to the authors and referees who hammered out the basic text; to the officers and staff of the Geological Society and of the 'Geoscientist' for their support and encouragement; to the Quaternary Research Association for generously subsidizing research student contributions to the symposium; to Professor Martin Menzies (Department of Geology, Royal Holloway, University of London, the successor to Bill Bishop's old department at Bedford College) and to Professor Jim Rose (Department of Geography, RHUL) for generous contributions towards editorial expenses; to the Production Editor, Angharad Hills and her colleagues at the Geological Society Publishing House for their understanding of the nature of the research process; to their fellow Bill Bishop Fund trustees – Professor Michael Day (Chairman, both of the Trust and of the Editorial Panel), the late and greatly missed Professor Bob Savage, Dr Meave Leakey, Dr David Keen and Mrs Sheila Bishop (Secretary) for their thoughts and guidance throughout.

Above all, our thanks are due to Sheila Bishop who made the first approaches to the Geological Society and who has since been actively involved in every aspect of the research symposium and of this volume. The editors are particularly grateful that Sheila recently undertook to sub-edit the entire text and, in that sense, this book is also a tribute to her.

This commemorative volume, then, is the outcome of the collaboration of those who wished to express their continuing high regard for the life and work of Bill Bishop.

P. Andrews
P. Banham

List of Contributors

Dr Peter Andrews
Department of Palaeontology
Natural History Museum
Cromwell Road
LONDON, SW7 5BD

Dr David Anderson
School of Geography
University of Oxford
Mansfield Road
OXFORD, OX1 3TB

Dr Peter Banham
Department of Geology
Royal Holloway
University of London
EGHAM
Surrey, TW20 OEX

Dr Laura C. Bishop
Department of Human Anatomy and Cell
    Biology
New Medical School
University of Liverpool
Ashton Street Building
LIVERPOOL, L69 3GE

Dr Julie L. Cormack
Department of Anthropology
University of California
BERKELEY,
CA 94720-3710
USA

Professor Michael Day
Department of Palaeontology
Natural History Museum
Cromwell Road
LONDON, SW7 5BD

Professor Alistair Dawson
Centre for Quaternary Science
Department of Geography
Coventry University
Priory Street
COVENTRY, CV1 5FB

Dr John Ego
National Oil Corporation of Kenya
P.O. Box 58567
NAIROBI
Kenya

Dr Christopher Gleed-Owen
Department of Geography (NES)
Coventry University
Priory Street
COVENTRY
CV1 5FB

Dr Dominique Gommery
Muséum National d Histoire Naturelle
Laboratoire de Paléontologie – URA 12 CNRS
8 rue Buffon
F-75005 PARIS
France

Dr John Gowlett
Department of Archaeology
The Hartley Building
University of Liverpool
P.O. Box 147
LIVERPOOL
L69 3BX

Dr Jane Hart
Department of Geography
University of Southampton
SOUTHAMPTON
SO17 1BJ

Professor Andrew Hill
Department of Anthropology
Yale University
Box 208277
NEW HAVEN
CT 06520-8277
USA

Dr David Keen
School of Environmental Sciences
Coventry University
Priory Street
COVENTRY
CV1 5FB

Dr John D. Kingston
Departments of Anthropology & Geology and
Geophysics
Yale University
P.O. Box 208277
NEW HAVEN
CT 06520-8277
USA

Dr Darrel Maddy
Department of Geography
Daysh Building
University of Newcastle
NEWCASTLE UPON TYNE
NE1 7RU

Dr Sally McBrearty
Department of Anthropology
U-176
University of Connecticut
STORRS
CT 06269
USA

Dr Joe McCall
Honorary Fellow, Liverpool University
44 Robert Franklin Way
SOUTH CERNEY
Glos. GL7 5UD

Dr Laura MacLatchy
Department of Anthropology
Boston University
BOSTON
MA 02215
USA

Dr Tim Mighall
Centre for Quaternary Science
Department of Geography
Coventry University
Priory Street
COVENTRY, CV1 5FB

Dr R. Bernhart Owen
Department of Geography
Hong Baptist University
KOWLOON TONG
Hong Kong
China

Dr Anthony Pearson
School of Geography
University of Oxford
Mansfield Road
OXFORD, OX1 3TB

Dr Martin Pickford
Muséum National d Histoire Naturelle
Laboratoire de Paléontologie – URA 12 CNRS
8 rue Buffon
F-75005 PARIS
France

Professor David Pilbeam
Department of Anthropology
Harvard University
CAMBRIDGE
MA 02138
USA

Dr Robin W. Renaut
Department of Geological Sciences
University of Saskatchewan
SASKATOON SK
S7N 5E2
Canada

Professor David Smith
Centre for Quaternary Science
Department of Geography
Coventry University
Priory Street
COVENTRY, CV1 5FB

Dr Brigitte Senut
Muséum National d Histoire Naturelle
Laboratoire de Paléontologie – URA 12 CNRS
8 rue Buffon
F-75005 PARIS
France

Dr Stephen Stokes
School of Geography
University of Oxford
Mansfield Road
OXFORD
OX1 3TB

Dr Jean-Jacques Tiercelin
UMR 6538 "Domaines Océaniques"
Institut Universitaire Européen de la Mer
Place Nicolas Copernic
29280 PLOUZANE
France

Dr Caroline Le Turdu
Research and Development Department
Elf Petroleum Norge
P.O. Box 168
Dusavik
4001 STAVANGER
Norway

Dr Richard Washington
School of Geography
University of Oxford
Mansfield Road
OXFORD, OX1 3TB

Dr James Wells
English Heritage
Ancient Monuments Laboratory
23 Savile Row
LONDON, W1X 1AB

Professor Bernard Wood
Department of Anthropology
George Washington University
2110 G St NW
WASHINGTON DC 20052
USA

Bill Bishop: a retrospective appreciation and bibliography

M. H. DAY & P. H. BANHAM

Walter William Bishop, always known as Bill, was a warm-hearted, open man who was an enthusiast for everything he touched, a man of tremendous drive and energy which was coupled with a sense of humour and underpinned by a serious academic mind. In the field he was a great companion, observant, patient and painstaking in his work, but genial and amusing on long drives through the bush or on the way back to camp, even-tempered when the Land Rover had to be dug out yet again! Bill Bishop was one of the outstanding geologists of his generation and one of the nicest men we have ever known; all who knew him still feel his loss and geology was deprived of one of its leading exponents.

Soon after his death, a group of his colleagues determined to keep his memory green in a way that we were sure he would have approved of. We collected together a small, but significant, fund that has the express purpose of helping post-graduate students complete their fieldwork – an area of funding that is often neglected by grant-giving bodies. Over the past 20 years we have given £10 268 divided between 58 students, a number of whom attended and contributed to this Symposium. We are proud of that record and are determined to continue the work.

For those who were not privileged to know Bill, we would like to give you a brief summary of his distinguished career and a bibliography of his published works. His first degree was an honours degree in Geography from Birmingham University, followed by a Certificate in Education, his intention being to teach. During his time as an undergraduate he gained the respect of his contemporaries and was elected President of the University of Birmingham Guild of Undergraduates. He was later made an Honorary Life Member of that Guild, an early recognition of his leadership qualities and his personality. He first became interested in Quaternary matters through his tutor Dr Gordon Warwick and, after spending a year training as a teacher, he joined Professor Fred Shotton in the Department of Geology at Birmingham, supported by bursaries from the William Piddock Foundation and the Charles Henry Foyle Trust. He was awarded his PhD in 1956 and his, now standard, work on the relationships between the Quaternary sequences and landforms of the South Midlands and the Thames Basin was read to the Royal Society by Professor Shotton and published in its *Philosophical Transactions* in 1958.

After the successful presentation of his PhD, he spent two three-year periods in East Africa. The first (1956–1959) was with the Geological Survey of Uganda and the second (1962–1965) as Curator of the National Museum of Uganda in Kampala. During these years Bill made many significant contributions to the study of the Cainozoic deposits and landforms of the East African Rift Valley. He refused to accept the orthodox generalizations of 'climate stratigraphy' and made important correlations between local successions established only after detailed mapping. During this period he often spoke of the benefit of fieldwork and of discussions with Professor Richard Flint during his tour of East Africa in 1957. Also while in Africa, Bill was inspired by Dr Louis and Dr Mary Leakey and the exciting work that was going on at Olduvai Gorge, Tanzania, including the discovery of the robust australopithecine, known at first as *Zinjanthropus*, and the smaller hominids later known as *Homo habilis*. Subsequently, he became interested in this field, concentrating on hominid ecology, palaeoenvironments, stratigraphy, taphonomy and dating as well as mammalian faunas, hominid evolution and palaeolithic technology. At the time of his death he was collaborating with Dr Richard Leakey and others in an international team working on the hominid-bearing Plio-Pleistocene deposits near Lake Turkana, north Kenya. Also, in an effort to close the gap in the more recent record, Bill, together with Dr Martin Pickford, was engaged in further international teamwork on younger deposits in Pakistan.

Between his spells in East Africa, he spent a few years (1959–1962) at the Hunterian Museum in Glasgow and became involved once more in attempting to solve the problems of the Late Glacial in this region, assisted at times in the field by members of the Lockerbie extra-mural class that he taught with great enthusiasm. He never lost his interest or authority in the British Quaternary despite his enormous commitment to the Plio-Pleistocene of East Africa. On his return to Britain Professor Basil King appointed

DAY, M. H. & BANHAM, P. H. 1999. Bill Bishop: a retrospective appreciation and bibliography. *In*: ANDREWS, P. & BANHAM, P. (eds) *Late Cenozoic Environments and Hominid Evolution: a tribute to Bill Bishop*. Geological Society, London, 1–4.

him a Lecturer in the Geology Department at Bedford College, University of London, where he continued to bring his experience as a stratigrapher to the British Pleistocene succession. With one of us (PB) and Professor Shotton, Bill contributed to an attempt to present a unified account of the Quaternary stratigraphy of Midland England, and later collaboration with Dr Russell Coope led to an original and penetrating account of Late Glacial and Postglacial environments in southwest Scotland. A book entitled *British Quaternary Studies* published after his death was dedicated to his memory.

Naturally in such a distinguished career honours and invitations abounded. He was the Bennett Lecturer, University of Leicester 1966, Silliman Lecturer, Yale University 1969, University Lecturer, Trinity College Dublin 1973, and invited lecturer at the Universities of Chicago, Iowa State, Boulder and the University of California, Berkeley. He was also Guest Lecturer at New York University during a National Science Foundation Conference on 'African Plio-Pleistocene Hominidae'. His most prestigious award, however, was the Prestwich Gold Medal of the Geological Society of London in 1976. After promotion to the position of Reader in the University of London in 1970, he was appointed to the Chair of Geology at Queen Mary College, London, in 1974, a position he held with distinction until his death in 1977. He had, however, been appointed as Director of the Peabody Museum and Professor of Geology at Yale University, confirmation of his international stature as a scholar. Sadly he never took up this latest appointment.

The contribution of Bill Bishop to life was not confined to academic matters, important though they are to us all. A lover of light opera, he had a pleasing voice and founded the Bedford College Light Opera Group; indeed he is the only Professor we know who concluded his Inaugural Lecture with a vocal rendition, in the style of Offenbach, on the subject of hominid evolution, to tremendous acclaim! With the death of Bill Bishop, the Earth Sciences lost a major player who would clearly have gone on to even greater things and who would have continued to stimulate and encourage all those with whom he taught. He would surely have made many more discoveries for our enlightenment. We all lost a good friend and colleague.

His two sons have both followed in his research footsteps, albeit in different disciplines, one a molecular biologist in East Africa, the other a biologist at his own alma mater, the University of Birmingham and shortly to take up a lectureship at the University of Wales, Bangor.

Tributes to Bill Bishop at the time of his death included the following:

'I have very pleasant memories of that first season at Kilombe, and would like to go back and do further work eventually. It was Bill's efforts and energies which started off the Kilombe project...we shall not forget what we owe to Bill, nor that the discovery and recognition of the Chesowanja sites was his work.'

'...you can rest assured that Bill was not only respected as a geologist, but loved and respected as a person in his own right. Geologists in particular often seem to forget that the latter is perhaps the more important.'

'I find it hard to accept that he is no longer with us. I was on the verge of writing to Bill to ask him about the possibility of working with him upon completion of my PhD.... From the time I first met him in 1963 Bill was always, to me, a kind and genuine friend and colleague. I shared many a happy field trip with him, at Baringo, at East Rudolf, at Olduvai, Olorgesailie, Magadi, Natron and of course at Laetolil where we all spent those cheery days together...I shall treasure this letter which was written in Bill's usual zest for life style. It is this zest and complete enjoyment that he not only obtained from but also contributed to life, that I shall remember Bill. There are few people that I associate wholly with East Africa and with all it meant to me. Bill is one of those few...Bill was not just another colleague, just another friend, just another human being. He was a key figure in the whole East African geological and palaeontological world.'

'Bill was in every way a great guy who lived every moment of his life to the full, and I hope that we his friends will remember him in that way.'

'Bill had contributed so much to the academic and social life of the university, and to geology as a science, it is tragic that his life should be cut short at a time when he still had so much to offer...I shall always have pleasant memories of Bill, who will surely be remembered with affection by hundreds of students'.

'He was such a kind-hearted, cheerful colleague and friend to us both in Africa and London, and we will miss him very much'.

'I cannot believe that someone so full of energy and yet so relaxed is dead. But he had a marvellous life he was so happy with you and the boys and he accomplished so much more than most people do'.

'People like D...will miss Bill sorely as a valued professional colleague, one of the top in his field. But we shall both miss a kindly and amusing friend as will the many other people who knew him well and who have enjoyed his company so often at different times and in a variety of places'.

The Bibliography of W.W. Bishop

BISHOP, W. W. 1958. The Pleistocene geology and geomorphology of three gaps in the Midland Jurassic escarpment. *Philosophical Transactions Royal Society of London*, **241B**(682), 225–306.
——1958. Miocene mammalia from the Napak Volcanics, Karamoja, Uganda. *Nature London*, **182**, 1480–1482.
——1958. Fossil apes and ivory. *The Bulletin of the Uganda Society*, 127–129.
——1958. Raised swamps of Lake Victoria. *Records of the Geological Survey of Uganda 1955–56*, 1–10.
——1959. Kafu stratigraphy and Kafuan artifacts. *South African Journal of Science*, **55**(5), 117–121.
——1960. *A review of the Pleistocene stratigraphy of the Uganda Protectorate*. Joint Meeting of the Regional Committees for Geology (Leopoldville 1958) CCTA, 91–105.
—— & POSNANSKY, M. 1960. Pleistocene environments and early Man in Uganda. *The Uganda Journal*, **24**, 44–61.
——1962. Pleistocene correlation in the Uganda section of the Albert-Edward rift valley. *Proceedings 4th Pan African Congress on Prehistory (Leopoldville 1959)*, 245–253.
——1962. A summary of the present position regarding Quaternary stratigraphical research in Uganda. *Proceedings 4th Pan African Congress on Prehistory (Leopoldville 1959)*, 209–217.
——1962. The mammalian fauna and geomorphological relations of the Napak volcanics, Karamoja. *Records of the Geological Survey of Uganda 1957–58*, 1–18.
——1962. Pleistocene chronology in East Africa. *Advancement of Science*, **18**, 75, 491–494.
—— & WHYTE, F. 1962. Tertiary mammalian faunas and sediments in Karamoja and Kavirondo, East Africa. *Nature London*, **196**(4861), 1283–1287.
——1963. Gully erosion in the Queen Elizabeth National Park. *Uganda Journal*, **26**(2), 161–165.
ALLBROOK, D. & BISHOP, W. W. 1963. New fossil hominoid material from Uganda. *Nature London*, **197**(4873), 1187–1190.
BISHOP, W. W. 1963. The later Tertiary and Pleistocene in Eastern Equatorial Africa. *In*: HOWELL, F. C. & BOURLIERE, F. (eds) *African Ecology and Human Evolution*. Aldine, Chicago, 246–275.

——1963. Uganda's animal ancestors. *Uganda Wildlife and Sport*, **3**(3), 1–7.
TRICKER, B. J. K., TAYLOR, W. H. & BISHOP, W. W. 1963. Fossils from Karamoja. *Uganda Journal*, **27**(1), 109–114.
BISHOP, W. W. 1963. Late-Glacial deposits near Lockerbie, Dumfriesshire. *Dumfriesshire and Galloway Natural History and Antiquarian Society Transactions*, **XL**, 117–132.
——1964. More fossil primates and other Miocene mammals from North-East Uganda. *Nature London*, **203**(4952) 1327–1331.
——1965. Quaternary geology and geomorphology in the Albertine Rift Valley, Uganda. *In*: WRIGHT, H. E. & FREY, D. G. (eds) *International Studies of the Quaternary*. Geological Society of America, Special Paper, **84**, 293–321.
——1966. The prelude to early toolmakers in Uganda. *In*: POSNANSKY, M. (ed.) *Prelude to East African History*. Oxford University, London, 186.
——1966. Stratigraphical geomorphology. *In*: DURY, G. H. (ed.) *Essays in Geomorphology*. Heinemann, London, 139–176.
—— & TRENDALL, A. F. 1967. Erosion-surfaces, tectonics and volcanic activity in Uganda. *Geological Society of London Quarterly Journal*, **122**, 385–420.
——1967. The Later Tertiary in East Africa Volcanica, sediments and faunal inventory. *In*: BISHOP, W. W. & CLARK, J. D. (eds) *Background to Evolution in Africa*. Chicago University, 31–56.
——1967. Annotated lexicon of Quaternary stratigraphical nomenclature in East Africa. *In*: BISHOP, W. W. & CLARK, J. D. (eds) *Background to Evolution in Africa*. Chicago University, 375–395.
——1967. Earlier, Middle and Later Pleistocene faunal distribution. *In*: CLARK, J. D. (ed.) *Atlas of African Prehistory*. Chicago University, 11–13, 22–28 plus 3 maps.
——1967. The Lake Albert Basin – An account of the Uganda Museum Baker Centenary expedition. *Geographical Journal*, **133**(4), 469–480.
——1968. The evolution of fossil environments in East Africa. Sixth Bennett Lecture of the University of Leicester (1966). *Transactions Leicester Literary and Philosophical Society*, **62**, 2–44.
——1968. Means of correlation of Quaternary successions in East Africa. *In*: MORRISON, R. B. & WRIGHT, H. E. (eds) *Proceedings VII INQUA Congress*, Vol. 8. University of Utah, 161–172.
——, MILLER, J. A. & FITCH, J. A. 1969. New potassium-argon age determination relevant to the Miocene fossil mammal sequence in East Africa. *American Journal of Science*, **267**, 669–699.
——1969. *Pleistocene Stratigraphy in Uganda*. Geological Survey of Uganda, Memoir **10**.
—— & CHAPMAN, G. R. Early Pliocene sediments and fossils from the Northern Kenya Rift Valley. *Nature London*, **226**, 914–918.
—— & DICKSON, J. H. 1970 Radiocarbon dates related to the Scottish Late-Glacial Sea in the Firth of Clyde. *Nature London*, **227**, 480–482.

——1971. Late Cenozoic history of East Africa in relation to hominoid evolution. *In*: TUREKIAN, K. K. (ed.) *The Late Cenozoic Glacial Ages.* Yale University, 493–527.

——, CHAPMAN, G. R., HILL, A. & MILLER, J. A. 1971. Succession of Cainozoic vertebrate assemblages from the Northern Kenya Rift Valley. *Nature London*, **233**, 389–394.

——1972. Stratigraphic succession 'versus' calibration in East Africa. *In*: BISHOP, W. W. & MILLER, J. A. (eds) *Calibration of Hominoid Evolution.* Scottish Academic, 219–246.

——1972. Post-conference commentary. *In*: BISHOP, W. W. & MILLER, J. A. *Calibration of Hominoid Evolution.* Scottish Academic, 455–477.

——1973. The tempo of human evolution. *Nature London*, **244**, 405–409.

——1973. Stratigraphical nomenclature in the Baringo area of the northern Kenya Rift Valley. *Proceedings of the Pan African Congress on Prehistory Dakar 1967*, 332–333.

WOLFF, R. G., SINGER, R. & BISHOP, W. W. 1975. Fossil Bear (*Agriotherium* Wagner 1837) from Langebaanweg, Cape Province, South Africa. *Quaternaria*, **XVII,** Roma 1973.

BISHOP, W. W. & PICKFORD, M. H. L. 1975. Geology, fauna and palaeoenvironments of the Ngorora Formation, Kenya Rift Valley. *Nature London*, **254**(2497), 185–192.

——, —— & HILL, A. 1975. New evidence regarding the Quaternary geology, archaeology and hominids of Chesowanja, Kenya. *Nature London*, **258**(5532), 204–208.

——1976. Pliocene problems relating to human evolution. *In*: ISAAC, G. & McCOWN, E. R. (eds) *Perspectives on Human Evolution, III.*, L. S. B. Leakey Memorial Volume, Staples, California.

——1976. Thoughts on the workshop – Stratigraphy, palaeoecology and evolution in the Lake Rudolf Basin'. *In*: COPPENS, Y., HOWELL, F. C., ISAAC, G. L. & LEAKEY, R. E. F. (eds) *Earliest Man and Environments in the Lake Rudolf Basin: stratigraphy, palaeo-ecology and evolution.* University of Chicago, 585–589.

——1976. Geochronological framework for the African Plio-Pleistocene Hominidae: As Cerberus sees it. *In*: JOLLY, C. (ed.) *African Hominidae of the Plio-Pleistocene: evidence, problems and strategies.* Butterworths, London.

——1976. Comparison of Australopithecine-bearing deposits in eastern and southern Africa a new look at a sixteen year old problem. *Proceedings South African Society for Quaternary Research 1975. Annals of South African Museum*, **71**, 225–237.

—— & COOPE, G. R. 1977. Stratigraphical and faunal evidence for Lateglacial and Flandrian environments in south-west Scotland. *In*: GRAY, J. M. & LOWE, J. J. (eds) *Studies in the Scottish Late-glacial Environments.* Pergamon, London, 61–88.

SHOTTON, F. W., BANHAM, P. H., & BISHOP, W. W. 1977. Glacial–interglacial stratigraphy of the Quaternary in Midland and eastern England. *In*: SHOTTON, F. W. (ed.) *British Quaternary Studies Recent Advances.* Oxford University, 267–286.

BISHOP, W. W. 1978. Geological framework of the Kilombe Acheulian archaeological site, Kenya. *In*: BISHOP, W. W. (ed.) *Geological Background to Fossil Man.* Scottish Academic, Edinburgh, 329–336.

——, HILL, A. & PICKFORD, M. 1978. Chesowanja: A revised geological interpretation. *In*: BISHOP, W. W. (ed.) *Geological Background to Fossil Man.* Scottish Academic, Edinburgh, 309–327.

Editor of:

Background to Evolution in Africa. 1967. (with CLARK, J. D.) Chicago University.

Calibration of Hominoid Evolution. 1972. (with MILLER, J. A.) Scottish Academic.

Journal of the Geological Society of London, Scientific Editor, 1969–1972.

Geological Background to Fossil Man – recent research in the Gregory Rift Valley. 1978. Geological Society of London–Scottish Academic, Edinburgh.

Part I. Early Miocene of Uganda

Bill Bishop worked in Uganda for six years during the 1950s and 1960s. During this time he initiated an extensive programme of field work in Miocene and later deposits in Uganda, both when he was with the Geological Survey and later when he took over as Curator of the Uganda Museum. An account of his activities in Uganda is given by Julie Cormack in the first chapter in this section, together with additional material on another noted Uganda geologist, E. J. Wayland. Between them they established geology as a scientific discipline in Uganda, at that time way ahead of comparable studies in other parts of East Africa, and the Uganda Museum was the foremost Museum, as Makerere University was the foremost University, in East Africa.

Two of the fossil sites for which Bill is best known are Moroto and Napak. He found large numbers of fossil apes at these localities, and because of his training he was able to set them in stratigraphic and taphonomic context which made them of greater value than many of the Kenya Miocene apes from the same period which often lacked context. He discovered a new site at Moroto, following that discovered by John Wilson of the Agriculture Department, situated on the flanks of the Moroto volcano, and the fossil ape specimens from these sites are the subject of the remaining two chapters in this section. The first is by Laura MacLatchy and David Pilbeam and is based on their field work in 1994 and 1995. For Pilbeam this is a continuation of the work he did for his doctorate, for Bill gave him the fossil ape collections from both Moroto and Napak to describe for his thesis. At that time he described all the apes as *Proconsul major*, the largest of the fossil apes also known from Kenya, but the discovery of postcranial material by their more recent expeditions has shown that the Moroto fossil is distinct from that species, and it was subsequently given the new name of *Morotopithecus bishopi* in honour of Bill Bishop. In their chapter, MacLatchy and Pilbeam describe the new material and its context, together with new dates that indicate an early Miocene age for the Moroto sediments.

The final chapter is by Martin Pickford, one of Bill's students and the one whose work overlapped most closely with Bill's own interests. He describes the geological context of the Moroto fossils, and in particular he questions the radiometric dating of the site on the grounds that the fauna indicates a younger, middle Miocene, age. Fifty years ago, before the programme of radiometric dates was initiated, there was no information on the absolute ages of fossil deposits such as those from Moroto, and it was the development of radiometric methods, that Bill used to such great effect, that established an absolute chronology. On some occasions, however, the absolute dates provided by methods such as potassium-argon dating proved to be out of phase with faunal dates, and where this happens caution is needed in accepting one or other of the dates. There is such a conflict for the Moroto deposits, brought out by Pickford in his chapter.

P. Andrews

Setting their sights/sites on Uganda:
Walter William Bishop and Edward James Wayland

JULIE L. CORMACK

*Department of Anthropology, University of Alberta, Edmonton,
Alberta T6G 2H4, Canada*

Abstract: Although Walter William (Bill) Bishop and Edward James Wayland were formally trained in Cenozoic geology, they directed this knowledge to palaeontological, archaeological, environmental and chronological questions. Particularly in terms of East African prehistory, their combined legacy has provided all subsequent Ugandan research with a solid, valuable, and integral framework. Between 1956 and 1959 Bishop worked at the Uganda Geological Survey; a period that not only coincided with Wayland's last visit to Uganda, but which came almost 40 years after Wayland's initial arrival. In an historical review of Quaternary research, Bishop noted that Wayland's work was 'of inestimable value and forms the keystone upon which all the later work depends.' This is apparent through Bishop's questioning of the Wayland climatic pluvial sequence and his reassessment of Wayland's identification of a Kafuan pebble culture. Wayland's initial fossil finds at Napak took on new importance after Bishop's work at Moroto; both sites served to complement East African Miocene localities in Kenya.

The combined efforts totalling some 35 years of Ugandan fieldwork by Edward James Wayland and Walter William (Bill) Bishop provided a solid and integral foundation for East African prehistory, geology and chronology from which all subsequent research has developed. Both of these geologically trained scholars worked in various parts of Uganda, but especially in the western (Albertine) and eastern (Gregory) rift valleys, on sediments dating from the early Miocene to the present day. The purpose of this paper is to review the scientific contributions of E. J. Wayland and W. W. Bishop as well as illustrating some of the parallels in their fieldwork, professional affiliations and their ideas on prehistory, geology and chronology. Figure 1 (see also fig. 1 in MacLatchy & Pilbeam 1999) is a map of Uganda.

From August 1956 to May 1959, Bill Bishop served as Pleistocene geologist for the Geological Survey of Uganda, where much of his time involved field mapping (Bishop 1962a, 1969). He first arrived in East Africa in 1956 subsequently spending two months at the Coryndon Museum in Nairobi in 1957 studying under Dr Louis Leakey. In 1962 to 1965, he took over Curatorship of the Uganda Museum. During that time, Bishop was also a part-time lecturer at the well-established Makerere University, in Kampala where he 'proved himself an inspiring lecturer and a person greatly concerned with the welfare

of students' (King 1978: v). In 1963, he was leader of the Baker Centenary Expedition to Lake Albert (described later). In 1965, at the invitation of Dr Basil C. King, a colleague from the 1959 Napak (Karamoja) fieldwork, he took a staff position at Bedford College, University of London. With this appointment, Bishop became co-organizer of the East African Geological Research Unit (EAGRU), one focus of which was the creation of well-established stratigraphical and radiometrically dated geological work in the Kenyan rift valley.

An exhibition including Bill Bishop and his East African work was displayed at Bedford

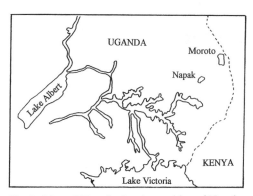

Fig. 1. Map of Uganda showing position of Napak and Moroto.

CORMACK, J. L. 1999. Setting their sights/sites on Uganda: Walter William Bishop and Edward James Wayland. *In*: ANDREWS, P. & BANHAM, P. (eds) *Late Cenozoic Environments and Hominid Evolution: a tribute to Bill Bishop.* Geological Society, London, 7–13.

College, University of London. His expertise is described as follows: he 'was not a vulcanologist, but a geomorphologist, palaeontologist and stratigrapher. He was to bring to the Rift Valley Project an insight into the depositional environments of such an area – river deposits, lake deposits and weathering deposits like laterites; a knowledge of vertebrate faunas – hippos, giraffes, elephants, antelope, pigs, as well as primates; and an awareness of the need for precision in the stratigraphic correlation of events in the Cenozoic' (cf. Bishop & Clark 1967).

In contrast, Bishop's predecessor, Edward James Wayland, focused his work in Uganda solely at the Geological Survey of Uganda (Cormack in press). He took up directorship in 1919, and eventually left the Survey in 1939, later returning to Uganda in the 1950s for fieldwork at Nsongezi.

In 1908, the oldest museum in East Africa (Posnansky 1963), the Uganda Museum was officially created from the Botanical, Forestry and Scientific Departments. Although Wayland did not have an affiliation with the Museum, in 1923, with Judge G. Smith and Alan Hogg, he founded The Uganda Literary and Scientific Society (becoming The Uganda Society) which was to be later associated with the Museum. The purpose of this Society was the 'encouragement of interest in the history, literature, culture and scientific knowledge of Uganda and neighbouring countries.' After its initial creation and success, it became inactive having not met since 1929. In 1933, it was reconstituted by Wayland and E.F. Twining along with its new journal, *The Uganda Journal*. Deming (1966: 11) writes that 'The Uganda Society wrote in January, 1948, asking if the Museum would welcome the idea of the two organizations being housed together'. This request took 16 years, and in 1964, the Uganda Museum and Uganda Society were brought together in the Museum's new Education Building.

Under the Curatorship of Dr Bishop from 1962 to 1965, the Uganda Museum prospered in terms of professional development and public exhibitions (Bishop 1964a). Dr Bishop became Curator in July 1962, after taking over from Dr Merrick Posnansky, a specialist in African archaeology. The following month, 'The Nile Quest' exhibition opened, one of 13 different exhibits for the Museum. In May 1963, the 'British Science Display' organized by the British Central Office of Information opened, and by November of that year, there were 175 000 visitors to the Museum. In addition to this display, in 1963 the Museum had 12 other temporary exhibits, including: Pottery in Africa (illustrat-

ing materials from both Nigeria and Uganda); Treasures from the Earth (showing mineral and fossil wealth in East Africa); and Child Development in East Africa (photographic display by Makerere University students).

During 1963, co-operation was established with other cultural institutions (i.e. Sorsbie Gallery in Nairobi, and the Rhodes National Gallery in Southern Rhodesia (Zimbabwe)) thus encouraging several travelling exhibitions throughout east and southern Africa (Bishop 1964a).

From June to August 1963, Bishop left the Museum briefly to lead the Baker Centenary Expedition to Lake Albert, a scientific research programme of geomorphology, archaeology and palaeontology to examine remote areas of the lake (Bishop 1967b). This expedition was in celebration of Sir Samuel White Baker's discovery of Lake Albert on 14 March 1864. Baker (in Bishop 1965: 295–296) describes the event as follows:

'I was about 1,500 feet above the lake, and I looked down from the steep granite cliff upon those welcome waters...I called this great lake 'the Albert Nyanza.' The flat sandy meadow that extends from the lake for about a mile to the foot of the precipitous cliffs of 1,500 feet, appears to have formed at one period the bottom of the lake. The lake was a vast depression far below the general level of the country, surrounded by precipitous cliffs, and bounded on the west and south-west by great ranges of mountains from five to seven thousand feet above the level of its waters – thus it was the one great reservoir into which everything must drain; and from this vast rocky cistern the Nile made its exit, a giant in its birth.'

To honour this event, on 11 March 1964 Dr John R. Baker, great nephew of Sir Samuel White Baker, opened an exhibition at the Museum entitled 'The Development of Lake Albert' (Bishop 1967b).

Immediately after the Baker Expedition, the Brathay Exploration Group led by Mr Brian Ware of Brathay, Ambleside, Westmorland, undertook geomorphological mapping of the Murchison Falls area (Bishop 1967b; Ware 1967). Bill Bishop and Merrick Posnansky acted as advisers for this project, spending some time in the field with the group.

Professional development of the Museum included new building construction as well as formal training for various Museum staff. The first major event occurred on 8 October 1962, the eve of Independence Day, when the Prime

Minister of Uganda opened the new permanent wing of the Museum housing the Independence Pavilion of Science and Industry (Bishop 1964a). The exhibition traced scientific and industrial development in Uganda including: the discovery of Lake Victoria (the source of the Nile) in 1862 by John Hanning Speke; the role of communication in industry; the fight against disease; and the future. Working models (e.g. printing press and a railway engine) and push-button displays made this exhibition interactive and generated much interest in the Museum.

In a 1964 article, Bishop described several planning additions to the Museum. An Education Building (and the new home for The Uganda Society) and Natural History Centre were to be opened to the public in November 1964, in addition to the construction of a visiting scientists' laboratory. 'In order to increase its "tourist" interest and also to preserve traditional crafts which are rapidly being lost, preliminary construction of a craft village has been commenced... Adjacent to the craft village will be an open-air theatre' (Bishop 1964a: 105).

In August 1963, the Museum established an Education Service using Ugandan Government funding with an active Canadian-trained African Education Officer. In 1963 and 1964, there was also foreign training for the Museum's Assistant in Switzerland and Great Britain, and for the Assistant Curator (C. Sekintu) in the United States. During this period, the Museum operated with a senior staff of six African and three European officers plus an African junior staff (Bishop 1964a).

As Director of the Geological Survey, Wayland spent much time becoming familiar with the landscapes and fossil evidence throughout Uganda. 'One of his first tasks was to walk right round Uganda, a journey of several months' (Davies 1967: 231). As early as 1920, Wayland recorded fossil mammals from the Karamoja District (Wayland 1921), where Bishop also spent much time. Both men also worked on the Kaiso sediment series along the western Lake Albert rift (Wayland 1926; Bishop 1962b). Generally though, Bishop's focus was on the northeastern Karamoja District in contrast to Wayland's assessment of archaeological sites around Lake Victoria–Sango Hills and the Kagera River (e.g. Nsongezi).

In June 1957, Professor and Mrs Richard Flint, Dr Louis Leakey, Dr Phillip Tobias, Bill Bishop and his wife Sheila boarded Leakey's boat – The Miocene Lady – for a short journey on Lake Victoria. In December 1997, as I write this brief paper in honour of Dr Bishop, I wonder if this short boating adventure in 1957 may have inspired and led him to his highly successful palaeontological discoveries of Miocene fossils in the Karamoja region the following year.

His work in Karamoja focused particularly around the Napak and Moroto volcanic mountains, where in 1958, he described the first *Proconsul* fossils from Uganda (Bishop 1958, 1964b, 1968b; Bishop & Posnansky 1960; Bishop & Whyte 1962; Allbrook & Bishop 1963; Tricker et al. 1963; Bishop et al. 1969). Figures 2–4 illustrate the Napak area and excavations. Between 1961 and 1965, he collected facial,

Fig. 2. Napak: front of caldera rim.

Fig. 3. Napak, 1964: site locality.

dental and vertebral remains of a large-bodied primate from the Moroto II locality. Figures 5–7 illustrate the Moroto area and excavations. In 1994–1995, Gebo *et al.* (1997) found more

hominoid postcranial evidence dating to at least 20.6 Ma BP, and proposed the new taxon *Morotopithecus bishopi* in honour of Bishop's original work at the site. According to Gebo *et al.* (1997: 403), '*Morotopithecus* represents the earliest evidence for a significantly apelike body plan in the primate fossil record.'

As mentioned above, Bishop also turned his field attentions to sediments of the Lake Albert rift and the Kazinga Channel which separates Lakes Edward and George (Bishop 1962*b*). These Kaiso Formation sediments revealed some of the first palaeontological evidence in Uganda which was eventually forwarded to the British Museum by J. S. Coates in 1909 (Andrews 1923; Wayland 1926; *cf.* Bishop 1965). This work by Wayland and colleagues in the Albertine rift was the first since the discovery of the lake in 1864 by Baker. The lacustrine Kaiso fauna includes abundant fish, mammal, reptile and mollusc remains (Hopwood, in Wayland 1926). Based on Wayland's work near the Kaiso village on Lake Albert, Cooke & Coryndon (1970) honoured Wayland with a species name of an East African Suidae ('*Sus*' *waylandi*), which most recently has been revised to *Nyanzachoerus waylandi* (Pickford 1989). Working along the Kazinga Channel, in 1958, Bishop conducted a small excavation near Mweya Lodge in Queen Elizabeth National Park, where he located numerous handaxes, hammerstones, cores and waste flakes.

Bishop's interest also lay in taphonomy, and stratigraphic calibration and chronology. In 1963, he studied recent natural kill sites in the

Fig. 4. Napak, 1964: beginning of the excavations.

Fig. 5. Moroto, January 1964: Moroto Mountain from Nakiloro Road.

Murchison Falls National Park (Bishop 1967*b*), and in Bishop (1968*b*) discussed the surface scatter patterns of the bones of a young buffalo which had been killed by a lion. *Calibration of*

Fig. 6. Moroto, January 1964: site locality.

Hominoid Evolution, a book edited by Bishop & Miller (1972), provided a central focus to current debates on East African chronology, from the essential law of superposition to the use of biostratigraphic markers, and various isotopic dating methods.

With Bishop's move to Bedford College, he shifted his research to Kenya, where for the next several years, the EAGRU (East African Geological Research Unit) programme concentrated its fieldwork, particularly geological mapping, in the Kavirondo and Lake Baringo regions. Various members of the EAGRU team were responsible for locating and describing hominoid and archaeological sites such as Chemeron, Chesowanja, Tugen Hills and Kilombe in the Baringo region.

There were also parallels in the scientific contributions of Bishop and Wayland to Ugandan geology and prehistory. Although both men made new archaeological and palaeontological discoveries, Bishop reinterpreted several of Wayland's original ideas on culture history, pluvial sequencing and stratigraphy. Three examples are given below.

Based on their work in 1926 and 1927 along the Kafu River, Wayland and his geologist T. Hirst believed that these river gravels contained evidence for a Stone Age culture based on pebble tools which Wayland termed the (pre-Chellean) Kafuan Pebble Culture (Wayland 1927, 1934; *cf.* van Riet Lowe 1952). These simple quartzite pebbles were hard to recognize as humanly made, and in 1959, Bishop criticized

Fig. 7. Moroto, January 1964: clearing the site.

these 'Kafuan artefacts' stating that human manufacture was difficult to distinguish from natural fracture which commonly occurred within these local river gravels. He dismissed the existence of this industry (Bishop 1959).

Wayland was a strong proponent of climatic pluvial sequences, attributing, for example, the terraces along the Kagera River to the 'Kageran' pluvial. Bishop questioned these climatic implications of stratigraphy (Bishop 1962a, 1967a, 1968a; Bishop & Clark 1967; cf. Cooke 1958; Flint 1959), and stated that, 'Solomon concluded as long ago as 1939:...the Pluvial hypothesis rests on very slender foundations...it will have to be replaced by palaeontological, archaeological and geomorphological methods' (Bishop 1968a: 165). Wayland (1926) established Kaiso stratigraphy, but in 1967, Bishop (1967a) suspended use of the term 'Epi-Kaiso'.

Both Wayland and Bishop are mentioned in the *Who's Who* series. Bill Bishop was listed in the *Who's Who in East Africa for 1963–1964*. He was Scientific Editor (in 1969) and continued as Secretary until 1975, for The Geological Society of London, and is fondly remembered for enhancing the reputation of the Society's journal. Wayland was listed in *Who Was Who, 1961–1970*. Both men also participated in the Pan African Congress on Prehistory meetings.

Bishop died at the young age of 45, just over ten years after Wayland's death in 1966. He not only built on the geological foundation that Wayland initiated in 1919, he also added dramatically to our knowledge of Miocene and Plio-Pleistocene fossils and archaeological remains in

Uganda. Ultimately, Bishop provided the essential framework on the chronology and stratigraphy required for a more complete understanding of the East African Cenozoic for future generations of scientists.

I am very grateful to S. Bishop for providing me with information and materials including original photographs which were scanned for my contributed poster presentation. I sincerely thank P. Andrews and J. Gowlett for the initial invitation to participate in this conference, and to have my poster displayed in my absence. For technical assistance, I appreciate the time and efforts given by L. Holm, in addition to use of the computer facilities of the Archaeological Research Facility, University of California, Berkeley.

References

ALLBROOK, D. & BISHOP, W. W. 1963. New fossil hominoid material from Uganda. *Nature*, **197**, 1187–1190.

ANDREWS, C. W. 1923. An African chalicothere. *Nature*, **112**, 696.

BISHOP, W. W. 1958. Miocene mammalia from the Napak volcanics, Karamoja, Uganda. *Nature*, **182**, 1480–1482.

——1959. Kafu stratigraphy and Kafuan artifacts. *South African Journal of Science*, **55**(5), 117–121.

——1962a. A summary of the present position regarding Quaternary stratigraphical research in Uganda. *In*: MORTELMANS, G. & NENQUIN, J. (eds) *Actes du IVe Congrès Panafricain de Préhistoire et de l'étude du Quaternaire, Leopoldville*. Musée Royal de l'Afrique Centrale, Tervuren, Belgium, 209–217.

——1962*b*. Pleistocene correlation in the Uganda section of the Albert-Edward Rift Valley. *In*: MORTELMANS, G. & NENQUIN, J. (eds) *Actes du IVe Congrès Panafricain de Préhistoire et de l'étude du Quaternaire, Leopoldville*. Musée Royal de l'Afrique Centrale, Tervuren, Belgium, 245–253.

——1964*a*. Le musée de l'Ouganda, Kampala. *Museum*, **XVII**(2), 99–102 (English translation on pages 103–105).

——1964*b*. More fossil primates and other Miocene mammals from north-east Uganda. *Nature*, **203**, 1327–1331.

——1965. *Quaternary geology and geomorphology in the Albertine Rift Valley, Uganda*. Geological Society of America, Special Paper **84**, 293–321.

——1967*a*. Annotated lexicon of Quaternary stratigraphical nomenclature in East Africa. *In*: BISHOP, W. W. & CLARK, J. D. (eds) *Background to Evolution in Africa*. University of Chicago, 375–395.

——1967*b*. The Lake Albert basin. *The Geographical Journal*, **133**, 469–480.

——1968*a*. Means of correlation of Quaternary successions in East Africa. *In*: MORRISON, R. B. & WRIGHT, H. E. JR (eds) *Means of Correlation of Quaternary Successions*. University of Utah, Salt Lake City, 161–172.

——1968*b*. The evolution of fossil environments in East Africa. *Leicester Literary and Philosophical Society*, **2**, 22–44.

——1969. *Pleistocene Stratigraphy in Uganda*. Geological Survey of Uganda, Memoir **X**.

—— & CLARK, J. D. (eds) 1967 *Background to Evolution in Africa*. University of Chicago.

—— & MILLER, J. A. (eds) 1972. *Calibration of Hominoid Evolution*. Scottish Academic, Edinburgh.

—— & POSNANSKY, M. 1960. Pleistocene environments and early man in Uganda. *Uganda Journal*, **24**(1), 44–61.

—— & WHYTE, F. 1962. Tertiary mammalian faunas and sediments in Karamoja and Kavirondo, East Africa. *Nature*, **196**, 1283–1287.

——, MILLER, J. A., & FITCH, F. J. 1969. New potassium-argon age determinations relevant to the Miocene fossil mammal sequence in East Africa. *American Journal of Science*, **267**, 669–699.

COOKE, H. B. S. 1958. Observations relating to Quaternary environments in East and Southern Africa. *Geological Society of South Africa, Bulletin*, **XX**.

—— & CORYNDON, S. C. 1970. Pleistocene mammals from the Kaiso Formation and other related deposits in Uganda. *In*: LEAKEY, L. S. B.

& SAVAGE, R. J. G. (eds) *Fossil Vertebrates of Africa*, Volume 2. Academic, London, 107–224.

CORMACK, J. L. (in press) Edward James Wayland. A Biography. *New Dictionary of National Biography*. Oxford University.

DAVIES, K. A. 1967. Obituary notice – Edward James Wayland. *Proceedings of the Geological Society of London*, **1642**, 231–232.

DEMING, L. M. 1966. *The history of the Uganda Museum*. Geological Survey of Uganda, Occasional Paper **10**.

FLINT, R. F. 1959. On the basis of Pleistocene correlation in East Africa. *Geological Magazine*, **46**(4), 265- 284.

GEBO, D. L., MACLATCHY, L., KITYO, R., DEINO, A., KINGSTON, J. & PILBEAM, D. 1997. A hominoid genus from the early Miocene of Uganda. *Science*, **276**, 401–404.

KING, B. C. 1978. In Memoriam. *In*: BISHOP, W. W. (ed.) *Geological Background to Fossil Man. Recent Research in the Gregory Rift Valley, East Africa*. Scottish Academic, Edinburgh, v–vi.

MACLATCHY, L. & PILBEAM, D. 1999. Renewed research in the Ugandan Early Miocene. *This volume*.

PICKFORD, M. 1989. New specimens of *Nyanzachoerus-waylandi* (Mammalia, Suidae, Tetraconodontinae) from the type area, Nyaburogo, (Upper Miocene), Lake Albert rift, Uganda. *Geobios*, **22**(5), 641–651.

POSNANSKY, M. 1963. The Uganda Museum, Kampala. *Museum*, **XVI**(3), 149–153.

TRICKER, B. J. K., TAYLOR, W. H. & BISHOP, W. W. 1963. II. Fossils from Karamoja. The fossiliferous sites. *Uganda Journal*, **27**, 109–114.

VAN RIET LOWE, C. 1952. *The Pleistocene Geology and Prehistory of Uganda. Part II. The Prehistory*. Geological Survey of Uganda, Memoir **VI**.

WARE, A. B. 1967. The Nile at the Murchison Falls: A survey by members of the Brathay Uganda Expedition. *The Geographical Journal*, **133**, 481–482.

WAYLAND, E. J. 1921. Geological Survey of Uganda 1919–1920. *Annual Report*, 38.

——1926. *The geology and palaeontology of the Kaiso bone bed*. Geological Survey of Uganda, Occasional Paper **2**.

——1927. *A possible age correlation of the Kafu gravels*. Geological Survey of Uganda, Annual Report for 1926.

——1934. Rifts, rivers, rains and early man in Uganda. *Journal of the Royal Anthropological Institute*, **64**, 333–352.

Renewed research in the Ugandan Early Miocene

LAURA MACLATCHY[1] & DAVID PILBEAM[2]

[1] *Department of Anthropology, Boston University, Boston, MA 02215, USA*
[2] *Department of Anthropology, Harvard University, Cambridge, MA 02138, USA*

Abstract: Hominoid fossils from two Moroto localities have recently been assigned to a new genus and species of Miocene hominoid, *Morotopithecus bishopi*. The new designation is based on a re-evaluation of previously known craniodental and vertebral specimens collected by Bill Bishop and co-workers, and a synthesis of these specimens with new postcranial material. Combined analysis of new and old fossils together with new dating reveals that *Morotopithecus* is the oldest hominoid to share with the extant apes features related to orthograde and suspensory behaviour. If these features are synapomorphies, it follows that Miocene hominoids (such as *Sivapithecus, Proconsul, Afropithecus* and *Kenyapithecus*) that do not share these derived postcranial characteristics with the extant hominoids may represent a different radiation from the one which gave rise to the living apes. Furthermore, the antiquity of the specimens indicates that significant aspects of the postcranial morphology of the extant apes was present before 20 Ma BP, much older than previously thought.

From 1958 to 1965, Bill Bishop undertook a detailed study of Lower Miocene fossil localities near the Napak and Moroto volcanoes in the Karamoja District of eastern Uganda. His work yielded an important faunal assemblage including an enigmatic large-bodied hominoid from Moroto. Between 1961 and 1965, Bishop's efforts at the Lower Miocene site Moroto II, north of the Moroto volcano, resulted in the recovery of hominoid facial, dental and vertebral remains, all of which were assigned to *Proconsul major* (Allbrook & Bishop 1963; Walker & Rose 1968). The assignment of the dental material to *P. major* was later disputed on the basis that its morphology warranted its placement in the genus *Afropithecus* (Leakey *et al.* 1988; Andrews 1992), but Ward (1991) later argued this point based on the derived morphology of the Moroto lumbar vertebra U.M.P. (Uganda Museum of Palaeontology) 67.28, which resembles the vertebrae of extant apes in several respects (Walker & Rose 1968; Ward 1993; Sanders & Bodenbender 1994). Assuming that the dental and vertebral remains were from the same species, which seems reasonable given that no other Miocene site contains more than one species of large hominoid (Gebo *et al.* 1997a), Ward proposed that since all known postcranial elements of *Proconsul* and *Afropithecus* are similar and compatible with generalized arboreal quadrupedal locomotor adaptations, and since the Moroto vertebra suggests a more orthograde posture, its assignment to either *Proconsul* or *Afropithecus* was questionable.

A suite of facial and dental characters that separate *Morotopithecus* from *Proconsul* and *Afropithecus* have since been identified (Gebo *et al.* 1997a). Features distinguishing it from *Afropithecus* include a greater degree of cingular development on cheek teeth, especially molars, a shorter premaxilla, a higher face, a broader nasal aperture, stylar wrinkling on the molars, a non-reduced M3, and a much wider incisive canal (Gebo *et al.* 1997a). *Morotopithecus* differs from both *Afropithecus* and *Proconsul* in its narrower interorbital region and larger premolars relative to M1, and from *Proconsul* in smaller M2 and M3 relative to M1. In addition, the more primitive postcranial remains attributed to *Proconsul* and *Afropithecus* (Walker & Pickford 1983; Rose 1983, 1993; Leakey *et al.* 1988; Ward 1993) compared to derived postcranial characters of *Morotopithecus*, suggested a generic level difference. This latter point might be disputed on the basis that while the recovered postcranial elements for *Proconsul* and *Morotopithecus* overlap for some (e.g. lumbar vertebra, proximal and distal femora), there are none shared by *Afropithecus* and *Morotopithecus*. Might the mosaic nature of Miocene hominoid postcranial adaptations lead to a combination of derived and primitive features in *Afropithecus*? Could *Afropithecus* have been orthograde, or more orthograde than *Proconsul*? Rose (1994)

MACLATCHY, L. & PILBEAM, D. 1999. Renewed research in the Ugandan Early Miocene. *In*: ANDREWS, P. & BANHAM, P. (eds) *Late Cenozoic Environments and Hominid Evolution: a tribute to Bill Bishop.* Geological Society, London, 15–25.

has judged *Afropithecus* to be indistinguishable from *Proconsul* in all known regions and at this time it seems reasonable to assume (as did Ward (1991)) that the vertebral morphology of *Afropithecus* was also like that of *Proconsul*. Even if *Afropithecus* is later shown to have some adaptations supporting suspensory and/or orthograde adaptations, craniodental differences, especially in the incisive canal morphology, support a generic distinction from *Morotopithecus*.

Analysis of the new fossil material and accurate dating allow a better determination of the role that the Moroto species played in hominoid evolution. In particular, the combined postcrania of *Morotopithecus* marks the earliest record of orthograde and forelimb suspensory behaviour in hominoids.

Discovery and context

There are two sites near the Moroto volcano, located about 13 and 16 km north of the summit of Moroto (Fig. 1). The Moroto I locality was found by J. G. Wilson in 1959; Bishop and Whyte collected there in 1961 and found a second site, Moroto II (Bishop & Whyte 1962). Bishop's work at Moroto ceased in 1965 and we know of no further collection until 1985, when Pickford and co-workers recovered a number of mammal specimens, including a large hominoid phalanx at Moroto I (Pickford *et al.* 1986). Almost ten years then passed until visits to Moroto in 1994 and 1995 resulted in the surface collection of MUZM (Makerere University Zoology Museum) 60, the glenoid region of a large hominoid scapula, at Moroto I and MUZM 80, partial right and left femora of a single hominoid, at Moroto II (MacLatchy *et al.* 1995).

The fossil-bearing sediments at Moroto I are deposited on top of basement complex and overlain by a basalt. The base of the sedimentary section is a conglomerate composed of metamorphic clasts which is overlain by fine red and green clays representing composite palaeosols or lacustrine deposits with minor pebble horizons. Fossils occur in both the coarse and fine deposits, are of variable size (rodent to proboscidean) and were probably transported in high energy contexts.

Sediments of Moroto II are exposed in a drainage just northeast of Kogole Hill. Deposits are mostly fluvial with minor fine grained lacustrine or ponding facies, perhaps with palaeochannel(s). These sediments were originally deposited within a relatively narrow channel (<50 m) cut into the basement metamorphic complex (mostly gneisses below Moroto II) and are capped by a basalt which forms Kogole Hill and adjacent ridges. The sediments traced laterally clearly lap onto the basement rock and indicate fairly steep walls to the palaeochannel (about 308). The base of the section is well exposed and coarse sandstone and conglomerate facies can clearly be seen onlapping against the basement gneiss.

Age estimates for the localities have varied considerably over the years: using conventional K/Ar dating of capping lavas, Bishop *et al.* (1969) obtained minimum estimates of 12.5 and 14.3 Ma for Moroto sites I and II respectively. Faunal comparisons by Pickford *et al.* (1986), however, indicated a minimum age of 17.5 Ma. The overlying basalts at Moroto I and II have since been redated at 20.6 Ma using ^{40}Ar/^{39}Ar incremental heating technique (Gebo *et al.* 1997a), making the underlying sites among the oldest hominoid localities in Africa.

Investigation of the environment of the Ugandan sites is underway and will hopefully improve our understanding of the environmental context in which *Morotopithecus* lived. Most of the sub-Saharan African record of Early and Middle Miocene (24 to 12 Ma ago) mammals comes from sites in Kenya and an important line of research is to investigate potential differences between the Ugandan and Kenyan fossil assemblages and palaeoecology. It is generally recognized that the older Kenyan sites of Songhor and Koru had wetter, less seasonal forests than later sites (Andrews *et al.* 1997) and it is of some interest to determine the situation at Moroto.

The Napak localities

The bulk of this paper deals with research at Moroto but the nearby Lower Miocene sites near the Napak volcanoes are also the object of ongoing research.

Bill Bishop's initial research at the Lower Miocene sites near Akisim near the Napak volcano (Bishop 1958, 1963, 1964, 1967; Bishop & Whyte 1962) resulted in the recovery of a number of primate species, including the lorisoids *Komba robustus*, *Komba minor*, *Progalago dorae* and *Mioeuoticus bishopi*, an indeterminate cercopithecoid, the small-bodied hominoids *Limnopithecus clarki* and *Micropithecus legetet* and the little known *Proconsul major*. The monkey tooth from Napak remains the oldest record of a cercopithecoid (Pilbeam & Walker 1968).

An age estimate of 19 Ma for the localities makes them broadly contemporaneous with well known sites in the Tinderet sequence of Kenya (Bishop *et al.* 1969), although redating these sediments is important. Collections at Napak I

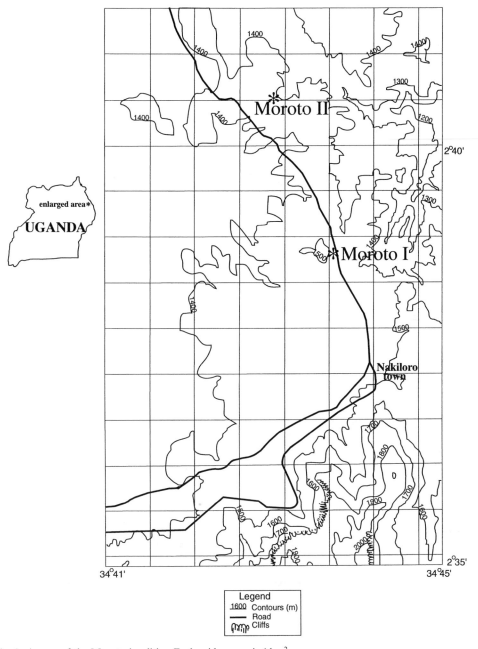

Fig. 1. A map of the Moroto localities. Each grid square is 1 km^2.

IV, V and IX in 1994 and 1995 resulted in the recovery of many new mammal, bird and reptile fossils. The localities preserve both small and large mammals: rodents (*Diamantomys, Afrocricetodon, Notocricetodon*), bats (*Propotto*), carnivores, anthracotheres, tragulids, rhinocerotids and proboscideans were among the specimens collected. New primate specimens from Napak include *P. major* and *Micropithecus* teeth and a lorisid distal humerus with lorisine affinities (Gebo *et al.* 1997*b*).

The Napak localities, along with the Tinderet localities in Kenya, are the only sites from which *Proconsul major* has been recovered. A tibia of

P. major collected by Bishop in 1958 at Napak has an estimated body weight in excess of 80 kg (Rafferty *et al.* 1995). This is of interest because large body size (in excess of 30 kg) may be correlated with the evolution of suspensory adaptations (Nengo 1995). The female gorilla size of *P. major* suggests that if it was arboreal, it would have been suspensory (Nengo 1995), distributing its body weight over multiple supports. The sparse postcranial evidence available for *P. major* is equivocal as to positional behaviours (e.g. Nengo & Rae 1992; Rose 1994; Rafferty *et al.* 1995) and it is not yet possible to determine if *P. major* was a largely terrestrial quadruped or an at least partially suspensory, arboreal species.

Postcranial material

Vertebra

The well preserved middle lumbar vertebra recovered by Bill Bishop at Moroto II remains one of the most important hominoid postcranial bones from the Miocene. Although its initial description by Walker & Rose (1968) clearly established its hominoid affinities, its significance was not recognized in the literature for more than two decades. As the paucity of hominoid-like postcrania in the Miocene became apparent, two detailed morphological studies on the Moroto vertebra were conducted, both of which have supported the initial report that the Moroto vertebra resembles the extant hominoid condition (Ward 1991, 1993; Sanders & Bodenbender 1994). Although the vertebral body proportions, including vertebral length, most closely resemble male baboons (Sanders & Bodenbender 1994), it shares many features with hominoids to the exclusion of cercopithecoids, including robust pedicles, lack of anapophyses, reduced ventral keeling and a caudally inclined spinous process (which is correlated with reduced dorsoventral mobility) (Ward 1991; Sanders & Bodenbender 1994). The location of origin and orientation of the transverse processes also resemble extant hominoids: the processes arise from the pedicle and are oriented dorsally (Sanders & Bodenbender 1994), increasing the moment arm of iliocostalis and longissimus dorsi to resist flexion (Shapiro 1993). This has been interpreted to mean that the Moroto hominoid had a stiff back, and that an orthograde posture and quadrumanous climbing were part of its positional repertoire. Such a behavioural pattern is in marked contrast with other early Miocene hominoids

such as *Proconsul nyanzae* and *heseloni* whose vertebrae are more like those of cercopithecoids and which have been reconstructed as generalized quadrupeds (Ward 1993).

The derived features of the Moroto lumbar vertebrae are rare among other Miocene hominoids. The lumbar morphology of other Early and Middle Miocene African hominoids, including *Afropithecus, Kenyapithecus* and *Otavipithecus*, is unknown; however, there are no features in any postcranial remains that argue for anything but pronograde quadrupedalism in these species (see recent reviews by Pilbeam 1996; Leakey & Walker 1997; McCrossin & Benefit 1997) although recent reports for Kenyapithecus from Maboko Island, Kenya, suggest hominoid-like features in the radius and cuboid (McCrossin 1997; McCrossin *et al.* 1998). Thus absence of well developed orthogrady/suspensory behaviour among other Miocene genera probably indicates that this was a rare positional behaviour and is not simply the result of an inadequate fossil record. It is not until the late Miocene of Europe that a lumbar morphology resembling that of extant hominoids is again documented, in the genera *Oreopithecus* and *Dryopithecus*. Although detailed descriptions of a new 9.5 million-year-old *Dryopithecus laietanus* skeleton from Can Llobateres, Spain, have not been published, Moyà-Solà & Köhler have reported that the lumbar vertebrae of *Dryopithecus* while 'somewhat elongated' are 'proportionally shorter than those of cercopithecoids and proconsulids' (Moyà-Solà & Köhler 1996: 158, 157). As recently reviewed by Shapiro (1993), shortening of the lumbar region, achieved by reducing the number of vertebrae and/or shortening the craniocaudal length of vertebral bodies, is thought to be related to locomotor modes involving orthogrady: brachiation (Keith 1923), bridging behaviour (Cartmill & Milton 1977) or vertical climbing at large body size (Jungers 1984) have all been implicated. As mentioned above, detailed metric comparisons by Sanders & Bodenbender (1994) have shown that *Morotopithecus* did not have short lumbar vertebrae. According to Moyà-Solà & Köhler (1996), however, *Dryopithecus* shares with *Morotopithecus* and extant hominoids transverse processes which arise from the pedicles and caudally directed spinous processes, both correlated with being 'stiff-backed'. *Oreopithecus bambolii* (dated at 8.4 Ma) lumbar vertebrae are reduced in length and number (relative to cercopithecoids; Shapiro 1993) and also have transverse processes which arise from the base of the pedicles (Harrison & Rook 1997). *Oreopithecus* and *Dryopithecus* are the only other non-hominine hominoid fossils with an inferred orthograde postural component to their positional behaviour.

Scapula

Pickford et al. (1999) question the attribution of the partial scapula from Moroto I to Morotopithecus. Although a preliminary report on the Morotopithecus scapula has been presented (Gebo et al. 1997a), detailed descriptions have not been published but are in progress. This paper is not the forum for the description or for detailed metric and functional comparisons. However, the following comments are offered.

A study of the structure and function of the primate scapula by Roberts (1974) remains one of the few comparative studies of the shoulder socket. Among palaeoanthropologists, this lack of attention may be due in part to the fact that fossil glenoid cavities are rarely recovered. Roberts divided glenoid fossae into two groups based on their outline: pear-shaped and ovate (Fig. 2). Most quadrupeds, both arboreal and terrestrial, have the pear-shaped outline; the ovate outline is found to some degree only in hominoids, some atelines and cursorial mammals such as the horse and deer (Roberts 1974). Roberts speculated that the ovate shape permits freedom of movement in primates and is an adaptation for rapid limb motion with a high acceleration increment in cursors. The Moroto glenoid (illustrated in Fig. 2) is clearly ovate, but cannot belong to the cursorial mammals with this morphology because the scapular spines of the cursors have a much more distal origin than do those of primates and the Moroto specimen. Some carnivores have glenoid fossae which *approach* an ovate shape, but these can be distinguished from hominoids by possession of

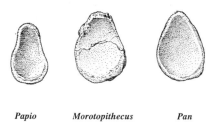

| Papio | Morotopithecus | Pan |

Fig. 2. The left glenoid fossae of *Papio*, *Morotopithecus* and *Pan*. The *Papio* specimen exemplifies the pear-shaped fossa characteristic of quadrupeds while both *Morotopithecus* and *Pan* have an ovate shaped fossa.

a craniodorsal notch, by prominent lipping at the edges of the glenoid fossa, or by the presence of an indentation or fossa between the spinoglenoid notch and the glenoid fossa margin. Those extant carnivores (including some felids (e.g. *Acinonyx*, *Felis*) and viverrids (e.g. *Genetta*, *Viverra*, *Civettictis*)) with *close* to an ovate morphology possess 'notches' on the craniodorsal and/or the cranioventral surface of the glenoid margin. This gives the glenoid outline an appearance intermediate to the pear and ovate outlines described above.

The craniodorsal margin is well preserved in the Moroto specimen and clearly shows that no craniodorsal notch was present. The presence of a glenoid notch on the cranioventral glenoid margin does not distinguish primates from carnivores, as some hominoids possess one (e.g. Museum of Comparative Zoology (M.C.Z.) specimens *Pan troglodytes* 23167 and 6244 and *Pongo pygmaeus* 50960). In any case, the cranial and cranioventral glenoid margins of the Moroto specimen are eroded, *and it is impossible to determine if a cranioventral notch was present*. Likewise, it is impossible to determine the relations between the supraglenoid tubercle and coracoid process (though Pickford et al. imply that it is possible) because both are broken off in the Moroto specimen. In carnivores, the glenoid margin is lipped, presumably to provide additional joint stability, and the attachment site of the glenoid labrum is rarely, and then only incipiently, visible. There is no lipping, and the attachment site of the glenoid labrum is clearly visible on the glenoid margin in the Moroto specimen, and is as in hominoids. Despite the fact that there is damage to the dorsal margin of the glenoid, the labrum attachment is preserved so the outline of all but the most cranial portion of the glenoid fossa can be accurately reconstructed, contra Pickford et al.

As Pickford et al. (1999) comment, the glenoid neck slopes gradually and obliquely in the Moroto specimen, and this is the condition seen in some *Pan* specimens (e.g. M.C.Z. 20041, 23163); in contrast, the dorsal wall is markedly curved in carnivores (due to the presence of a fossa) and the neck is often narrow. Pickford et al. imply that the scapular neck of the Moroto specimen is appreciably thicker dorsoventrally than in primates. Rather, the ratio of dorsoventral neck width to glenoid fossa width is 0.624 in *Morotopithecus*, well within the ranges seen in extant great apes. The mean values of this ratio (± standard deviation) are 0.605 ± 0.114 in *Pan troglodytes* $(n = 21)$, 0.670 ± 0.111 in *Gorilla gorilla* $(n = 16)$ and 0.505 ± 0.058 in *Pongo pygmaeus* $(n = 12)$. It is true, as Pickford et al.

report, that the infraglenoid tubercle is wide and rugose in *Morotopithecus*, but this is also the case for many *Pan* specimens (e.g. M.C.Z. 10736, 26847). However, the scarcely visible trabecular orientation cannot be used to infer the loading environment of the gleno-humeral joint. First, the complex, three-dimensional trabecular morphology of the glenoid region cannot be accurately gauged from the outside of the specimen. Second, no comparative study has ever been conducted to determine if there are differences in glenoid fossa trabecular morphology between suspensory and non-suspensory primates. Third, while it is suspected there may be differences in trabecular density and thickness in the glenoid region of habitual suspensors vs. quadrupeds, it is unclear why the trabecular *orientation* would be different under these different loading regimes. Fourth, if differences do exist between suspensory and quadrupedal primates (and it is not known if they do), for species such as *Pan* which are both suspensory and quadrupedal, knuckle-walking would load the shoulder in compression and potentially mask the effects of less frequent suspension. Note that it has already been suggested that *Morotopithecus* was at least partially quadrupedal based on its proximal femoral morphology (MacLatchy & Bossert 1996; Gebo *et al.* 1997*a*).

Finally, the shape of the glenoid itself, which is gently curved along both dorsoventral and craniocaudal axes, is a morphology we have not observed in any non-suspensory primate or in an extant carnivore. This morphology would seem to favour rotational arm movements and indicate a highly mobile shoulder joint. In contrast, quadrupedal mammals with pear-shaped fossae have glenoid articular surfaces that are more curved along the craniocaudal axis, due to the cranial 'lip' which prevents dislocation of the gleno-humeral joint (Roberts 1974).

It seems unlikely that there was a large-bodied, highly arboreal carnivore in the Miocene that expanded its dorsoventral scapular dimensions, lost marginal lipping and developed a hominoid pattern of curvature, especially given the range of positional behaviours known for extant and fossil carnivores (Martin 1989; Taylor 1989). In particular, there are no highly arboreal carnivores with a large body size (i.e. >30 kg). It is thus more parsimonious to attribute the glenoid fragment to the only large-bodied, suspensory primate known from Moroto.

As stated above, few other glenoid regions have been described for catarrhines. *Oreopithecus* has a glenoid that is broad dorsoventrally (Harrison & Rook 1997) while *Pliopithecus* has a pear-shaped glenoid.

Femora

As with the scapula, detailed descriptions of the new femoral material are in progress. The two partial femora recovered from Moroto II include a left femur consisting of the femoral head and a proximal portion that excludes the neck but extends below the lesser trochanter, and a right femur that preserves both articular ends but is missing perhaps one-half of the shaft. The morphology of the proximal femur is generally more primitive than in living hominoids (Gebo *et al.* 1997*a*). For instance, the femoral head is small relative to distal articular dimensions when compared to living hominoids, and the trochanteric fossa extends well below the mid-point of the femoral neck, unlike extant hominoids where the fossa is restricted distally (Fig. 3). A prominent tubercle is present on the posterior aspect of the neck; early catarrhines, Miocene hominoids and some gibbons possess this trait but it is entirely absent among the great apes.

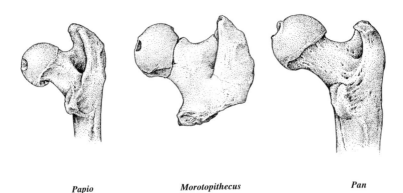

Papio   Morotopithecus   Pan

Fig. 3. A posterior view of the right proximal femora of *Papio*, *Morotopithecus* and *Pan*.

The distribution of articular surface on the femoral head is similar to that of monkeys in that there is relatively more articular surface on the anterior aspect of the femoral head. Chimpanzees differ from this pattern in having an articular surface that is more evenly distributed, permitting a wider range of lateral rotation and abduction than in monkeys (MacLatchy & Bossert 1996). The monkey-like configuration of the articular surface margin in the Moroto hominoid suggests a greater emphasis on adducted limb postures than in *Pan*, and implies quadrupedal hip use.

The femoral shaft and distal femoral proportions are both robust; the femoral cortical bone is extremely thick, the biepicondylar region is broad mediolaterally and the intercondylar notch is well buttressed. The distal femur has a deep popliteal groove and a prominent adductor tubercle. Overall, the femur documents features such as a shallow trochlea, broad condyles and moderately high neck angle that suggest joint mobility, as well as those such as the proximal femoral articular surface that suggest hip adduction was not infrequent.

The assertion by Pickford *et al.* (1999) that the two femora are not left and right femora from the same individual is unlikely. Although one of us (MacLatchy) recently visited the Uganda National Museum and was told that there were pieces found by Bishop that fit on to the femur found by our expedition, these pieces could not be produced and so have not been seen by this team. We reiterate that the two femoral heads are of identical size and the differences in trochanter morphology in the specimens we recovered that Pickford *et al.* describe are very slight and affected by the wear of the left femur.

Body size

Body mass estimates from dental remains often differ from those derived from postcranial remains, especially since some Miocene hominoids are megadont relative to extant species (Rafferty *et al.* 1995). Although a few cranial parameters have been found to be quite robust body size indicators, postcranial estimates are generally viewed as more accurate since the functional links with body mass are presumably more direct (Aiello & Wood 1994). For *Morotopithecus*, body mass estimates inferred from postcranial proportions vary depending on the region used. Femoral head dimensions suggest a body size of approximately 30 kg, diaphyseal cortical area suggests a mass of 50 kg, and biepicondylar breadth yields estimates approaching 40 kg (Table 1). Among living apes and monkeys,

femoral articular and diaphyseal dimensions do not yield such disparate estimates. The combination of a small femoral head with such a robust shaft is unlike extant catarrhines and *P. nyanzae* (Ruff *et al.* 1989; Ward *et al.* 1993) and may imply a significant difference in the loading conditions of the femur of *Morotopithecus* compared to these other catarrhines. Since the femoral shaft is broken, the approximate locations of the mid (50%) and proximal (80%) shaft lengths can only be estimated. Despite this, the two estimates give similar results. Regressions for both cercopithecoid monkeys and hominoids are provided for the femoral dimensions since scaling relationships differ markedly in these two groups and it is not clear which sample provides a more appropriate comparison for *Morotopithecus*. We suspect that the relatively small femoral head size of *Morotopithecus* compared to extant hominoids causes the hominoid-based femoral head regressions to yield an erroneously low body mass estimate. The femoral estimates, combined with Sanders & Bodenbender's (1994) body mass estimate of 38 kg based on the vertebra, are compatible with a 40 kg animal, about the size of a female chimpanzee, at Moroto II. The estimate from the Moroto I glenoid fossa is slightly higher at 48 kg. The large body size of *Morotopithecus* indirectly argues for suspensory adaptations since an above-branch quadruped of this size would be severely limited in its use of arboreal substrates.

Suspension and orthogrady in Miocene hominoids

Recent reviews by Rose (1993, 1994) have emphasized the quadrupedal nature of most Miocene hominoids. However, suspensory adaptations have implicitly been considered a significant component of the Miocene hominoid repertoire and it is only recently that it has been recognized that modern hominoid-like suspensory adaptations are found in only three genera: *Oreopithecus, Morotopithecus* and perhaps *Dryopithecus* (Harrison 1986; Moyà-Solà & Köhler 1996; Pilbeam 1996). *Morotopithecus* further stands out as the only Early or Middle Miocene hominoid for which suspensory adaptations may be inferred, a full 10 Ma before a similar grade of adaptations is found anywhere else.

A major research aim is to determine whether the postcranial similarities of *Oreopithecus, Morotopithecus, Dryopithecus* and their extant cousins are homologous or homoplastic (McCrossin & Benefit 1994; Pilbeam 1996; Larson 1998). A few

Table 1. *Body mass estimates of* Morotopithecus

Parameter	Sample	Equation/source (all least squares regression)	Estimated mass (kg)
Femoral head AP diameter (FHAP)	Cercopithecoid* (*Nasalis, Mandrillus, Macaca, Presbytis*)	Ln (FHAP) = 1.881 + 0.417 Ln(mass) R = 0.993	30
	Hominoid† (*Hylobates, Pan, Pongo, Gorilla*)	Ln(FHAP) = 2.199 + 0.339 Ln(mass) R = 0.998	25
	Combined catarrhine sample‡ (*Nasalis, Mandrillus, Macaca, Presbytis, Hylobates, Pan, Pongo, Gorilla*)	Ln(FHAP) = 1.979 + 0.39 Ln(mass) R = 0.990	29
Femoral shaft cortical area at estimated 20% length	'Total' (*Homo, Pan, Gorilla, Pongo, Macaca*)	Least-squares equations from Ruff 1987	54
	'Hominoid' (*Homo, Pan, Gorilla, Pongo*)		54
at estimated 50% length	'Total' (*Homo, Pan, Gorilla, Pongo, Macaca*)		53
	'Hominoid' (*Homo, Pan, Gorilla, Pongo*)		53
at estimated 80% length	'Total' (*Homo, Pan, Gorilla, Pongo, Macaca*)		51
	'Hominoid' (*Homo, Pan, Gorilla, Pongo*)		52
Femoral bicondylar width	Combined catarrhine platyrhine sample (21 species)	Least-squares regressions from Aiello & Wood (1994)	39
	Hominoid (*Homo, Pan, Gorilla, Pongo*)		37
Maximum width glenoid cavity (GLW)	Hominoid (*Pan troglodytes, Pan paniscus, Pongo, Gorilla, Hylobates, Symphalangus*)§	Unpublished data provided by William Jungers Ln(mass) = 2.744Ln(GLW) − 4.917 R = 0.991	48
Vertebral body surface area	26 catarrhine species	Sanders & Bodenbender (1994)	38

* Linear regressions were performed on sex-specific mean values. Sample size is 10 individuals per species with the sexes evenly split except for *Mandrillus* where $n = 7$ for males and $n = 3$ for females. Body masses were known except for *Mandrillus*, where body mass estimates provided by Jungers (1985) were used.
† Linear regressions were performed on sex-specific mean values. Sample size is 10 individuals per species with the sexes evenly split. Body masses were known for *Hylobates* and some *Pongo*. Body mass estimates from Jungers (1985) were used for for *Pan, Gorilla* and some *Pongo* specimens.
‡ Linear regressions were performed on sex-specific mean values for the combined data set described in footnotes * and † above.
§ Linear regressions were performed by Jungers on sex-specific means of animals of known body weight.

researchers think they are likely to be homologous: '... the postcranial characteristics shared by *Oreopithecus* and the extant hominoids are so pervasive throughout the skeleton that it is almost impossible to consider that these could have been developed independently to such a remarkable degree of detail in *every* anatomical region' (Harrison & Rook 1997: 347). 'It is indeed likely that some fraction of hominoid postcranial similarities in fact represent homoplasies, but I doubt that this is a significant fraction' (Pilbeam 1996: 160). Many Miocene workers, however, think that homoplasy in the postcranial system might be substantial (e.g. Begun & Kordos 1997; Begun *et al.* 1997; Kelley 1997; Ward 1997).

It is widely accepted that many forelimb (and axial) features of hominoids are also well developed in atelines (Ericson 1963). Larson (1998) has recently attempted to determine what proportion of hominoid upper limb features conventionally thought to be synapomorphies are in fact unique to hominoids. Skeletal elements considered included the sternum, clavicle, scapula, humerus, ulna, radius, lunate and capitate; Larson also looked at the shape of the thorax. Of 34 traits, Larson found only seven to be distinctive to hominoids; 11 were shared by hominoids and *Ateles* and the rest (16 traits – almost half) were also shared with some other primate. A major finding of this study '... that the list of distinctive postcranial features for the living apes is not quite as long as many workers believe' (Larson 1998: 95) is overshadowed by fact that many of the 'distinctive' traits could not be attributed to functional convergence, since so many of the traits were found in at least one other non-suspensory species. This is rather unsettling since it suggests a widespread oversimplification of the relationship between morphological features and their corresponding behavioural implications.

A similar survey has not been attempted for the hindlimb or the rest of the axial skeleton. An examination of the phylogenetic distribution of lumbar vertebral features would be of great interest since this is an element shared by all three 'modern' Miocene hominoids. For instance, only the great apes and humans have transverse processes which arise from the pedicles rather than the body (Shapiro 1993); the distribution of this trait argues for it being a derived character. Smaller hylobatids and atelines, as well as the subfossil lemurs *Megaladapis* and *Paleopropithecus* show a different pattern with transverse processes that arise at the junction of pedicle and the vertebral body (Shapiro 1993, pers. comm.); however, the siamang resembles *Pongo* (Pilbeam pers. obs.). Since the transverse processes of *Morotopithecus* have a more dorsal origin than do those of small hylobatids, and since *Morotopithecus* is likely to be the sister group to all living hominoids (Gebo *et al.* 1997*a*), including gibbons, the point of origin of the transverse process morphology would have had to become more ventral in the smaller hylobatids, assuming their ancestor had a *Morotopithecus*-like (or *Pongo*- or *Symphalangus*-like) lumbar morphology.

While it is recognized that there are functional correlates to being 'stiff-backed' it is not clear if this trait is necessary for forelimb suspension, vertical climbing or bridging (Shapiro 1993); however, like lumbar reduction *per se*, it is probably related to controlling movements between the pelvis and thorax (Cartmill & Milton 1977) and is perhaps less likely to be attributable only to size constraints (i.e. is an adaptation to resist buckling during erect postures) since the gibbons also have modified lumbar regions. It is worth noting that the length of the functional lumbar region (using the zygopophyseal definition) of the relatively small-bodied atelines is greater than it is in gibbons and other hominoids (Shapiro 1993). If gibbons evolved from a much larger ancestor with a more derived lumbar morphology, such as *Morotopithecus*, then large body size may indeed play an important role in the origin, or origins, of a 'stiff-back'.

It is still difficult to determine whether the entire suite of hominoid lumbar features could have evolved independently in different hominoid lineages. Given the rareness of these features among extant primates and in the fossil record, it seems plausible that they are synapomorphies. If so, later Miocene hominoids that lack these features either 're-evolved' quadrupedalism, or are more distantly related to extant hominoids than is *Morotopithecus*.

Summary

Morotopithecus was an arboreal hominoid whose locomotor repertoire probably included forelimb-dominated climbing, orthograde suspension and some quadrupedalism. Its hip lacked the mobility of extant hominoids, so its overall suspensory capabilities probably fell short of that seen in extant hominoids. However, with back and shoulder morphology suggesting orthograde, suspensory adaptations, *Morotopithecus* represents our best model of the ancestral ape morphotype. Hence *Morotopithecus* is a key taxon in understanding the evolution of modern hominoid postcranial adaptations and positional behaviour. For instance, the size and antiquity of the Moroto hominoid supports the view that the small body size of living hylobatids is derived, and not the ancestral condition for the living apes.

Morotopithecus is the oldest hominoid to share postcranial features, and presumably locomotor characteristics, with the extant apes. This modern ape-like morphology was present 10 Ma before a similar grade of adaptations is again documented. If features related to orthograde and suspensory adaptations are synapomorphies among the living hominoids, the postcranial material of *Morotopithecus* suggests that Miocene apes such as *Proconsul*, *Afropithecus*, *Sivapithecus* and perhaps *Kenyapithecus*, which do not share many derived postcranial characteristics with the extant hominoids, may be members of a different radiation from the one which gave rise to extant hominoids.

We wish to thank P. Andrews and S. Bishop for inviting us to participate in this symposium, and D. Gebo, J. Kingston and R. Kityo for their fieldwork and collaboration at Moroto and Napak. We are very grateful to the Uganda National Council for Science and Technology for permission to conduct research in Uganda, and to the Zoology Department of Makerere University for their many efforts. Funding was provided by the L. S. B. Leakey Foundation.

References

AIELLO, L. & WOOD, B. 1994. Cranial variables as predictors of hominine body mass. *American Journal of Physical Anthropology*, **95**, 409–426.

ALLBROOK, D. & BISHOP, W. W. 1963. New fossil hominoid material from Uganda. *Nature*, **97**, 1187–1190.

ANDREWS, P. 1992. Evolution and environment in the Hominoidea. *Nature*, **360**, 641–646.

——, BEGUN, D. R. & ZYLSTRA, M. 1997. Interrelationships between functional morphology and paleoenvironments in Miocene hominoids. *In*: BEGUN, D. R., WARD, C. V. & ROSE, M. D. (eds) *Function, Phylogeny and Fossils Miocene Hominoid Evolution and Adaptations.* Plenum, New York, 29–58.

BEGUN, D. R. & KORDOS, L. 1997. Phyletic affinities and functional convergence in *Dryopithecus* and other Miocene and living hominids. *In*: BEGUN, D. R., WARD, C. V. & ROSE, M. D. (eds) *Function, Phylogeny and Fossils Miocene Hominoid Evolution and Adaptations.* Plenum, New York, 291–316.

——, WARD, C. V. & ROSE, M. D. 1997. Events in hominoid evolution *In*: BEGUN, D. R., WARD, C. V. & ROSE, M. D. (eds) *Function, Phylogeny and Fossils Miocene Hominoid Evolution and Adaptations.* Plenum, New York, 389–416

BISHOP, W. W. 1958. Miocene Mammalia from the Napak volcanics, Karamoja, Uganda. *Nature*, **182**, 1480–1482.

——1963. The Later tertiary and Pleistocene in Eastern equatorial Africa *In*: CLARK HOWELL, F. & BOURLIERE, F. (eds) *African Ecology and Human Evolution.* Aldine, Chicago, 146–175.

——1964. More fossil primates and other Miocene mammals from North-East Uganda. *Nature*, **203**, 1327–1331.

——1967. The later tertiary in East Africa – volcanics, sediments and faunal inventory *In*: BISHOP, W. W. & DESMOND CLARK, J. (eds) *Background to Evolution in Africa.* University of Chicago, 31–55.

—— & WHYTE, F. 1962. Tertiary mammalian faunas and sediments in Karamoja and Kavirondo, East Africa *Nature*, **196**, 1283–1287.

——, MILLER, J. A. & FITCH, F. J. 1969. New Potassium–Argon age determinations relevant to the Miocene fossil mammal sequence in East Africa. *American Journal of Science*, **267**, 669–699.

CARTMILL, M. & MILTON, K. 1977. The lorisiform wrist joint and the evolution of 'brachiating' adaptations in the Hominoidea. *American Journal of Physical Anthropology*, **47**, 249–272.

ERICSON, G. E. 1963. Brachiation in New World Primates and in anthropoid apes. *Symposia of the Zoological Society, London*, **10**,135–164.

GEBO, D. L., MACLATCHY, L., KITYO, R., DEINO, A., KINGSTON, J. & PILBEAM, D. 1997a. A hominoid genus from the Early Miocene of Uganda. *Science*, **276**, 401–404.

——,—— & ——1997b. A new lorisid humerus from the Early Miocene of Uganda. *Primates*, **38**, 423–427.

HARRISON, T. 1986. A reassessment of the phylogenetic relationships of *Oreopithecus bambolii* Gervais. *Journal of Human Evolution*, **15**, 541–583.

—— & ROOK, L. 1997. Enigmatic anthropoid or misunderstood ape? The phylogenetic status of *Oreopithecus bambolii* reconsidered. *In*: BEGUN, D. R., WARD, C. V. & ROSE, M. D. (eds) *Function, Phylogeny and Fossils Miocene Hominoid Evolution and Adaptations.* Plenum, New York, 327–362.

JUNGERS, W. L. 1984. Scaling of the hominoid locomotor skeleton with special reference to lesser apes. *In*: PREUSCHOFT, H., CHIVERS, D., BROCKELMAN, W. & CREEL, N. (eds) *The Lesser Apes.* Edinburgh University, 146–169.

——1985. Body size and scaling of limb proportions in primates. *In*: JUNGERS, W. L. (ed.) *Size and Scaling in Primate Biology.* Plenum, New York, 345–381.

KEITH, A. 1923. Man's posture: its evolution and disorders. *The British Medical Journal*, **1**, 451–454.

KELLEY, J. 1997. Paleobiological and phylogenetic significance of life history in Miocene hominoids. *In*: BEGUN, D. R., WARD, C. V. & ROSE, M. D. (eds) *Function, Phylogeny and Fossils Miocene Hominoid Evolution and Adaptations.* Plenum, New York, 173-208

LARSON, S. 1998. Parallel evolution in the hominoid trunk and forelimb *Evolutionary Anthropology*, **6**(3), 87–99.

LEAKEY, M. & WALKER, A. 1997. *Afropithecus* function and phylogeney. *In*: BEGUN, D. R., WARD, C. V. & ROSE, M. D. (eds) *Function, Phylogeny and Fossils Miocene Hominoid Evolution and Adaptations.* Plenum, New York, 225–239

LEAKEY, R., LEAKEY, M. G. & WALKER, A. C. 1988. Morphology of *Afropithecus turkanensis* from Kenya. *American Journal of Physical Anthropology*, **76**, 289–307.

MACLATCHY, L. & BOSSERT, W. 1996. An analysis of the articular surface distribution of the femoral head and acetabulum in anthropoids with implications for hip function in miocene hominoids. *Journal of Human Evolution*, **31**, 425–453.

MACLATCHY, L. M., GEBO, D. & PILBEAM, D. 1995. New primate fossils from the Lower Miocene of northeast Uganda. *American Journal of Physical Anthropology Supplement*, **18**, 139.

MARTIN, L. 1989. Fossil history of the terrestrial Carnivora. *In*: GITTLEMAN, J. (ed.) *Carnivore Behavior, Ecology and Evolution, Volume 1.* Cornell University, New York, 356–368

McCrossin, M. 1997. New postcranial remains of *Kenyapithecus* and their implications for understanding the origins of hominoid terrestriality. *American Journal of Physical Anthropology Supplement*, **24**, 164.

McCrossin, M. L. & Benefit, B. R. 1994. Maboko Island and the evolutionary history of the Old World monkeys and apes. *In*: Corruccini, R. S. & Ciochon, R. L. (eds) *Integrative Paths to the Past*. Prentice Hall, New Jersey, 95–122.

—— & ——1997. On the relationships and adaptations of *Kenyapithecus*, a large-bodied hominoid from the Middle Miocene of eastern Africa. *In*: Begun, D. R., Ward, C. V. & Rose, M. D. (eds) *Function, Phylogeny and Fossils Miocene Hominoid Evolution and Adaptations*. Plenum, New York, 241–268.

——, —— & Gitau, S. N. 1998. Functional and phylogenetic analysis of the distal radius of Kenyapithecus with comments on the origin of the African great ape and human clade. *American Journal of Physical Anthropology Supplement*, **26**, 158.

Moyà-Solà S. & Köhler, M. 1996. A *Dryopithecus* skeleton and the origins of great ape locomotion, *Nature*, **379**, 156–159.

Nengo, I. 1995. Large-bodied early Miocene catarrhines and the origin of apes. *Amererican Journal of Physical Anthropology Supplement*, **20**, 159–160.

—— & Rae, T. 1992. New hominoid fossils from the Early Miocene site of Songhor, Kenya. *Journal of Human Evolution*, **23**, 423–429.

Pickford, M., Senut, B., Hadoto, D., Musisi, J. & Kariira, C. 1986. Recent discoveries at the Miocene sites at Moroto, North-East Uganda: biostratigraphical and paleoecological implications. *C. R. Acad. Sc. Paris*, **302**, 681–687.

——, —— & Gommery, D. 1999. Sexual dimorphism in *Morotopithecus bishopi*, an early Middle Miocene hominoid from Uganda and a reassessment of its geological and biological contexts. *This volume*.

Pilbeam, D. 1996. Genetic and morphological records of the Hominoidea and hominid origins: a synthesis. *Molecular Phylogenetics and Evolution*, **5**, 155–168.

—— & Walker, A. 1968. Fossil monkeys from the Miocene of Napak, northeastern Uganda. *Nature*, **220**, 657–660.

Rafferty, K. L., Walker, A., Ruff, C. B., Rose, M. D. & Andrews, P. J. 1995. Postcranial estimates of body weight in *Proconsul*, with a note on a distal tibia of *P. major* from Napak, Uganda. *American Journal of Physical Anthropology*, **97**, 391–402.

Roberts, D. 1974. Structure and function of the primate scapula. *In*: Jenkins, F. A. (ed.) *Primate Locomotion*. Academic, New York, 171–200.

Rose, M. D. 1983. Miocene hominoid postcranial morphology: Monkey-like, ape-like, neither or both? *In*: Ciochon, R. L. & Corruccini, R. S. (eds) *New Interpretations of Ape and Human Ancestry*. Plenum, New York, 405–417.

——1993. Locomotor anatomy of Miocene Hominoids. *In*: Gebo, D. L. (ed.) *Postcranial Adaptations in Nonhuman Primates*. Northern Illinois University, DeKalb, 252–272.

——1994. Quadrupedalism in some Miocene catarrhines. *Journal of Human Evolution*, **26**, 387–411.

Ruff, C. B. 1987. Structural allometry of the femur and tibia in Hominoidea and *Macaca Folia Primatologica*, **48**, 9–49.

——, Walker, A. & Teaford, M. K. 1989. Body mass, sexual dimorphism and femoral proportions of *Proconsul* from Rusinga and Mfangano Islands, Kenya. *Journal of Human Evolution*, **18**, 515–536.

Sanders, W. J. & Bodenbender, B. E. 1994. Morphometric analysis of lumbar vertebra U.M.P. 67–28: Implications for spinal function and phylogeny of the Miocene Moroto hominoid. *Journal of Human Evolution*, **26**, 203–237.

Shapiro, L. 1993. Functional Morphology of the vertebral column in primates *In*: Gebo, D. L. (ed.) *Postcranial Adaptations in Nonhuman Primates*. Northern Illinois University, DeKalb, 121–149.

Taylor, L. 1989. Locomotor adaptations by carnivores. *In*: Gittleman, J. (ed.) *Carnivore Behavior, Ecology and Evolution, Volume 1*. Cornell University, New York, 382–409.

Walker, A. & Pickford, M. 1983. *In*: Ciochon, R. L. & Corruccini, R. S. (eds) *New Interpretations of Ape and Human Ancestry*. Plenum, New York, 325–351.

—— & Rose, M. 1968. Fossil hominoid vertebra from the Miocene of Uganda. *Nature*, **217**, 980–981.

Ward, C. V. 1991. *Functional anatomy of the lower back and pelvis of the Miocene hominoid* Proconsul nyanzae *from Mfangano Island, Kenya*. PhD thesis, Johns Hopkins University.

——1993. Torso morphology and locomotion in *Proconsul nyanzae*. *American Journal of Physical Anthropology*, **92**, 291–328.

——, Walker, A., Teaford, M. F. & Odhiambo, I. 1993. Partial skeleton of *Proconsul nyanzae* from Mfangano Island. *American Journal of Physical Anthropology*, **90**, 77–111.

Ward, S. 1997. The taxonomy and phylogenetic relationships of Sivapithecus revisited. *In*: Begun, D. R., Ward, C. V. & Rose, M. D. (eds) *Function, Phylogeny and Fossils Miocene Hominoid Evolution and Adaptations*. Plenum, New York, 269–290.

Sexual dimorphism in *Morotopithecus bishopi*, an early Middle Miocene hominoid from Uganda, and a reassessment of its geological and biological contexts

MARTIN PICKFORD,[1,2] BRIGITTE SENUT[2] & DOMINIQUE GOMMERY[2]

[1] *Chaire de Paléoanthropologie et de Préhistoire, Collège de France,*
11 Place M. Berthelot, 75005 Paris, France
[2] *Laboratoire de Paléontologie, URA 12 du CNRS, Muséum National d'Histoire Naturelle,*
8 rue Buffon, 75005 Paris, France

Abstract: A large-bodied hominoid from Uganda, recently named *Morotopithecus bishopi*, is based on a number of fossils from Moroto II (the type locality) and Moroto I a nearby site. The material from Moroto II was considered by Gebo *et al.* to belong to a single individual. Reanalysis of the material reveals that the sample from Moroto II is heterogeneous in size and morphology, suggesting the presence of at least two individuals. Other fossils from the site include a previously undescribed upper canine of female morphology which is appreciably smaller than the canines in the Moroto palate. The size and morphological differences between the various specimens from Moroto II, even though restricted in number, are compatible with the hypothesis that *M. bishopi* was a sexually dimorphic hominoid with large males and small females. A fragment of scapula from Moroto I which was assigned to *M. bishopi* is not from a primate, but belongs instead to a terrestrial quadruped. There is, however, a phalanx from the site which belongs to a large-bodied hominoid, probably *M. bishopi*. Analysis of the fauna from Moroto I and II reveals that it correlates closest to Faunal Set III of Pickford and is not as old as Faunal Set II as previously reported by Pickford *et al.* or even older. The sediments are probably aged between 15 and 17 Ma.

This volume commemorating Bill Bishop's contribution to science provides us with an opportunity to examine the history of discovery and interpretation of Moroto, one of the fossil sites in northeastern Uganda that will always be associated with his name. Bill was himself a multidisciplinary scientist and published extensively on fossil hominoids from the site, and on aspects of its geomorphology, geochronology, depositional environments and palaeoecology. The recent upturn in interest in Moroto following the belated baptism of *Morotopithecus bishopi*, the first pieces of which were found in 1961, prompts the authors to delve into the history of interpretation of the site and to describe a few fossils that have been found subsequent to Bill's pioneering work there. The aim of this contribution, apart from being a homage to Bill Bishop, is to examine diverse aspects of the site and its fossil record, all of which would have been of keen interest to him.

Discovery of the Moroto Palate and associated fossils

The fossils assigned to the holotype of *Morotopithecus bishopi* were recovered by W. W. Bishop

and colleagues over a period of several years from 1961 until 1965. At the so-called *P. major* site at Moroto II (Fig. 1) and the opposite side of the gully, called Moroto IIA, Bishop's team screened the surface rubble and superficial sediments in the gully bottom down to a depth of 'about one foot', in the process finding many of the missing teeth and much of the face belonging to the palate, parts of the left and right mandibles, three vertebrae and parts of two femora (details extracted from field notes written by Sonia Cole in 1964 and 1965). Further parts of two femora which fit onto the pieces recovered by Bishop in 1964 are reported to have been found in 1994 (Gebo *et al.*, 1997). Table 1 summarizes the long-drawn-out process of recovery of the material.

In 1985, the Uganda Palaeontology Expedition visited Moroto I and II. At Moroto I a partial phalanx of a large hominoid was found, and is here described for the first time. The outcrops at Moroto II were examined carefully during this survey, special attention being focused on the two flanks of the *P. major* gully and its bottom, but no primate fossils were found. Only a few scraps of indeterminate bone occurred on the uphill bank of the gully.

PICKFORD, M., SENUT, B. & GOMMERY, D. 1999. Sexual dimorphism in *Morotopithecus bishopi*, an early Middle Miocene hominoid from Uganda, and a reassessment of its geological and biological contexts. *In*: ANDREWS, P. & BANHAM, P. (eds) *Late Cenozoic Environments and Hominid Evolution: a tribute to Bill Bishop*. Geological Society, London, 27–38.

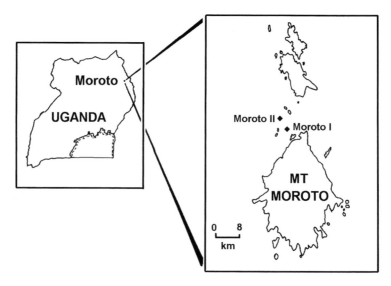

Fig. 1. Location of Moroto I and II, northern Uganda.

Table 1. *Discovery history of specimens from Moroto II, Uganda assigned to* Morotopithecus bishopi

Date	Specimen	Collectors
August 1961	Left maxilla (edentulous), fragment of right mandible	W. W. Bishop & F. Whyte
December 1961	Right maxilla and two fragments upper jaw	D. Allbrook and students
20 January 1964	3rd left molar in part of jaw, 2nd right molar, 1st left premolar, 1st right premolar, 2nd left premolar, right canine, fragment of left canine, left lateral incisor, 9 skull fragments, 11 possible primate bone fragments	S. Cole & W. W. Bishop
22 January 1964	3rd right molar, part of canine, 4 skull? fragments, 1 piece of shattered long bone (preservation cf *P. major*), 2 fragments vertebrae, 3 fragments mandible with tooth roots *P. major*, 1 part of canine, 2 fragments of mandible (one part of ascending ramus)	S. Cole & W. W. Bishop
9 February 1965	3rd molar crown, 2 mandibular fragments with tooth roots, 3 pieces of bone probably belong	S. Cole & W. W. Bishop
10 February 1965	Lower part about 1 foot depth: 1 vertebra ?taken by W.B., 22 fragments of bone (some very rolled)	S. Cole & W. W. Bishop
Unknown date (?1961)	Unworn right lower third premolar	Unknown
1994	2 primate partial femora + ?shaft fragments	D. Gebo & L. MacLatchy

In 1994, Gebo *et al.* (1997) found a fragmentary scapula at Moroto I which they assigned to *M. bishopi* and they reported finding parts of two primate femora from the *P. major* site. In October 1997, at the request of the Department of Antiquities and Museums, Kampala, the Uganda Palaeontology Expedition visited Moroto in order to introduce Ugandan palaeontologists to the area. During this brief visit the upper canine of a large-bodied hominoid was found at a site some 150 m from the Moroto II *P. major* site, and this fossil is described here.

Geological context and age of the Moroto deposits

The Moroto sediments accumulated in valleys incised into Basement Rocks of the Mozambique Belt (Bishop 1964; Bishop *et al.* 1967;

Pickford & Tassy 1980). They are overlain by basalt flows which baked the upper surface of the sediments. Initial radio-isotopic age determinations of these lavas suggested a Middle Miocene age for the Moroto deposits (Bishop *et al.* 1967; Pickford 1986*a*; Pickford *et al.* 1986). Sample MB/6 from Loitakero (= Moroto I) yielded ages of 12.5 ± 0.4 and 12.6 ± 0.4 Ma and sample MB/7 from Kogole (= Moroto II) yielded an age of 14.3 ± 0.3 Ma.

Gebo *et al.* (1997) resampled the basalt lavas which overlie the sediments at Moroto I and II and, even though, according to the authors, the samples were not of high quality, they yielded an age of 20.6 Ma at Moroto I and a poor age estimate from Moroto II. From this the authors concluded that the Moroto hominoid was about 21 Ma. After study of the Moroto fauna Pickford *et al.* (1986) reported that the site was perhaps earlier than 17.5 Ma, principally on the basis of the presence of *Pterodon nyanzae* and *Brachyodus aequatorialis* in the sample. However, the known range of *B. aequatorialis* spans the period 22.5 Ma (Meswa Bridge) to Moruorot (*c.* 16.8 Ma; Boschetto *et al.* 1992) and Gebel Zelten (*c.* 16.5 Ma; Pickford 1991) and that of *Pterodon nyanzae* ranges from 22.5 Ma (Meswa Bridge) to *c.* 15 Ma (Maboko) (Pickford 1981, 1991; Feibel & Brown 1991). Thus the presence of these two species at Moroto can no longer be taken as evidence for an age older than 17.5 Ma, their chronological ranges now extending upwards to 16.5 and 15 Ma respectively. The Moroto proboscideans *Eozygodon morotoensis* and cf *Archaeobelodon* (Pickford & Tassy 1980; Tassy & Pickford 1983) have been recorded from Moruorot (aged *c.* 16.8 Ma; Boschetto *et al.* 1992), Rusinga (aged 17.8 Ma; Drake *et al.* 1988) and Buluk, the latter site aged about 17.2 Ma (McDougall & Watkins 1985; Watkins 1989). These two proboscidean taxa have also recently been found in Auchas, Namibia in strata aged about 19–18 Ma, and their known range is from *c.* 19 to 16.8 Ma. New fossil discoveries at Moroto I and II include a small tayassuid in which the transverse lophs of the molars are scored centrally by a deep groove (Pickford 1998). The only other East African sites at which such suiforms have been recorded are Maboko, western Kenya, dated about 14.8 Ma (Feibel & Brown 1991), Muruyur, Baringo District, Kenya, which is aged *c.* 15 Ma (Pickford 1986*c*, 1988; Hill *et al.* 1991), a site which, like Moroto, has also yielded the rodent *Diamantomys*, and Kirimun, Kenya, aged *c.* 15 Ma (Matsuda *et al.* 1986). Even though the fauna from Moroto is restricted in diversity, it suggests a Middle Miocene age (Faunal Set III) meaning that the

sediments are unlikely to be as old as 20.6 Ma, but probably lie somewhere between 15 and 17 Ma, a suggestion already made by Pickford (1986*b*).

Gebo *et al.* (1997) have proposed major changes to scenarios of hominoid evolution based on the Moroto specimens and their purported age greater than 20.6 Ma. The present authors consider that the Moroto hominoid is closely related to *Proconsul major* from Napak, Songhor and Chamtwara and that it is younger than these specimens, rather than being older than them. The evolutionary scenarios will obviously be rather different depending upon the age assigned to them.

Material assigned to the Moroto hominoid

Skull

As described by Pilbeam (1969) and Gebo *et al.* (1997) the skull of *Morotopithecus bishopi* consists of the greater part of the palate (UMP 62–11) with all the teeth except for the right central incisor which was lost some time prior to death of the individual, as revealed by the spongy texture of the infilling of its alveolus. In addition there are parts of the face leading up to the intraorbital region with its prominent nasals (Pilbeam 1969: fig. 19). The size and shape of the canines reveals that this individual is probably a male. A consequence of the massive canines is the enlarged aspect of the anterior end of the snout which, in palatal view, widens anteriorly towards the canines.

The teeth have been described in detail by Pilbeam (1969) and it is not necessary to repeat his studies save to point out that the premolars are anteroposteriorly short, the molars bunodont with wrinkled enamel and prominent, beaded lingual cingula. Superficially the teeth of *Morotopithecus bishopi* recall those of *Proconsul major* from Napak (Uganda) and Songhon in Kenya, but, as noted by Martin (1981), the upper incisors, canines and premolars and the third molar in the Moroto palate are appreciably larger than those from the Kenyan sample whilst the first and second molars are similar in size.

Upper female canine

An upper left canine of a large-bodied hominoid was found 150 m from the Moroto palate site. The cervix of the canine (Fig. 2/2) is narrower than the crown, and the root possesses a waist below the cervix. This morphology contrasts with that of the partially reconstructed canines

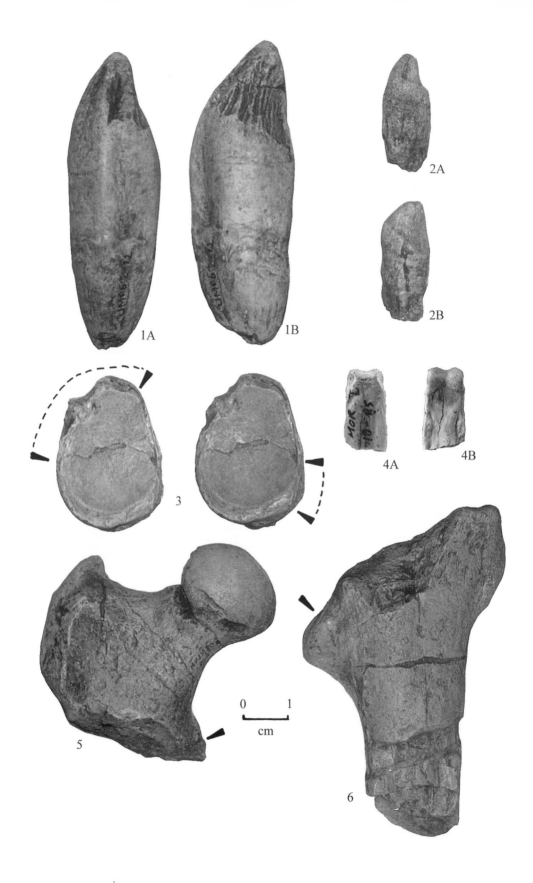

1A   1B   2A

2B

3   4A   4B

0   1
cm

5   6

Table 2. *Measurements (in mm) of upper canines from Moroto II*

Specimen	Mesio-distal length	Bucco-lingual breadth	Labial crown height
UMP 62–11 left	18.6	15.0	27.6
UMP 62–11 right	18.1	15.7	25.0
UMP 62–12 left	17.6	16.1	22.0
Moroto IIa left	11.4	9.1	11.5

Measurements of UMP 62–11 are estimated from reconstructions.

in the Moroto palate in which the crowns are widest at cervix and in which there is no waisting of the root. The isolated upper canine UMP 62–12, also from Moroto II (Fig. 2/1) is comparable to those in the Moroto palate (Pilbeam 1969). The overall shape of the new canine indicates that it is most probably that of a female individual. The mesial surface of the crown possesses a deep groove that extends from the apex towards the cervix, ending at a prominent cingulum. There is a crest from apex to cervix along the disto-labial edge of the crown which has been enhanced by wear against the P_3. The base of the crown on the labial side sports a cingulum. This tooth is appreciably smaller and lower crowned than the canines in the Moroto palate, which evidently represents a male individual. Measurements of the hominoid canines from Moroto are presented in Table 2.

Mandible

The mandible from Moroto II was described by Pilbeam (1969: fig. 20). The more complete of the two corpora is the left one which, even though badly broken and eroded, is continuous from the front of the canine root to the lower part of the ramus. The canine root is massive, indicating that it is probably a male individual, and its discovery locus suggests that it may well belong to the same individual as the palate. The maximum and minimum dimensions of the left lower canine root, measured near the cervix are 18 mm × 12.5 mm.

An unnumbered right P_3 of a large hominoid collected at Moroto, probably in 1961, is

unworn. The base of the crown is not present, but the tooth is otherwise in good condition. Maximum preserved length is 11.7 mm and the maximum preserved breadth is 9 mm. The mesial crest ends in a low tubercle just above cervix level and the honing surface, even though unworn, is flat and has a wide triangular outline. There is a narrow cingulum on the mesio-lingual aspect of the crown. Three crests descend from the tip down the distal aspect of the crown comprising large lingual and distal crests with a third, smaller, crest between them. The distal crest ends in a small tubercle immediately above the cervix. This tooth most probably belongs to *Morotopithecus bishopi* on account of its size and discovery locus. The large honing surface suggests that it represents a male individual.

Scapula

The left scapula fragment from Moroto I assigned to *Morotopithecus bishopi* by Gebo *et al.* (1997) and described briefly by MacLatchy (1995) and MacLatchy *et al.* (1995) consists of part of the glenoid cavity, neck and the proximal part of the spine base. About a third of the margin of the glenoid cavity is broken away on either side of the glenoid notch and on the margin of the cavity opposite the notch. Thus the margin of the glenoid cavity, as preserved, does not reflect its original outline. The specimen lacks the coracoid process and the supraglenoid tubercle. A remnant of a deep and narrow glenoid notch is visible (Fig. 2/3), being a non-hominoid feature (Senut 1981). A little of the neck of the scapula is preserved, but there is

Fig. 2.1 (A) Mesial and (B) lingual views of left upper male canine (cast) from Moroto II, Uganda 2 (A) Mesial and (B) lingual views of UMP 62–12 left upper female canine (cast) from Moroto II, Uganda. 3 Stereo view of glenoid cavity of a non-hominoid scapula from Moroto I Uganda (cast). Note the remnants of a glenoid notch (irregular depression in upper left sector of the cavity) and the broken and damaged perimeter of the piece (dashed lines between arrows). 4 MOR I 10′85, the distal end of a phalanx from Moroto I provisionally assigned to *Morotopithecus bishopi*: (A) dorsal view; (B) volar view. 5 Anterior aspect of MUZM 80, right femur (cast) from Moroto II showing orientation of lesser trochanter (arrow). 6 Anterior aspect of MUZM 80, left femur (cast) from Moroto II showing orientation of lesser trochanter (arrow). Note the additional piece of shaft added to the original specimen described and figured by Gebo *et al.* (1997). Scale bar for all parts is 1 cm.

part of the base of the acromion present. There is a continuous broken surface between the base of the spine and the part where the coracoid process has broken away. The latter was probably confluent with the supraglenoid tubercle, another non-hominoid character. The bone is over 10 mm thick in this area, whereas in primates this region is usually appreciably thinner. The infraglenoid tuberosity is wide and corrugated. In *Pan* the glenoid process flares towards its margins from a dorsoventrally narrow neck, whereas in the Moroto scapula the slope from the glenoid towards the blade is flatter and more uniform as in many artiodactyls and carnivores. The dorsal and ventral aspects of the glenoid process possess a system of trabeculae running parallel to the margin of the glenoid cavity. The strength and disposition of these trabecular ridges indicate that the scapula was habitually under compressive forces and not in tension as is the case with climbing and suspensory apes. Whilst we have been unable to identify the species to which the Moroto scapula belongs we are confident that it differs so widely from those of great apes and humans that it is unlikely to represent a hominoid.

Vertebrae

Parts of three hominoid lumbar vertebrae are known from Moroto II (MOR 1'61 (= UMP 67–28), Mor II 61 (two fragments) and MOR IIa Jan 62 (two fragments)). One of these has been described in detail by Walker & Rose (1968) and has been reassessed by Ward (1993, 1997), Sanders & Bodenbender (1994) and Gebo *et al.* (1997). The other two specimens are fragmentary parts of vertebral bodies and neural arches and add little additional information about the species. The morphology of the specimens accords with their being assigned to a large-bodied hominoid such as *Morotopithecus bishopi*, as does their discovery at the same locality and at the same time as the mandible and maxillae of this species. We agree that this species probably had a lower back which was closer in its morphofunctional relationships to that of extant African apes than it is to that of smaller *Proconsul* species.

Femora

There are parts of two primate femora from Moroto II. One, from the right side, is relatively well preserved but lacks a significant proportion of the diaphysis, while the other, from the left side, is much more fragmentary and has been rolled and abraded, thereby losing an appreciable amount of cortical bone in places. Never-

theless, enough of the proximal end remains for its gross morphology to be made out, especially when the piece collected by Bishop is added (Fig. 2/6). Comparison of the proximal portions of these two femora (Fig. 2/5, 6) reveals the presence of significant size and morphological differences of a degree that is greater than occurs in two femora from the same individual, from which we conclude that the rolled femur probably does not belong to the same individual as the better preserved specimen, and in all likelihood it represents a smaller individual.

In posterior aspect the right femur has a lesser trochanter which projects laterally to a marked extent. In the left femur, the lesser trochanter projects more distally (Fig. 2/6). Furthermore, in the right femur the anterior margin of the lesser trochanter forms a steep angle with the basal part of the neck of the femur, whereas in the left femur this angle is more open. The small fossa located anterior to the lesser trochanter is better developed in the right femur than it is in the left one. The greater trochanter of the right femur is uniformly convex from its anterior end to the point where it merges with the diaphysis, while in the left femur there is a distinct concavity in its profile near its distal limit. Whilst some of the differences noted above may have been slightly enhanced by erosion of the left femur with consequent minor loss of cortex, the overall appearance of the two specimens suggests that they belong to two different morphological groups. It remains to be determined whether the differences are due to the presence of two taxa in the deposits or whether they reflect sexual differences in a single species, although, on the basis of available evidence, we consider the latter possibility to be more likely.

Phalanx

MOR 10'85 is the distal half of a phalanx (Fig. 2/4) of a large primate found at Moroto I by members of the Uganda Palaeontology Expedition in 1985. Its size is compatible with what would be expected for *Morotopithecus bishopi*. In volar aspect there is a flattened shaft bordered medially and laterally by low but strong ridges for the flexors. The dorsal surface is more evenly curved, but possesses a shallow gutter which merges distally into the open valley which divides the articular surface into two halves. In dorsal view the shaft narrows distally towards the articular facets. On each side of the distal end there are prominent crests for ligamentous attachments. In lateral view the shaft is curved, especially the articular part which bends substantially volarly. The distal articular facets are 8.7 mm wide at their widest part and are 6.1 mm high. The curved shaft of this phalanx indicates that it was probably from an arboreal animal. Its size and overall morphology suggest that it is from a large-bodied ape, and we here provisionally assign it to *Morotopithecus bishopi*.

Dental sexual dimorphism in *Morotopithecus*

There is no consensus in the literature about what degree of variation in fossil primates can be subsumed under sexual dimorphism. Pickford's (1986*b*) study of dimorphism in various *Proconsul* species was severely criticised by Teaford *et al.* (1993) and Plavcan (1993) who insisted that the Rusinga sample of *Proconsul* must contain two species (*P. nyanzae* and *P. heseloni*) instead of a single highly dimorphic species (*P. nyanzae*). Both of these commentators approached the question from a neontological angle, backing up their approach with a plea for uniformitarianism. However, uniformitarianism is to do with processes and not outcomes or events. Whilst it is evident that the various degrees of

sexual dimorphism that we observe in extant primates are the result of evolutionary processes, they cannot be interpreted within a strict uniformitarian framework. Modern samples may be used as an actualistic guide but no more. There are several reasons for this, one of which is that all available samples of extant primates underestimate the degree of dimorphism in the species for the simple reason that the specimens have been garnered from a minute proportion of the population of that species and from an infinitesimally short period of its existence. Thus modern analogues will always underestimate the totality of dimorphisms that a lineage exhibited during its lifetime. The concept that Teaford *et al.* have used is not uniformitarianism – it is actualism, which is quite a different concept and which also has its limitations for interpreting the past.

That said, the presence of two kinds of hominoid canines at Moroto can mean one of two things. Either there are two species of large-bodied hominoid at the site, or there is a single sexually dimorphic hominoid in which dimorphism was as marked as it is in *Gorilla gorilla* (Fig. 3). It is as great as dimorphism inferred for *Proconsul* from Rusinga Island (Pickford 1986*b*)

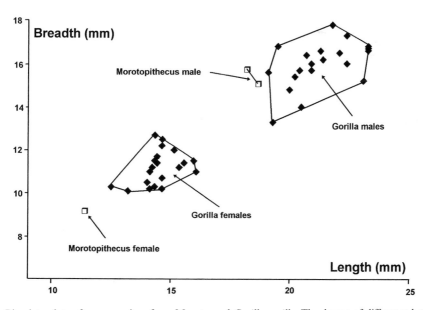

Fig. 3. Bivariate plots of upper canines from Moroto and *Gorilla gorilla*. The degree of difference between the Moroto sample is compatible with its interpretation as an example of sexual dimorphism within a single species *Morotopithecus bishopi*. It is less likely that the small canine of female morphology represents a second species of hominoid at the site.

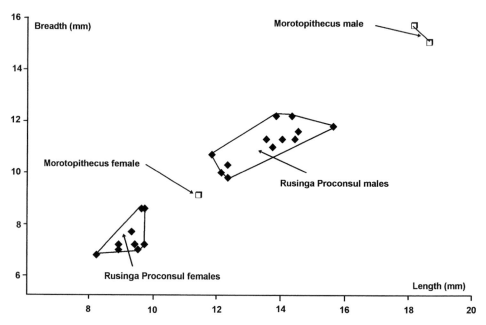

Fig. 4. Bivariate plots of upper canines from Moroto and pooled samples of *Proconsul* from Rusinga Island.

(Fig. 4) and *Kenyapithecus* from Nachola (Ishida *et al*. 1991). In order to throw light on the matter we made metric comparisons with these taxa (*Gorilla, Proconsul* and *Kenyapithecus*).

Pickford (1986*b*) examined a sample of 24 upper canines from Rusinga (nine females, 15 males) assigned to *Proconsul*, and concluded that even though the degree of dimorphism at Rusinga was greater than in any extant primate, only a single sexually dimorphic species occurred there (Fig. 4). The main reason for proposing this conclusion was that subdivision of the sample into two species would have led to the unlikely result that one of the species was represented only by males and the other only by females. The dimorphism index (mean basal crown area of males/mean basal crown area of females rounded out to the nearest 10) for this species, *Proconsul nyanzae*, was calculated to be 210% which is greater than that of the gorilla (190%) and the chimpanzee (160%) (Ishida *et al*. 1991). Teaford *et al*. (1993) were unable to accept such a high index of dimorphism and opted instead for a subdivision of the Rusinga sample into two species. The problem of sex representation remains, however, with their species *P. nyanzae*

being represented only by males and their species *Proconsul heseloni* being represented only by females.

Ishida *et al*. (1991) presented data from a homogeneous sample of *Kenyapithecus* from the Aka Aiteputh Formation at Nachola, Northern Kenya. The specimens came from a small area and from a thin bed of shales intercalated between basalt lavas. Their sample consisted of 15 upper canines which could be measured. The measurements clustered into two groups which the authors interpreted to represent males and females of a single species, an interpretation supported by considerations of gross morphology. Calculations yielded a dimorphism index of 225% for the upper canines from Nachola. Thus at Nachola, variability is greater than in any extant hominoid. As with the Rusinga sample, a subdivision of the Nachola sample into two species in order to make it conform to expectations based on actualism, would lead to the same result – the larger species would be represented only by male specimens, the smaller one only by females. It is less likely that, in the sample, there are two morphologically similar but dimorphic species with overlapping variation.

The degree of dimorphism that Pickford accepted at Rusinga and that Ishida *et al.* (1991) demonstrated for the Nachola hominoid, is indeed greater than that known for any extant primate species. But the Rusinga and Nachola samples are not the only ones available that show such elevated degrees of dimorphism. Similar degrees of dimorphism have been documented in hominoids from Songhor, Koru, Maboko and Fort Ternan (Kelley 1986; Pickford 1985, 1986*b*). In all these sites large hominoid canines possess male morphology and small ones have female morphology. Similar degrees of dimorphism have been recorded in Chinese hominoid samples (Kelley & Xu 1991) and other samples from Eurasia. Now, a similar situation arises at Moroto. With the approach employed by Teaford *et al.* (1993) and Plavcan (1993) the hominoids from each of these sites would have to be subdivided into two taxa, one of which would be represented only by males, the other only by females. This seems to be a misunderstanding of what can be explained by actualism. It seems more realistic biologically to accept the premise that some species of fossil hominoids exhibited greater degrees of dimorphism than any living species.

The canine dimorphism for the small sample of Moroto canines (three males and one female) has been calculated using the same formula as the one used by Ishida *et al.* (1991). The procedure yields a figure of 271% which at first glance seems excessive. If, however, we take the second largest male specimen and the second smallest female specimen from Nachola and perform the same exercise, an index of 288% is obtained, a figure which is appreciably greater than that for Moroto. If we perform a similar calculation on gorilla specimens, figures as high as 376% can be obtained depending upon the specimens included in the calculation. From this we infer that the single female canine available from Moroto is from the small end of the range of variation, and that the most plausible hypothesis is that the Moroto sample of canines represents a single species. If we don't accept this degree of dimorphism, then once again we must postulate the presence of two species at the site, one known only from males, the other only from a female.

Thus, of the two possibilities – two sexes or two taxa – we consider it more likely that *Morotopithecus bishopi* was sexually dimorphic to an extent that is as great as that documented in Nachola *Kenyapithecus* and Rusinga *Proconsul* and that all the large-bodied hominoid remains found thus far at Moroto probably represent a single species.

Taxonomic history of the Moroto palate and associated fossils

Despite the completeness of the Moroto palate, the specimen has had a chequered taxonomic history. Initially it was described as being a classic example of *Proconsul major* (Bishop 1963, 1964; Allbrook & Bishop 1963). In 1963, Leakey wrote that it was not *Proconsul* but a pongid ancestral to *Gorilla*, and he repeated this claim in 1970. In view of current debates about the affinities of *Proconsul* and the Moroto hominoid (Ward 1993, 1997; Sanders & Bodenbender 1994; Gebo *et al.* 1997), Leakey's (1963) classification and phylogenetic interpretation, even though not supported by any anatomical evidence, appears prophetic, yet it has seldom been acknowledged or discussed in the literature.

Letters housed in the archives of the Palaeontology Division, Uganda Museum, Kampala, have proved to be an interesting source for understanding early interpretations of the Moroto hominoid. In a letter to W. W. Bishop dated 7 October 1964, D. Pilbeam wrote that 'the material is particularly splendid. The palate is certainly "*Proconsul major*"'. In a letter to B. Campbell dated 28 December 1964, W. W. Bishop wrote that he was hoping that he would find more of the beast to prove without any question that it was *Proconsul major* and not yet another new and exciting primate to complicate the already overcrowded family tree. By 1965, L. S. B. Leakey had formed the opinion that the Moroto palate represented a genus distinct from *Proconsul*, and in a letter to W. W. Bishop dated 9 April 1965, suggested the name '*Perigorilla*' for it. Bishop agreed that it could represent a new genus, but replied to Leakey on 18 April 1965 that he could observe no significant differences between the Moroto palate and the Kenyan fossils assigned to *Proconsul major*. In view of the fact that Kenyan *P. major* and the Moroto hominoids share some derived characters not found in other species of *Proconsul* (Martin 1981), Bishop's suggestion that the two belong to a genus distinct from *Proconsul* also merits the credit which until now has not been acknowledged. Leakey (1967, 1970) wrote that he was preparing a note in which he intended to create a new genus for the Moroto hominoid, but apparently this paper was never published. Gebo *et al.* (1997) reported that Leakey had referred the Moroto palate to *Pseudogorilla*, but the reference cited (Leakey 1962) mentions neither the Moroto palate nor the name *Pseudogorilla*. In 1967, Leakey wrote that he was preparing to create a new genus for the palate (Leakey 1967) and in 1970 he discussed the material without using a name for it, only saying that it was not *Proconsul major* (Leakey 1970). The first mention attributing the name *Pseudogorilla* to Leakey (1962) appears to be that of Schwartz (1986) but the basis for this citation appears to be erroneous.

In 1969, Pilbeam (1969) concluded that the Moroto palate was only subgenerically distinct from European *Dryopithecus* and that it should be designated *Dryopithecus (Proconsul) major*. Andrews (1978) classified the Moroto specimens as *Proconsul (Proconsul) major*. With the discovery of a set of upper teeth at Chamtwara, Kenya, and some material from Meswa Bridge which belong to *Proconsul major* (Andrews *et al.* 1981; Martin 1981) it became clear that the Moroto palate did not represent the same species as the Kenyan fossils assigned to *P. major*. In 1981, Martin concluded that the Moroto palate differed from the expanded Kenyan sample of *Proconsul major* in several important respects and that it could no longer be considered to belong to this species. This view was reiterated by Pickford (1986*b*) and Pickford *et al.* (1986).

The Moroto palate subsequently lay in taxonomic limbo for a number of years until the description of *Afropithecus* by Leakey *et al.* (1988), whereupon it was suggested that it belonged to this genus, being only specifically distinct from it. Leakey *et al.* (1988) and Leakey & Walker (1997) suggested that it is probable that the Kalodirr material (*Afropithecus turkanensis*) and the Moroto palate are congeneric but specifically distinct. Andrews (1992; Andrews *et al.* 1997) agreed with this view by classing the specimens as *?Afropithecus turkanensis*. Kelley & Pilbeam (1986) and Ward (1997), in contrast, considered that the Moroto palate differed so widely from both *Proconsul* and *Afropithecus* in maxillary and dental anatomy, that its current taxonomic status was thereby rendered indeterminate. The diversity of views is remarkable considering that the Moroto palate is one of the most complete specimens of a large-bodied hominoid known from the Miocene of Africa. Much more fragmentary specimens appear to have caused considerably less difficulty for most palaeoanthropologists.

Recently, Gebo *et al.* (1997) reinterpreted the Moroto II hominoid fossils and described some bones (femora from Moroto II, scapula from Moroto I) that had not previously been published, and named the new genus and species *Morotopithecus bishopi*. The presence of shared dental morphology in *Morotopithecus* and *Proconsul major* from Kenya such as blade-like tips to the canines as opposed to pointed canine tips that occur in *P. nyanzae* and *P. africanus*

(Martin 1981), suggests that these two taxa may well share a closer relationship than either of them does to any other known Miocene hominoid. Thus, *P. major* may have to be removed from the genus *Proconsul* as suggested (but never published) by Bishop in 1965. Previous (Rafferty *et al.* 1995) and ongoing studies of postcranial elements from Napak assigned to *P. major* (Gommery *et al.* 1998) may throw some light on the problem, in particular whether *P. major* should be retained within the genus *Proconsul*. The old assumption that *P. major* is virtually an upscaled version of *P. nyanzae* and *P. africanus* may be incorrect, and if so, this would affect many published scenarios about its affinities.

Phylogenetic interpretations of *Morotopithecus*

Gebo *et al.* (1997) agreed with Ward (1993) and Sanders & Bodenbender (1994) that the vertebral column of *Morotopithecus* is more derived towards the pattern that occurs in extant great apes and humans than is that of *Proconsul*. If the supposed antiquity of Moroto according to Gebo *et al.* (1997) (predating most known *Proconsul* fossils) is accepted, then the timing of phylogenetic events among early Miocene African hominoids will need revision, in particular the timing of the evolution of a vertebral column of modern (derived) aspect. However, if the age of Moroto II is revised upwards, as we believe should be the case, then the origin of this derived morphology could have occurred considerably later and could therefore have evolved from the (primitive) *Proconsul* pattern of the vertebral column as expressed in *Proconsul nyanzae* (in which we include *P. heseloni*).

The proposal that *Morotopithecus* belongs to a clade along with the extant African apes and humans, led Gebo *et al.* (1997) to exclude *Graecopithecus*, *Otavipithecus*, *Afropithecus* and *Kenyapithecus* from having any role in the evolution of extant African and Asian apes. But *Morotopithecus* is not the only Miocene hominoid to possess derived morphology of the vertebral column. The atlas of *Otavipithecus* from late Middle Miocene deposits of Namibia is morphologically close to that of the chimpanzee (Senut & Gommery 1997) and for this and other reasons, including its mandibular and dental morphology (Conroy *et al.* 1992) and its elbow morphology (Senut & Gommery 1997) we would not exclude it from having lain close to or within the lineage that eventually gave rise to extant African apes and humans.

We feel sure that, had he been able to, Bill Bishop would have closely followed the debate that has centred on the Moroto palate and the locality from which it came and would no doubt be amused to know that he had found bits of its femora which fit onto pieces collected almost 30 years to the day after his own discoveries.

We thank S. Bishop for encouragement to contribute a paper to the proceedings of the Bill Bishop Memorial Symposium. An article highlighting the history of some of Bill's discoveries at Moroto is appropriate, especially in view of recent reinterpretations of the hominoid fossils found there. This paper could not have been written had it not been for the excellent co-operation that we have had with the Ministry of Tourism, Wildlife and Antiquities, Uganda (P. Wamala), the Department of Antiquities and Museums, Kampala where the Moroto fossils are curated (E. Kamuhangire, E. Musiime), the Geology Department, Makerere University, Kampala (I. Ssemnanda), the Uganda National Council for Science and Technology, Kampala, (Z. Nyiira, J. F. Kakule, C. Mugoya), the Uganda Geological Survey and Mines Department, Entebbe, (S. Mboijana, D. Hadoto), the French Ministry of Foreign Affairs (A. Peltier, J. C. Hainglaise), the National Museum of Natural History, Paris, (Ph. Taquet), and the Collège de France, (Y. Coppens). Funding for the UPE was provided by the DGRCST of the French Ministry of Foreign Affairs (J.-C. Jacq), the Collège de France (Y. Coppens) and GDR 983 of the CNRS. Thanks to T. Harrison for the reference to Schwartz (1986).

References

ALLBROOK, D. & BISHOP, W. W. 1963. New fossil hominoid material from Uganda. *Nature*, **197**, 1187–1190.

ANDREWS, P. J. 1978. A revision of the Miocene Hominoidea of East Africa. *Bulletin of the British Museum of Natural History*, **30**, 85–224.

ANDREWS, P. 1992. Evolution and environment in the Hominoidea. *Nature*, **360**, 641–646.

——, BEGUN, D. & ZYLSTRA, M. 1997. Interrelationships between Functional Morphology and Paleoenvironments in Miocene Hominoids. *In*: BEGUN, D. R. WARD, C. V. & ROSE, M. D. (eds) *Function, Phylogeny, and Fossils: Miocene Hominoid Evolution and Adaptations*. Plenum, New York, 29–58.

——, HARRISON, T., MARTIN, L. & PICKFORD, M. 1981. Hominoid Primates from a new Miocene locality named Meswa Bridge in Kenya. *Journal of Human Evolution*, **10**, 123–128.

BISHOP, W. W. 1963. Uganda's animal ancestors. *Wildlife and Sport*, **3**(3), 1–8.

——1964. More fossil Primates and other Miocene mammals from north-east Uganda. *Nature*, **203**, 1327–1331.

——, MILLER, J. A. & FITCH, F. W. 1967. New potassium-argon age determinations relevant to the Miocene fossil mammal sequence in East Africa. *American Journal of Science*, **267**, 669–699.

BOSCHETTO, H. B., BROWN, F. H. & McDOUGALL, I. 1992. Stratigraphy of the Lothidok Range, northern Kenya, and K-Ar ages of its Miocene Primates. *Journal of Human Evolution*, **22**, 47–71.

CONROY, G., PICKFORD, M., SENUT, B., VAN COUVERING, J. A. & MEIN, P. 1992. *Otavipithecus namibiensis*, first Miocene hominoid from southern Africa. *Nature*, **356**, 144–148.

DRAKE, R., VAN COUVERING, J. A., PICKFORD, M., CURTIS, G. & HARRIS, J. A. 1988. New chronology for the early Miocene mammalian faunas of Kisingiri, Western Kenya. *Journal of the Geological Society of London*, **145**, 479–491.

FEIBEL, C. S. & BROWN, F. H. 1991. Age of the Primate-bearing deposits on Maboko Island, Kenya. *Journal of Human Evolution*, **21**, 221–225.

GEBO, D. L., MACLATCHY, L., KITYO, R., DEINO, A., KINGSTON, J. & PILBEAM, D. 1997. A hominoid genus from the Early Miocene of Uganda. *Science*, **276**, 401–404.

GOMMERY, D., SENUT, B. & PICKFORD, M. 1998. New hominoid postcranial remains from the early Miocene of Napak, Uganda. *Annales de Paléontologie*, **84**, 287–306.

HILL, A., BEHRENSMEYER, K., BROWN, B., DEINO, A., ROSE, M., SAUNDERS, J. WARD, S. & WINKLER, A. 1991. Kipsaramon: A lower Miocene hominoid site in the Tugen Hills, Baringo District, Kenya. *Journal of Human Evolution*, **20**, 67–75.

ISHIDA, H., MBUA, E. NAKANO, Y. & YASUI, K. 1991. Sexual dimorphism in canine size of *Kenyapithecus* from Nachola, Northern Kenya. *In*: EHARA, A. (ed.) *Primatology Today*, Elsevier, Amsterdam, 517–520.

KELLEY, J. 1986. Species recognition and sexual dimorphism in *Proconsul* and *Rangwapithecus*. *Journal of Human Evolution*, **15**, 461–495.

—— & PILBEAM, D. R. 1986. The dryopithecines: taxonomy, comparative anatomy and phylogeny of Miocene large hominoids. In: SWINDLER, D. R. & IRWIN, J. (eds) *Comparative Primate Biology*. Liss, New York, 361–411.

—— & XU, Q. 1991. Extreme sexual dimorphism in a Miocene hominoid. *Nature*, **352**, 151–153.

LEAKEY, L. S. B. 1962 (1961). A new lower Pliocene fossil primate from Kenya. *Annals and Magazine of Natural History*, **13**(4), 689–697.

——1963. East African fossil Hominoidea and the classification within this super-family. *In*: WASHBURN, S. L. (ed.) *Classification and Human Evolution*. Aldine, Chicago, 32–49.

——1967. Notes on the mammalian faunas from the Miocene and Pleistocene of East Africa. *In*: BISHOP, W. W. & CLARK, J. D. (eds) *Background to Evolution in Africa*. Chicago University, 7–28.

——1970. Introduction. *In*: LEAKEY, L. S. B. *The Stone Age Races of Kenya*. Oxford University.

LEAKEY, M. G. & WALKER, A. 1997. *Afropithecus* Function and Phylogeny. *In*: BEGUN, D. R., WARD, C. V. & ROSE, M. D. (eds) *Function, Phylogeny, and Fossils: Miocene Hominoid Evolution and Adaptations*. Plenum, New York, 225–239.

LEAKEY, R. E., LEAKEY, M. G. & WALKER, A. 1988. Morphology of *Afropithecus turkanensis* from Kenya. *American Journal of Physical Anthropology*, **76**, 289–307.

MACLATCHY, L. M. 1995. Postcranial adaptations in Miocene hominoids. *Journal of Vertebrate Paleontology, Abstracts*, **15**(3), 41A.

MACLATCHY, L. GEBO, D. & PILBEAM, D. 1995. New primate fossils from the Lower Miocene of Northeast Uganda. *American Journal of Physical Anthropology, Supplement*, **20**, 139.

MARTIN, L. 1981. New specimens of *Proconsul* from Koru, Kenya. *Journal of Human Evolution*, **10**, 139–150.

MATSUDA, T., TORII, M., KOYAGUCHI, T., MAKINOU-CHI, T., MITSUSHIO, H. & ISHIDA, S. 1986. Geochronology of Miocene hominoids east of the Kenya Rift Valley. *In:* ELSE, J. G. & LEE, P. C. (eds) *Primate Evolution*. Cambridge University, 35–47.

MCDOUGALL, I. & WATKINS, R. 1985. Age of hominoid-bearing sequence at Buluk, northern Kenya. *Nature*, **318**, 175–178.

PICKFORD, M. 1981. Preliminary Miocene Mammalian biostratigraphy for Western Kenya. *Journal of Human Evolution*, **10**, 73–97.

——1985. A new look at *Kenyapithecus* based on recent collections from Western Kenya. *Journal of Human Evolution*, **14**, 113–143.

——1986a. The geochronology of Miocene higher primate faunas of East Africa. *In:* ELSE, J. G. & LEE, P. C. (eds) *Primate Evolution*. Cambridge University, 19–33.

——1986b. Sexual dimorphism in *Proconsul*. *Human Evolution*, **1**, 111–148.

——1986c. A revision of the Miocene Suidae and Tayassuidae of Africa. *Tertiary Research Special Paper*, **7**, 1–83.

——1988. Geology and fauna of the Mid-Miocene Muruyur Beds, Baringo District, Kenya. *Human Evoution*, **3**, 381–390.

——1991. Biostratigraphic correlation of the middle Miocene mammal locality of Jabal Zaltan, Libya. *In:* SALEM, M. J. (ed.) *The Geology of Libya*, Vol. 4. Elsevier, Amsterdam, 1483–1490.

——1998. A new genus of Tayassuidae (Mammalia) from the middle Miocene of Uganda and Kenya. *Annales de Paléontologie*, **84**, 275–285.

—— & TASSY, P. 1980. A new species of *Zygolophodon* (Mammalia, Proboscidea) from the Miocene hominoid localities of Meswa Bridge and Moroto (East Africa). *Neues Jahrbuch fur Geologie und Palaeontologie Abhandlungen*, **4**, 235–251.

——, SENUT, B., HADOTO, D., MUSISI, J. & KARIIRA, C. 1986. Découvertes récentes dans les sites Miocènes de Moroto (Ouganda oriental): aspects biostratigraphiques et paléoécologiques. *Comptes-rendus de l'Academie des Sciences de Paris*, **302**, 681–686.

PILBEAM, D. R. 1969. Tertiary Pongidae of East Africa: Evolutionary relationships and taxonomy. *Bulletin of the Peabody Museum of Natural History*, **31**, 1–185.

PLAVCAN, M. 1993. Catarrhine dental variability and species recognition in the fossil record. *In:* KIMBEL, W. H. & MARTIN, L. B. (eds) *Species, Species Concepts, and Primate Evolution*, Plenum, New York, 239–264.

RAFFERTY, K. L., WALKER, A., RUFF, C. ROSE, M. D. & ANDREWS, P. J. 1995. Postcranial estimates of body weights in *Proconsul*, with a note on a distal tibia of *P. major* from Napak, Uganda. *American Journal of Physical Anthropology*, **97**, 391–402.

SANDERS, W. J. & BODENBENDER, B. E. 1994. Morphometric analysis of lumbar vertebra UMP 67–28: Implications for spinal function and phylogeny of the Miocene Moroto hominoid. *Journal of Human Evolution*, **26**, 203–237.

SENUT, B. 1981. L'humérus et ses articulations chez les hominidés plio-pléistocènes. *Cahiers de Paléontologie (Paléoanthropologie)*, 1–141.

—— & GOMMERY, D. 1997. Squelette postcrânien d'*Otavipithecus*, Hominoidea du Miocène moyen de Namibie. *Annales de Paléontologie*, **83**, 267–284.

SCHWARTZ, J. 1986. Primate systematics and a classification of the Order. *In:* SWINDLER, D. R. (ed.) *Comparative Primate Biology, Vol. 1, Systematics, Evolution and Anatomy*. Liss, New York, 1–41.

TASSY, P. & PICKFORD, M. 1983. Un nouveau mastodonte zygolophodonte (Proboscidea, Mammalia) dans le Miocène inférieur d'Afrique orientale: systématique et paléoenvironnement. *Geobios*, **16**, 53–77.

TEAFORD, M.. WALKER, A. & MUGAISI, G. S. 1993. Species discrimination in *Proconsul* from Rusinga and Mfwangano Islands, Kenya. *In:* KIMBEL, W. H. & MARTIN, L. B. (eds) *Species, Species Concepts, and Primate Evolution*. Plenum, New York, 373–392.

WALKER, A. & ROSE, M. 1968. Fossil hominoid vertebra from the Miocene of Uganda. *Nature*, **217**, 980–981.

WARD, C. V. 1993. Torso morphology and locomotion in catarrhines: Implications for the positional behavior of *Proconsul nyanzae*. *American Journal of Physical Anthropology*, **92**, 291–328.

——1997. Functional anatomy and phyletic implications of the hominoid trunk and hindlimb. *In:* BEGUN, D. R. WARD, C. V. & ROSE, M. D. (eds) *Function, Phylogeny, and Fossils: Miocene Hominoid Evolution and Adaptations*. Plenum, New York, 101–130.

WARD, S. 1997. The taxonomic and phylogenetic relationships of *Sivapithecus* revisited. *In:* BEGUN, D. R., WARD, C. V. & ROSE, M. D. (eds) *Function, Phylogeny, and Fossils: Miocene Hominoid Evolution and Adaptations*. Plenum, New York, 269–290.

WATKINS, R. T. 1989. The Buluk Member, a fossil hominoid-bearing sedimentary sequence of Miocene age from Northern Kenya. *Journal of African Earth Sciences*, **8**, 107–112.

Part II. Middle Miocene to Pleistocene of the Tugen Hills, Kenya

After his return to England, initially to Bedford College and later as Professor of Geology at Queen Mary College, both colleges of the University of London, Bill Bishop turned his attentions to Kenya. He already had good connections there with Louis Leakey and through his dating work on East African fossiliferous sediments generally, and he joined B. C. King in the East Africa Geological Research Unit (EAGRU). This combined a mapping programme with a study area for training students, and the area chosen for the main activities was the area around Lake Baringo in northern Kenya, including the Tugen Hills. This is a beautiful part of the Gregory Rift Valley, and it proved to be an inspired choice for it encompassed sediments ranging from over 15 million years old almost to the present. Much of the present section is by students or associates of Bill's who worked in this area, and the eight chapters of this section are a direct continuation of the work initiated by Bill Bishop.

The first chapter is by Robin Renaut and associates. They describe the mineralogy of several lacustrine sedimentary sequences in the Tugen Hills and Kerio Valley region, including parts of the Ngorora, Tambach and Kapthurin Formations. They show the presence of closed basin and strongly alkaline palaeolakes similar to Lake Bogoria in the Kenya rift today, and they draw attention to the confusion that can be engendered when fauna (or artefacts) indicating one type of environment are washed into sediments that actually were accumulated under different conditions. The second chapter by Joe McCall also considers the sedimentary environment, in this case of the tuffaceous rocks from the Silali volcano to the north of Lake Baringo.

There then follow three papers on the environments, faunas and hominoids of the Tugen Hills succession. The first, by John Kingston, is based on isotopic analysis of fossil herbivore enamel and soil carbonates, and it shows that over the last 15.5 million years woodland-like conditions prevailed, very much like the environments in the region today, and at no time were environments dominated by open grasslands. There was, however, an increase in dietary importance of C_4 grasses later in time. The second paper by Andrew Hill describes the work of the Baringo Palaeontological Research Group (BPRP), the successor to EAGRU. It documents the Baringo Basin succession in terms of the constituent faunas, and it highlights a number of significant faunal events, in particular the occurrence of the earliest cercopithecid monkey, possibly the earliest hominin and the earliest known occurrence of the genus *Homo*. The fossil faunas, including the hominoids are briefly described. Finally, a joint paper by Hill and Kingston together with Laura Bishop describes the fossil suids from the later part of the Tugen Hills succession. Eleven species are described, and their ecomorphology and isotope analysis suggests that forest and woodland habitats were present throughout the Pliocene and early Pleistocene.

The final part of this section is devoted to human remains, both fossil bones and artefacts. Bernard Wood provides a concise summary of all the fossil hominins from the Baringo Basin deposits, in particular illustrating the Baringo mandible described many years ago but not illustrated at the time. The fossils from the Kapthurin Formation are compared with similar aged fossils from other parts of East Africa and the taxonomic question of these middle Pleistocene hominins is discussed. Then follows a detailed review of the Kapthurin Formation by Sally McBrearty, describing the sedimentary facies, fauna and archaeology. A middle Pleistocene biface-free lithic industry is described that is contemporaneous with Acheulian industries elsewhere, and at another site the earliest occurrence of reliably dated blades is documented. Higher up the sequence is a Middle Stone Age core reduction industry, again the earliest reliably dated MSA occupation in Africa. The final chapter by John Gowlett reviews the archaeology of the region, again with emphasis on the Kapthurin Formation.

P. Andrews

Saline, alkaline palaeolakes of the Tugen Hills–Kerio Valley region, Kenya Rift Valley

ROBIN W. RENAUT,[1] JOHN EGO,[2] JEAN-JACQUES TIERCELIN,[3]
CAROLINE LE TURDU[4] & R. BERNHART OWEN[5]

[1] *Department of Geological Sciences, University of Saskatchewan,
Saskatoon SK, S7N 5E2, Canada*
[2] *National Oil Corporation of Kenya, PO Box 58567, Nairobi, Kenya*
[3] *UMR 6538 'Domaines Océaniques', Institut Universitaire Européen de la Mer, Place
Nicolas Copernic, 29280 Plouzané, France*
[4] *Research and Development Department, Elf Petroleum Norge, PO Box 168, Dusavik, 4001
Stavanger, Norway*
[5] *Department of Geography, Hong Kong Baptist University, Kowloon Tong,
Hong Kong, China*

Abstract: The Neogene sedimentary rocks of the region west of Lake Baringo, Kenya, contain a remarkably rich and diverse mammalian fauna that includes hominids. The mineralogy of these sediments, particularly the lacustrine facies, has received little attention. The authigenic minerals in the lacustrine sediments and palaeosols can provide clues to the hydrochemistry of the former surface waters and shallow groundwaters, and to the palaeoclimate. Several lacustrine sequences have been examined in the Tugen Hills and Kerio Valley region, using X-ray diffraction, scanning electron microscopy and electron microprobe methods. These include lacustrine facies of the Miocene Tambach Formation and Ngorora Formation, and the Pleistocene Kapthurin Formation.

Mineralogical results show that many of the Neogene palaeolakes were strongly saline and alkaline for much of their histories, punctuated by dilute (freshwater) phases of variable duration. The lacustrine sediments are commonly rich in zeolites (analcime, clinoptilolite, mordenite) and contain a diverse authigenic mineral suite that includes quartz, K-feldspar, fluorite and dolomite. Sedimentary structures and facies provide supporting evidence for variable lake levels and periodic desiccation. The Ngorora (Member C) palaeolake at Kapkiamu was probably meromictic at times, forming organic-rich shales analogous to the sapropelic oozes currently forming in Lake Bogoria. At other times, the lakes dried up to form shallow playa-lakes similar to Lake Nakuru. The Kapthurin palaeolake was also strongly saline and alkaline for part of its history. This new evidence has implications for the interpretation of the associated hominid and archaeological sites in the region.

The Lake Baringo region contains one of the best exposed sequences of Neogene sedimentary rocks in the Kenya Rift, spanning the time from the early stages of rift development through to the present day. Many sedimentary formations in the Tugen Hills (Kamasia) have yielded rich vertebrate faunas, including hominids. Following preliminary studies by several workers (Gregory 1921; Fuchs 1950; Shackleton 1951; McCall *et al.* 1967), the stratigraphic framework of these rocks was formally established by Bishop & Chapman in the 1970s, supported by palaeontological studies by Hill, Pickford and others (e.g. Bishop & Chapman 1970; Bishop

et al. 1971; Pickford 1975*a,b*, 1978). Although there have been other studies on the geochronology (Chapman & Brook 1978; Tauxe *et al.* 1985; Hill *et al.* 1986; Deino *et al.* 1990), palaeontology (Hill *et al.* 1985, 1992; Hill 1995, 1999), and archaeology (e.g. McBrearty *et al.* 1996; McBrearty 1999) of the basin during the last two decades, few detailed sedimentological studies have been undertaken since the initial research directed by Bill Bishop.

During the late 1980s interest in the Tugen Hills succession came from the petroleum industry, led by the National Oil Corporation of Kenya (NOCK). It was recognized that several

RENAUT, R. W., EGO, J., TIERCELIN, J.-J., LE TURDU, C. & OWEN, R. B. 1999. Saline, alkaline palaeolakes of the Tugen Hills–Kerio Valley region, Kenya Rift Valley. *In*: ANDREWS, P. & BANHAM, P. (eds) *Late Cenozoic Environments and Hominid Evolution: a tribute to Bill Bishop*. Geological Society, London, 41–58.

of the lacustrine sequences could potentially have sourced hydrocarbons, given that rift lakes commonly develop very high organic productivity (Melack 1981; Talbot 1988; Renaut & Tiercelin 1994). High regional heat-flow, coupled with the excellent potential for structural traps, made the region attractive for oil exploration. The Miocene Tambach and Ngorora formations were considered good targets. Member C of the Ngorora Formation, in particular, was already known to contain organic-rich lacustrine shales (Pickford 1975*a*, 1978).

In co-operation with NOCK, the mineralogy and sedimentology of these two formations were examined in order to understand better the depositional setting of the potential source and reservoir rocks. In this paper, we present results of preliminary mineralogical and sedimentological studies of the lacustrine facies of the Tambach Formation, Member C of the Ngorora Formation, and the mid-Pleistocene Kapthurin Formation. The authigenic mineral suites include abundant zeolites, fluorite, authigenic K-feldspar and quartz. The mineralogy confirms that each of these palaeolakes was at times saline and highly alkaline, similar in composition to modern Lake Bogoria and Lake Nakuru.

Methods

Most sediment samples, collected from sections measured in the field, were examined using standard petrographic methods and X-ray diffraction (XRD), using a Rigaku rotating anode diffractometer. Selected polished thin sections were examined on JEOL JXA 8600 electron microprobe for determination of mineral compositions. Other samples were gold-coated and examined on a JEOL 840 scanning electron microscope (SEM). To determine total organic carbon (TOC), samples were air dried, ground to <100 mesh, then digested with hot HCl. The samples then underwent combustion in a Leco induction furnace with measurement of organic carbon as CO_2.

Geological setting

The Kenya Rift at the latitude of Lake Baringo (1°N) is structurally complex and has features unique in the Kenya Rift (Fig. 1). The western edge of the rift is defined by the 1500 m high Elgeyo Escarpment, a major border fault (Chapman *et al.* 1978; Morley *et al.* 1992). Approximately 90 km to the east, the Laikipia Escarpment forms the eastern rift boundary.

Two sub-basins lie between the rift borders: the Kerio sub-basin and the Baringo–Bogoria half-graben. Lake Baringo lies in the Quaternary axial trough and is the main modern depocentre in this part of the rift. The uplifted Tugen Hills fault-block rises abruptly west of Lake Baringo, almost reaching the elevation of the Elgeyo Escarpment. Much of the Neogene succession of sedimentary and volcanic rocks is exposed in the Tugen Hills. West of its crest, the dip slope of the fault block descends toward Elgeyo and is buried on its eastern edge by younger sediments of the Kerio Valley (Fig. 1). Although appearing to be a simple half-graben, the Kerio sub-basin underwent two main phases of rifting. The early phase (Palaeogene?) produced a full graben that underlies the N–S axis of the Kerio Valley (Mugisha *et al.* 1997). The Kerio sub-basin contains up to 6 km of Tertiary and younger strata that rest on late Proterozoic basement.

Sedimentary stratigraphy

The stratigraphy of the Tugen Hills–upper Kerio Valley region (Fig. 2) was established in the late 1960s and 1970s by Bill Bishop, Gregory Chapman and members of the East African Geological Research Unit, based at Bedford College, University of London (e.g. Bishop *et al.* 1971; Chapman *et al.* 1978). Most sedimentary formations lie between series of lava flows. These lavas, together with tuffs, have yielded many radiometric ages that provide the chronostratigraphic framework.

The oldest sediments exposed, the Kamego Formation, are mainly arkosic fluviatile sandstones shed from basement rocks. The Kimwarer Formation, located at the southern end of the Kerio Valley, contains green, waxy, laminated tuffaceous shales that are probably the oldest exposed lacustrine sediments in the region. The Tambach Formation comprises a series of fluvial and lacustrine sediments, exposed in the Elgeyo Escarpment. The Tugen Hills succession consists of six major sedimentary formations (Muruyur, Ngorora, Mpesida, Lukeino, Chemeron and Kapthurin) and several lesser ones, dated between 16 Ma and late Pleistocene (Hill 1995, 1999).

Tambach Formation

Geological setting

The Miocene Tambach Formation contains one of the oldest sequences of lacustrine sediments in the central Kenya Rift. Where exposed, the

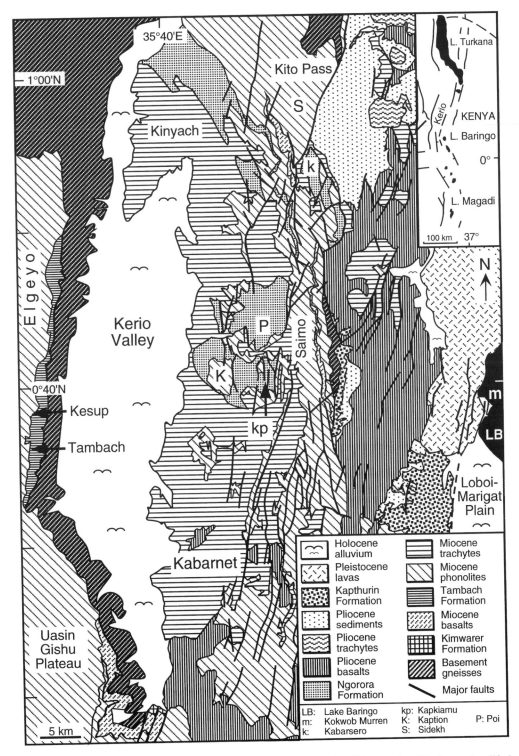

Fig. 1. Geological map of the Tugen Hills–Kerio Valley region, showing localities mentioned in the text (modified from Chapman *et al.* 1978).

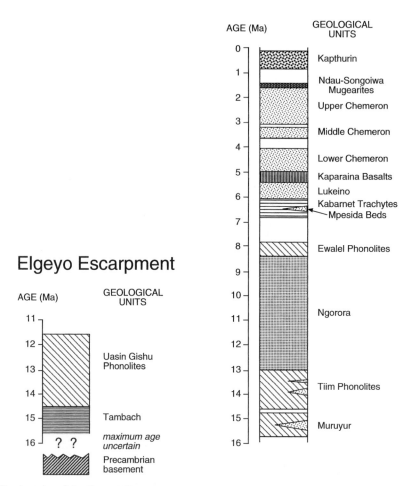

Fig. 2. Stratigraphy of the Tugen Hills and Kerio sub-basin (modified from Chapman *et al.* 1978; Hill 1995).

formation comprises *c.* 400 m of colluvial, fluviatile and lacustrine sedimentary rocks, with an intercalated phonolitic lava flow, trachytic and phonolitic tuffs, and small intrusions of ankaramite and basanite (Murray-Hughes 1933; Shackleton 1951; Lippard 1972). The sedimentary rocks are exposed discontinuously on the face of the Elgeyo Escarpment between latitudes 0°33'N and 0°49' (Figs 1, 3, 4a). The Tambach sediments lie upon an irregular palaeotopography of late Proterozoic Mozambiquan Belt gneisses, amphibolites, schists and quartzites that have a steep E-dipping foliation (Chapman *et al.* 1978; Hetzel & Strecker 1994). The sediments are overlain unconformably by phonolite lavas of the Uasin Gishu Phonolite Formation, dated from 14.5–12 Ma (Lippard 1973).

Few outcrops of Tambach sediments are seen west of the Elgeyo Escarpment owing to the extensive (up to 500 m) cover of phonolites, but Sanders (1963) mentions 6 m (20 feet) of 'tuffs and grits' lying on basement rocks near Eldoret that may be of equivalent age or older. The western margin of the Tambach basin may have been located 40–50 km west of the Elgeyo border fault. Geophysical interpretations indicate an eastern margin at least as far as the Tugen Hills (Mugisha *et al.* 1997). The southern and northern limits of the Tambach depositional basin are poorly constrained.

Based on the distribution of the Uasin Gishu Phonolites, Morley *et al.* (1992) suggested that the Tambach basin was a broad depression that was initiated as a sag; Chapman *et al.* (1978)

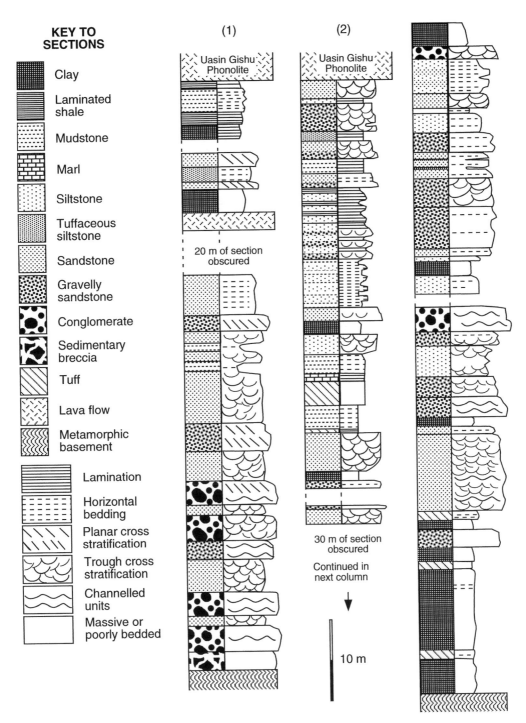

Fig. 3. Stratigraphic sections of the Tambach Formation. Section 1 was measured along the Kabarnet–Tambach road, approximately 2–3 km south of Tambach. Section 2 is taken from Shackleton (1951).

Fig. 4. (a) Tambach Formation, showing outcrop 4 km south of Tambach village. Elgeyo Escarpment in background. (b) Poorly sorted paraconglomerate (debris flow deposit), near base of Tambach Formation, road outcrop 3 km south of Tambach. Section is 3 m high. (c) Fluviatile sediments, road outcrop 2.5 km south of Tambach. Pale trough-cross-stratified arenites (sandy braided stream channel?) are overlain by poorly sorted conglomerates (gravelly braided stream). (d) Lacustrine shales, 1 km south of Tambach. (e) Small deltaic sand bodies with NE-dipping foresets, interbedded with lacustrine shales, 1.5 km south of Tambach. (f) SEM photomicrograph showing analcime (a) from Tambach Formation shales at Kesup. Later clays (smectite?) coat the euhedral crystal.

termed it a downwarp. The sag basin probably had its depocentral axis near the concealed Kerio Fault, where the sediments are >500 m thick (Mugisha *et al.* 1997). The sag basin formed through thermal subsidence between about 16 Ma and 12 Ma, following the initial phase of rifting that formed the Kerio Fault and graben (Mugisha *et al.* 1997). After eruption of the Uasin Gishu phonolites, the second major phase of rifting took place. Movement on the Elgeyo Fault downfaulted the Tambach sediments below the Kerio Valley where they became covered by younger lavas and sediments (Morley *et al.* 1992; Mugisha *et al.* 1997).

Although exposures are generally good, the outcrop on the escarpment is essentially two dimensional. This limits the detailed reconstruction of the Tambach basin palaeogeography.

Stratigraphy and sedimentology

The overall depositional sequence is fining upward, with alluvial fan and gravelly braided stream deposits near the base of the sequence, passing upward through ephemeral and perennial(?) sandy braided stream deposits, to shallow deltaic and lacustrine sediments at the top part of the sequence (Fig. 3). Intercalated airfall and waterlain tuffs are common. Deposition began upon a highly irregular surface. In places, coarse colluvial conglomerates and quartz-cemented sedimentary breccias rest directly on basement; elsewhere there is a deeply weathered basal claystone, part of which may be a palaeosol. The irregular substrate resulted in highly variable local stratigraphic variations, including thickness. Higher in the sequence, units appear to become more laterally continuous as sedimentation progressively infilled and blanketed the palaeotopography.

The presence of bouldery conglomerates and paraconglomerates (debris-flow deposits) near the base of the sequence (Fig. 4b) implies that there was considerable local topography during the initial stages of Tambach sedimentation. The clasts in the conglomerates near the base of the sequence are mainly basement gneisses and quartz pegmatites. Palaeocurrent indicators (mainly cross-bedding and imbrication) show that most of the exposed fluvial sediments derived from the west, southwest and south. Sediments also probably originated from the eastern margin, but the evidence is concealed below the Kerio Valley. These coarse sediments may have been shed from adjacent uplands that resulted from formation of the sag depression and movements on the Kerio Fault. The bulk of the lower part (c. 200 m) of the succession is composed of fluvial conglomerates and sandstones. These include both gravelly and sandy braided stream deposits (Fig. 4c), and lensoid crevasse-splay siltstones. Although dominated by basement clasts, conglomerates containing phonolite and nephelinite clasts become common in the middle and upper parts of the formation.

The sandstones are generally moderately to poorly sorted, and are composed mainly of litharenites and arkoses towards the base of the section, with an increase in volcanic grains towards the top of the section. A few sandstones are well sorted and quartz-rich, reflecting their predominant basement provenance. Cements are mainly calcite and iron oxides, with thin local quartz or albite overgrowths in some sandstones. Authigenic smectite and illite are also common. Feldspathic floodplain silts become common toward the top of the sequence, with local development of palaeosols, calcareous rhizoliths and a few thin calcrete horizons. Rare, abraded vertebrate bone fragments were found in the channel sands and gravel units.

Lacustrine sediments

Although thin lacustrine sequences are present in the lower part of the sequence, only those from the upper part of the succession (Fig. 3) were examined. The samples analysed by XRD were taken in the road-cut exposures c. 1 km south of Tambach and at Kesup.

The lacustrine facies from the upper part of the sequence are dominated by pale green, grey and white shales that are interbedded with greenish mudstones and claystones, or brownish grey siltstones and fine sandstones (Fig. 4d). Many shales, mudstones and claystones are slightly waxy in feel and appearance; some are tuffaceous. Two styles of lamination are common. Many green or white shales and claystones are finely laminated with laminae <2 mm thick ('paper shales'), forming depositional units centimetres to decimetres thick. Other shales have thicker laminae (2–10 mm), some of which are upward fining, arranged in units up to several metres thick. The latter are locally interbedded with siltstones or fine rippled sandstone beds or lenses from centimetres to several decimetres thick. In places, thicker (50–150 cm) sandstone units with Gilbert-type foresets interfinger with the shales, representing delta progradation into the former lake (Fig. 4e).

Greenish, more massive mudstones and claystones are also commonly interbedded with the shales, and locally are brecciated into small (1–2 cm) granules, some of which were reworked to form an intraclast breccia. Bedding planes locally reveal small mudcracks; these are more abundant in the green units. Microfaulting is common.

Several levels in the shales are fossiliferous, containing fish bones, ostracods, insect carapaces, and locally abundant plant debris. Fish preservation is generally poor; most fish are disarticulated and are rarely complete. Near Kesup, however, bedding planes with small whole fish fossils (3–8 cm long) are present. Diatoms were not seen in any samples examined. Plant remains include scattered small leaves on bedding planes, and disseminated vegetal debris preserved as brown carbonized films. Root marks are locally present in the green mudstones and claystones.

A total of 26 samples of lacustrine shale, mudstone and claystone were analysed by X-ray diffraction. The silt and fine sand fraction is consistently dominated by K-feldspar, quartz and sodic plagioclase. Calcite is a minor component in some of the coarsely laminated shales. The clay fraction in the white, grey and greenish grey shales and mudstones is mainly smectite with subsidiary illite. Chlorite and kaolinite are present in some samples, but are rarely major components. In some green waxy shales and mudstones, analcime ($Na_{16}(Al_{16}Si_{32}O_{96}).16H_2O$) is common, accounting for up to 20–25% of the rock (Fig. 4f). SEM observations show that most analcime is in the form of trapezohedral crystals, 5–20 μm long. The crystals form pore-filling cement between detrital clays and are themselves locally coated by younger illuvial or authigenic clay minerals (smectite and illite).

Lacustrine palaeoenvironments

Detailed reconstruction of the Tambach palaeo-lakes is not possible because of the restricted outcrop, but the sedimentary features and mineralogy provide sufficient evidence to determine the general character of the palaeolake in which the upper part of the sequence was deposited.

The rivers that deposited the fluvial sediments in the lower part of the formation may have fed a palaeolake north of the outcrop belt, but this is only speculation. By the stage when the main Tambach lake became established at Tambach–Kesup, the sag basin had been largely filled by fluviatile sediments. The overall fining-upward succession implies reduced stream gradients, at least in the area of outcrop. The Tambach lake was fed by streams draining a mixed volcanic–basement catchment, as indicated by detrital grain compositions.

The palaeolake fluctuated in surface level and in chemistry. At times, the waters were apparently fresh enough to support a substantial fish population, but there remains the possibility that many could have been washed in from rivers. However, the ostracods indicate fresh to slightly brackish waters. Diatoms may have been present, but have succumbed to diagenetic dissolution. The variations in lamination are possibly related to water depth, the coarse laminae representing more proximal facies, with finer clays and shales in relatively deeper water. The latter could also mark periods of low siliciclastic influx.

However, the common presence of analcime shows that the waters for periods became saline and highly alkaline. Its euhedral form and relationship to detrital grains confirm that the analcime is authigenic rather than detrital. Analcime is a common authigenic mineral in saline, alkaline lakes (e.g. Hay 1970; Surdam & Eugster 1976; Remy & Ferrell 1989; Renaut 1993). Although it may precipitate as a cement, it more commonly forms by the diagenetic alteration of a precursor silicate mineral where in contact with $NaCO_3$-rich lake or pore waters. The composition of the precursor mineral can sometimes be determined by analysing the Si/Al ratio of the analcime (Coombs & Whetton 1967; Iijima & Hay 1968). For the Tambach analcimes, the Si/Al ratio is approximately 2.15–2.26. This low ratio implies that a clay mineral precursor is likely (Ego 1994). No other zeolites were found in the sediments, but the sample size was small.

The analcime probably formed during prolonged periods of low lake level when high evaporative concentration increased the salinity and alkalinity of the lake brines and interstitial pore fluids. Alkaline pore fluids would also readily dissolve any diatoms. During such stages lake level would have fallen, exposing shorelines. However, the analcime does not appear restricted to massive and brecciated mudstones, so some analcime probably formed below alkaline lake brines, as for example has happened at lakes Magadi (Eugster 1980) and Bogoria (Tiercelin 1981; Renaut & Tiercelin 1994).

The evidence for high salinity and alkalinity also shows that the Tambach palaeolake was, at least for part of its history, a hydrologically closed basin in a region with high net evaporation. Outflow, possibly to the north, may have existed during dilute phases, but when saline, the lake was probably confined to the sag depression.

The Ngorora Formation

Geological setting

The Miocene Ngorora Formation is a series of volcaniclastic, colluvial, fluviatile and lacustrine sediments, up to c. 400 m thick, that were deposited over a period of about 4 Ma (Bishop & Chapman 1970; Bishop & Pickford 1975; Hill 1995). The sediments lie upon lavas of the Tiim Phonolite Formation (13.1 Ma) and are unconformably overlain by the Ewalel Phonolite Formation (c. 9 Ma). During sedimentation, the western and eastern basin margins were the Elgeyo Escarpment and the Laikipia Plateau, respectively. Tiati central volcano formed the northern boundary, while the southern margins were defined by the gradual rise of the rift floor (Bishop & Pickford 1975; Pickford 1978). Kaption volcano, located in the southern half of the basin, was active during the initial stages of Ngorora sedimentation (Pickford 1975a).

The sediments were deposited in several distinct fault-bounded basins, defined by the Saimo, Kito Pass, Cherial and Kaption faults, that were separated by intervening uplands at Saimo, Sidekh and Kaption (Fig. 1). The Ngorora basin remained tectonically active, and the sediment source and recharge areas changed throughout the period of sedimentation. Because of their periodic or partial isolation, each sub-basin exhibits a different stratigraphic succession and thickness.

Stratigraphy and sedimentology

Bishop & Chapman (1970) subdivided the Ngorora Formation into five members, A to E designating a type-section at Kabarsero. Member A is composed largely of volcaniclastic, fluviatile sediments and lahar deposits, whereas members B and D comprise mainly fluviatile sediments. Two of the members, C and E are predominantly lacustrine. However, there are many local variations in the several sub-basins.

Pickford (1975a, 1978), who studied the geology and palaeontology in detail, established the broad palaeogeographical setting throughout the period of sedimentation. Later studies focused on the palaeontology (e.g. Hill *et al.* 1985; Jacobs & Kabuye 1987), geochronology (e.g. Tauxe *et al.* 1985; Deino *et al.* 1990) and palaeoenvironmental reconstructions (Owen 1981; Kingston *et al.* 1994), with an emphasis on determining the context of the several hominoids that have been discovered in the formation (Hill 1995, 1999). Relatively little detailed sedimentological analysis has been published since the initial work of Pickford (1975a).

Description of Member C

Sediments and facies. Of the two lacustrine members, C and E Member C was of primary interest in this study because Pickford (1978) had reported petroliferous sediments from this member, and Bishop & Pickford (1975) suspected that some of the sediments were 'chemical precipitates'. The lacustrine shales of Member E at Kabarsero are rich in fossil fish and contain diatomaceous silts and diatomites, dominated by *Aulacoseira* spp. (Owen 1981). Although many levels lack diatoms, the Member E palaeolake was relatively fresh for at least part of its history.

The lacustrine sediments of Member C were examined and sampled in the Kapkiamu sub-basin, both at Kapkiamu and at Poi (Figs 5 and 6a). They consist predominantly of lacustrine shales, claystones and siltstones, locally inter-calated with coarser ephemeral-stream deposits and tephra. The Kapkiamu sub-basin, interpreted as a graben by Bishop & Pickford (1975), was bordered to the southwest by Kaption volcano (then dormant or extinct), and along its eastern edge by the Cherial fault and Saimo Horst (Fig. 5). The maximum sediment thickness in the Kapkiamu sub-basin is *c.* 200 m. The Kapkiamu sub-basin had steep sides and a small watershed (Pickford 1978), which limited the potential for coarse siliciclastic sediment influx.

A 35 m section of Member C near Kapkiamu village was measured and sampled at *c.* 1 m intervals for XRD analysis (Fig. 5). The sediments consist mainly of white to pale green, fissile shales, mudstones, siltstones and fine sandstones (Fig. 6a). Coarse and fine laminae are present, similar to those described for the Tambach Formation. The coarser silts and fine sands are commonly ripple-marked, with both current and wave ripples (Fig. 6b). Desiccation cracks (1–15 cm wide), mudstone intraclast breccias, and clastic dykes are common throughout the sequence. Less common are salt pseudomorphs after gaylussite(?) and halite, and raindrop imprints that are found on mudcracked surfaces. Bird footprints are abundant on some bedding planes. The shales and mudstones are rich in carbonaceous plant debris; rootmarks and thin, fossiliferous clay-rich palaeosols are found at several levels. A few units contain whole and fragmented fossil fish (*Tilapia* sp., *Clarias* sp.?) on bedding planes. The upper part of Member C at Kapkiamu and Poi is extensively silicified and porcellanous in appearance. In places, thin (10–40 cm) beds and lenses of massive chert are present. Elsewhere the silicification cuts across lithological boundaries.

Intercalated with the lacustrine shales are pale-brown tuffaceous siltstones and fine sandstones with slightly erosive base contacts. Their upper boundaries are commonly gradational, either coarsening into sandstones, or fining into mudstones. Small bone fragments are locally present in this facies. Thin lenticular units of conglomerate and fine tuffaceous sandstones, in units up to 50 cm thick that show small-scale planar cross-stratification, interfinger with the siltstones and shales. The conglomerates are weakly imbricated with rounded lava pebbles and erosive basal contacts. These coarser sediments are interpreted to be products of unchannelled flow and shallow ephemeral streams crossing exposed littoral plains.

At Poi, petroliferous shales (up to 4.3% TOC) forming depositional units up to 1.4 m thick are present, especially near the base of the section (Fig. 6c). The shales are dark greenish grey,

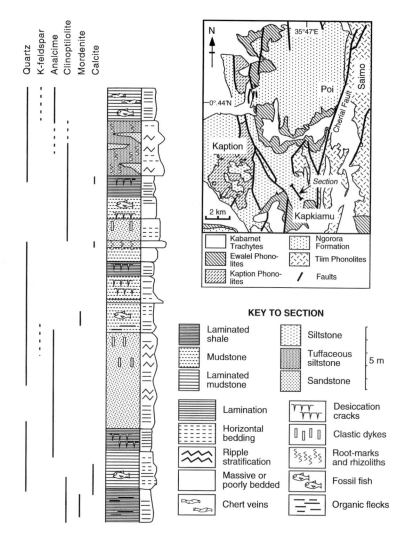

Fig. 5. Measured section and mineralogy of Member C Ngorora Formation at Kapkiamu. Inset shows geological setting of the Kapkiamu sub-basin (from Chapman *et al.* 1973) and location of section.

moderately well lithified, and contain fossil fish and leaf fragments. Poorly preserved stromatolites, oncoids and thin (10–15 cm) beds of marl and limestones are also present (see Pickford 1975*a* for details).

Mineralogy. The shales and mudstones contain abundant zeolites, together with authigenic clay minerals (mainly smectite and illite), calcite, quartz, opal-CT and K-feldspar. The zeolites are principally clinoptilolite [$(Na,K)_6(Al_6Si_{30}O_{72})$. $20H_2O$)] (also termed silica-rich heulandite; Tschernich 1992) and analcime (Fig. 6d, e). Minor mordenite [$Na_3KCa_2(Al_8Si_{40}O_{96}).28H_2O$]

accompanies clinoptilolite in a few samples. The euhedral K-feldspar (Fig. 6f) is compositionally different from the detrital feldspars in the catchment. The authigenic minerals are typically present in several associations: (1) smectite + calcite; (2) smectite + clinoptilolite; (3) analcime; (4) analcime + K-feldspar. Authigenic quartz is present in several associations. In places, the shales are nearly pure zeolitites, composed almost entirely of clinoptilolite and (or) analcime. The coarser sediments are mainly detrital sanidine, anorthoclase and plagioclase, with lesser quartz. Calcite and iron oxide cements are common in the siltstones and sandstones.

Fig. 6. Ngorora Formation, Member C. (**a**) Lacustrine shales dipping gently westward towards the Elgeyo Escarpment (on horizon); Kapkiamu. (**b**) Bedding plane surface of lacustrine shales with parallel wave ripples; Poi. (**c**) Laminated greyish green, organic-rich shales; Poi. (**d**) SEM photomicrograph showing authigenic clinoptilolite. (**e**) SEM photomicrograph showing authigenic analcime (a), coated by later smectite (s) that was probably precipitated from relatively dilute groundwater. (**d**) SEM photomicrograph showing authigenic K-feldspar (k) and iron oxide minerals (f). Scale bar is 10 μm.

Traces of fluorite were found in a few analcime-bearing mudstones. Gypsum, previously mentioned by Pickford (1978), is locally present as selenitic crystals on outcrop surfaces and along joints, but is evidently a late product, probably related to oxidation of former pyrite by circulating groundwater.

The silica associated with silicification is mainly microquartz, but includes some opal-CT. The silica is both replacive of earlier mineral grains or cements, and acts as a cement in some siltstones and sandstones.

Interpretation of Member C

Lacustrine palaeoenvironments. The new evidence from Kapkiamu and Poi confirms the suggestion of Bishop & Pickford (1975) that the Member C palaeolake(s) in the Kapkiamu basin was strongly saline and alkaline throughout much of its history. The basin was almost certainly hydrologically closed and ponded to the north by a fault block (Pickford 1978: fig. 16.4C). The relatively low amount of coarse siliciclastic sediment supports Pickford's interpretation of a small catchment area. Most sediment was probably washed into the lake by ephemeral streams, represented by the cross-bedded sandstones and rippled coarse siltstones that are intercalated with the finer lacustrine sediments.

The sedimentological evidence for frequent subaerial exposure indicates that the lake fluctuated repeatedly in surface level. At times the lake water was relatively fresh. During these stages the surface waters were able to support fish. Calcified stromatolites formed along the shoreline, which implies that the waters were fresh enough to hold some calcium ions. The cyclicity of some laminae may be evidence of seasonality (Bishop & Pickford 1975). Their lateral continuity may also be evidence of phases when a perennial lake was present.

However, for much of its history the Kapkiamu lake was saline and alkaline, fluctuating markedly in salinity. Repeated exposure surfaces indicate periodic shoreline regression. Frequent fluctuations in lake level are shown by the numerous mudcracked surfaces, halite and gaylussite(?) pseudomorphs, and mud intraclast breccias. At such stages, the lake shrank to a shallow playa-lake bordered by exposed mudflats which were traversed by ephemeral washes. Silts and fine sands would have been introduced by ephemeral washes from the basin margins, or by deflation. The salt pseudomorphs probably resulted from crystal growth on mudflat surfaces or from very shallow intrasedimentary brines that were subject to capillary evaporation. It is unclear if the lake ever precipitated lacustrine evaporites (e.g. trona, nahcolite) in the basin centre, but it is certainly plausible. Although not a full analogue, modern lakes Nakuru and Elmenteita have many sedimentological similarities to the inferred overall setting for 'low-stage' Kapkiamu palaeolake.

The depositional setting of the organic-rich shales is unclear. They are found in sequences with few mudcracked surfaces, which implies that the lake was perennial during the period of formation. The analysed organic-rich shales contain analcime, which indicates high salinity and alkalinity, although this may be a later diagenetic overprint from a succeeding phase of low lake level. The high TOC, however, suggests that sedimentation may have occurred in a stratified lake with anoxic bottom waters. Modern Lake Bogoria may provide a partial analogue.

Although shallow (9 m deep), Lake Bogoria is meromictic with an anoxic monimolimnion. Organic-rich zeolitic muds accumulated in the deeper parts of the lake at several stages during the late Quaternary (Tiercelin & Vincens 1987; Renaut & Tiercelin 1994). Unlike Lake Bogoria, however, the Kapkiamu palaeolake appears to have had little coarse siliciclastic sediment input, resulting in purer zeolitic sediments.

Diagenesis. The diagenetic history of the rocks is complex and only a summary is presented here. Some details are given in Ego (1994) and additional supporting data will be presented elsewhere. The original lake sediments at Kapkiamu were probably weathering products of local phonolites and volcaniclastic sediments, possibly augmented by airfall tephra. These sediments probably contained abundant volcanic glass. Surface waters and groundwaters that fed the lake initially acquired a $Na-Ca-HCO_3$ composition, resulting mainly from silicate mineral hydrolysis during weathering. With evaporative concentration, they evolved into saline, alkaline brines as they moved toward the centre of the lake basin. Those fluids, as either lake water or shallow groundwater, reacted with the fine-grained siliciclastic sediment to yield a range of authigenic silicate minerals. Reactions may have taken place below the alkaline lake waters or in shallow, lake-marginal groundwaters at times when the lake was low, saline and had retreated to the centre of the basin.

The authigenic mineral assemblage closely resembles those described from several Neogene lakes in the western United States (e.g. Sheppard & Gude 1968; Surdam & Parker 1972; Surdam & Sheppard 1978), where distinct authigenic mineral zones are present that reflect the increasing salinity and alkalinity of shallow lake water, and (or) groundwaters that flowed gradually toward the basin centre. At Kapkiamu, the glass altered to smectite in the more dilute waters near the basin margins. Calcite precipitated from the fluids as cements, probably by near-surface degassing of CO_2, which depleted the waters in their Ca^{2+}. In more saline waters, glass and possibly some smectite altered to clinoptilolite. With further evaporative concentration, the clinoptilolite was replaced by analcime. Authigenic K-feldspar then formed in the most concentrated alkaline brines. The analcimes at Kapkiamu have high Si/Al ratios of 2.4–2.8 (Ego 1994), which supports an origin as an alteration product of a silica-rich precursor zeolite that formed from volcanic glass. The K-feldspar, in turn, probably formed from alteration of analcime or other zeolites in the most concentrated brines near the centre of the lake basin. Thus, the general diagenetic sequence inferred can be summarized as:

Volcanic glass → clinoptilolite → analcime
→ K-feldspar

This pattern is essentially the same as that for several palaeolakes of the Eocene Green River Formation in Wyoming (cf. Surdam & Sheppard 1978). Thus, the mineral zones observed in the Kapkiamu section and at Poi indicate fluctuations in the chemistry of the lake water and groundwaters at different stages during the history of the lake.

The processes that led to silicification of the lake sediments near the top of the sequence have not been fully investigated. Although very high alkalinity is implied by the analcime and K-feldspar, unequivocal Magadi-type cherts (cf. Eugster 1980), which might be expected to be present, were not recognized. However, silicification was widespread and is present in the sediments at the same general level in the Kabarsero type-section. Textural relationships show that the silica commonly postdated the zeolites. Reworked silicified mudstone clasts imply some early silicification. The silica was probably mobilized in highly alkaline pore fluids passing through the shales, with precipitation perhaps induced by an abrupt drop in pH. This may have resulted from dilution by fresher waters, or may have been induced by decay of organic matter in the sediments. In additional to 'normal' weathering sources, silica is a by-product of the clinoptilolite to analcime reaction, but is consumed when analcime changes to K-feldspar. Diatoms, probably present during dilute lake stages, are another possible silica source. Some silica may have been introduced by circulating hydrothermal waters.

Kapthurin Formation

The Pleistocene Kapthurin Formation is a series of predominantly fluviatile sediments that crop out west of Lake Baringo (McCall et al. 1967; Walsh 1969; Martyn 1969; Tallon 1976, 1978). The sediments, which are up to c. 125 m thick, were deposited in the contemporary axial rift depression following uplift of the Saimo Escarpment (Fig. 1), which rejuvenated the local drainage systems. The formation consists mainly of lava pebble conglomerates that are intercalated with pale brown feldspathic siltstones and fine sandstones. These sediments were deposited in alluvial fans, braided stream channels and on

floodplains and littoral plains that were subjected to unchannelled wash. Palaeosols, including calcretes, are common in the finer sediments, as are several important archaeological sites (Leakey et al. 1969; Martyn 1969; McBrearty et al 1996; McBrearty 1999). Martyn (1969) subdivided the formation into five members: the Lower, Middle and Upper Silts and Gravels members are separated by two volcaniclastic units – the Pumice Tuff and Bedded Tuff.

The rivers flowed eastward into a 'Central Rift Lake' (Tallon 1978) in a setting broadly similar to that of the modern Baringo basin. The northern and southern limits of the basin may have been constrained in part by NW–SE transverse structures similar to those that define the modern Baringo basin (cf. Le Turdu et al. 1995, in press). Most lacustrine sediments of the Kapthurin Formation have been downfaulted to the east and buried by younger sediments. However, a small area of Kapthurin lake sediments that belongs mainly to the Middle Silts and Gravels Member is exposed near the Bartekero River (Fig. 7). From vertebrate faunal evidence, Tallon (1978) concluded that the Kapthurin palaeolake was fresh.

Sediment samples were collected for XRD analysis from the Pumice Tuff and lacustrine facies of Middle Silts and Gravels members near the Bartekero River. Just above the contact with the Pumice Tuff, the Middle Silts and Gravels Member consists of reddish silty and sandy clays and clayey silts containing scattered small gravel clasts and $CaCO_3$ concretions. These sediments are locally tuffaceous and greenish. The reddish sediments pass transitionally upward into dark brown and blackish clays and silts (Fig. 7). In places, layers of calcite concretions with minor siderite, up to 25 cm in diameter, are present in both units. These are probably products of bacterial reduction. Large (up to 1 m high) columnar stromatolites and oncoids (calcite) are found at several levels in the lacustrine sediments; in places, they lie directly upon volcanic rocks that served as a stable substrate. An analogous situation exists at northern Kokwob Murren (Fig. 1), where recent calcite stromatolites containing erect cyanobacterial filaments encrust the rocky shoreline of Lake Baringo. The black clays pass upward into bedded silts and sands that locally contain calcite rhizoliths and thin palaeosols.

The XRD data show that the red and greenish clays and silts contain zeolites (principally analcime), authigenic quartz, fluorite, calcite and traces of dolomite. Although detailed studies have not been undertaken, the zeolites and fluorite imply that the Kapthurin palaeolake was at times saline and highly alkaline.

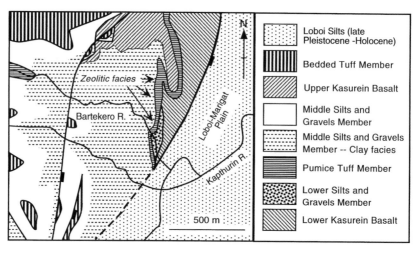

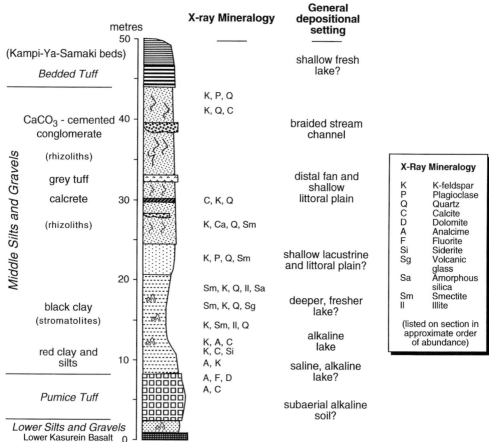

Fig. 7. Geological map and section of lacustrine facies of Kapthurin Formation (after Tallon 1978), showing X-ray mineralogy.

These sediments are commonly granular, probably due in part to disaggregation upon repeated subaerial exposure. Analcime is locally abundant in the Pumice Tuff, although its depositional environment is unclear. Zeolites were not found in the overlying black clays, samples of which were dominated by smectite, with lesser illite, chlorite and kaolinite. The silt and sand fractions are predominantly alkali feldspars, with lesser plagioclase and quartz. Calcite is a common cement in the black clays and overlying silts and fine sands. Minor selenitic gypsum in the black clays may have resulted from oxidation of pyrite.

Although sparse, the XRD data imply that the Kapthurin palaeolake was probably very shallow and became highly alkaline for periods during and following deposition of the Pumice Tuff. The lake became deeper and fresher during deposition of the black clays and silts, which have a diverse fauna including crocodile, hippo and *Tilapia* (McBrearty *et al.* 1996). These muds and silts are similar to those accumulating on the floor of modern Lake Baringo (cf. Tiercelin 1981; Tiercelin & Vincens 1987), which is only *c.* 4 m deep. The succeeding silts and sands represent regression, due to an eastward progradation of the alluvial–littoral plain, a fall in lake level, or subsidence of rift floor.

Discussion

The three examples described confirm that saline, alkaline lakes commonly developed during the Neogene in the Baringo–Kerio region. This is not surprising, given the predominance of hydrologically closed basins in the modern Kenya Rift. Similar alkaline palaeolakes are also known from the Turkana (Cerling 1979) and Magadi basins (e.g. Eugster 1980). Although not discussed here, authigenic zeolites, Magadi-type cherts and other minerals diagnostic of high salinity and alkalinity have also been found in lacustrine sediments and palaeosols from other formations in the Baringo region, including the Lukeino, Chemeron, Ilosowuani and Chesowanja formations (Renaut 1993, and unpublished data).

The closed drainage basins that are essential to the development of saline, alkaline lakes result in large part from the structural setting of sedimentary basins in the rift. Bill Bishop (pers. comm. 1976) stressed the importance of the combination of rift faulting and volcanic barriers (lava flows and central volcanoes) in providing basins for the accumulation of sediments. The distinctive shape of the modern Baringo basin results from the interference of the N–S (0–10°N) trend of the Tertiary Rift with the NW–SE transverse zones

that are inherited from Precambrian basement rocks (Coussement 1995; Le Turdu *et al.* 1995, in press). These tectonic trends play a major role in defining the basin morphology, drainage patterns, topographic and hydrological closure, rates of subsidence, and location of the depocentre. Similarly, many central volcanoes and hot springs are located at the intersection of these two tectonics trends (Dunkley *et al.* 1993; Le Turdu *et al.* 1995). It is probable that these tectonic lineaments also influenced the location and evolution of many of the earlier Neogene basins of the Tugen Hills and Kerio Valley regions, possibly including the northern and southern limits of the Kapthurin basin. Similar trends are evident on SPOT satellite imagery of the Ngorora and Tambach basins, but are partly masked by the cover of later lavas and sediments.

In addition to hydrological closure, the other prerequisites for development of saline, alkaline waters are reliable recharge and evaporative concentration. Weathering of the abundant volcanic rocks and ash by silicate hydrolysis results in runoff and groundwaters that have $Na-Ca-HCO_3$ compositions (Eugster 1980). However, most rift lakes are also fed, at least in part, by subaerial and (or) sublacustrine hot springs. Virtually all modern rift lakes in the East African rift have some hydrothermal recharge. In some basins, they are a trivial source of recharge (e.g. Lake Turkana), whereas in others they supply a major proportion of the annual inflow (e.g. Lake Magadi and Nasiki Engida). Much of this recharge is saline and alkaline, resulting from mineral–water interaction during underground circulation and the supply of CO_2 from deep crustal sources. The hydrothermal component becomes most significant during dry climatic phases when lake levels are low. Sedimentary evidence for hydrothermal recharge, in the form of travertine or sinter, is very localized and absent in some basins (Renaut & Tiercelin 1994; Renaut *et al.* 1998). It is likely that most of the Neogene palaeolakes at Baringo basin were partly fed by hydrothermal waters that were discharged from fault-line hot springs. They may have been particularly important in the Kapkiamu basin. The paucity of coarse peripheral siliciclastics, coupled with thick lacustrine sedimentary fill, are possible clues to a significant hydrothermal influx during sedimentation.

The results of this preliminary research confirm that mineralogical analyses of lacustrine sediments have great potential for providing useful information to help interpret the palaeoenvironmental setting of the many hominid and archaeological sites. Hay (1970, 1976) successfully pioneered this approach at Olduvai Gorge,

Tanzania, and it has equal potential in the Tugen Hills. Authigenic silicate minerals, in particular, can help to clarify the palaeosalinity of lake waters, and remove some of the potential ambiguity of many lacustrine vertebrate fossils and pollen assemblages found in Neogene sedimentary rocks.

Observations at modern saline, alkaline rift lakes have shown some of the potential problems of interpretation of fossil analogues. At modern Lake Bogoria, for example, catfish (*Clarias* sp.) are seasonally washed into the northern sub-basin from the Sandai River. The dead fish are washed up on muddy shorelines or buried in proximal deltaic sediments. Molluscs (*Melanoides tuberculata*) are currently being reworked from late Pleistocene sediments that were deposited when the lake was fresher and at higher levels, and are being incorporated in the modern littoral sediments with little or no damage to the shells (Renaut & Owen 1991). If preserved in ancient sediments, the catfish and molluscs would be taken to indicate fresh water, yet the mixolimnion of the modern lake has a salinity of $>60\,g\,l^{-1}$ TDS (total dissolved solids). Without supporting mineralogical or geochemical evidence (e.g. stable isotope data from contemporary carbonates), the palaeoenvironmental interpretation of the fossil-bearing sediments might be incorrect – the palaeontological indicators support dilute lake waters.

Similar arguments can apply to hominid artefacts. Obsidian and chert blades, scrapers and debitage are locally present in the matrix of littoral gravels and on mudflats around the shoreline of modern Lake Bogoria. Some artefacts are probably of late Pleistocene or Holocene age (cf. Farrand *et al.* 1976) and are unrelated to the modern lake and its contemporary human population. If fossilized in the geological record, the association of fish bones, freshwater molluscs and obsidian artefacts might be interpreted as evidence of hominid exploitation of lacustrine food resources. However, the contemporary lake has a salinity twice that of seawater and almost all its living biomass is microbial. Mineralogical and geochemical analyses of the associated sediments may in some cases demonstrate whether the artefacts, fossils and sediments are likely to have been both contemporary and compatible.

Conclusions

XRD, electron microprobe and SEM analyses of lacustrine sediments from several Neogene formations from the Tugen Hills–Kerio Valley region, west of Lake Baringo, have shown that many of the palaeolakes became highly saline and alkaline at different stages in their histories. The Miocene Tambach and Ngorora formations both contain authigenic zeolites that formed from $NaCO_3$-rich lake and pore waters. At Kapkiamu, the Ngorora Member C palaeolake varied from being an alkaline perennial lake to a shallow ephemeral saline, alkaline playa-lake. During its low stages, an authigenic mineral zonation developed (smectite–clinoptilolite–analcime–K-feldspar) that reflected the increasing salinity of the pore fluids. The mid-Pleistocene Kapthurin Formation had a highly alkaline stage, also marked by formation of zeolites. Detailed mineralogical analyses have considerable potential to refine the palaeoenvironmental interpretation of many of the Neogene sedimentary sequences in the Tugen Hills.

This research was supported by several agencies, including the Natural Sciences and Engineering Research Council of Canada, the National Oil Corporation of Kenya (NOCK), the Canadian International Development Agency (CIDA) and Elf-Aquitaine. We are grateful to the Office of The President, Republic of Kenya, for granting research permission, and our colleagues at NOCK for their generous support, especially J. K. Kwambai and F. M. Mbatau. Thanks are expressed to G. Chapman and an anonymous reviewer for their suggestions to improve the manuscript. RWR and RBO express special thanks to the late Bill Bishop, who initiated our research in Kenya, and who was both our supervisor and friend.

References

BISHOP, W. W. & CHAPMAN, G. R. 1970. Early Pliocene sediments and fossils from the northern Kenya Rift. *Nature*, **226**, 914–918.
——, HILL, A. & MILLER, J. A. 1971. Succession of Cainozoic vertebrate assemblages from the northern Kenya Rift Valley. *Nature*, **233**, 389–394.
—— & PICKFORD, M. H. L. 1975. Geology, fauna and palaeoenvironment of the Ngorora Formation, Kenya Rift Valley. *Nature*, **254**, 185–192.
CERLING, T. E. 1979. Palaeochemistry of Plio-Pleistocene Lake Turkana, Kenya. *Palaeogeography, Palaeoclimatology, Palaeoecology*, **27**, 247–285.
CHAPMAN, G. R. & BROOK, M. 1978. Chronostratigraphy of the Baringo basin, Kenya Rift Valley. *In*: BISHOP, W. W. (ed.) *Geological Background to Fossil Man*. Scottish Academic, Edinburgh, 207–223.
——, LIPPARD, S. J. & MARTYN, J. E. 1973. *Geological map of the northern Tugen Hills* (Degree Sheet No. 34 North East Quarter; 1:125,000). East African Geological Research Unit, Bedford College, University of London.
——, —— & ——1978. The stratigraphy and structure of the Kamasia Range, Kenya Rift Valley. *Journal of the Geological Society, London*, **153**, 265–281.

COOMBS, D. S. & WHETTON, J. T. 1967. Composition of analcime from sedimentary and burial metamorphic rocks. *Geological Society of America Bulletin*, **78**, 269–282.

COUSSEMENT, C. 1995. *Structures traverses et extension intracontinentale. Le role des zones de failles d'Assoua et Tanganyika–Rukwa–Malawi dans la cinématique néogène du système de Rift Est-africain*. PhD thesis, Université de Bretagne Occidentale, France.

DEINO, A., TAUXE, L., MONAGHAN, M. & DRAKE, R. 1990. $^{40}Ar/^{39}Ar$ age calibration of the litho- and paleomagnetic stratigraphies of the Ngorora Formation, Kenya. *Journal of Geology*, **98**, 567–587.

DUNKLEY, P. N., SMITH, M., ALLEN, D. J. & DARLING, W. G. 1993. *The geothermal activity and geology of the northern sector of the Kenya Rift Valley*. British Geological Survey Research Report **SC/93/1**.

EGO, J. K. 1994. *Sedimentology and diagenesis of Neogene sediments in the central Kenya Rift Valley*. MSc thesis, University of Saskatchewan.

EUGSTER, H. P. 1980. Lake Magadi, Kenya, and its precursors. *In:* NISSENBAUM, A. (ed.) *Hypersaline Brines and Evaporitic Environments*. Developments in Sedimentology, No. 28, Elsevier, Amsterdam, 195–232.

FARRAND, W. R., REDDING, R. W., WOLPOFF, M. H. & WRIGHT, H. T. 1976. *An archeological investigation on the Loboi Plain, Baringo District, Kenya*. Technical Report, Museum of Anthropology, University of Michigan, **4**.

FUCHS, V. E. 1950. Pleistocene events in the Baringo Basin. *Geological Magazine*, **87**, 149–174.

GREGORY, J. W. 1921. *The Rift Valleys and Geology of East Africa*. Seeley Service, London.

HAY, R. L. 1970. Silicate reactions in three lithofacies of a semi-arid basin, Olduvai Gorge, Tanzania. Mineralogical Society of America, Special Paper **3**, 237–255.

——1976. *Geology of the Olduvai Gorge*. University of California, Berkeley.

HETZEL, R. & STRECKER, M. R. 1994. Late Mozambique Belt structures in western Kenya and their influence on the evolution of the Cenozoic Kenya Rift. *Journal of Structural Geology*, **16**, 189–201.

HILL, A. 1995. Faunal and environmental change in the Neogene of East Africa: evidence from the Tugen Hills sequence, Baringo District, Kenya. *In:* VRBA, E. S., DENTON, G. H., PARTRIDGE, T. C. & BURKLE, L. H. (eds) *Paleoclimate and Evolution with Emphasis on Human Origins*. Yale University, New Haven, 178–193.

——1999. The Baringo Basin, Kenya: from Bill Bishop to BPRP. *This volume*.

——, CURTIS, G. & DRAKE, R. 1986. Sedimentary stratigraphy of the Tugen Hills, Baringo, Kenya. *In:* FROSTICK, L. E., RENAUT, R. W., REID, I. & TIERCELIN, J.-J. (eds) *Sedimentation in the African Rifts*. Geological Society, London, Special Publications, **25**, 289–295.

——, DRAKE, R., TAUXE, L. *et al.* 1985. Neogene palaeontology and geochronology of the Baringo Basin, Kenya. *Journal of Human Evolution*, **14**, 759–773.

——, WARD, S., DEINO, A., CURTIS, G. & DRAKE, R. 1992. Earliest *Homo. Nature*, **355**, 719–722.

IIJIMA, A. & HAY, R. L. 1968. Analcime composition in the Green River Formation of Wyoming. *American Mineralogist*, **33**, 184–200.

JACOBS, B. F. & KABUYE, C. H. S. 1987. Environments of early hominoids: evidence for Middle Miocene forest in East Africa. *Journal of Human Evolution*, **16**, 147–155.

KINGSTON, J. D., MARINO, B. D. & HILL, A. 1994. Isotopic evidence for Neogene hominid paleoenvironments in the Kenya Rift Valley. *Science*, **264**, 955–959.

LEAKEY, M., TOBIAS, P. V., MARTYN, J. E. & LEAKEY, R. E. F. 1969. An Acheulian industry with prepared core technique and the discovery of a contemporary hominid at Lake Baringo, Kenya. *Proceedings of the Prehistoric Society*, **35**, 4876.

LE TURDU, C., TIERCELIN, J. J., COUSSEMENT, C., ROLET, J., RENAUT, R. W., RICHERT, J. P., XAVIER, J. P. & COQUELET, D. 1995. Basin structure and depositional patterns interpreted using a 3D remote sensing approach: the Baringo–Bogoria basins, central Kenya Rift, East Africa. *Bulletin des Centre de Recherche Exploration-Production Elf-Aquitaine*, **19**, 1–37.

——, ——, RICHERT, J. P., ROLET, J., XAVIER, J.-P., RENAUT, R. W., LEZZAR, K. E. & COUSSEMENT, C. (in press). Influence of pre-existing oblique discontinuities on the geometry and evolution of extensional fault patterns: evidence from the Kenya Rift using SPOT imagery. *In:* MORLEY, C. (ed). *American Association of Petroleum Geologists Memoirs*.

LIPPARD, S. J. 1972. *The stratigraphy and structure of the Elgeyo Escarpment, southern Kamasia Hills and adjoining areas, Rift Valley Province, Kenya*. PhD thesis, University of London.

——1973. The petrology of phonolites from the Kenya Rift. *Lithos*, **6**, 217–234.

MARTYN, J. E. 1969. *The geological history of the country between Lake Baringo and the Kerio River, Baringo District, Kenya*. PhD thesis, University of London.

MCBREARTY, S. 1999. The archaeology of the Kapthurin Formation. *This volume*.

——, BISHOP, L. C. & KINGSTON, J. D. 1996. Variability in traces of Middle Pleistocene hominid behavior in the Kapthurin Formation, Baringo, Kenya. *Journal of Human Evolution*, **30**, 563–580.

MCCALL, G. J. H., BAKER, B. H. & WALSH, J. 1967. Late Tertiary and Quaternary sediments of the Kenya Rift Valley. *In:* BISHOP, W. W. & CLARK, J. D. (eds) *Background to Evolution in Africa*. University of Chicago, 191–220.

MELACK, J. M. 1981. Photosynthetic activity of phytoplankton in tropical African soda lakes. *Hydrobiologia*, **81**, 71–85.

MORLEY, C. K., WESCOTT, W. A., STONE, D. M., HARPER, R. M., WIGGER, S. T. & KARANJA, F. M. 1992. Tectonic evolution of the northern Kenyan Rift. *Journal of the Geological Society, London*, **149**, 333–348.

MUGISHA, F., EBINGER, C. J., STRECKER, M. & POPE, D. 1997. Two-stage rifting in the Kenya Rift: implications for half-graben models. *Tectonophysics*, **278**, 61–81.

MURRAY-HUGHES, R. 1933. *Notes on the geological succession, tectonics and economic geology of the western half of Kenya Colony*. Report of the Geological Survey of Kenya, **3**.

OWEN, R. B. 1981. *Quaternary diatomaceous sediments and the geological evolution of lakes Turkana, Baringo and Bogoria, Kenya Rift Valley*. PhD thesis, University of London.

PICKFORD, M. H. L. 1975a. *Stratigraphy and palaeoecology of five Late Cainozoic formations in the Kenya Rift Valley*. PhD thesis, University of London.

——1975b. Late Miocene sediments and fossils from the northern Kenya Rift Valley. *Nature*, **256**, 279–284.

——1978. Geology, palaeoenvironments and vertebrate faunas of the mid-Miocene Ngorora Formation, Kenya. *In:* BISHOP, W. W. (ed.) *Geological Background to Fossil Man*. Scottish Academic, Edinburgh, 237–262.

REMY, R. R. & FERREL, R. E. 1989. Distribution and origin of analcime in the marginal lacustrine mudstones of the Green River Formation, south-central Uinta Basin, Utah. *Clays and Clay Minerals*, **37**, 419–432.

RENAUT, R. W. 1993. Zeolitic diagenesis of late Quaternary fluviolacustrine sediments and sediments and associated calcrete formation in the Lake Bogoria Basin, Kenya Rift Valley: *Sedimentology*, **40**, 271–301.

—— & OWEN, R. B. 1991. Shore-zone sedimentation and facies in a closed rift lake: the Holocene beach deposits of Lake Bogoria, Kenya. *In:* ANADÓN, P., CABRERA, L. & KELTS, K. (eds) *Lacustrine Facies Analysis*. International Association of Sedimentologists, Special Publications, **13**, 175–195.

—— & TIERCELIN, J.-J. 1994. Lake Bogoria, Kenya Rift Valley: a sedimentological overview. *In:* RENAUT, R. W. & LAST, W. M. (eds) *Sedimentology and Geochemistry of Modern and Ancient Saline Lakes*. Society for Sedimentary Geology (SEPM), Special Publication, **50**, 101–123.

——, JONES, B. & TIERCELIN, J.-J. 1998. Rapid *in situ* silicification of microbes at Loburu hot springs, Lake Bogoria, Kenya Rift Valley. *Sedimentology*, **45**, 1083–1104.

SANDERS, L. D. 1963. *Geology of the Eldoret Area*. Report of the Geological Survey of Kenya, **64**.

SHACKLETON, R. M. 1951. A contribution to the geology of the Kavirondo Rift Valley. *Quarterly Journal of the Geological Society, London*, **106**, 345–392.

SHEPPARD, R. A. & GUDE, A. J. 1968. *Distribution and genesis of authigenic silicate minerals in tuffs of Pleistocene Lake Tecopa, Inyo County, California*. US Geological Survey Professional Paper **597**.

SURDAM, R. C. & EUGSTER, H. P. 1976. Mineral reactions in the sedimentary deposits of the Lake Magadi region, Kenya. *Geological Society of America Bulletin*, **87**, 1739–1752.

—— & PARKER, R. B. 1972. Authigenic aluminosilicate minerals in the tuffaceous rocks of the Green River Formation, Wyoming. *Geological Society of America Bulletin*, **83**, 689–700.

—— & SHEPPARD, R. A. 1978. Zeolites in saline, alkaline-lake deposits. *In:* SAND, L. B. & MUMPTON, F. A. (eds) *Natural Zeolites: Occurrence, Properties, Use*. Pergamon, Oxford, 145–174.

TALBOT, M. R. 1988. The origins of lacustrine oil source rocks: evidence from the lakes of tropical Africa. *In:* FLEET, A. J., KELTS, K. & TALBOT, M. R. (eds) *Lacustrine Petroleum Source Rocks*. Geological Society, London, Special Publications, **38**, 93–102.

TALLON, P. W. J. 1976. *The stratigraphy, palaeoenvironments and geomorphology of the Pleistocene Kapthurin Formation, Kenya*. PhD thesis, University of London.

——1978. Geological setting of hominid fossils and Acheulian artefacts from the Kapthurin Formation, Baringo District, Kenya. *In:* BISHOP, W. W. (ed.) *Geological Background to Fossil Man*. Scottish Academic, Edinburgh, 361–378.

TAUXE, L., MONAGHAN, M., DRAKE, R., CURTIS, G. & STAUDIGEL, H. 1985. Paleomagnetism of Miocene East African Rift sediments and the calibration of the geomagnetic reversal time scale. *Journal of Geophysical Research*, **90B**, 4639–4646.

TIERCELIN, J. J. 1981. *Rifts continentaux, tectonique, climats, sédiments. Exemples: la sédimentation dans le Nord du Rift Gregory, Kenya, et dans le rift de l'Afar, Ethiopie, depuis le Miocène*. PhD thesis, Université Aix-Marseille II.

—— & VINCENS, A. (eds) 1987. Le demi-graben de Baringo–Bogoria, Rift Gregory, Kenya. 30000 ans d'histoire hydrologique et sédimentaire. *Bulletin des Centre de Recherche Exploration-Production Elf-Aquitaine*, **11**, 249–540.

TSCHERNICH, R. W. 1992. *Zeolites of the World*. Geoscience, Phoenix.

WALSH, J. 1969. *Geology of the Eldama Ravine Kabarnet area*. Report of the Geological Survey of Kenya, **84**.

Silali Volcano, Baringo, Kenya: sedimentary structures at the western fringe

JOE MCCALL

44 Robert Franklin Way, South Cerney, Gloucestershire GL7 5UD, UK

Abstract: A brief description is given of exposures of tuffaceous rocks near Kapedo in the Gregory Rift Valley, eruptives of the Quaternary (400 ka–7 ka) Silali Volcano, situated to the north of Lake Baringo, Kenya. These sequences are marked by a transition from unrelieved trachytic tuff sequences in the east to sequences containing interleaved tuffaceous sediments and torrent wash towards the west; sedimentary structures such as cross-bedding, graded bedding and channelling, indicating deposition in a fluviatile and/or lacustrine environment. There are also structures indicative of tectonic deformation, related to fault movements and slumping during the sedimentation. The structures and the three likely sources within the volcano are illustrated by a series of photographs.

The author was first involved in the geological mapping of the Baringo District in 1958–1960 when he mapped the quarter degree sheet 35SW including the then Lake Hannington (now Bogoria) for the Geological Survey of Kenya (McCall 1967). At that time considerable doubt, initiated by H. B. S. Cooke, was held concerning the concept of 'Kamasian' Lake Beds (Gregory 1921; Leakey & Solomon in Leakey 1931). Both the author and the late John Walsh recognized that there were several sedimentary sequences in the Baringo Basin of quite different ages. With the support of the Geological Survey, they, with the late Brian Baker, carried out a reconnaissance of the exposures in the river valleys to the west of Lake Baringo, identifying and naming the quite separate Chemeron and Kapthurin sequences, the latter unconformable on the former. This work attracted the interest of Bill Bishop and the account of it was published under his joint editorship (McCall *et al.* 1967).

At this time the author noticed the caldera volcano of Silali north of Lake Baringo and carried out two expeditions to it in 1965 and 1967 supported by the Geological Survey of Kenya and the East African Geological Research Unit in which Bill Bishop, then at Bedford College, was active. This was the first geological coverage of Silali. The author's original map, which was utilized to compile part of the EAGRU 1:125,000 sheet (EAGRU 1978), is now held in the archives of the British Geological Survey. Silali Volcano has since been described in the literature by McCall (1968*a,b* 1970), McCall & Hornung (1972), Dunkley *et al.* (1994), Smith *et al.* (1995) and Macdonald *et al.* (1995).

The last time that the author went into the field with Bill Bishop was in the summer of 1967, when they examined some very interesting and unusual sedimentary structures within the tuffaceous deposits on the western fringe of Silali Volcano, around the small village trading centre of Kapedo. The deposits containing these are the subject of this account. A week after Bill Bishop's visit the author discovered the Karmosit vertebrate fossil locality in much older (*c.* 3.4 Ma) sediments some kilometres to the south and his collections were studied and described by Bishop *et al.* (1971).

The recent volcano of Silali – active 400–220 ka up to 7 ka – is the largest caldera volcano in the northern part of the Gregory Rift Valley in Kenya (Fig. 1). Its early pre-caldera development was dominated by per-alkaline trachyte lavas and pyroclasts, and these were succeeded by mildly alkaline to transitional basalts (Smith *et al.* 1995). The tuffaceous deposits near Kapedo, described and illustrated here, relate to part of the earlier of these two pre-caldera eruptive sequences. They have only been briefly mentioned in the literature and the sedimentary structures within them have not been illustrated. They are the Upper Pyroclastic Deposits shown near Kapedo in fig. 3A of Smith *et al.* 1995 (Table 1). Dunkley *et al.* (1994: 47) wrote:

'immediately east of Kapedo village (AM 1780 1300) up to 10 m of bedded pumiceous tuffs mantle the topography of the underlying Mission Basalt and are in turn overlain by trachyte lavas. Individual beds are up to 0.75 m thick, are internally stratified, and

McCALL, G. J. H. 1999. Silali Volcano, Baringo, Kenya: sedimentary structures at the western fringe. *In*: ANDREWS, P. & BANHAM, P. (eds) *Late Cenozoic Environments and Hominid Evolution: a tribute to Bill Bishop*. Geological Society, London, 59–68.

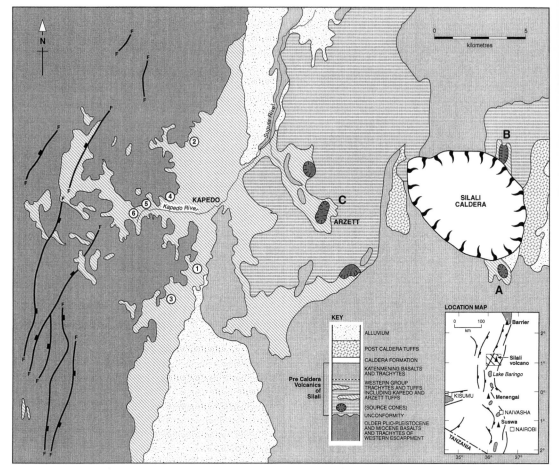

Fig. 1. Geological sketch map of Silali volcano and the Kapedo tuff exposures (derived from EAGRU 1978). Inset shows location within the Gregory Rift valley. A, B and C are the possible sources of the tuffs in the Silali Volcano. Note that the basalt flow down the course of the Suguta River is a flow older than the Katenmening Basalts; it underlies the Kapedo tuffs, and was named the Mission Basalt. The sites illustrated in Figs 2A–E and 4A–E are located at sites 1–6 on this figure, as indicated in the captions. The four views illustrated in Figs 2D, E and 4A, B are very close together, likewise those illustrated in Figs 4D, E.

contain sub-rounded lithic clasts of trachyte and obsidian. A sample from this locality has yielded an Ar/Ar date of 131(+ or −3) ka. Further south, sections in the Suguta and Kapedo rivers expose up to 20 m of well-bedded trachytic pumice-lapilli tuff and ash. These deposits are locally intercalated with, and cut by fluvial conglomerates and sand-stones ... cross-bedding, parallel lamination and slumps are common. These features indicate that in this area the Kapedo Tuffs were deposited within a fluviolacustrine envir-onment and were probably reworked.'

These authors also note the draping of the Kapedo tuffs to the west of Kapedo onto the Murgisian basalt and older Pliocene and Mio-cene strata, and suggest a source in Plinian-style eruptions from a series of cones located on the eastern half of the former summit area of Silali Volcano (Figs 1 and 2), though Arzett cone on the western flank may have also contributed. These probable sources are accepted by the present author.

Description of the outcrops

Along the floor of the Rift Valley east of Kapedo flows the Suguta River emanating from vigorous hot springs immediately east of Kapedo Village, and joined immediately to the east of the village

Table 1. *The stratigraphic sequence of Silali Volcano*

Volcanic lithostratigraphy			Major lithology	Thickness or extent	Age	Evolution and style of activity	
Post-Caldera Group	Extra-Caldera	Recent Basalts	Basalts	6–8 km²	<1 ka	Fissure eruption among N–S and NNE trending fissures, scoria cones and lava domes	Post-caldera activity
		Pyroclastic Deposits	Trachytic pumice lapilli / Tuffs and breccias	1–2 m / 15 km²	<10 ka		
		Black Hills Trachytes	Trachytes, benmoreites / Phonolites, basalt		7–9±2 ka		
	Intra-Caldera	Basalts	Hawaiites	8 km²	9±9 ka		
		Trachytes	Trachytes	8 km²	8±ka		
Pre-Caldera Group	Katenmening Lavas	Katenmening Basalts	Basalts, trachytes and mixed rocks.	50 m	63±11 ka	Widespread fissure eruptions on flank and summit area, pit crater formation and magma drainage	Pre- to syn-caldera collapse
		Katenmening Trachytes	Trachytes	10–40 m			
		Flank Fissure Baslats	Basalts	>50 m	100 ka		
Western Flank Group		Summit Trachyte Arzett Tuffs	Trachytes / Trachytic pumic lapilli tuffs, air-fall and surge deposits	300 m / 40 m	>100 ka / 123 ka	Plinian eruptions, scoria cones and eruptions from circumferential fissures	Pre-caldera flank eruptions
		Discoid Trachyte	Trachytes	50 m			
Caldera Wall Group	Kapedo Tuffs	Upper Pyroclastic Deposits	Trachytic ash flow and air fall deposits	>120 m	130–135 ka	Plinian eruptions from large scoria cones	Late shield
		Intermediate Lavas	Trachytes, hawaiites and basalts	95 m		Fissure eruptions	
		Lower Pyroclastic Deposits	Trachytic breccias and lavas	>150 m		Plinian eruptions, cone formation	
		Lower Trachytes	Trachytes	?	216–?400 ka		Early shield
		Mission Basalt	Basalt	?	?	? Fissure eruptions	Platform

Older Plio-Pleistocene and Miocene volcanic rocks (trachytes and basalts)

After Smith *et al.* (1995).

by the Kapedo River, flowing out from the west through a gap in the fault scarp of Plio-Pleistocene and Miocene volcanic rocks immediately to the west of the village. Both rivers cut into yellow to buff coloured trachytic pumiceous tuffs which have been named the Kapedo tuffs (McCall & Hornung 1972).

The sections along the Suguta River, around Kapedo, and along the Kapedo River where it cuts through the scarp to the west, are extremely interesting because these deposits represent a transition between pyroclastic deposits (*sensu stricto*) and continental sediments containing mainly pyroclastic material reworked, but with an admixture of gravelly torrent wash material off the high and steep escarpment to the west of Kapedo.

To the east of Kapedo and in the narrow defile to the south of the village, where the old dirt road approached the village from the south, the sections display only rather thickly stratified pumice tuffs (Fig. 2A). These tuffs are entirely similar in character to those exposed in the caldera wall, interleaved with trachyte lavas, and in two cones on the edge of the eastern part of the caldera (A,B in Figs 1 and 3), and in and around the Arzett cones on the western flank of the volcano (C in Figs 1 and 3). There is no reason to believe that they are anything but airfall tuffs: they show coarse bedding and are quite distinct from the very widespread developments of pyroclastic flows displaying welding, eutaxitic and *fiamme* structure of this rift valley volcanic province (McCall 1964). A chemical analysis, average of three samples of these trachytic pumice tuffs of Silali, is given by McCall & Hornung (1972).

Along the foot of the scarp east of Kapedo there are two exposures, to the south of the village, where these tuffs are visibly unconformable on the older Pliocene trachytic volcanics of the escarpment (Fig. 2B).

As one moves westwards up the Kapedo River valley from Kapedo village, the tuff sections change in character. There are still some developments of thickly bedded tuff and also some quite massive tuff units (for example, as seen in Fig. 4D), but within the sequence sedimentary structures are evident. These structures are of three types:

(a) *Cross-bedding*. Finer tuffaceous layers, largely composed of pumice fragments, make their appearance and these may display cross-bedding (Figs 2E and 4B). Elsewhere there is also some large-scale tabular cross-bedding in thick units (Fig. 4C).

(b) *Graded bedding*. Coarse to fine grades are also evident in some sections of finer pumiceous material (Fig. 2D).

(c) *Wash-out scours*. These are of three types:
   (i) small-scale scours evident in the finely layered sequences described above (Figs 2E and 4B);
   (ii) scours filled with torrent-wash cobble gravel, composed of lava fragments derived from the older volcanics of the western escarpment and not from the Silali Volcano, from which the tuffaceous component is derived (Fig. 4A). The finer sediments also contain scattered clasts of such material (Fig. 2E);
   (iii) very large-scale channelling structures, affecting thick layered units (Fig. 4D).

These structures can only represent deposition in water and some are only compatible with a fluviatile environment.

Deformation structures related to faulting and slumping

Outcrops south of Kapedo expose the monotonous tuff sequence draped steeply over the Murgisian Basalt, the youngest of the lava units

Fig. 2. (A) Stratified pumice tuff immediately east of Kapedo village (Site 1 on Fig. 1). This appears to be a sequence of quite well sorted air-fall tuffs, with no reworked tuffaceous sediment intercalations evident, such as appear in the sections as one goes towards the west, though there is just a trace of cross-bedding at the bottom. (B) Stratified pumice tuffs, similar to those in (A) at the foot of the fault scarp north of Kapedo village (Site 2 on Fig. 1) showing unconformity and draping on the older Pliocene trachytic volcanic rocks (Unit Rc4 on EAGRU 1978). (C) Similar pumice tuffs, quite steeply mantling the Pleistocene(?) Murgisian basalt (e' on EAGRU 1978), part of the older volcanic assemblage of the western escarpment, south of Kapedo village (Site 3 on Fig. 1). The dips of the beds here reach 40° in a series of disrupted blocks along the line of the escarpment, though the tuffs in the foreground are disposed horizontally. The fronting cliff is 3 m high. (D) Graded bedding in alternating fine and medium coarse grained layers, overlying a pocket of coarse angular and sub-rounded clasts, Kapedo River section (Site 4 on Fig. 1). The section shown is 1 m high. (E) Cross-bedding and a wash-out in a similar sequence. There are scattered angular trachyte lava clasts derived from the older rocks of the escarpment and pockets of such clasts, which mark the incipient development of larger scale channelling features filled with such clasts, seen in Fig. 4A. Kapedo River section (Site 4 on Fig. 1).

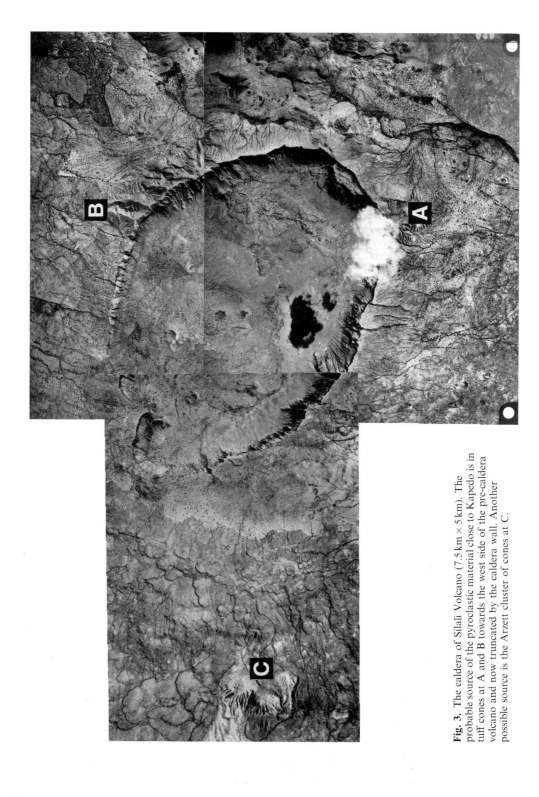

Fig. 3. The caldera of Silali Volcano (7.5 km × 5 km). The probable source of the pyroclastic material close to Kapedo is in tuff cones at A and B towards the west side of the pre-caldera volcano and now truncated by the caldera wall. Another possible source is the Arzett cluster of cones at C.

of the sequence of older rocks of the Western Scarp (Fig. 2C). The tuffs in the foreground of the photograph are disposed horizontally, but those proximal to the scarp are tilted eastwards at quite steep angles in a series of dislocated blocks; dips reach as much as 40°. Normal fault movements in the centre of the rift valley occurred here up to very recent times – the floor is characterized by successive arrays of 'grid' or *touche de piano* sets (McCall 1967), and this development must be due to very recent faulting affecting the Kapedo tuff sequence – probably a renewal of movement along the fault bounding the eastern escarpment.

An outcrop near the western end of the Kapedo River section exposed 'broken beds' (Fig. 4E) and these are clearly both underlain and overlain by undisturbed beds. The interpretation tentatively placed on this is that the broken beds are the product of contemporaneous slumping movements during the deposition of the Kapedo tuffs. The broken beds appear to scour out the undisturbed beds below and are overlain and abutted on abruptly by an undisturbed cross-bedded layer. It seems probable that this structure is the product of contemporaneous slumping, related to fault movements while the sequence was being deposited.

Age of the Kapedo tuffs

Smith *et al.* (1995: 303) report an ^{40}Ar/^{39}Ar determination on a tuff sample from close to Kapedo village, yielding an age of 132 (+ or −3) ka; this fits in well with another determination from the top of the caldera wall of 135 (+ or −3) ka. However, as these authors note, one cannot exclude a source for part of the Kapedo tuff sequence at Arzett (C on Figs 1 and 3) which gave an age of about 123 ka (Table 1). An age range of 135–123 ka thus seems likely for the entire sequence.

Discussion

It is very difficult for geologists to differentiate in ancient sequences between air-fall pyroclastics and reworked sediments composed of pyroclastic material, either by drawing boundaries on the map or in petrographic description. We see here that, even in these Quaternary sequences, close to a major volcano and in a very restricted drainage system, there is interfingering between air-fall pyroclasts and water-laid sediments dominantly composed of pyroclasts from the same source, reworked in water and mixed with torrent-wash gravels, unrelated to the volcano, in a continental setting. Even in such a geologically young setting, in which the field relationships and character of the rocks have not been modified by later processes, there are no hard and fast mappable boundaries between water-laid sediments and air-fall pyroclasts, the only field boundaries that are seen being on a very small scale, within the outcrops. Field or petrographic separation of direct air-fall material from reworked material is probably completely impossible. The term 'Lake Beds' was early applied widely to any water-laid sediments within the rift valley but it is something of a misnomer. The tuffaceous sediments within the rift valley may be fluviatile, deposits of small localized pondings or deposits of larger lakes such as the present Lakes Naivasha, Elmenteita, Nakuru, Bogoria, Baringo and Turkana. The Kapedo deposits are probably a combination of torrent wash, tuffaceous fluviatile deposits and deposits in small pondings. They are probably not deposits of extensive lakes.

Conclusion

The Kapedo tuffs close to Kapedo are normal, stratified air-fall pumice tuffs, but as one goes west, draping on the scarp of older Pliocene and Pleistocene volcanics is apparent and dips may

---

Fig. 4. (overleaf) (**A**) A scour channelling fine pumiceous beds and filled with bouldery torrent-wash gravels, derived from the rocks seen below the unconformities in Fig. 2B, C; the older Pliocene rocks forming the western escarpment material not related to Silali Volcano. These are here mixed with the tuffaceous material from Silali Volcano. The channel is 1m wide. Kapedo River section (Site 4 on Fig. 1). (**B**) An exposure of fine tuffaceous sediments, displaying cross-bedding and multiple scour channels washing out the beds below. Width of view is 1.5m. Kapedo River section (Site 4 on Fig. 1). (**C**) Outcrop about 5km west from Kapedo along the Kapedo River showing a middle layer with large-scale tabular cross-bedding in a three-fold section, about 4m thick (Site 5 on Fig. 1). (**D**) A two-fold section displaying a steep 3m thick layer of layered pumiceous material, washed out and infilled by a 4m thick horizontally disposed layer of similar material (Site 6 on Fig. 1) (**E**) A three-fold section about 3m thick, close to the sites of Fig. 4C, D, showing a lower horizontal layer of fine, layered pumiceous material, washed out by a layer of 'broken beds', a chaotic assemblage of slumped(?) fragments of similarly layered pumiceous material, and above another layer of coarser pumiceous material filling another wash-out (Site 6 on Fig. 1).

Table 2. *The sedimentary sequences of diverse ages now established in the Baringo Basin*

Name	Age
Kobwob beds	Holocene
Kapedo River beds (Silali)	131 ka (+ or −3)
Kapthurin Formation	top 240 ka
	bottom 780 ka
Chemoguit beds (Chesowanja)	1.1–1.2 Ma
Chemeron Formation	<1.5 Ma
	(Ndau trachymugearite 1.57 Ma)
Karmosit beds	3.4 Ma
Aterir beds	>4 Ma
Kaperyon Formation	5 Ma
Lukeino Member	6–6.7 Ma
Mpesida beds	6.3–7 Ma
Ngorora Formation	10–12.6 Ma
Alengerr beds	12–14 Ma
Muruyur beds	13–14 Ma

Derived from Bishop *et al.* (1971), P. Andrews (pers. comm.) and this study.

be as much as 40° off the scarp; although this may be partly a draping effect, the localized linear zone of disrupted blocks and high dips appears rather to be due to tectonic disturbance related to reactivation of a fault. As one goes westwards also, tuffaceous sediments appear, with cross-bedding, graded bedding and channelling, and there is an intermixture of the airfall tuffs with Silali-derived pumiceous sediments, reworked air-fall tuffs, and clasts of the older Pliocene lava, shed off the western fault scarp and carried by fast-flowing streams, and quite unrelated to the Silali eruptions. The latter material appears both as scattered isolated clasts and small pockets of clasts, and also forms sizeable channel fillings of angular gravel within the tuffaceous material. Further west again very large-scale sedimentary structures appear: tabular cross-bedding, channels several metres wide and deep, and quite spectacular 'broken-beds' infilling large channels and themselves cut by channels, probably slump deposits. These appear to be related to tectonic disturbance involving faulting and slumping, during the deposition of the Kapedo tuffs.

This sequence could very well reward a much more detailed study as it represents a remarkably well exposed section of the transition between air-fall tuffs and water-laid sediments, including both such material reworked and extraneous material, in a continental, still tectonically active rift valley setting.

We have progressed in the Baringo basin from the concept of a great, extensive 'Lake Kamasia', through the distinction of the Chemeron and Kapthurin Beds, to the recognition of a succession of a number of sedimentary formations of widely different ages (Table 2). The age of the sediments within the Kapedo tuffs is apparently younger than that of the well studied Kapthurin Beds to the south (Table 2), but the same type of transition might well apply to those sequences. The exposures near Kapedo could well reveal vertebrate fossils on detailed examination.

References

BISHOP, W. W., CHAPMAN, G. R., HILL, A. & MILLER, J. A. 1971. Succesion of Cainozoic Vertebrate Assemblages from the Northern Kenya Rift Valley. *Nature, Physical Science*, **233**, 389–394.

DUNKLEY, P. N., SMITH, M., ALLEN, D. J. & DARLING, W. E. 1994. *The Geothermal Activity and Geology of the Northern Sector of the Kenya Rift Valley*. British Geological Survey Research Report SC/93/1.

EAST AFRICAN GEOLOGICAL RESEARCH UNIT (EAGRU) 1978. *Geology of the Kapedo and Emuruangogolak Area*. Map of degree sheet 27 SW, Scale 1:125,000, prepared for the Geological Survey of Kenya.

GREGORY, J. W. 1921. *The Rift Valleys and Geology of East Africa*. Seeley Service, London.

LEAKEY, L. S. B. 1931. *The Stone Age Cultures of Kenya Colony*. Cambridge University Press.

McCALL, G. J. H. 1964. Froth-flows in Kenya. *Geologische Rundschau*, **54**, 1148–1195.

——1967. *Geology of the Nakura–Thomson's Falls– Lake Hannington Area*. Reprint No. 78, Geological Survey of Kenya.

——1968a. Silali, another major caldera volcano in the Rift Valley of Kenya. *Proceedings of the Geological Society, London*, **1644**, 267–268.

——1968*b*. The five caldera volcanoes of the central rift valley in Kenya. *Proceedings of the Geological Society, London,* **1647**, 54–59.

——1970. Gabbroic and ultramafic nodules – high level intracrustal occurrences in alkali basalts and associated volcanics from Kenya, described and compared with those of Hawaii. *Physics of the Earth and Planetary Interiors,* **3**, 255–272.

—— & HORNUNG, G. 1972. A geochemical study of Silali volcano, Kenya, with special reference to the origin of the intermediate-acid eruptives of the central rift valley, *Tectonophysics,* **15**, 97–113.

——, BAKER, B. H. & WALSH, J. 1967. Late Tertiary and Quaternary sediments of the Kenya Rift Valley. *In*: BISHOP, W. W. & CLARK, J. D. (eds) *Background to Evolution in Africa.* University of Chicago Press, 191–200.

MACDONALD, R., DAVIES, G. R., UPTON, B. G. J., DUNKLEY, P. N., SMITH, M. & LEAT, P. T. 1995. Petrogenesis of Silali volcano, Gregory Rift, Kenya. *Journal of the Geological Society,* **152**, 703–720.

SMITH, M., DUNKLEY, P. N., DEINO, A., WILLIAMS, L. A. J. & McCALL, G. J. H. 1995. Geochronology, stratigraphy and structural evolution of Silali Volcano, Gregory Rift Valley, Kenya. *Journal of the Geological Society,* **152**, 297–310.

Environmental determinants in early hominid evolution: issues and evidence from the Tugen Hills, Kenya

JOHN D. KINGSTON

Department of Anthropology and Department of Geology and Geophysics,
PO Box 208109, Yale University, New Haven, CT 06520-8109, USA

Abstract: Evidence of hominid/hominoid palaeoenvironments collected from the Tugen Hills succession has been key in appreciating the diversity of habitats that characterized the East African Rift Valley over the last 15.5 Ma. Isotopic analyses of fossil herbivore enamel, palaeosol carbonates and preserved organic matter from the Tugen Hills provide a means of reconstructing plant biomass based on differences in photosynthetic processes. In modern tropical ecosystems, carbon isotopic variation can be used to distinguish different physiognomic types of plant communities – in general differentiating 'open' vs 'closed' habitats. Isotopic data from palaeosol horizons in this sequence indicate that throughout this interval of time, at various locations in the Tugen Hills, slightly open woodland-like environments were available for hominoids and early hominids to exploit and that environments similar to modern East African grasslands at no time dominated this part of the rift valley. Analyses of a number of fossil herbivore taxa from the sequence indicate an increase in the dietary importance of C_4 grasses in the late Miocene. Cumulatively these data, in conjunction with palaeobotanical evidence, suggest that past environments in the Tugen Hills region were heterogeneous in both space and time from the middle Miocene through the Pleistocene.

When Darwin (1871) first suggested that hominid origins might be linked to environmental change he established a paradigm which remains central to most theories of human evolution. Many of the behavioural and morphological changes documented in the fossil hominid record have tentatively been linked to the general notion that forests were replaced by more open grassland and woodland habitats in East Africa during the late Miocene and Pliocene, presumably as a response to increasing aridity and cooler temperatures. The tempo and mode of this vegetational succession, informally referred to as the savanna hypothesis, has never been explicitly articulated but has nevertheless become entrenched as a theme in palaeoanthropological literature. This theoretical perception remains an attractive construct as it reconciles well with the traditional premise that major stages of human evolution unfolded as a response to increasingly open environments. In addition, directional global climatic change through the Neogene, well documented in the marine record, appears to support the possibility of progressively more arid and seasonal terrestrial conditions in Africa (Miller *et al.* 1987; Crowley & North 1991; deMenocal & Rind 1993; Kennett 1995). While most researchers interested in the role of environmental factors in hominid evolution recognize this scenario as probably somewhat simplistic and generally unsubstantiated, they also appreciate that it potentially incorporates elements of truth. As such, the savanna hypothesis has endured to the extent that it is typically invoked in examining aspects of hominid evolution without reference to any supporting data. The circularity of linking early hominid traits interpreted as adaptations to open terrain with the concept of grasslands replacing forest in East Africa has been noted by previous researchers (such as Hill 1987) and recently there have been a number of discussions expressly challenging the hypothesis (Kingston *et al.* 1994; Hill 1995; Potts 1996; Shreeve 1996; Feibel 1997). Based on accumulating evidence, the emerging consensus is shifting to the view that the evolution of landscapes in East Africa relative to early hominids is complex. Simply invoking the directional development of open habitats as selective pressure for hominid speciation or extinction events is insufficient and possibly misleading. This perspective is also not novel. In 1962 after six years of field investigations in East Africa, Bill Bishop wrote:

'It seems probable that with a combination of climatic variations and a diversified landscape containing a wide range of vegetation zones within a small compass, together with numerous lake basins of changing form, East Africa provided a patchwork of environmental niches

Kingston, J. D. 1999. Environmental determinants in early hominid evolution: issues and evidence from the Tugen Hills, Kenya. *In*: Andrews, P. & Banham, P. (eds) *Late Cenozoic Environments and Hominid Evolution: a tribute to Bill Bishop*. Geological Society, London, 69–84.

which were ideally suited to man's development of varied techniques and ways of life.'

Although this comment was framed in the
context of the Pleistocene, it is clear that the
considerations that led to this deduction apply
equally well to earlier periods in the Neogene.

Nature of the fossil record

The difficulty in discussing early human evolution within the context of a palaeoecological
framework is due primarily to the poor quality
and resolution of the hominid/hominoid, faunal,
floral and environmental fossil records available
for study. While the course of human evolution
was surely mediated by environmental change,
empirical evidence from East Africa as yet
remains too incomplete to support or refute
these long-term directional environmental trends
and potential correlations between evolutionary
change and environmental shifts. In addition,
distortions to the record related to taphonomic
and collection biases further complicate interpretations.

A scrutiny of the assumptions underlying the
notion that environmental factors direct the path
of early hominid evolution reveals a number of
fundamental, unresolved issues which need to
be addressed in justifying this approach. One
rudimentary question involves the relative significance of biotic and abiotic factors as driving
mechanisms of evolution. Are physical changes
in the environment necessary for speciation and
extinction, or are biotic interactions such as
competition, predation, parasitism and mutual-
ism sufficient engines of evolution? Although a
number of theoretical models advocating either
biotic factors or perturbations in the physical
environment as primary forces in evolution have
been proposed (Van Valen 1973; Stenseth &
Maynard Smith 1984; Vrba 1985a, 1995a), the
fossil record, especially in the terrestrial realm,
has yet to provide unequivocal support for any
of these models. Alternatively, both biotic and
abiotic factors are involved and the relative
importance shifts depending on the specifics of
intrinsic and extrinsic environmental and evolutionary factors.

Sidestepping the abiotic/biotic debate, a number of studies have implicated major global
changes in climate and environment as the
driving force in the evolution of early hominids (Bonnefille 1984; Prentice & Denton 1988;
Stanley 1992, 1995; deMenocal 1995; Vrba et al.
1995). The underlying assumption in these hypotheses is that while biotic forces may have been
factors, major physical perturbations of the

ecosystems were critical to what are perceived
to be major adaptive shifts in our ancestry. The
origin of Hominidae, provisionally defined by
the advent of bipedality, has been linked to a
shift to more open environments in East Africa
which in turn has been linked to the Mediterranean Messinian salinity crisis between 5.6 and
5 Ma (Brain 1981; Laporte & Zhilman 1983;
Ambrose 1995). Similarly, the apparent radiation of hominid species during the Pliocene has
been linked to global cooling (Brain 1981;
Bonnefille 1984; Grine 1986; Prentice & Denton
1988; Stanley 1992; deMenocal 1995; Vrba et al.
1989; Vrba 1995a, b). Although the specifics of
hominid phylogeny are currently debated (e.g.
Wood 1992; Wood et al. 1994; Suwa et al. 1996),
the Plio-Pleistocene hominid fossil record of
Africa indicates that there were at least four
species within the genus Australopithecus, two or
three species of Paranthropus, and up to four
species of the genus Homo. Coincident with the
earliest appearance of the genus Homo (Hill et al.
1992) is the oldest evidence for lithic artifacts
dated 2.6–2.5 Ma (Semaw et al. 1997). In general,
it has been assumed that the increase in species
diversity and evidence of behavioural changes
within the human lineage during this interval
also reflect the replacement of forest environments by more open woodland and grassland
environments. This increase in habitat diversity
is linked in turn to the onset of northern hemisphere glacial cycling and resultant increase in
low-latitude aridity.

While it is tempting to invoke global climatic
change as a causal mechanism for hominid
evolution, it is unclear how or if major climatic
shifts detected in marine cores are reflected in the
interior of continents. During the late Pleistocene, increased fluxes of aeolian dust to marine
sediments off the African coast (deMenocal &
Rind 1993), abrupt lowering of lake level in
central and East Africa (Street-Perrott & Perott
1990) and expansion of arid African vegetational
zones (Pokras & Mix 1985) are coincident with
high-latitude glacial advances. Recent analyses
of terrestrial detritus in marine cores sampled off
the African coast (deMenocal 1995; deMenocal
& Bloemendal 1995) indicate that at 2.8 Ma
the African climate became dependent on the
rhythm of high-latitude glacial cycling, manifested by the onset and intensification of seasonally cooler and arid cycles in Africa. These
changes are linked to ecological fragmentation
and establishment of arid-adapted species in
Africa. Although these data indicate that the
African climate in general was tracking global
shifts in the Pliocene and possibly earlier on
in the Miocene, the effects on specific hominid

habitats and ecology remain unclear. Superimposed on the influence of global climatic change are alterations in local hominid habitats induced by crustal doming, volcanism and graben formation in East Africa. In addition to creating topographic and hence habitat heterogeneity, orographic effects probably had a significant influence on regional atmospheric circulation. Eruption of volcanic debris can have profound effects on a regional and even global scale, disrupting atmospheric circulation patterns and drastically altering ecosystems proximal and, in some cases, distal to the eruptive centre. Teasing apart the relative contribution of local, regional and global events to changes in East African environment remains extremely difficult given the complex interrelationships between these extrinsic factors as well as the fragmentary nature of the local palaeoenvironmental record.

Fossil fauna associated with early hominid specimens potentially provides the most relevant and detailed information on possible habitat alteration and resulting ecological pressures on the various hominid species. Environmental shifts implicated in hominid evolution would mostly likely be detected in the evolutionary pathway of contemporaneous taxa. The difficulty in this approach, however, is controlling for all the interpretive, taphonomic and ecological factors that can either obscure or mimic true links between extrinsic factors and faunal turnover. Even recognition and characterization of faunal turnovers in general are problematic and require extensive temporal and geographic continuity in faunal data sets (Barry 1995; White 1995) as well as high resolution chronological control and uniform taxonomic classification. Typically raw palaeontological data from the terrestrial realm lack these attributes. Vrba (1985a) articulated a 'turnover pulse hypothesis' which proposes that faunal change resulting from climatic events should be synchronous in separate lineages. Turnovers in bovid taxa (Vrba 1985b) and micromammal taxa (Wesselman 1985) between 2.7 and 2.5 Ma in Africa have been cited as support for the turnover pulse hypothesis. The validity of this theory has been questioned (Hill 1987, 1995; Prothero 1995) and recently more specific biostratigraphic analyses by Bishop (1994), Bishop et al. (1999), White (1995) and Behrensmeyer et al. (1997) suggest that the speciation and extinction of East African fauna between 3 and 2 Ma does not track climatic change in any obvious way. A key element in understanding and interpreting potential links between environmental and evolutionary factors is resolving the specific timing of events.

Are environmental shifts abrupt or gradual? Is there a lag time required for communities to respond to changing abiotic conditions? Do different types of taxa or assemblages of taxa respond differentially? Are environmental shifts directional over the course of geological time or do they oscillate about a norm? Potts (1996) has suggested that hominid evolution is linked to a pattern of dramatic, episodic environmental oscillations rather than discrete events.

Assuming that the fossil taxa respond to environmental change induced by climatic shifts, it becomes necessary to differentiate faunal turnover due to in situ speciation and extinction from immigration, which may also correlate with climatic fluctuations. Faunal interchange is viewed as a significant process in the evolution and differentiation of terrestrial mammalian communities during the Neogene (Flynn et al. 1991; Janis 1993; Barry 1995; Opdyke 1995). The timing and location of these intercontinental migratory events are controlled to an extent by climatic events but also by tectonic change which can facilitate dispersal by the formation of 'corridors' in regions where interchange was previously restricted by geographical or ecological barriers. As barriers are transgressed, speciation and extinction occur as introduced faunas interact with novel ecosystems. Major faunal turnovers in terrestrial successions have been linked with the creation of 'corridors' formed by low sea level stands or by the tectonic reshuffling of land masses (Barry et al. 1985; Thomas 1985). Alternatively, the formation of barriers can separate previously continuous populations resulting in speciation by vicariance.

Correlating hominid evolution with environmental change ultimately requires developing a detailed palaeoecological perspective based on empirical data collected from terrestrial sequences in East Africa rather than relying on global climatic and tectonic events or habitat reconstructions documented elsewhere. Existing information for the late Miocene and Pliocene of East Africa is limited and interpretation of palaeohabitats based on different lines of evidence often appear incongruous (e.g. Fort Ternan: Andrews & Nesbit Evans 1979; Bonnefille 1984; Shipman 1986; Dugas & Retallack 1993; Cerling et al. 1997a). These apparent discrepancies most likely relate to the complex nature of past ecosystems as well as comparison of data from different stratigraphic levels rather than flawed analyses. These studies emphasize the need to develop and synthesize as many approaches to palaeoenvironmental reconstruction as possible. Within the past decade, stable isotopic analyses of fossil material which forms

in equilibrium with vegetation has been used
to constrain interpretations of the vegetational
physiognomy of palaeohabitats as well as aspects
of palaeodiet. This technique provides an additional tool for semi-quantitative reconstruction of palaeoenvironments. Isotopic analyses
of palaeosol components and fossil herbivore
enamel collected from the Tugen Hills succession provide information on palaeohabitats in
the Baringo Basin over the last 15.5 Ma.

Tugen Hills

In the northern Kenya Rift Valley, the rift
structure consists of a half-graben, characterized
by marked asymmetry (Frostick 1997). In the
Tugen Hills region of the rift, the Elgeyo
Escarpment forms the main boundary (border)
fault on the western escarpment while the eastern margin of the rift is characterized by
antithetic and synthetic faults with much smaller
throws which cut the structure into a series

of tilted fault blocks (Fig. 1). The Tugen Hills
is a complex fault block uplifted along a synthetic fault (Saimo or Kamasia Fault) between
the Elgeyo Escarpment and the axial Baringo–
Suguta trench (Chapman *et al.* 1978). The rift in
this area was initiated as a downwarped trough
in the early to middle Miocene and served
as a depositional basin for thick sedimentary
sequences interbedded with intermittent phonolitic and basaltic lava flows. About 7 Ma, the
'proto-Tugen Hills' was formed by extensive normal faulting along the main Kamasia (Saimo)
fault. After considerable erosion, late Miocene/
Pliocene volcanics and sediments were deposited
and then tilted and faulted in a second major rift-
faulting episode (2–0.5 Ma). This event resulted
in final uplift of the range and exposure of
Miocene/Pliocene sequences in fault scarps along
the eastern foothills of the Tugen Range.

As a result of its complex depositional and
structural history, the Tugen Hills succession
(Fig. 2) exists as a series of disjunct fault-
bounded blocks. Sedimentation within each of

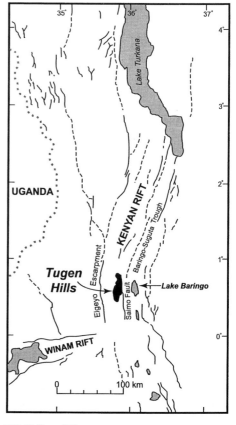

Fig. 1. Location of the Tugen Hills within the East African Rift Valley of Kenya.

Age (Ma)

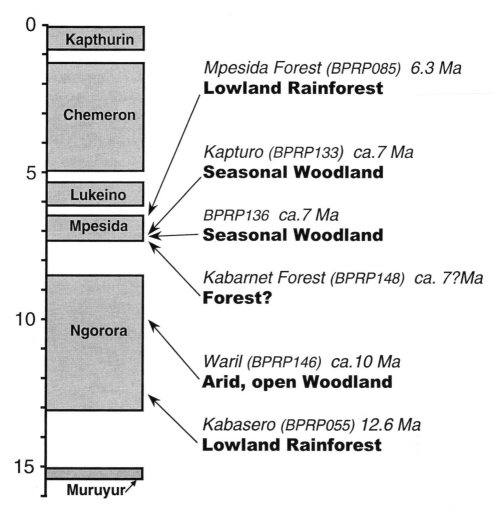

Fig. 2. Middle to late Miocene palaeohabitat reconstructions in the Tugen Hills succession based on palaeobotanical assemblages (Jacobs & Kabuye 1987, 1989; Jacobs & Winkler 1992; Jacobs & Deino 1996; Jacobs pers. comm.). Temporal span and formational designations of sedimentary units are depicted in the shaded rectangles. BPRP numbers refer to Baringo Paleontological Research Project site designations.

these blocks was localized and there is considerable lateral facies variation complicating direct correlation between structurally displaced sections. Establishment of a stratigraphic framework has relied on palaeomagnetic studies as well as geochemical analysis and radiometric dating of interbedded volcanic flows and associated volcaniclastic units (Chapman & Brook 1978; Dagley *et al.* 1978; Tauxe *et al.* 1985; Deino *et al.* 1990). Details of the 3000+ m of intercalated Miocene and Pliocene sediments and volcanics exposed in fault scarps and eroded

surfaces along the eastern foothills of the Tugen Hills are described in Martyn (1969), Bishop *et al.* (1971), Chapman (1971), King & Chapman (1972), Pickford (1975, 1978*a*,*b*), Hill *et al.* (1986) and Hill (1994, 1995, 1999).

The long succession of fossiliferous sediments exposed in the Tugen Hills provides an opportunity to investigate the pattern of African Neogene faunal change in some detail, sampling intervals of time not well documented elsewhere in sub-Saharan Africa. The sequence has also yielded palaeofloral samples and biogeochemical data that contribute to our understanding of the ecological context for the origin and development of the Ethiopian fauna including early hominids. Significantly, this sequence also provides the opportunity to document environmental change within a discrete portion of the rift, circumventing the confounding effects of splicing together a composite profile based on data collected from sites of different ages that are hundreds of kilometres apart. Faunal change can be detected between all five major formations and also within the duration of the Ngorora and Chemeron Formations (Fig. 2) (Barry et al. 1985; Hill et al. 1985, 1986; Hill 1987, 1994, 1995, 1999). The most notable interval of faunal change occurs between the Ngorora assemblages and the Mpesida Beds which includes the appearance of whole new families such as the Elephantidae and the first leporids in sub-Saharan Africa, the rhinoceros *Ceratotherium* and various new species in established genera.

Isotopic evidence for palaeoecological reconstructions in the Tugen Hills

Theoretical background

Partitioning of two naturally occurring stable isotopes of carbon, ^{12}C and ^{13}C, in terrestrial plants, soil carbonates, soil and sediment organic matter, and ultimately herbivore tissue is in part a function of different ecophysiological adaptations of plants. During the first stage of photosynthesis (carboxylation), as plants assimilate carbon from the atmospheric CO_2 reservoir, the lighter isotope (^{12}C) is preferentially incorporated into the organic matrix, resulting in substantially lower ratios of ^{13}C /^{12}C in the plant tissue relative to atmospheric CO_2. This discrimination against ^{13}C (fractionation) is due to small differences in physical and chemical properties imparted by the difference in mass between ^{12}C and ^{13}C. The extent of this isotopic fractionation varies significantly depending on the photosynthetic pathway utilized by a plant (Craig 1953; Park & Epstein 1960; Smith & Epstein 1971; O'Leary 1981; Farquhar et al. 1982). There are three major photosynthetic types referred to as C_3 (Calvin–Benson), C_4 (Hatch-Slack or Kranz) and CAM (Crassulacian acid metabolism) pathways, each of which has a characteristic range of ^{13}C /^{12}C values. These metabolic pathways represent adaptations to variable atmospheric and climatic conditions including pCO_2, moisture availability, temperature and irradiance.

Nearly all trees, shrubs, herbs and some sedges, as well as grasses growing in temperate, high altitude or shaded habitats, fix carbon using the C_3 photosynthetic pathway. C_3 vegetation dominates terrestrial environments and accounts for approximately 85% of all plant species (Salisbury & Ross 1985). The isotopic composition of C_3 flora, expressed as $\delta^{13}C$, ranges from −22‰ to −3‰ with a mean $\delta^{13}C$ value of −27.1‰ (O'Leary 1988). Isotopic ratios are expressed relative to the standard PDB (Pee Dee Belemnite) where

$$\delta^{13}C \ (‰)$$
$$= [(^{13}C \ /^{12}C)_{sample}/(^{13}C/^{12}C)_{standard} - 1]$$
$$\times 1000$$

The isotopic variation in C_3 plants is due primarily to environmental influences, including water stress, nutrient availability, light intensity, CO_2 partial pressure, temperature, and extent of forest canopy (Farquhar et al. 1982; van der Merwe & Medina 1989; Tieszen 1991).

C_4 physiology is linked almost exclusively to tropical and subtropical grasses. This pathway fixes CO_2 more efficiently than C_3 metabolism at lower atmospheric pCO_2 levels ($<c. 400$ ppmV) and high temperatures (30–45°C) and C_4 plants, in general, tolerate higher water stress. The C_4 photosynthetic pathway represents a modification of the C_3 mechanism and is considered to have evolved independently a number of times (Renvoize & Clayton 1992), possibly as a response to decreasing levels of CO_2 relative to O_2 in the atmosphere (Ehleringer 1991). A mean $\delta^{13}C$ value of 13.1‰ ± 1.2‰ has been calculated for C_4 plants (O'Leary 1988) with a range of −9 to −15‰, about half that of C_3 plants.

CAM plants are mostly succulents, including the cacti (Cactaceae) and stonecrops (Crassulaceae). Like C_4 plants, they utilize both the C_3 and C_4 pathways but CAM plants differentially utilize the two pathways depending on environmental conditions resulting in $\delta^{13}C$ values which span the range of values covered by C_3 and C_4 plants (Deines 1980; O'Leary 1981). The strategy of CAM plant physiology to endure extremely xeric conditions severely limits their ability to take in and fix CO_2 and in general they compete poorly with C_3 and C_4 plants under less extreme conditions. It is unlikely that CAM plants constituted a significant portion of the plant biomass in palaeoenvironments supporting large vertebrate populations and CAM plants will not be considered further here.

Determining the relative proportions of C_3 and C_4 vegetation in the past provides a valuable tool for estimating aspects of environmental conditions and plant physiognomy in palaeohabitat reconstructions. Specifically, the link between C_4 metabolism and grasses provides a means of identifying open woodland to grassland tropical/subtropical ecosystems in the past. After the evolution of C_4 plants, sometime in the middle to late Miocene, a greater C_4 component relative to C_3 potentially indicates more open habitats in low altitude/low latitude regions. However, the large variety of C_3-dominated habitats, ranging from lowland rainforest to arid bushland to temperate grasslands, limits the resolving power of a C_3 isotopic signal in reconstructing vegetation. In addition, in adopting a uniformitarian approach, modern ecosystems typically provide the template for interpreting isotopic records of the past. Past habitats may in fact have no modern analogues. The possibility that C_3 grass-dominated tropical ecosystems existed before the evolution and spread of C_4 grasses, in particular, complicates interpretations of past landscapes.

A number of isotopic approaches have been developed to retrieve estimates of the relative proportions of plants using the C_3 and C_4 photosynthetic pathways in the past, including isotopic analyses of: (1) preserved organic plant matter in palaeosols (Ambrose & Sikes 1991; Kingston et al. 1994); (2) proxy material such as palaeosol carbonates which form in isotopic equilibrium with palaeovegetation (Cerling & Hay 1986; Quade et al. 1989a; Sikes 1994; Kingston in press); and (3) bone or enamel which reflects available dietary plants (Lee-Thorp & van der Merwe 1987; Morgan et al. 1994; Cerling et al. 1997b).

Palaeosols in the Tugen Hills

The isotopic composition of carbon in modern soils has been shown to closely reflect prevailing climatic and ecological conditions including the proportion of surface vegetation utilizing the C_3 or C_4 photosynthetic pathway (O'Brien & Stout 1978; Deines 1980; Cerling 1984; Amundson & Lund 1987; Quade et al. 1989b). These isotopic signals are retained in paleosols and have been retrieved from the fossil record to reconstruct aspects of the plant biomass in ancient landscapes (Kelly et al. 1991; Cerling 1992; Kingston et al. 1994; Sikes 1994; Quade & Cerling 1995). Although palaeosol components are not, in general, subjected to the types of taphonomic and sampling filters which can seriously bias interpretation of faunal and floral components, they may be subjected to differential preservation. For example, soils forming in high energy, non-stable environments such as on alluvial fans, hill sides or adjacent to major river channels

may be selectively destroyed and be underrepresented in the fossil record. If certain ecosystems are typically associated with these depositional settings, these settings may not be reflected in palaeosol studies.

Palaeosols, interbedded primarily with volcaniclastic alluvial fan, fluvial and lacustrine facies, constitute a conspicuous but in general minor component ($<5\%$) of the sedimentary sequences exposed in the Tugen Hills. Palaeosols are unevenly distributed both laterally and vertically in the succession, most likely reflecting complex palaeotopography and the extremely localized nature of depositional regimes within the structurally complex inner rift. Intervals of time such as those represented by deposits of the Mpesida Beds and lower Ngorora Formation are characterized by significant influxes of volcaniclastic debris to the extent that soil development, preservation and recognition are generally poor.

$\delta^{13}C$ values of pedogenic carbonate nodules from the succession (Fig. 3a) record a complex distribution of C_3 and C_4 vegetation through time, indicating primarily a persisting mixed C_3/C_4 mosaic. Most of the individual values fall within the range suggesting a contribution of carbon by both C_3 and C_4 vegetation, although values are heavily weighted towards the C_3 end of the spectrum. The lateral variation at any given level suggests a heterogeneous landscape although the $\delta^{13}C$ ranges for all the fossil horizons are statistically more negative than the modern Baringo vegetation, indicating less of a C_4 component in the past. Excluding the modern data, only one palaeosol from the succession yielded carbonates with a $\delta^{13}C$ value clearly indicating biomass composed almost exclusively of C_4 grasses. In general, the palaeosol carbonate isotopic values, where present, suggest woodland-type habitats although the specifics of these environments remain unknown.

Even though the isotopic variation in palaeosol carbonates is statistically consistent throughout the succession, there are a number of issues to be considered in evaluating this data set. First, the temporal resolution in sampling frequency is limited and it is conceivable that habitat shifts may have occurred during intervals not represented by the isotopic profile. In addition, palaeosols typically form over hundreds or even thousands of years and thus preserve a palaeoenvironmental record averaged over an interval spanning many generations of plants. Vegetational succession, however, can occur over time scales of only 100 to 1000 years as a result of fires, immigration or emigration of fauna, and climatic perturbations, all of which

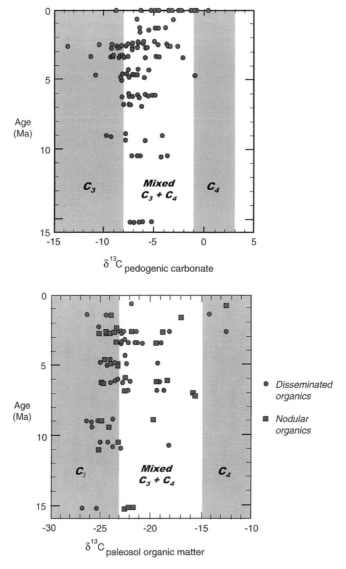

Fig. 3. (**a**) Stable carbon isotopic composition (δ^{13}C) of paleosol carbonate sampled from horizons within the Tugen Hills succession. (**b**) δ^{13}C of bulk palaeosol organic matter from the Tugen Hills succession. Circles denote disseminated organics within the palaeosol matrix and the squares organic residue isolated from the carbonate matrix of pedogenic nodules. (**c**) Plot showing the δ^{13}C values of the enamel apatite of various taxa sampled from the Tugen Hills succession.

can occur relatively rapidly (tens of years). In these cases environmental interpretations based on isotopic analyses of soil components may lack the resolution to distinguish perturbations in the ecosystem and would in effect average the relative proportion of C_3 and C_4 biomass, obscuring abrupt shifts in palaeovegetation. A further consideration in interpreting these data relates to assumptions that a consistent

isotopic signature of C_3 relative to C_4 plant biomass through time in the Baringo Basin implies static environmental conditions. A C_3 component potentially reflects vegetation ranging from grasses to large trees and a persisting C_3/C_4 signal would not necessarily record changes in the specific plants contributing a C_3 isotopic signal. Finally, pedogenic carbonate was notably absent in palaeosols at a number of localities in

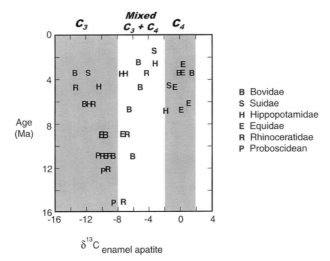

Fig. 3. (*continued*).

the Tugen Hills. These non-calcareous palaeo-sols may be indicative of environmental conditions which inhibit formation or preservation of pedogenic nodules such as forested habitats with acidic soils or heavy precipitation which leaches carbonates from the soil profiles. Such biomes would not be represented in this type of analysis. Interestingly, at sites in the Tugen Hills with fossil/macrofossil assemblages indicative of localized, if not widespread, forest environments, local palaeosols were devoid of pedogenic carbonate.

Although carbon isotopic analyses of associated palaeosol organic matter (disseminated and nodular) (Fig. 3b) also indicate lateral variation throughout the succession, there is significantly less evidence for a C_4 component before c. 6.5 Ma. $\delta^{13}C$ values of the organic matter from formational and subformational groups indicate ranges of up to 12‰ but, as with the palaeosol carbonates, the isotopic values cluster more toward the C_3 endmember. Organic residue yielding isotopic signatures characteristic of essentially pure C_4 vegetation occurs at three sites, all less than 2.3 Ma. The isotopic signatures of organic matter suggest an increase in the C_4 component during an apparent gap in the fossil record between uppermost units of the Ngorora Formation (Ngeringerowa Beds at 8.5–9 Ma) and horizons within the Mpesida Beds (c. 6.5 Ma).

Theoretical models (Cerling 1984; Quade et al. 1989b) predict that differences in the isotopic signatures of carbonate nodules and associated organic residue ($\Delta\delta$) are 14‰ and 15.5‰ at temperatures of 25°C and 15°C respectively.

Although the means for the $\Delta\delta$ for both disseminated and nodular organics fall within this theoretical envelope (15.3‰ and 15.4‰), the standard deviation is significant (5.0‰ and 4.1‰). Discrepancies may relate to differential preservation of the various fossil records or to the way that each of these components records aspects of palaeoenvironments.

Fossil herbivore enamel from the Tugen Hills

An alternative and complementary method of documenting relative proportions of C_3 and C_4 vegetation in the past involves the isotopic analyses of the dietary carbonate preserved in the enamel of fossil herbivores. The carbon isotopic composition of modern herbivore tissue, including tooth enamel, is directly related to the $\delta^{13}C$ value of the primary photosynthesizing plants in the food chain (DeNiro & Epstein 1978; Tieszen et al. 1983; Ambrose & DeNiro 1986). Unlike bone apatite, the mineral portion of enamel is highly resistant to diagenetic alteration and the biogenic dietary signal is preserved during fossilization (Lee-Thorp 1989). This signal can be used to reconstruct proportions of C_3 and C_4 vegetation in the diet of extinct taxa. Application of isotopic analyses to fossil enamel strictly for palaeodietary studies has been limited (Ericson et al. 1981; Lee-Thorp et al. 1989b), and instead its use has been primarily for palaeo-ecological reconstruction (Thackeray et al. 1990; Kingston 1992; Quade et al. 1992, 1994; Wang et al. 1993; Morgan et al. 1994; MacFadden et al. 1996; Cerling et al. 1997b).

The carbon isotopic composition of enamel carbonate from 58 fossil tooth samples collected from the Tugen Hills sequence was analysed. Sampling strategy emphasized collection of potential grazing forms such as equids, high-crowned bovids and hippopotamids which might provide constraints on the timing and nature of the introduction and continuity of C_4 grasses into the Baringo Basin. The isotopic profile generated by analyses of fossil apatite represents a different type of record in that the environment is not sampled directly but rather through a dietary filter. The selectivity of animals, competitive exclusion, seasonal migrations and long-term biogeographic changes can all potentially complicate interpretation of fossil apatite for palaeovegetation reconstructions. With this in mind, analyses included a wide range of herbivore taxa through the succession with the assumption that dietary shifts associated with significant alteration of habitat might be detected.

During enamel formation, the lighter carbon (^{12}C) is discriminated against and the isotopic signature of biological apatite is significantly heavier than dietary components (DeNiro & Epstein 1978). These physiological fractionation effects typically result in a 12–14‰ enrichment of enamel relative to diet (Sullivan & Kreuger 1981; Lee-Thorp et al. 1989a) although some researchers note less enrichment (DeNiro & Epstein 1978; Ambrose & Norr 1993). The $\delta^{13}C$ of herbivore enamel from the Tugen Hills succession indicates that although there is a dietary C_4 component as early as 15.5 Ma, there is no evidence for a significant C_4 or an exclusive C_4 component in diets until c. 6.5 Ma. Between 7 and 2 Ma, analysis of fossil enamel apatite records a wide range of $\delta^{13}C$ values indicating dietary regimes ranging from pure C_3 to pure C_4. In assessing the potential contribution of C_4 vegetation to palaeodiets it is necessary to appreciate that the isotopic demarcation distinguishing essentially pure C_3 diets from mixed C_3/C_4 diets is actually represented by a range reflecting interpretive differences. The distinction between these dietary groups is dependent on assumptions made regarding: (1) a +1.5‰ correction for preindustrial atmospheric $\delta^{13}C$ values (Marino & McElroy 1991); (2) the physiological fractionation of carbon in enamel formation (estimates range from 9.5‰ to 15‰); (3) environmental factors such as water stress or high irradiance which might cause an enrichment in C_3 plants; and (4) differential fractionation in animals with different body sizes. Based on interpretations of these variables, estimates of this dietary boundary as detected isotopically

in enamel apatite range from −12‰ to −8‰ (Cerling et al. 1997b). In documenting early evidence for a C_4 diet, a conservative approach would be to adopt a $\delta^{13}C$ values of greater than −8‰ as reflecting a C_4 dietary component. By these criteria, enamel samples from Muruyur and the Ngorora Formation horizons record a minor C_4 component by as early as the middle Miocene. Alternatively, although less likely, these values may reflect a dietary reliance on CAM plants or C_3/C_4 intermediates.

Discussion

While the isotopic analyses of palaeosol carbonates indicate heterogeneous, mixed C_3/C_4 environments throughout the 15.5 Ma spanned by sediments in the Tugen Hills succession, the isotopic signatures of associated organic matter and enamel carbonate suggest an increase in the C_4 component during the late Miocene. These latter data sets provide support for a global increase in C_4 biomass between 8 and 6 Ma possibly related to a decrease in atmospheric CO_2 (Cerling et al. 1993) or intensification of monsoonal patterns (Quade et al. 1989a). The implications of this isotopic transition for late Miocene landscapes remain unclear as C_3 grasses clearly were significant components of ecosystems before this shift and may have occupied the modern C_4 niche, forming extensive temperate and tropical grasslands as well as grassy substrata in more wooded habitats. The earliest evidence for grasses in Africa is pollen contained in core sediments from coastal Cameroon in the early Eocene (Salard-Cheboldaeff 1979, 1981). Grass pollen, however, is absent from this core during the middle Oligocene and into the early Miocene which marks the terminus of the core. Grass pollen and charred grass cuticle, interpreted to have formed as a result of savanna fires, are intermittently abundant in early Miocene to Pleistocene core samples taken from the Niger Delta (Morley & Richards 1993). Moderate rises in the relative abundance of these grassland components during the middle Miocene and a significant increase during the late Miocene are thought to indicate periods of marked aridity with strong seasonality of rainfall, with savanna habitats extending over most of the Niger delta region. In East Africa, autochthonous assemblages of grass blades (Dugas & Retallack 1993) and a pollen assemblage dominated by grass pollen (54%) (Bonnefile 1984) preserved in volcanic ash at the vertebrate-rich locality of Fort Ternan have been dated to about 14 Ma (Shipman et al. 1981). Although there has been considerable debate concerning the habitat represented by the fossil record (Andrews & Nesbit Evans 1979; Shipman 1986; Cerling *et al.* 1992, 1997*a*; Retallack 1992; Dugas & Retallack 1993), the presence of abundant grass components in upper levels of the stratigraphic section exposed at Fort Ternan indicate that at some point in the middle Miocene, C_3 grasses constituted a significant portion of the Fort Ternan ecosystem, at least locally.

The apparent isotopic transition during the late Miocene may simply reflect the displacement of C_3 grasses in woodland/bushland or grassland biomes by C_4 grasses, requiring minimal perceptual change in the vegetational physiognomy of East African habitats. Alternatively, the transition involved the replacement of more forested habitats by grasslands. This latter interpretation would have significance for hominid evolution as it provides support for the savanna hypothesis. To attempt resolution of these potential interpretations, it becomes necessary to examine other data sets that provide information of palaeohabitats. Within the Tugen Hills, a number of macrofloral sites have been and are currently being investigated (summarized in Fig. 2). A fossil macrofloral assemblage from the Ngorora Formation dated to 12.6 Ma at the site of Kabasero records 57 taxa with affinities to lowland to submontane wet to moist rainforests (Jacobs & Kabuye 1987, 1989; Jacobs & Winkler 1992). Palaeobotanical evidence from the site of Waril, about 10–9 Ma based on stratigraphic position, suggests a seasonally dry wooded savanna habitat although no grass remains have been documented in the assemblage (Jacobs pers. comm.). Environmental reconstructions based on sedimentological and mineralogical evidence collected from lacustrine horizons penecontemporaneous to the Waril site in the Ngorora Formation also indicate that warm, arid conditions prevailed in this area *c.* 10 Ma (Renaut *et al.* 1999). Sediments of the Mpesida Beds at the site of Kapturo constrained to about 6.8 Ma contain numerous plants interpreted as representing a deciduous woodland (Jacobs & Deino 1996). Also within Mpesida sediments, about 10 km south-southwest of the Kapturo locality, are abundant fossil wood fragments preserved in an ash flow deposit exposed over an area $>10\,km^2$. Preliminary analyses of the fossil wood indicate affinities to central and West African forest (Jacobs pers. comm.). These data, especially when coupled with the isotopic data indicating significant C_4 grasses by the late Miocene, reflect a range of habitats suggesting a diverse, dynamic vegetative structure in the Baringo Basin from the middle Miocene onwards. Also significant,

the isotopic and palaeobotanical data indicate that at no time in the past was this portion of the rift valley dominated by C_3 or C_4 grasslands.

Exposures of the Tugen Hills succession are locally extensive ($>800\,km^2$) and palaeoecolgical data derived from the sequence have the potential to document local heterogeneity inherent in a rift valley setting. Based on the diverse landscapes present today in the rift valley, not only on a local but also on a regional scale, it would be unrealistic to extrapolate the type and range of habitat diversity documented in the Baringo Basin as representative of East Africa in general during the Neogene. Nevertheless, these data record the vegetation in an area of the rift where fossil evidence indicates that early hominids and hominoids ranged and as such are relevant to discussions of the role of shifting environments in the evolution of the human lineage. No obvious phytogeographical trend is revealed by the data and although globally, and to an extent locally, there is an isotopic shift indicating a spread of C_4 grasses during the late Miocene (8.5 to 6.5 Ma)(Cerling *et al.* 1997*b*), the effect of this transition on African hominid habitats is unknown. This interval also incorporates the establishment of vertebrate communities more similar to modern fauna but the timing and ecological basis of this faunal change during the late Miocene is also not well constrained.

Summary

Environmental change has no doubt influenced the morphological and behavioural innovations characterizing early hominid evolution during the late Miocene and Pliocene in Africa. Basic questions of how and when and to what extent remain unanswered. Detailing the evolution of landscapes in Africa during this period is ultimately critical to addressing these questions yet at this point not much is known. This lack of data has forced us to adopt or accept simplified versions of environmental trends involving to some extent a monotonic replacement of forests by more open habitats during the Neogene. While data from late Miocene and Pliocene localities in Africa may ultimately in part support this scenario on a large-scale basis, emerging evidence implicates more heterogeneous, fluctuating landscapes during early hominid evolution. It is likely that the source of many of the selection pressures directing the course of human evolution lies in the specifics of African ecosystems and the complicated interrelationships between constituent faunas and floras as

well as with extrinsic climatic factors. Enhancing
the resolution of the fossil record to a level at
which we can address these issues remains one of
the challenges of palaeoanthropology.

I am grateful to the organizers of the Bill Bishop
Memorial Conference for inviting me to participate in
the meeting and present some of my ongoing research
in the Tugen Hills. By emphasizing a multidisciplinar-
ian approach, Bill Bishop helped establish the foundation for understanding the evolution of East African
landscapes, which has proved essential to theories
of human evolution. I thank the members of the
Baringo Palaeontological Research Project, in particular A. Hill, for their collaboration and camaraderie.
This work was funded by grants from National Science
Foundation, L. B. S. Leakey Foundation, the Bill
Bishop Memorial Trust and the Louise Brown
Foundation.

References

AMBROSE, S. H. 1995. Paleoecology and paleobiogeography of late Miocene hominoid/hominid clado-
genesis: Was the trichotomy a reality. *4th Annual
Meeting Paleoanthropological Society, Oakland,
CA* (abstract).
AMBROSE, S. H. & DeNIRO, M. J. 1986. Reconstruction of African human diet using bone collagen
carbon and nitrogen isotope ratios. *Nature*, **319**,
321–324.
—— & NORR, L. 1993. Experimental evidence for the
relationship of the carbon isotope ratios of whole
diet and dietary protein to those of bone collagen
and carbonate. *In*: LAMBERT, J. L. & GRUPE, G.
(eds) *Prehistoric Human Bone: Archaeology at the
Molecular Level*. Springer, Berlin, 1–13.
—— & SIKES, N. E. 1991. Soil carbon isotope evidence
for Holocene habitat change in the Kenya Rift
Valley. *Science*, **253**, 1402–1405.
AMUNDSON, R. G. & LUND, L. J. 1987. The stable isotope chemistry of a native and irrigated typic
natrargid in the San Joaquin Valley of California.
Soil Science Society of America Journal, **51**(3),
761–767.
ANDREWS, P. & NESBIT EVANS, E. 1979. The environ-
ment of *Ramapithecus* in Africa. *Paleobiology*,
5(1), 22–30.
BARRY, J. C. 1995. Faunal turnover and diversity in
the terrestrial Neogene of Pakistan. *In*: VRBA,
E. S., DENTON, G. H., PARTRIDGE, T. C. &
BURCKLE, L. H. (eds) *Paleoclimate and Evolution,
with Emphasis on Human Origins*. Yale University
Press, New Haven, 115–134.
——, JOHNSON, N. M., RAZA, S. M. & JACOBS, L. L.
1985. Neogene faunal change in southern Asia:
Correlations with climatic, tectonic, and eustatic
events. *Geology*, **13**, 637–640.
BEHRENSMEYER, A. K., TODD, N. E., POTTS, R. &
McBRINN, G. E. 1997. Late Pliocene faunal turn-
over in the Turkana Basin, Kenya and Ethiopia.
Science, **278**, 1589–1594.

BISHOP, L. C. 1994. *Pigs and the ancestor: hominids,
suids and environments during the Plio-Pleistocene
of East Africa*. PhD Thesis, Yale University.
——, HILL, A. & KINGSTON, J. D. 1999. Palaeoecology
of Suidae from the Tugen Hills, Baringo, Kenya.
This volume.
BISHOP, W. W. 1962. Pleistocene chronology in East
Africa. *Advancement of Science*, January **1962**.
——, CHAPMAN, G. R., HILL, A. & MILLER, J. A.
1971. Succession of Cainozoic vertebrate assem-
blages from the northern Kenya Rift Valley.
Nature, **233**, 389–394.
BONNEFILLE, R. 1984. Cenozoic vegetation and
environments of early hominids in East Africa.
In: WHYTE, R. O. (ed.) *The Evolution of the East
Asian Environment. II Palaeobotany, Palaeozool-
ogy, and Palaeoanthropology*. University of Hong
Kong, 579–612.
BRAIN, C. K. 1981. The evolution of man in Africa:
Was it a consequence of Cainozoic cooling? Alex
L. du Toit Memorial Lecture 17. *Transactions of
the Geological Society of South Africa*, annex **84**,
1–19.
CERLING, T. E. 1984. The stable isotopic composition
of modern soil carbonates and its relationship to
climate. *Earth and Planetary Science Letters*, **71**,
229–240.
—— & HAY, R. L. 1986. An isotopic study of paleosol
carbonates from Olduvai Gorge. *Quaternary
Research*, **25**, 63–78.
——1992. Development of grasslands and savannas in
East Africa during the Neogene. *Palaeogeography,
Palaeoclimatology, Palaeoecology (Global and
Planetary Change Section)*, **97**, 241–247.
——, KAPPELMAN, J., QUADE, J., AMBROSE, S. H.,
SIKES, N. E. & ANDREWS, P. 1992. Reply to comment on the paleoenvironment of *Kenyapithecus*
at Fort Ternan. *Journal of Human Evolution*,
23, 371–377.
——, WANG, Y. & QUADE, J. 1993. Expansion of
C_4 ecosystems as an indicator of global ecological change in the late Miocene. *Nature*, **361**,
344–345.
——, HARRIS, J. M., AMBROSE, S. H., LEAKEY, M. G.
& SOLOUNIAS, N. 1997a. Dietary and environmental reconstruction with stable isotope analyses
of herbivore tooth enamel from the Miocene
locality of Fort Ternan, Kenya. *Journal of Human
Evolution*, **33**, 635–650.
——, ——, MACFADDEN, B. J., LEAKEY, M. G.,
QUADE, J., EISENMANN, V. & EHLERINGER, J. R.
1997b. Global vegetation change through the Mio-
cene/Pliocene boundary. *Nature*, **389**, 153–158.
CHAPMAN, G. R. 1971. *The geological evolution of the
northern Kamasia Hills, Baringo District, Kenya*.
PhD Thesis, University of London.
—— & BROOK, M. 1978. Chronostratigraphy of the
Baringo Basin, Kenya. *In*: BISHOP, W. W. (ed.)
Geological Background to Fossil Man. Scottish
Academic, London, 207–223.
——, LIPPARD, S. J. & MARTYN, J. E. 1978. The strati-
graphy and structure of the Kamasia Range, Kenya
Rift Valley. *Journal of the Geological Society of
London*, **135**, 265–281.

CRAIG, H. 1953. The geochemistry of the stable carbon isotopes. *Geochimica et Cosmochimica Acta*, **3**, 53–92.

CROWLEY, T. J. & NORTH, G. R. 1991. *Paleoclimatology*. Oxford University, New York.

DAGLEY, P., MUSSETT, A. E. & PALMER, H. C. 1978. Preliminary observations on the paleomagnetic stratigraphy of the area west of Lake Baringo, Kenya. *In*: BISHOP, W. W. (ed.) *Geological Background to Fossil Man*. Scottish Academic, London, 225–235.

DARWIN, C. 1871. *The Descent of Man, and Selection in Relation to Sex*. Murray, London.

DEINES, P. 1980. The isotopic composition of reduced organic carbon. *In*: FRITZ, P. & FONTES, J. C. (eds) *Handbook of Environmental Isotope Geochemistry. V. 1. The Terrestrial Environment*. Elsevier, New York, 329–406.

DEINO, A., TAUXE, L., MONOGHAN, M. & DRAKE, R. 1990. ^{40}Ar/^{39}Ar age calibration of the litho- and paleomagnetic stratigraphies of the Ngorora Formation, Kenya. *Journal of Geology*, **98**, 567–587.

DEMENOCAL, P. B. 1995. Plio-Pleistocene African climate and the paleoenvironment of human evolution. *Science*, **270**, 53–59.

——— & BLOEMENDAL, J. 1995. Plio-Pleistocene climatic variability in subtropical Africa and the paleoenvironnment of hominid evolution. *In*: VRBA, E. S., DENTON, G. H., PARTRIDGE, T. C. & BURCKLE, L. H. (eds) *Paleoclimate and Evolution, with Emphasis on Human Origins*. Yale University Press, New Haven, 262–288.

——— & RIND, D. 1993. Sensitivity of Asian and African climate to variations in seasonal insolation, glacial ice cover, sea-surface temperature, and Asian orography. *Journal of Geophysical Research*, **98** (D4), 7265–7287.

DENIRO, M. J. & EPSTEIN, S. 1978. Influence of diet on the distribution of carbon isotopes in animals. *Geochimica et Cosmochimica Acta*, **42**, 341–351.

DUGAS, D. P. & RETALLACK, R. J. 1993. Middle Miocene fossil grasses from Fort Ternan, Kenya. *Journal of Paleontology*, **67**(1), 113–128.

EHLERINGER, J. R. 1991. Climate change and the evolution of C_4 photosynthesis. *Trends in Ecology and Evolution*, **6**, 95–99.

ERICSON, J. E., SULLIVAN, C. H. & BOAZ, N. T. 1981. Diets of Pliocene mammals from Omo, Ethiopia, deduced from carbon isotope ratios in tooth apatite. *Palaeogeography, Palaeoclimatology, Palaeoecology*, **36**, 69–73.

FARQUHAR, G. D., O'LEARY, M. H. & BERRY, J. A. 1982. On the relationship between carbon isotope discrimination and the intercellular carbon dioxide concentration in leaves. *Australian Journal of Plant Physiology*, **9**, 121–137.

FEIBEL, C. S. 1997. Debating the environmental factors in hominid evolution. *GSA Today*, **7**(3), 1–7.

FLYNN, L. J., TEDFORD, R. H. & ZHANXIANG, Q. 1991. Enrichment and stability in the Pliocene mammalian fauna of North China. *Paleobiology*, **17**(3), 246–265.

FROSTICK, L. E. 1997. The East African rift basins. *In*: SELLEY, R. C. (ed.) *African Basins. Sedimentary Basins of the World Vol. 3*. Elsevier Science, Amsterdam, 187–209.

GRINE, F. E. 1986. Ecological causality and the pattern of Plio-Pleistocene hominid evolution in Africa. *South Africa Journal of Science*, **82**, 87–89.

HILL, A. 1987. Causes of perceived faunal change in the later Neogene of East Africa. *Journal of Human Evolution*, **16**, 583–596.

———1994. Late Miocene and Early Pliocene hominoids from Africa. *In*: CORRUCCINI, R. S. & CIOCHON, R. L. (eds) *Integrative Paths to the Past*. Prentice Hall, Englewood Cliffs, 123–145.

———1995. Faunal and environmental change in the Neogene of East Africa: evidence from the Tugen Hills Sequence, Baringo District, Kenya. *In*: VRBA, E. S., DENTON, G. H., PARTRIDGE, T. C. & BURCKLE, L. H. (eds) *Paleoclimate and Evolution, with Emphasis on Human Origins*. Yale University, New Haven, 178–193.

———1999. The Baringo Basin, Kenya: from Bill Bishop to BPRP. *This volume*.

——— (in press). Evidence for African vertebrate faunas and environments between 8 Ma and 4 Ma. *In*: WHYBROW, P. J. & HILL, A. (eds) *Fossil Vertebrates of Arabia*. Yale University, New Haven.

———, CURTIS, G. & DRAKE, R. 1986. Sedimentary stratigraphy of the Tugen Hills. *In*: FROSTICK, L. E. et al. (eds) *Sedimentation in the African Rifts*. Geological Society, London, Special Publications, **25**, 285–295.

———, DRAKE, R., TAUXE, L. et al. 1985. Neogene paleontology and geochronology of the Baringo Basin, Kenya. *Journal of Human Evolution*, **14**, 759–773.

———, WARD, S., DEINO, A., GARNISS, C. & DRAKE, R. 1992. Earliest *Homo*. *Nature*, **355**, 719–722.

JACOBS, B. F. & DEINO, A. L. 1996. Test of climate–leaf physiognomy regression models, their application to two Miocene floras from Kenya, and ^{40}Ar/^{39}Ar dating of the late Miocene Kapturo site. *Palaeogeography, Palaeoclimatology, Palaeoecology*, **123**, 259–271.

——— & KABUYE, C. H. S. 1987. A middle Miocene (12.2 Ma) forest in the East African Rift Valley, Kenya. *Journal of Human Evolution*, **6**, 147–155.

——— & KABUYE, C. H. S. 1989. An extinct species of *Pollia* Thunberg (Commelinaceae) from the Miocene Ngorora Formation, Kenya. *Review of Paleobotany and Palynology*, **59**, 67–76.

——— & WINKLER, D. A. 1992. Taphonomy of a middle Miocene autochthonous forest assemblage, Ngorora Formation, central Kenya. *Palaeogeography, Palaeoclimatology, Palaeoecology*, **99**, 31–40.

JANIS, C. M. 1993. Tertiary mammal evolution in the context of changing climates, vegetation, and tectonic events. *Annual Review of Ecology and Systematics*, **24**, 467–500.

KELLY, E. F., AMUNDSON, R. G., MARINO, B. D. & DE NIRO, M. J. 1991. Stable carbon isotopic composition of carbonate in Holocene grassland soils. *Soil Science Society of America Journal*, **55**(6), 1651–1657.

KENNETT, J. P. 1995. A review of polar climatic evolution during the Neogene, based on the Marine sediment record. *In*: VRBA, E. S., DENTON, G. H., PARTRIDGE, T. C. & BURCKLE, L. H. (eds) *Paleoclimate and Evolution, with Emphasis on Human Origins*. Yale University Press, New Haven, 49–64.

KING, B. C. & CHAPMAN, G. R. 1972. Volcanics of the Kenya rift valley. *Philosophical Transactions of the Royal Society, London. Series A*, **271**, 185–208.

KINGSTON, J. D. 1992. *Stable isotopic evidence for hominid paleoenvironments in East Africa*. PhD thesis, Harvard University.

—— (in press). Isotopes and environments of the Baynunah Formation, Emirate of Abu Dhabi, United Arab Emirates. *In*: WHYBROW, P. J. & HILL, A. (eds) *Fossil Vertebrates of Arabia*. Yale University, New Haven.

——, MARINO, B. D. & HILL, A. 1994. Isotopic evidence for Neogene hominid paleoenvironments in the Kenya Rift Valley. *Science*, **264**, 955–959.

LAPORTE, L. F. & ZHILMAN, A. L. 1983. Plates, climate and hominoid evolution. *South African Journal of Science*, **79**, 96–110.

LEE-THORP, J. A. 1989. *Stable carbon isotopes in deep time: The diets of fossil fauna and hominids*. PhD thesis, University of Cape Town.

—— & VAN DER MERWE, N. J. 1987. Carbon isotope analysis of fossil bone apatite. *South African Journal of Science*, **83**, 71–74.

——, SEALY, J. C. & VAN DER MERWE, N. J. 1989a. Stable carbon isotope ratio differences between bone collagen and bone apatite, and their relationship to diet. *Journal of Archaelogical Science*, **16**, 585–599.

——, VAN DER MERWE, N. J. & BRAIN, C. K. 1989b. Isotopic evidence for dietary differences between two extinct baboon species from Swartkrans. *Journal of Human Evolution*, **18**, 183–190.

MACFADDEN, B. J., CERLING, T. E. & PRADO, J. 1996. Cenozoic terrestrial evolution in Argentina: Evidence from carbon isotopes of fossil mammal teeth. *Palaios*, **11**, 319–327.

MARINO, B. D. & MCELROY, M. B. 1991. Isotopic composition of atmospheric CO_2 inferred from carbon in C_4 plant cellulose. *Nature*, **349**, 127–131.

MARTYN, J. E. 1969. *The geological history of the country between Lake Baringo and the Kerio River, Baringo District, Kenya*. PhD thesis, University of London.

MILLER, K. G., FAIRBANKS, R. G. & MOUNTAIN, G. S. 1987. Tertiary oxygen isotope synthesis, sea level history, and continental margin erosion. *Paleoceanography*, **2**(1), 1–19.

MORGAN, M. E., KINGSTON, J. D. & MARINO, B. D. 1994. Carbon isotopic evidence for the emergence of C_4 plants in the Neogene from Pakistan and Kenya. *Nature*, **367**, 162–165.

MORLEY, R. J. & RICHARDS, K. 1993. Gramineae cuticle: a key indicator of Late Cenozoic climatic change in the Niger Delta. *Review of Palaeobotany and Palynology*, **77**, 119–127.

O'BRIEN, B. J. & STOUT, J. D. 1978. Movement and turnover of soil organic matter as indicated by carbon isotope measurements. *Soil Biology and Biochemistry*, **10**, 309–317.

O'LEARY, M. H. 1981. Carbon isotope fractionation in plants. *Phytochemistry*, **20**, 553–567.

——1988. Carbon isotopes in photosynthesis. *Bioscience*, **38**, 328–336.

OPDYKE, N. D. 1995. Mammalian migration and climate over the last seven million years. *In*: VRBA, E. S., DENTON, G. H., PARTRIDGE, T. C. & BURCKLE, L. H. (eds) *Paleoclimate and Evolution, with Emphasis on Human Origins*. Yale University Press, New Haven, 109–114.

PARK, R. & EPSTEIN, S. 1960. Carbon isotope fractionation during photosynthesis. *Geochimica et Cosmochimica Acta*, **21**, 110–126.

PICKFORD, M. 1975. *Stratigraphy and palaeoecology of five late Cainozoid formations in the Kenya Rift Valley*. PhD thesis, University of London.

——1978a. Geology, paleoenvironments and vertebrate faunas of the mid-Miocene Ngorora Formation, Kenya. *In*: BISHOP, W. W. (ed.) *Geological Background to Fossil Man*. Scottish Academic Press, London, 237–262.

——1978b. Stratigraphy and mammalian paleontology of the late-Miocene Lukeino Formation, Kenya. *In*: BISHOP, W. W. (ed.) *Geological Background to Fossil Man*. Scottish Academic Press, London, 263–278.

POKRAS, E. M. & MIX, A. C. 1985. Eolian evidence for spatial variability of late Quaternary climates in tropical Africa. *Quaternary Research*, **24**, 137–149.

POTTS, R. 1996. Evolution and climate variability. *Science*, **273**, 922–923.

PRENTICE, M. L. & DENTON, G. H. 1988. The deepsea oxygen isotope record, the global ice sheet system and hominid evolution. *In*: GRINE, F. E. (ed.) *Evolutionary History of the "Robust" Australopithecines*. Aldine de Gruyter, New York, 383–403.

PROTHERO, C. R. 1995. Faunal response to climatic events: Testing the turnover pulse hypothesis. *North American Paleontological Convention, 6th, Abstracts of Papers*. Paleontology Society, Special Publications, **8**, 314.

QUADE, J. & CERLING, T. E. 1995. Expansion of C_4 grasses in the Late Miocene of Northern Pakistan: evidence from stable isotopes in paleosols. *Palaeogeography, Palaeoclimatology, Palaeoecology*, **115**, 91–116.

——, ——, BARRY, J. C. *et al*. 1992. A 16 Ma record of paleodiet using carbon and oxygen isotopes in fossil teeth from Pakistan. *Chemical Geology*, **94**, 183–192.

——, —— & BOWMAN, J. R. 1989a. Development of Asian monsoon revealed by marked ecological shift during the latest Miocene in northern Pakistan. *Nature*, **342**, 163–166.

——, —— & BOWMAN, J. R. 1989b. Systematic variations in the carbon and oxygen isotopic composition of pedogenic carbonate along elevation transects in the southern Great Basin, United States. *GSA Bulletin*, **101**, 464–475.

——, SOLOUNIAS, N. & CERLING, T. E. 1994. Stable isotopic evidence from paleosol carbonates and fossil teeth in Greece for forest or woodlands over the past 11 Ma. *Palaeogeography, Palaeoclimatology, Palaeoecology*, **108**, 41–53.

RENAUT, R., EGO, J., TIERCELIN, J. J., LE TURDU, C. & OWEN, R. B. 1999. Saline, alkaline palaeolakes of the Tugen Hills–Kerio Valley region, Kenya Rift Valley. *This volume*.

RENVOIZE, S. A. & CLAYTON, W. D. 1992. Classification and evolution of the grasses. *In*: CHAPMAN, G. P. (ed.) *Grass Evolution and Domestication*. Cambridge University, 3–37.

RETALLACK, G. J. 1992. Comment on the paleoenvironment of Kenyapithecus at Fort Ternan. *Journal of Human Evolution*, **23**, 365–371.

SALARD-CHEBOLDAEFF, M. 1979. Palynologie Maestrichtienne et Tertiaire du Cameroun. Etude qualitative et reparitition verticale des principles especes. *Review of Palaeobotany and Palynology*, **28**, 365–388.

——1981. Palynologie Maestrichtienne et Tertiaire du Cameroun. Resultats botaniques. *Review of Palaeobotany and Palynology*, **32**, 401–439.

SALISBURY, F. B. & ROSS, C. W. 1985. *Plant Physiology*. Wadsworth, Belmont.

SEMAW, S., HARRIS, J. W. K., FEIBEL, C. S., RENNE, P., BERNOR, T. L., FESSAHA, N. & MOWBRAY, K. 1997. The oldest archaeological sites with an early Oldowan Industry from the Gona River deposits of Ethiopia. *Nature*, **385**, 333–336.

SHIPMAN, P. 1986. Paleoecology of Fort Ternan reconsidered. *Journal of Human Evolution*, **15** 193–204.

——, WALKER, A., VAN COUVERING, J. A., HOOKER, P. J. & MILLER, J. A. 1981. The Fort Ternan hominoid site, Kenya: geology, age, taphonomy, and paleoecology. *Journal of Human Evolution*, **10**, 49–72.

SHREEVE, J. 1996. Sunset on the savanna. *Discover*, **17**(7), 116–124.

SIKES, N. E. 1994. Early hominid habitat preferences in East Africa: Paleosol carbon isotopic evidence. *Journal of Human Evolution*, **27**, 25–45.

SMITH, B. N. & EPSTEIN, S. 1971. Two categories of $^{13}C/^{12}C$ ratios for higher plants. *Plant Physiology*, **47**, 380–384.

STANLEY, S. M. 1992. An ecological theory for the origin of *Homo*. *Paleobiology*, **18**, 237–257.

——1995. Climatic forcing and the origin of the human genus. *In*: KENNETT, J. & STANLEY, S. M. (eds) *Effects of Past Global Change on Life*. Studies in Geophysics, National Academy, Washington DC, 233–243.

STENSETH, N. C. & MAYNARD SMITH, J. 1984. Coevolution in ecosystems: Red Queen evolution or stasis? *Evolution*, **38**(4), 870–880.

STREET-PERROTT, F. A. & PERROTT, R. A. 1990. Abrupt climate fluctuations in the tropics: the influence of Atlantic Ocean circulation. *Nature*, **343**, 607–612.

SULLIVAN, C. H. & KRUEGER, H. W. 1981. Carbon isotope analysis of separate chemical phases in modern and fossil bone. *Nature*, **292**, 333–335.

SUWA, G., WHITE, T. D. & HOWELL, F. C. 1996. Mandibular postcanine dentition from the Shungura Formation, Ethiopia: Crown morphology, taxonomic allocations, and Plio-Pleistocene hominid evolution. *American Journal of Physical Anthropology*, **101**, 247–282.

TAUXE, L., MONAGHAN, M., DRAKE, R., CURTIS, G. & STAUDIGEL, H. 1985. Paleomagnetism of Miocene East African rift sediments and the calibration of the Geomagnetic Reversal Timescale. *Jounal of Geophysical Research*, **90**, 4639–4646.

THACKERAY, J. F., VAN DER MERWE, N. J., LEE-THORP, J. A., SILLEN, A., LANHAM, J. L., SMITH, R., KEYSER, A. & MONTEIRO, P. M. S. 1990. Changes in carbon isotope ratios in the late Permian recorded in therapsid tooth apatite. *Nature*, **347**, 751–753.

THOMAS, H. 1985. The early and middle Miocene land connection of the Afro-Arabian plate and Asia: a major event for hominoid dispersal. *In*: DELSON, E. (ed.) *Ancestors: The Hard Evidence*. Liss, New York, 42–50.

TIESZEN, L. L. 1991. Natural variations in the carbon isotope values of plants: Implications for archaeology, ecology, and paleoecology. *Journal of Archaeological Science*, **18**, 227–248.

——, BOUTTON, T. W., TESDAHL, K. G. & SLADE, N. A. 1983. Fractionation and turnover of stable carbon isotopes in animal tissues: implications for the ^{13}C analysis of diet. *Oecologia (Berlin)*, **57**, 32–37.

VAN DER MERWE, N. J. & MEDINA, E. 1989. Photosynthesis and $^{13}C/^{12}C$ ratios in Amazonian rain forests. *Geochimica et Cosmochimica Acta*, **53**, 1091–1094.

VAN VALEN, L. 1973. A new evolutionary law. *Evolutionary Theory*, **1**, 1–30.

VRBA, E. S. 1985a. Environment and evolution: Alternative causes of the temporal distribution of evolutionary events. *South African Journal of Science*, **81**, 229–236.

——1985b. African Bovidae: Evolutionary events since the Miocene. *South African Journal of Science*, **81**, 263–266.

——1995a. On the connection between paleoclimate and evolution. *In*: VRBA, E. S., DENTON, G. H., PARTRIDGE, T. C. & BURCKLE, L. H. (eds) *Paleoclimate and Evolution, with Emphasis on Human Origins*. Yale University Press, New Haven, 24–45.

——1995b. The fossil record of African Antelopes (Mammalia, Bovidae) in relation to human evolution and paleoclimate. *In*: VRBA, E. S., DENTON, G. H., PARTRIDGE, T. C. & BURCKLE, L. H. (eds) *Paleoclimate and Evolution, with Emphasis on Human Origins*. Yale University Press, New Haven, 385–411.

——, DENTON, G. H., PARTRIDGE, T. C. & BURCKLE, L. H. (eds) 1995. *Paleoclimate and Evolution, with Emphasis on Human Origins*. Yale University Press, New Haven.

——, —— & PRENTICE, M. L. 1989. Climatic Influences on early hominid behavior. *OSSA*, **14**, 127–156.

WANG, Y., CERLING, T. E., QUADE, J., BOWMAN, J. R.,
SMITH, G. A. & LINDSAY, E. H. 1993. Stable
isotopes of paleosols and fossil teeth as paleoecol-
ogy and paleoclimate indicators: An example from
the St. David Formation, Arizona. *In*: SWART,
P. K., LOHMANN, K. C., MCKENZIE, J. A. & SAVIN,
S. (eds) *Climate Change in Continental Isotopic
Records.* Geophysical Monograph, **78**, 241–248.
WESSELMAN, H. B. 1985. Fossil micromammals as
indicators of climatic change about 2.4 Myr ago in
the Omo valley, Ethiopia. *South African Journal of
Science*, **81**, 260–261.

WHITE, T. D. 1995. African omnivores: Global climatic
change and Plio-Pleistocene hominids and suids.
In: VRBA, E. S., DENTON, G. H., PARTRIDGE, T. C.
& BURCKLE, L. H. (eds) *Paleoclimate and Evolu-
tion, with Emphasis on Human Origins.* Yale
University Press, New Haven, 369–384.
WOOD, B. 1992. Origin and evolution of the genus
Homo. Nature, **355**, 783–790.
——, WOOD, C. & KONIGSBERG, L. 1994. *Paranthro-
pus boisei*: An example of evolutionary stasis?
American Journal of Physical Anthropology, **95**,
117–136.

The Baringo Basin, Kenya: from Bill Bishop to BPRP

ANDREW HILL

Department of Anthropology, Yale University, PO Box 208277,
New Haven, CT 06520, USA

Abstract: The sediments and fossils of the Baringo Basin in the Kenya Rift Valley were a major focus of Bill Bishop's later work. Investigations have continued in the region, conducted by the Baringo Palaeontological Research Project (BPRP). In the western portion of the basin, the Tugen Hills preserve fossiliferous sediments ranging in age from 15.5 Ma to 200 ka. Many of these fossiliferous units span time periods not otherwise represented in Africa and are unique in permitting the documentation of Ethiopian faunal development through the later part of the Neogene. Perhaps the major faunal change is seen between 8.5 Ma and 6.5 Ma, with the appearance of a number of elements that characterize modern African communities. Various palaeoecological indicators allow these events to be viewed in an environmental context. The succession is very well calibrated, making it possible to judge the tempo of change within the sequence, and also to make correlations with other sites elsewhere. A number of significant events in primate evolution are recorded: for example, the last victoriapithecid, the earliest cercopithecid and earliest colobine, possibly the earliest hominid, the earliest member of genus *Homo*, and perhaps one of the last representatives of *Australopithecus boisei*.

When Bill Bishop first visited the Lake Baringo Basin in the northern Rift Valley of Kenya, he realized how interesting it was. This was in the mid-1960s; a time when in Africa very little radiometric or palaeomagnetic work had been carried out to date terrestrial vertebrate sites or to correlate between them. Despite this, it was obvious that there was a lack of information about African faunas for the long period between the early Miocene sites of western Kenya and eastern Uganda, and the later sites containing hominids such as Olduvai in Tanzania. It was a time before any fossil hominids earlier than *Homo sapiens* had yet been discovered in Kenya. And as far as palaeoenvironments were concerned, Louis Leakey and others explained climatic fluctuations in eastern Africa by the 'Pluvial hypothesis' (Brooks 1914). Indeed, the Tugen Hills themselves had been used as a basis for the Kamasian Pluvial (Leakey & Solomon 1929). Writers like Robert Ardrey (1961) had vividly popularized the idea of a 'Pliocene drought' to explain the absence of sediments and fossil evidence for that time period.

Bishop recognized the importance of this new area for clarifying these issues, and his achievement was to begin work collecting solid data and forming ideas about them, based upon normal and rigorous stratigraphic procedures (Bishop 1967, 1971, 1972, 1976; Bishop & Chapman 1970; Bishop et al. 1971, 1975, 1978; Bishop &

Pickford 1975). It soon became apparent that the succession preserved fossiliferous sediments from at least some of the otherwise missing time gap in Africa, later known to extend from 14 to 4 Ma. The area also quickly produced the first fossil hominid from Kenya (Martyn 1967; Tobias 1967). The succession as a whole held out the possibility of understanding the palaeoenvironmental and palaeoecological context of hominoid evolution through the Neogene.

In this paper I review some of the results of work in the Baringo Basin since Bill Bishop's time there, and in so doing hope to show the continued importance of the area for understanding the evolution of fossil vertebrate animals and environments. This includes the evolution of humans and their ancestors. Bishop was rightly insistent on the primacy of a chronological framework for palaeontological and palaeoanthropological work, and I allude to some issues of calibration of the sediments before discussing their fossil content. As there are now many sites – over 200 of different ages – known in the Tugen Hills, I discuss only a few, or evidence from packages of related sites, in order to provide windows on time through the section. Fossil primates, including hominids and other hominoids, were one of Bill Bishop's main interests, as they are of the present Baringo Project. Selection has consequently been guided by those sites that preserve important primate

HILL, A. 1999. The Baringo Basin, Kenya: from Bill Bishop to BPRP. *In*: ANDREWS, P. & BANHAM, P. (eds) *Late Cenozoic Environments and Hominid Evolution: a tribute to Bill Bishop.* Geological Society, London, 85–97.

specimens. In discussing these sites I take the opportunity to comment on the current status of these specimens.

The Baringo Basin and its investigation

Although there are also fossiliferous sediments on the east side of the Baringo Basin, the principal relevant feature of the area is the Tugen Hills (Fig. 1). Situated west of Lake Baringo, they are formed by a complicated uplifted fault block between the Elgeyo escarpment to their west and the central line of the Rift to the east. Further east is the Laikipia escarpment. The prominent Saimo scarp forms the eastern face of the hills, and faulted dip-slopes extend to the west into the Kerio Valley. About 3000 m of fossiliferous sediments are exposed in the scarp and the eastern foothills.

The Tugen Hills were relatively little known geologically until the mid-1960s when a syste-

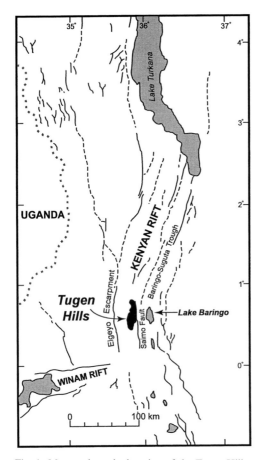

Fig. 1. Map to show the location of the Tugen Hills.

matic programme of investigation was initiated by the East African Geological Research Unit (EAGRU) under the direction of Basil King, based at Bedford College, University of London. Gregory (1896, 1921) had earlier seen the Hills when he explored and described the Rift in 1892/93. He was the first to use the term 'Lake Kamasia' to explain the origin of some of the sediments. In 1930 and 1931 Fuchs (1950) visited and collected some fossils as part of the Second African Lakes Expedition. Later, the Kenya Geological Survey began work in the southern parts (McCall et al. 1967), and divided Gregory's and Fuchs' Kamasia sediments into two separate units, the Chemeron and Kapthurin.

The work of EAGRU, starting with such people as Martyn (1969) and Chapman (1971; see also Chapman et al. 1978), began to produce a much more detailed geological framework for the region which resulted in a large number of fossil sites being discovered, one or two producing hominoids. As a result of this Bill Bishop formed an additional group of students, of whom I was the first, in order to investigate these more closely. Further systematic work on the sequence was begun in 1980 by the Baringo Palaeontological Research Project (BPRP), initially directed by David Pilbeam, and since 1985 by myself. It is a continuing project, now based at Yale University, working in association with the National Museums of Kenya and involving a number of researchers from various parts of the world.

The region remains as interesting as it was in Bill Bishop's time. On the whole, sites throughout eastern Africa are now well dated, there are relatively abundant hominoids from some time levels in the region, and much more is known about palaeoenvironments. However, there remains a general absence of fossil sites in Africa between 14 Ma and about 6 Ma. And this absence applies to the whole of the African continent. This period saw the origins of the modern Ethiopian fauna, which included the divergence of hominids and modern African apes. The Tugen Hills fills this gap by presenting a long section from 16 Ma into the Pleistocene, including many parts of this otherwise missing time period. It is very well calibrated, and provides a standard for other more temporally isolated sites in sub-Saharan Africa. It documents first and last appearances for many taxa, including hominids and other primates (Hill 1985a, b, 1987, 1995; Hill et al. 1985, 1986, 1992a; Barry et al. 1985). In addition, good palaeoenvironmental information now comes from a variety of approaches and data in the Tugen Hills (e.g. Jacobs and Kabuye, 1987; Morgan et al. 1994; Kingston et al. 1994; Kingston 1999).

Stratigraphical framework and dating

EAGRU and Bishop's group established a basic stratigraphical scheme for the succession (Bishop *et al.* 1971; Chapman *et al.* 1978). They gradually accumulated relevant radiometric dates, mainly whole-rock K/Ar analyses carried out by the laboratories of Miller and Fitch at Cambridge, the Institute of Geological Sciences Geochemistry Division in London, Liverpool University (Sub-department of Geophysics), and by Evernden and Curtis at Berkeley. Results up to 1978 were collated and summarized by Chapman and Brook (1978). Dagley *et al.* (1978) carried out an early palaeomagnetic survey.

BPRP has continued and greatly expanded this programme, with age determinations often being performed in conjunction with finds of significant primate specimens (Hill 1985*a*; Hill *et al.* 1985, 1986, 1992*b,c*; Deino *et al.* 1990; Deino & Hill in press).

Figure 2 presents the current stratigraphical framework. There are six major fossiliferous sedimentary formations in the Tugen Hills succession, with approximate bracketing dates as follows:

Muruyur	15.5–15 Ma
Ngorora	13–8.5 Ma
Mpesida	7–6.2 Ma
Lukeino	6.2–5.6 Ma
Chemeron	5.6–1.6 Ma
Kapthurin	700–<200 ka

Stratigraphically above these are a few other units such as the Loboi Silts, that extend into the Holocene (Farrand *et al.* 1976; Tallon 1978).

On the eastern side of Lake Baringo the time interval just above the apparent termination of the Chemeron Formation in the main sequence is represented by the Chemoigut Formation, the fauna dating to about 1.4 Ma (Carney *et al.* 1971). The Chemoigut Formation is overlain by the middle Pleistocene Mukutan Beds (Bishop *et al.* 1975, 1978)

Recently BPRP dating has primarily been carried out by single-crystal laser fusion argon/argon methods, along with palaeomagnetic stratigraphy. We have age determinations on lavas separating major units, but also on many tuffs within individual sedimentary sequences. A number of points are worth noting.

- Many of these sedimentary units are exposed extensively, over relatively large geographical areas.
- For many parts of the sequence there is now very good calibration indeed. The combination of radiometric determinations and

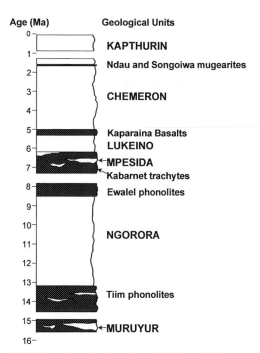

Fig. 2. Stratigraphical section of the Tugen Hills sequence showing major volcanic and sedimentary units (sedimentary units named in upper case; volcanic units shaded and named in lower case).

palaeomagnetic stratigraphy through the Kabasero section of the Ngorora Formation, for example, suggested modifications to deep-sea spreading rates, and a revision to the Global Geomagnetic Reversal Timescale (GRTS) (Tauxe *et al.* 1985; Deino *et al.* 1990). It is now used as the standard for GRTS by a number of palaeomagnetists for this part of the Miocene. (This represents a considerable change from the days when Bill Bishop and I wandered around Baringo pointing a fluxgate magnetometer at basalt.)

- For much of the time period represented by the section, these are the only fossiliferous sediments yet known in the whole of Africa.
- Some of these units are of very long duration, notably the Ngorora and Chemeron. There is not an 'Ngorora site'; there are many sites, as is indeed the case for all of these units. It makes little sense to discuss 'the Ngorora fauna', or to talk of an 'Ngororan' faunal stage. The Ngorora and Chemeron Formations each represent about 4 Ma. To speak of the 'Ngorora fauna' or the 'Chemeron fauna' would be equivalent to lumping together as a single community all East African animals from today back to Laetoli.

In addition to calibration by radiometric and palaeomagnetic methods, BPRP has begun a programme of tuff fingerprinting. Some volcanic eruptions in the Pliocene were of huge magnitude, their tephras extending across much of Africa. A number of tuffs in the Chemeron Formation have already been identified with ones that also occur elsewhere (Namwamba 1993; Brown 1994). At the site complex of Kipcherere several tuffs correlate with those in the Turkana Basin; our Reed tuff equates with the Lokochot tuff (about 3.5 Ma by interpolation). Slightly higher at Kipcherere another tuff is equivalent to the Tulu Bor (≡ Sidi Hakoma Tuff of Hadar, 3.32 Ma), and elsewhere in the Chemeron Formation is another tuff that equates with the Lokalalei (2.52 Ma, ≡ Tuff D in the Shungura, also detected at Gadeb in Ethiopia). These tephras are also found in western Uganda and in marine cores from the Gulf of Aden. Another tuff in the Tugen Hills equates with one in the Kanapoi sequence. In addition we believe that a tuff which occurs near the top of the Tabarin exposures in the Chemeron Formation is the same as the Moiti Tuff (3.89 Ma), known near the base of the Omo Group, but this is still subject to geochemical confirmation.

The exciting feature of this work is that such extensive tuffs represent time intervals of very short duration, a matter of days or weeks. They make it possible to establish highly resolved time-lines across great distances, and to control for time when comparing faunas and palaeoenvironments which are very widely separated geographically. They thus provide the opportunity to assess contemporaneous palaeoecological variation across a significant part of eastern Africa.

The Tugen Hills succession and faunal change

The rest of this paper is concerned with describing in general terms the faunas through the succession and commenting upon faunal change. It emphasizes slightly the record for hominoids and other primate specimens that are important for the timing of the origin and disappearance of clades. There is a general assumption that vertebrate species evolve in relation to their environment, be it in response to changes in vegetation and associated fauna, in relation to other changes in local environment, to global climatic change, or to some combination of these elements. If we are to correlate such environmental changes reliably with speciation, if in fact

we are going to understand anything about the tempo and mode of human evolution, then we have to establish reliable dates for first and last appearances of taxa. These need to be established not just for hominoids, but for the rest of their associated fauna throughout the Neogene.

Muruyur Formation

The oldest level from which significant fossils come in the Tugen Hills is in the Muruyur Formation, and many sites are exposed at several stratigraphical levels in the Kipsaramon site complex (Hill et al. 1991). At 15.5 Ma is a very extensive bone bed (BPRP# 89), up to 20 cm thick and extending laterally for at least 2500 m^2. It contains a diverse fauna, with specimens ranging in size from rodent teeth to proboscidean heads. The fauna is basically similar to other early to mid-Miocene faunas elsewhere in Africa, such as at Maboko in western Kenya, although with a number of unique taxa. There are three genera of proboscideans, *Protanancus, Choerolophodon* and *Deinotherium*. There is at least one species of rhinoceros, a hippopotamus (*Kenyapotamus*), one or more suids (*Nguruwe* and perhaps *Lopholistriodon*), a sanithere (*Diamantohyus*), a giraffid (*Palaeotragus*) and a tragulid (*Dorcatherium*). An extensive collection of small mammals belongs to seven families, and these are particularly useful for assessing aspects of palaeoecology (Winkler 1992, in press). Some open area is suggested by the presence of spring hares (Peditidae), but flying squirrels (*Anomalurus*) imply the existence of forest. Among primates are isolated teeth and a mandible of *Victoriapithecus macinnessi, Kalepithecus* sp., and at least one tooth referable to *Proconsul* (Hill et al. 1991). A possible *Proconsul* talus comes from another site in the Kipsaramon site complex at a slightly higher level (BPRP# 91; Hill & Ward, 1988).

Also slightly younger in the Kipsaramon site complex, at about 15.3 Ma, is a locality (BPRP# 122) preserving a partial skeleton (KNM-TH 28860) and over 40 teeth of a hominoid referable to *Kenyapithecus africanus*, along with a few teeth of *Nyanzapithecus* (Brown et al. 1991). There are at least seven individuals of *Kenyapithecus*, with a number of teeth coming from the same jaws. The partial skeleton (Ward et al. 1996), at present being described, preserves parts of the head, both shoulders, arms and hands, and much of the thoracic cage, which reveal much that is new about this taxon. The current inventory consists of a mandibular corpus of an adult male with all teeth in excellent condition except for right I_1 and M_2, which are missing. The left M_1 is damaged, missing its entoconid. There is a left clavicle, and a left proximal humerus with 4 cm of diaphysis. The right humerus is missing its head, but is otherwise complete. The right ulna has a complete olecranon and three-quarters of its diaphysis. Similarly the right radius has complete head and three-quarters of its diaphysis. There is a left distal radius with about half of its diaphysis. The left distal ulna is fragmentary but has the styloid process and a radial articular surface. There is a right scaphoid, a right hamate, and numerous metacarpals and phalanges in articulation. There are numerous ribs and fragmented cervical and thoracic vertebrae. We also have the right and left maxillary incisors of the same individual.

The clavicle and the elbow region of this specimen of *Kenyapithecus* are especially interesting. The latter preserves all three joints (humerus–ulnar, radial–humeral and radial–ulnar). In addition the scaphoid shows facets for a free os centrale, the hamate shows a triquetral facet distinctive from *Proconsul* and similar to *Dryopithecus*, and the fingers appear to have a relatively long proximal phalangeal segment. The mandible is the largest known for *Kenyapithecus* and has a distinct inferior transverse torus, lateral corpus hollowing, and a robust base. Overall the preserved morphology shows an interesting mix of features, and the forelimb anatomy suggests a different locomotor pattern from that of *Proconsul* (Ward *et al.* 1996).

There are no other partial skeletons, and few mandibles, of *Kenyapithecus* described, and this example presents many parts of the skeleton not otherwise known from isolated specimens. *Kenyapithecus* remains a rare and intriguing taxon; this is the best specimen known, and this Kipsaramon site is one of the best three for the genus. However, apart from hominoids, there appear to be no other large mammals preserved here.

Ngorora Formation

The Ngorora Formation extends from about 13 Ma to 8.5 Ma, a long period of time not otherwise represented at sites elsewhere in Africa. Thus there are no contemporary fossil faunas with which it may be compared, and many of the taxa found are unique to the formation. There are many sites in the formation from many different levels. It has been particularly well calibrated by BPRP both radiometrically and by palaeomagnetic stratigraphy (Hill *et al.* 1985; Tauxe *et al.* 1985; Deino *et al.* 1990).

Low in the section a volcanic ash, dated at about 12.6 Ma, preserves a remarkable assemblage of leaves, some of them attached to branches. The more than 50 taxa identified suggest a lowland wet rainforest environment, with West African floral affinities (Jacobs 1994; Jacobs & Deino, 1996; Jacobs & Kabuye 1987; Jacobs & Winkler, 1992).

Just a little higher stratigraphically, and in the same vicinity, is a particularly interesting locality (BPRP#38) which offers a diverse fauna, about 12.5 Ma in age. It was the first fossil site to be recorded by Chapman while working with EAGRU when he came across the rocks that now constitute the Ngorora Formation. Some faunal differences exist between this level and the Muruyur sites at 15.5 Ma, but it remains essentially mid-Miocene in character, and records the last occurrences of some earlier forms. This particular local fauna includes representatives of four families of carnivore, an aardvark, a hyrax, a proboscidean, a rhinoceros, and a range of artiodactyls. There is an anthracothere, a suid (*Lopholistriodon*), a palaeomerycid (*Climacoceros*), a giraffid (*Palaeotragus*), a tragulid (*Dorcatherium*), and at least four species of bovid. There are three identified species of rodent (Winkler in press). As for primates, the last known Victoriapithecid monkey occurs here, a new species of *Victoriapithecus* so far unique to this site. Along with this are teeth of a hominoid that may be attributable to *Proconsul*. This specimen, or maybe a premolar at another site dated at just younger than 12.42 Ma (KNM-BN 10489 from BPRP#65; Hill *et al.* 1985; Hill & Ward 1988; Deino *et al.* 1990) would be the last *Proconsul* known in the record. Other Ngorora sites of about this age supplement the list. Additional representatives of rodents, carnivores and creodonts are known, along with insectivores. There is *Choerolophodon ngororae* and *Prodeinotherium* among proboscidea, and three species of rhinoceros, a hippopotamus (*Kenyapotamus*), another species of *Dorcatherium*, and additional giraffids and bovids.

An interesting primate occurs in the sequence at about 12 Ma (KNM-BN 1378 from BPRP#60). It is a left upper molar of an otherwise unknown species of hominoid retrieved by Chapman at the beginning of Bill Bishop's work in the area (Bishop & Chapman 1970; Hill & Ward 1988; Hill 1994). Work in the years since then has unfortunately revealed no further evidence of this intriguing taxon.

By about 9 Ma, at the top of the Ngorora Formation, a distinct change in the nature of the fauna has occurred, as is shown by localities in the Ngeringerowa site complex. At this level is the first evidence for the arrival of equids in sub-Saharan Africa, for example, and we see the beginning of modern tribes of antelopes such as the first reduncine bovids. Among primates are the first cercopithecoids in sub-Saharan Africa. There are the first colobines as well, rather small ones, described as *Microcolobus tugenensis* by Benefit and Pickford (1986) (see also Gundling & Hill in press).

Mpesida Beds

Faunas from the Mpesida Beds reinforce this impression of an apparently significant change, though exactly how suddenly the change occurs remains an open question. In the Tugen Hills succession it does coincide with a substantial gap in the sequence, from about 8.5 to 6.5 Ma, and so it is difficult to monitor the actual tempo and mode of the change. In contrast to the Ngorora Formation, the Mpesida Beds are rather narrowly restricted in space and time, although we now believe that they are geographically more extensive than formerly supposed. There is as yet relatively little radiometric control within the formation itself, but localities are well constrained by bounding ages to about 6.5 Ma, and one site that is probably in this formation has been dated to 6.7–7.2 Ma (BPRP# 133; Jacobs & Deino 1996). From sites in the unit are the first elephantids in the form of *Primelephas*, the first of the genus *Anancus*, the first of the modern genera of rhinos, *Ceratotherium*, and the first leporids in sub-Saharan Africa. Among primates is the earliest occurrence of colobines of modern size. In addition there is another proboscidean, *Stegotetrabelodon*. There are new species of genera known in the Ngorora Formation, such as the rhinoceros *Brachypotherium* and the equid *Hipparion*. There is a chalicothere, hippopotami, a giraffe, and bovids include members of modern tribes and genera, such as *Tragelaphus*, *Kobus*, *Madoqua* and *Gazella* or *Raphiceros*.

Further palaeoenvironmental information is provided by fossil trees, leaves, branch fragments and trunks embedded in a surge deposit ash flow. These suggest lowland rainforest habitats (Jacobs pers. comm.). Plant remains at a site dated to 6.7–7.2 Ma indicate a deciduous woodland (Jacobs & Deino 1996).

Lukeino Formation

The Lukeino Formation provides evidence of fauna from about 6.2 Ma to 5.6 Ma. These assemblages indicate continued faunal change,

with an increasing number of modern elements, such as the first modern kinds of pigs, in the form of *Nyanzachoerus syrticus* (see Bishop *et al.* 1999). Groups in the Mpesida Beds continue to be represented, such as leporids, rhinos, hipparionine equids, giraffids including the modern genus *Giraffa*, members of some contemporary tribes of bovids, hippopotami, proboscidea, carnivora and aardvarks. Some of these are new species. In addition is the oldest known porcupine, and the oldest of the chalicothere genus *Ancylotherium*. There are also a number of cercopithecoid specimens.

From one site currently believed to be in this unit is a particularly intriguing hominoid specimen, a lower first molar (KNM-LU 335 from BPRP# 29), first described by Andrews in Pickford (1975). Work by several people (e.g Corruccini & McHenry 1980; McHenry & Corrucini 1980; Hill & Ward 1988; Ungar *et al.* 1994), has pointed out resemblances to chimpanzee, and also to hominids. Ungar *et al.* (1994) indicated similarities to chimpanzees and also to what is now known as *Australopithecus anamensis* (Leakey *et al.* 1995). No further remains of this species are yet known, which is unfortunate as the hominoid appears to be one of the more interesting from the Tugen Hills succession.

Chemeron Formation

Like the Ngorora Formation, the Chemeron Formation is another unit in the Tugen Hills succession that preserves sediments and fossils extending for a considerable range of time, in this case from about 5.6 Ma to 1.6 Ma. Once we believed that the upper and lower portions of the formation would prove to be distinct mappable units, requiring separate formational names. However, recent work shows stratigraphical continuity throughout the entire formation.

There are many sites near the base of the Chemeron Formation, in the interval between 5.6 and 4 Ma. Tabarin (BPRP# 77) is one that spans this range. The fauna at these levels is essentially similar to that in the underlying Lukeino Formation, although members of some new taxa appear, such as one of the first representatives of the modern genus of African elephant, *Loxodonta*. There is also *Elephas recki*, and the earlier *Stegotetrabelodon* is now absent. Other proboscideans are *Deinotherium* and *Anancus*. Changes occur in the pigs, with *Nyanzachoerus jaegeri* and *Ny. kanamensis* replacing *Ny. syrticus* (Hill *et al.* 1992*a*; Bishop *et al.* 1999). The chalicothere *Ancylotherium*, the rhino *Ceratotherium praecox* and hipparionine equids remain. There are bovids, giraffids, rodents, carnivores and cercopithecoids among other groups.

From the site of Tabarin also comes what is probably the earliest hominid known (KNM-TH 13150; Hill 1985a; Ward & Hill 1987). The specimen is a fragment of mandible with M_1, M_2 and partial root of M_3 found by BPRP in 1984. When first described (Hill 1985a), I identified it as being similar to *Australopithecus afarensis*, but also commented that if we could find more material then it might prove to be a new species. However, I felt that it was not at all appropriate to use this specimen to name a new taxon and for it to become the type, because it possesses only a small number of relatively undiagnostic morphological traits, many of which could be primitive for Hominidae in general. This was the conclusion also reached in a later, more detailed analysis (Ward & Hill 1987). Now that White and colleagues have described *Ardipithecus ramidus* from Aramis in the Middle Awash (White *et al.* 1994, 1995), it is possible to see similarities with that taxon as well, such as molars slightly narrower than those of *Au. afarensis*. Although it cannot be definitively diagnosed, it may best be provisionally, but not certainly, identified as cf *Ar. ramidus*. The hominid from Tabarin may be just slightly older than those from Aramis, being dated at about between 4.4 and 4.5 Ma. The Aramis specimens are currently dated at just younger than 4.39 Ma.

BPRP has new age determinations at Tabarin, soon to be published, which provide fine calibration through the sequence. In addition we are carrying out tuff fingerprinting to establish time lines between the Tugen Hills at this level and Aramis. This exercise will be interesting palaeoenvironmentally as well as chronometrically, as we will then be able to compare the details of distant and different contemporary Pliocene environments. Aramis seems clearly to reflect a forest environment (WoldeGabriel *et al.* 1994), whereas Tabarin is best regarded as woodland (Kingston 1992, 1999).

From another site at a similar level (KNM-BC 1745 from BPRP# 30) is a proximal hominid humerus (Pickford *et al.* 1983). This specimen is perhaps more convincingly hominid, as among other derived features it has a shallow intertubercular groove, unlike African apes (Hill & Ward, 1988; Hill 1994).

Faunal specimens of particularly high quality are found at over 30 sites between about 3 Ma and 2.4 Ma. There is an almost entire skeleton of the pig *Kolpochoerus* for example, a number of complete pig crania, a whole giant land turtle, and some particularly good primates. In 1966 Bill Bishop discovered a complete monkey skeleton at site JM 90/91 (BPRP# 97). This became the type of *Paracolobus chemeroni*, excavated and described by Richard Leakey (1969). At this same site was a monkey skull that became the type of *Theropithecus baringensis* (Leakey 1969).

These taxa represent a change in the fauna from earlier in the formation. Other new elements include the modern species of rhino *Ceratotherium simum*, and among proboscideans a new species of Loxodonta, *L. exoptata*, and a new form of *Elephas recki*. Pigs include *Kolpochoerus afarensis*, *K. limnetes*, *Notochoerus scotti* and *N. eulius* (see Bishop *et al.* 1999).

At 2.43 Ma is the hominid specimen known as the Chemeron temporal (KNM-BC 1). It is a largely complete right temporal bone. The specimen is of some historical importance, particularly in this context, as Bill Bishop was closely involved in events immediately following its discovery. Also it was the first fossil hominid specimen, other than late specimens of *Homo sapiens*, to be found in Kenya. More recently it has taken on renewed interest as it has been described as the earliest member of genus *Homo* (Hill *et al.* 1992b, c). Consequently it is worth taking this opportunity to document the circumstances of its discovery.

John Kimengich found this specimen at site JM 85 (BPRP# 2) in late October 1965, while working for, and in the presence of, John Martyn of EAGRU. It was discovered early in the course of John Martyn's work. It was one of the very first fossils, and JM85 one of the very first fossil sites, he discovered in the area. Martyn did not recognize the specimen as hominid, and took it with other fossils to Jonathan Leakey, who lives in the area. Leakey identified the item as a hominid. As a consequence of all this, Bill Bishop visited the site, and in 1966 Mary and Louis Leakey, along with Richard and Margaret Leakey, came to the region with a team of collectors from Olduvai. The Leakeys carried out a number of unrelated projects in their 1966 field season. For example, Richard Leakey excavated the almost complete skeleton of a large proboscidean from site JM 514 (BPRP# 23) which is now on display in the Kenya National Museum. A hominid mandible and some postcranials were found in the Middle Pleistocene Kapthurin Formation, and Margaret Leakey excavated artefacts in that unit (Leakey *et al.* 1969; see McBrearty *et al.* 1996; McBrearty 1999). Finally, Mary Leakey and her staff conducted a large excavation at the Chemeron Formation site where the temporal bone had been found.

Explaining the background to their 1966 work in the Kapthurin Beds, Leakey *et al.* (1969) report:

'... During the course of mapping, J. E. Martyn and his assistants found a number of fossils in the Chemeron beds. He showed these to Mr Jonathan Leakey who noticed an incomplete hominid temporal bone amongst them. In view of this find it was decided that a closer examination of the area was necessary in order to ascertain the exact provenance of the specimen and to look for further remains of the same individual. The ensuing excavation and sieving were carried out under the supervision of Mrs M. D. Leakey. The operation was, however, unsuccessful, although it is likely that the temporal bone had eroded out of the Upper Fish Beds of the Chemeron formation'.

It is not uncommon in such circumstances for no further hominid remains to be found in excavation, although in this case there were other mammals and very many fish bones. In their final report Mary and Louis Leakey (nd) gave more details:

'The temporal is lightly rolled and exhibits small areas of strongly cemented gritty matrix, visible particularly in the interstices of the lambda suture. The matrix contains well-rounded particles of coarse sand grade and appear (sic) entirely similar to a horizon which occurs at the summit of the slope on which the specimen was found. The degree of abrasion visible on the bone is also consistent with it having been derived from this horizon since other beds on the higher part of the slope are all fine-grained.'

The specimen was described by Tobias (1967), as Hominidae indet., and Martyn (1967) described the geology and provided a section of the site with the location of the discovery indicated. Martyn in that paper establishes the particular horizon within the short section of the excavation that the fossil most probably comes from, based on adhering matrix, microstratigraphy, and the local geomorphological situation. His conclusion agrees with that of the Leakeys cited above, and substantiates the account he gave in a letter to Basil King on December 1st 1965, only a month after the specimen was found (Manuscript letter, KNM Archives: John Martyn to Basil King, 1 December 1965):

'...it could not have come from anywhere except from some horizon between 4 and 8 ft above the Lower Tuffs (see section). Some matrix clinging to the bone showed that it came from a grit consisting of subrounded fragments of volcanic rock cemented by calcite. There are a number of stringy beds of grit, sometimes cemented sometimes not but the most promising, bearing in mind the location

of the bone appears to lie about 8 ft above the lower tuffs.'

At that time the geological sequence was not well dated, and there were very few other hominid fossils available with which to compare the specimen.

Subsequently the fossil received little additional comment. In 1973 Richard Leakey, who had examined the site not long after the hominid's discovery, wrote rather perceptively:

'Although the fossil was located on the surface, there is no reason to doubt the reported provenance and approximate age of between fossil 2 and 3 million years. The fragmentary condition of the specimen makes it difficult to assess its taxonomic affinities but there are several features that suggest differences from Australopithecus sensu lato.'

Details of the specimen and its context were recorded in standard catalogues such as Oakley et al. (1977) and Day (1977). Howell (1978) discusses it and its geological situation (see also Howell 1972). He comments on its 'apparent substantial antiquity', suggests that its morphology diverges from that found in Australopithecus boisei, and 'very tentatively' refers it to Au. africanus.

In 1992 BPRP identified the specimen to genus Homo, and dated the site at 2.43 Ma (Hill et al. 1992a, b). At that time this made it the oldest known member of Homo by half a million years. More detailed recent work substantiates these conclusions (Sherwood et al. 1996, in press; Deino & Hill in press). In a comment on the original paper Wood (1992) suggested that the specimen might belong to H. rudolfensis, but at present we prefer to remain conservative about species attribution. Other mammalian fauna from this particular site and horizon includes Alcelaphine bovids (Gentry 1978), hippopotami, and suids (Kolpochoerus limnetes; Bishop et al. 1999).

Since the Chemeron temporal was redescribed, other specimens attributed to Homo have appeared in this time range. There is now a maxilla from the Middle Awash at 2.33 Ma (Kimbel et al. 1996, 1997), and also a mandible from Malawi (Schrenk et al. 1993; Bromage et al. 1995). A date of 2.4 Ma was originally given for the Malawi specimen, but this seems to be based upon a misunderstanding of Chemeron biostratigraphy by the authors (Hill 1995). In later publications (e.g. Bromage et al. 1995) they appear to temper their earlier assertions. Based on information generally available, the Malawi mandible is in fact not well dated and it could be much younger than 2.4 Ma. At present the Chemeron temporal remains the oldest known member of the genus *Homo*.

Chemoigut Formation

On the east side of Lake Baringo is another geological unit that represents time just later than the Chemeron Formation in the east. At Chesowanja the Chemoigut Formation crops out and provides an extensive fauna, including a partial cranium of *Australopithecus boisei* (KNM-CH 1), a few fragments of additional *Au. boisei* individuals, and Oldowan artefacts.

I found the australopithecine cranium in 1970 (Carney *et al.* 1971), at which time it was only the third cranium of *Au. boisei* known. The original description points out several apparently advanced or derived features. The specimen has a very steeply set frontal, and appears to have no signs of marked ridges for *temporalis*, for example. These features were perceived as advanced at the time and concordant with the age of the specimen. However, subsequent material from elsewhere in East Africa has demonstrated an interestingly large range of contemporary variation in the hypodigm (Brown *et al.* 1993), with some individuals showing a mix of apparently 'primitive' and 'advanced' features. This perception has been reinforced by a recently described skull from Ethiopia (Suwa *et al.* 1997). Apart from the first paper (Carney *et al.* 1971), and a second short note clarifying a few anatomical points (Walker 1972), KNM-CH 1 has never been described in any detail, and BPRP has plans to carry out further preparation and analysis.

Two additional robust australopithecine teeth belonging to at least one other individual were found on our subsequent expedition to Chesowanja with Bill Bishop, at which time revisions were made to the geological interpretation of the region (Bishop *et al.* 1975, 1978). A later expedition retrieved cranial fragments of a further individual from another site within the area (Gowlett *et al.* 1981).

BPRP is carrying out renewed dating at Chesowanja. If earlier estimates of about 1.4 Ma for the age of the cranium are confirmed (Hooker & Miller 1979), either it or the Ethiopian skull (Suwa *et al.* 1997) would be the last known *Au. boisei* (see Kimbel 1995).

Kapthurin Formation

The Kapthurin Formation is the most recent of the significant fossiliferous units in the Baringo Basin. It spans much of the mid-Pleistocene, ranging from about 700 ka to less than 200 ka, and contains an extensive fauna including hominids. Also, archaeological occurrences attributed to several distinct industries are distributed throughout the section. Since 1990 the formation has been the focus of an independent but allied project, directed by McBrearty (see McBrearty *et al.* 1996; McBrearty 1999).

Summary

Fossiliferous sediments in the Baringo Basin span the time from about 16 Ma into the Pleistocene. There are many fossil sites distributed through the succession. These provide the only evidence in Africa of faunas and palaeoenvironments for long periods of time in the Neogene, notably that between 14 Ma and 6 Ma. The Tugen Hills sequence establishes a succession, finely calibrated by radiometric and palaeomagnetic means, that constitutes a reference section for less dateable sites elsewhere.

Fossil material from Tugen Hills sites permits the documentation of the Ethiopian fauna and changes in it through time. Many species are known only from the succession. The Tugen Hills sequence provides data for first and last appearances of these and many others taxa (Fig. 3).

Among primates, the Tugen Hills succession supplies all the evidence for African monkeys (except for one tooth) between 14 Ma and about 6 Ma (Gundling & Hill in press). At 12.5 Ma it supplies the last victoriapithecid, which is a new species of *Victoriapithecus*. The earliest cercopithecoid (which is also the earliest colobine)

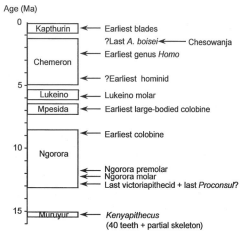

Fig. 3. Section of the Tugen Hills sequence with some prominent events in Primate evolution indicated.

occurs at about 8.5 Ma. The earliest modern sized colobine follows at 6.5 Ma. The types of *Paracolobus chemeroni* and *Theropithecus baringensis* occur at 3.2 Ma.

For hominoids, the Tugen Hills sequence provides some of the best evidence of *Kenyapithecus,* at about 15.3 Ma, in the form of many teeth and a partial skeleton. From about 12 Ma is a tooth of an otherwise unknown hominoid, and perhaps the last known representative of *Proconsul.* At 6 Ma or 6.5 Ma is a very interesting molar tooth of another otherwise unknown hominoid that shows resemblances to both chimpanzee and hominids, particularly to *Au. anamensis.*

At Tabarin the Tugen Hills succession has produced the earliest hominid, at about 4.5 Ma, and the earliest representative of genus *Homo* from BPRP#2 at 2.4 Ma. At Chesowanja there is one of the last known members of *Au. boisei* at 1.4 Ma.

Evidence of palaeoenvironments is available not only from the fauna, but from fossil macroflora, and isotopic analyses of palaeosol carbonates, mammal teeth and diatoms.

It is still as true now, as it was in Bill Bishop's day, that if we wish to study African hominoids and the rest of the Ethiopian fauna between 14 ma and 6 Ma, then at present the Baringo Basin is about the only place to look. Bill was very interested in human evolution. But he also recognized the importance of detailed information about context, and relating human evolution to changes in the rest of the African fauna and the environment. If we follow his example and continue this strategy, then I am optimistic that we may replace our relatively static view of time successive hominid species with a more profound understanding of the actual dynamics of evolutionary change in our lineage.

Palaeoanthropological work in the Tugen Hills since 1980 has been carried out by the Baringo Palaeontological Research Project (BPRP), based at Yale University and operating in conjunction with the National Museums of Kenya. It is a multidisciplinary project involving participants from several countries; currently the USA, England, France and Kenya. Among these are A. Deino (Berkeley Geochronology Laboratory) who is responsible for the dating programme, J. Kingston (Yale) who as well as performing stratigraphical work has used various biogeochemical techniques to investigate environmental change. B. Jacobs (Southern Methodist University) investigates the macroflora. S. Ward, B. Brown (Northeastern Ohio Universities College of Medicine) and myself have overall responsibility for the study of the hominoids, with considerable help from R. Sherwood (University of Wisconsin, Madison) on the Chemeron temporal. Of Kenyan expedition participants I particularly thank K. Cheboi and B. Kimeu. The basic funding has come primarily from grants to A. Hill from the National Science Foundation, USA (most recently NSF SBR-9208903), the Louise Brown Foundation, the Ingalls Foundation, J. Clayton Stephenson, the L. S. B. Leakey Foundation, and several disbursements from Yale University. Individual BPRP participants have also received their own funding from various sources applied to aspects of the project, including some, such as Laura Bishop and John Kingston, who have benefited from grants from the Bill Bishop Memorial Trust. We thank the Government of the Republic of Kenya for research permission. I thank J. Martyn for a number of discussions concerning KNM-BC 1. I am grateful to Sally McBrearty for her very detailed criticism of the draft, and other helpful comments were provided by G. Chapman, J. Kingston and J. Rossie.

References

ARDREY, R. 1961. *African Genesis.* MacMillan, London.

BARRY, J., HILL, A. & FLYNN, L. 1985. Variation de la faune au Miocene inférieur et moyen de l'Afrique de l'est. *L'Anthropologie* (Paris) , **89**, 271–273.

BENEFIT, B. & PICKFORD, M. 1986. Miocene fossil cercopithecoids from Kenya. *American Journal of Physical Anthropology*, **69**, 441–461.

BISHOP, L. C., HILL, A. & KINGSTON, J. D. 1999. Palaeoecology of Suidae from the Tugen Hills, Baringo, Kenya. *This volume.*

BISHOP, W. W. 1967. Stratigraphical nomenclature in the Baringo area of the northern Kenya Rift Valley. *Proceedings of the Pan-African Congress of Prehistory: Dakar*, 332–333.

——1971. The late Cenozoic history of East Africa in relation to Hominid evolution. *In*: TUREKIAN, K. K. (ed) *The Late Cenozoic Glacial Ages.* Yale University, New Haven, 493–527.

——1972. Stratigraphic succession 'versus' calibration in East Africa. *In*: BISHOP, W. W. (ed.) *Calibration of Hominoid Evolution.* Scottish Academic, Edinburgh, 1–28.

——1976. Pliocene problems relating to Human Evolution. *In*: ISAAC, G. LL. & McCOWN, E. R. (eds) *Human Origins: Louis Leakey and the East African Evidence.* Benjamin, California, 139–153.

—— & CHAPMAN, G. R. 1970. Early Pliocene sediments and fossils from the northern Kenya Rift Valley. *Nature*, **226**, 914–918.

—— & PICKFORD, M. 1975. Geology, fauna and palaeoenvironments of the Ngorora Formation, Kenya Rift Valley. *Nature*, **254**, 185–192.

——, CHAPMAN, G. R., HILL, A. & MILLER, J. A. 1971. Succession of Cainozoic vertebrate assemblages from the northern Kenya Rift Valley. *Nature*, **233**, 389–394.

——, HILL, A. & PICKFORD, M. 1978. Chesowanja: a revised geological interpretation. *In*: BISHOP, W. W. (ed.) *Geological Background to Fossil Man.* Scottish Academic, Edinburgh, 309–327.

——, PICKFORD, M. & HILL, A. 1975. New evidence regarding the Quaternary geology, archaeology, and hominids of Chesowanja, Kenya. *Nature*, **258**, 204–208.

BROMAGE, T. G., SCHRENK, F. & ZONNEVELD, F. W. 1995. Paleoanthropology of the Malawi Rift: an early hominid mandible from the Chiwondo Beds, northern Malawi. *Journal of Human Evolution*, **28**, 71–108.

BROOKS, C. E. P. 1914. The meteorological conditions of an ice-sheet and their bearing on the dessication of the globe. *Royal Meteorological Society Quarterly Journal*, **40**, 53–70.

BROWN, B., HILL, A. & WARD, S. 1991. New Miocene large hominoids from the Tugen Hills, Baringo District, Kenya. *American Journal of Physical Anthropology*, (Supplement 12), 55.

——, WALKER, A. C., WARD, C. V. & LEAKEY, R. E. 1993. New *Australopithecus boisei* calvaria from east Lake Turkana, Kenya. *American Journal of Physical Anthropology*, **91**, 137–159.

BROWN, F. H. 1994. Development of Pliocene and Pleistocene chronology of the Turkana Basin, east Africa, and its relation to other sites. *In*: CORRUCCINI, R. S. & CIOCHON, R. L. (eds) *Integrative Paths to the Past: Paleoanthropological Advances in Honor of F. Clark Howell*. Prentice Hall, New Jersey, 285–312.

CARNEY, J., HILL, A., MILLER, J. A. & WALKER, A. 1971. Late Australopithecine from Baringo District, Kenya. *Nature*, **230**, 509–514.

CHAPMAN, G. R. 1971. *The geological evolution of the northern Kamasia Hills, Baringo District, Kenya*. Doctoral dissertation, University of London.

—— & BROOK, M. 1978. Chronostratigraphy of the Baringo Basin, Kenya Rift Valley. *In*: BISHOP, W. W. (ed.) *Geological Background to Fossil Man*. Geological Society, London, Scottish Academic, Edinburgh, 207–223.

——, LIPPARD, S. J. & MARTYN, J. E. 1978. The stratigraphy and structure of the Kamasia Range, Kenya Rift Valley. *Journal of the Geological Society, London*, **135**, 265–281.

CORRUCCINI, R. S. & MCHENRY, H. M. 1980. Cladometric analysis of Pliocene hominoids. *Journal of Human Evolution*, **9**, 209–221.

DAGLEY, P., MUSSETT, A. E. & PALMER, H. C. 1978. Preliminary observations on the palaeomagnetic stratigraphy of the area west of Lake Baringo, Kenya. *In*: BISHOP, W. W. (ed.) *Geological Background to Fossil Man*. Geological Society, London, Scottish Academic, Edinburgh, 225–235.

DAY, M. H. 1977. *Guide to Fossil Man* (3rd edn). University of Chicago.

DEINO, A. L. & HILL, A. (in press). ^{40}Ar/^{39}Ar dating of the Chemeron Formation strata encompassing the site of hominid KNM-BC 1 Tugen Hills, Kenya. *Journal of Human Evolution*.

——, TAUXE, L., MONAGHAN, M. & DRAKE, R. 1990. ^{40}Ar/^{39}Ar age calibration of the litho- and paleomagnetic stratigraphies of the Ngorora Formation, Kenya. *Journal of Geology*, **98**, 567–587.

FARRAND, W. R., REDDING, R. W., WOLPOFF, M. H. & WRIGHT, H. T. 1976. *An archaeological investigation on the Loboi Plain, Baringo District, Kenya*. Museum of Anthropology, University of Michigan, Technical Reports **4**.

FUCHS, V. E. 1950. Pleistocene events in the Baringo Basin. *Geological Magazine*, **87**, 149–174.

GENTRY, A. W. 1978. The fossil Bovidae of the Baringo Area, Kenya. *In*: BISHOP, W. W. (ed.) *Geological Background to Fossil Man*. Geological Society, London, Scottish Academic, Edinburgh, 293–308.

GOWLETT, J. A. J., HARRIS, J. W. K., WALTON, D. & WOOD, B. A. 1981. Early archaeological sites, hominid remains and traces of fire from Chesowanja, Kenya. *Nature*, **294**, 125–129.

GREGORY, J. W. 1896. *The Great Rift Valley*. Murray, London.

——1921. *The Rift Valley and Geology of East Africa*. Seeley, London.

GUNDLING, T. & HILL, A. (in press). Geological context of fossil Cercopithecoidea from eastern Africa. *In*: WHITEHEAD, P. F. & JOLLY, C. J. (eds) *Old World Monkeys*. Cambridge University.

HILL, A. 1985a. Early hominid from Baringo, Kenya. *Nature*, **315**, 222–224.

——1985b. Les variations de la faune du Miocène récent et du Pliocène d'Afrique de l'est. *L'Anthropologie* (Paris), **89**, 275–279.

——1987. Causes of perceived faunal change in the later Neogene of East Africa. *Journal of Human Evolution*, **16**, 583–596.

——1994. Late Miocene and early Pliocene Hominoids from Africa. *In*: CORRUCCINI, R. S. & CIOCHON, R. L. (eds) *Integrative Paths to the Past: Paleoanthropological Advances in Honor of F. Clark Howell*. Prentice Hall, New Jersey, 123–145.

——1995. Faunal and environmental change in the Neogene of east Africa: evidence from the Tugen Hills sequence, Baringo District, Kenya. *In*: VRBA, E. S., DENTON, G. H., PARTRIDGE, T. C. & BURCKLE, L. H. (eds) *Paleoclimate and Evolution, with Emphasis on Human Origins*. Yale University, New Haven, 178–193.

—— & WARD, S. 1988. Origin of the Hominidae: the record of African large hominoid evolution between 14 My and 4 My. *Yearbook of Physical Anthropology*, **31**, 49–83.

——, BEHRENSMEYER, A. K., BROWN, B., DEINO, A., ROSE, M., SAUNDERS, J., WARD, S. & WINKLER, A. J. 1991. Kipsaramon: a lower Miocene hominoid site in the Tugen Hills, Baringo District, Kenya. *Journal of Human Evolution*, **20**, 67–75.

——, CURTIS, G. & DRAKE, R. 1986. Sedimentary stratigraphy of the Tugen Hills, Baringo District, Kenya. *In*: FROSTICK, L. E. RENAUT, R. W., REID, I. & TIERCELIN, J.-J. (eds) *Sedimentation in the African Rifts*. Geological Society, London, Special Publications, **25**, 285–295.

——, DRAKE, R., TAUXE, L., *et al.* 1985. Neogene palaeontology and geochronology of the Baringo Basin, Kenya. *Journal of Human Evolution*, **14**, 749–773.

——, WARD, S. & BROWN, B. 1992a. Anatomy and age of the Lothagam mandible. *Journal of Human Evolution,* **22**, 439–451.

——, ——, DEINO, A., CURTIS, G. & DRAKE, R. 1992b. Earliest *Homo. Nature,* **335**, 719–722.

——, ——, ——, —— & ——1992c. Earliest *Homo* debate. *Nature,* **358**, 289–290.

HOOKER, P. J. & MILLER, J. A. 1979. K-Ar dating of the Pleistocene fossil hominid site at Chesowanja, north Kenya. *Nature,* **282**, 710–712.

HOWELL, F. C. 1972. Pliocene/Pleistocene Hominidae in eastern Africa: absolute and relative ages. *In*: BISHOP, W. W. & MILLER, J. A. (eds) *Calibration of Hominoid Evolution.* Scottish Academic, Edinburgh, 331–368.

——1978. Hominidae. *In*: MAGLIO, V. J. & COOKE, H. B. S. (eds) *Evolution of African Mammals.* Harvard University, Cambridge, 154–248.

JACOBS, B. F. 1994. Paleoclimate reconstructions using middle to late Miocene paleofloras from central Kenya. *American Journal of Botany,* **81** (Supplement), 94.

—— & DEINO, A. L. 1996. Test of climate–leaf physiognomy regression models, their application to two Miocene floras from Kenya, and ^{40}Ar/^{39}Ar dating of the Late Miocene Kapturo site. *Palaeogeography, Palaeoclimatology, Palaeoecology,* **123**, 259–271.

—— & KABUYE, C. H. S. 1987. A middle Miocene (12.2 my old) forest in the East African Rift Valley, Kenya. *Journal of Human Evolution,* **16**, 147–155.

—— & WINKLER, D. A. 1992. Taphonomy of a middle Miocene autochthonous forest assemblage, Ngorora Formation, central Kenya. *Palaeogeography, Palaeoclimatology, Palaeoecology,* **99**, 31–40.

KIMBEL, W. H. 1995. Hominid speciation and Pliocene climatic change. *In*: VRBA, E. S., DENTON, G. H., PARTRIDGE, T. C. & BURCKLE, L. H. (eds) *Paleoclimate and Evolution, with Emphasis on Human Origins.* Yale University, New Haven, 425–437.

——, JOHANSON, D. C. & RAK, Y. 1997. Systematic assessment of a maxilla of *Homo* from Hadar, Ethiopia. *American Journal of Physical Anthropology,* **103**, 235–262

——, WALTER, R. C., JOHANSON, D. C., *et al.* 1996. Late Pliocene *Homo* and Oldowan tools from the Hadar Formation (Kadar Hadar Member), Ethiopia. *Journal of Human Evolution,* **31**, 549–561.

KINGSTON, J. D. 1992. *Stable isotopic evidence for hominid paleoenvironments in East Africa.* Doctoral dissertation, Harvard University, Cambridge, MA.

——1999. Environmental determinants in early hominid evolution: issues and evidence from the Tugen Hills, Kenya. *This volume.*

——, MARINO, B. & HILL, A. 1994. Isotopic evidence for Neogene hominid paleoenvironments in the Kenya Rift Valley. *Science,* **264**, 955–959.

LEAKEY, L. S. B. & SOLOMON, J. D. 1929. East African archaeology. *Nature,* **124**, 9.

LEAKEY, M. G., FEIBEL, C. S., MCDOUGALL, I. & WALKER, A. 1995. New four-million-year-old hominid species from Kanapoi and Allia Bay, Kenya. *Nature,* **376**, 565–571.

LEAKEY, M., TOBIAS, P. V., MARTYN, J. E. & LEAKEY, R. E. F. 1969. An Acheulian industry with prepared core technique and the discovery of a contemporary hominid at Lake Baringo, Kenya. *Proceedings of the Prehistorical Society,* **35**, 48–76.

LEAKEY, M. D. & LEAKEY, L. S. B. (nd) Notes by M. D. LEAKEY and L. S. B. LEAKEY, F.B.A. *Archives of the National Museums of Kenya* (typewritten).

LEAKEY, R. E. F. 1969. New Cercopithecoidea from the Chemeron Beds of Lake Baringo, Kenya. *In*: LEAKEY, L. S. B. (ed.) *Fossil Vertebrates of Africa (Vol. 1).* Academic, London, 53–70.

——1973. Australopithecines and hominines: a summary of the evidence from the early Pleistocene of eastern Africa. *Symposium of the Zoological Society of London,* **33**, 53–69.

MARTYN, J. E. 1967. Pleistocene deposits and new fossil localities in Kenya. *Nature,* **215**, 476–477.

——1969. *The geological history of the country between Lake Baringo and the Kerio River, Baringo District, Kenya.* Doctoral dissertation, University of London.

MCBREARTY, S. 1999. The archaeology of the Kapthurin Formation. *This volume.*

——, BISHOP, L. C. & KINGSTON, J. D. 1996. Variability in traces of Middle Pleistocene hominid behavior in the Kapthurin Formation, Baringo, Kenya. *Journal of Human Evolution,* **30**, 563–580.

MCCALL, G. J. H., BAKER, B. H. & WALSH, J. 1967. Late Tertiary and Quaternary sediments of the Kenya Rift Valley. *In*: BISHOP, W. W. & CLARK, J. D. (eds) *Background to Evolution in Africa.* Chicago: Chicago University, 191–220.

MCHENRY, H. M. & CORRUCCINI, R. S. 1980. Late Tertiary hominoids and human origins. *Nature,* **285**, 397–398.

MORGAN, M. E., KINGSTON, J. D. & MARINO, B. D. 1994. Carbon isotopic evidence for the emergence of C4 plants in the Neogene from Pakistan and Kenya. *Nature,* **367**, 162–165.

NAMWAMBA, F. L. 1993. *Tephrostratigraphy of the Chemeron Formation, Baringo Basin, Kenya.* Masters dissertation, University of Utah.

OAKLEY, K. P., CAMPBELL, B. G. & MOLLESON, T. I. 1977. *Catalogue of Fossil Hominids Part I: Africa* (2nd edn). Trustees of the British Museum (Natural History), London.

PICKFORD, M. 1975. Late Miocene sediments and fossils from the northern Kenya Rift Valley. *Nature,* **256**, 279–284.

——, JOHANSON, D. C., LOVEJOY, C. O. & WHITE, T. D. 1983. A Hominoid humeral fragment from the Pliocene of Kenya. *American Journal of Physical Anthropology,* **60**, 337–346.

SCHRENK, F., BROMAGE, T. G., BETZLER, C. G., RING, U. & JUWAYEYI, Y. M. 1993. Oldest *Homo* and pliocene biogeography of the Malawi Rift. *Nature,* **365**, 833–836.

SHERWOOD, R. J., WARD, S. & HILL, A. 1996. Mandibular fossa anatomy of the Chemeron temporal bone (KNM-BC 1). *American Journal of Physical Anthropology*, (Supplement 22), 214–215.

——, —— & —— (in press). The taxonomic status of the Chemeron temporal (KNM-BC 1). *Journal of Human Evolution*.

SUWA, G., ASFAW, B., BEYENE, Y., *et al.* 1997. The first skull of *Australopithecus boisei*. *Nature*, **389**, 489–492.

TALLON, P. W. J. 1978. Geological setting of the hominid fossils and Acheulian artifacts from the Kapthurin Formation, Baringo District, Kenya. *In*: BISHOP, W. W. (ed.) *Geological Background to Fossil Man*. Geological Society, London, Scottish Academic, Edinburgh, 361–373.

TAUXE, L., MONAGHAN, M., DRAKE, R., CURTIS, G. & STAUDIGEL, H. 1985. Paleomagnetism of Miocene East African Rift sediments and the calibration of the Geomagnetic Reversal Time Scale. *Journal of Geophysical Research*, **90**, 4639–4646.

TOBIAS, P. V. 1967. Pleistocene deposits and new fossil localities in Kenya. *Nature*, **215**, 478–480.

UNGAR, P. S., WALKER, A. & COFFING, K. 1994. Reanalysis of the Lukeino Molar (KNM-LU 335). *American Journal of Physical Anthropology*, **94**, 165–173.

WALKER, A. 1972. Chesowanja Australopithecine. *Nature*, **238**, 108–109.

WARD, S. & HILL, A. 1987. Pliocene hominid partial mandible from Tabarin, Baringo, Kenya. *American Journal of Physical Anthropology*, **72**, 21–37.

——, BROWN, B. & HILL, A. 1996. Forelimb of *Kenyapithecus africanus* from the Tugen Hills, Baringo District, Kenya. *American Journal of Physical Anthropology*, (Supplement 22), 240.

WHITE, T. D., SUWA, G. & ASFAW, B. 1994. *Australopithecus ramidus*, a new species of early hominid from Aramis, Ethiopia. *Nature*, **371**, 306–312.

——, —— & ——1995. *Australopithecus ramidus*, a new species of early hominid from Aramis, Ethiopia: corrigendum. *Nature*, **375**, 88.

WINKLER, A. J. 1992. Systematics and biogeography of middle Miocene rodents from the Muruyur Beds, Baringo District, Kenya. *Journal of Vertebrate Paleontology*, **12**, 236–249.

—— (in press). Neogene paleobiogeography and east African paleoenvironments: contributions from the Tugen Hills rodents and lagomorphs. *Journal of Human Evolution*.

WOLDEGABRIEL, G., WHITE, T. D., SUWA, G., RENNE, P., DE HEINZELIN, J., HART, W. K. & HEIKEN, G. 1994. Ecological and temporal placement of early Pliocene hominids at Aramis, Ethiopia. *Nature*, **371**, 330–333.

WOOD, B. 1992. Old bones match old stones. *Nature*, **355**, 678–679.

Palaeoecology of Suidae from the Tugen Hills, Baringo, Kenya

LAURA C. BISHOP,[1]* ANDREW HILL[2] & JOHN D. KINGSTON[3]

[1] *Department of Human Anatomy and Cell Biology, New Medical School, University of Liverpool, Ashton Street Building, Liverpool L69 3GE, UK*
[2] *Department of Anthropology, Yale University, POBox 208277, New Haven, CT 06520–8277, USA*
[3] *Department of Anthropology and Department of Geology and Geophysics, Yale University, PO Box 208277, New Haven, CT 06520–8277, USA*

Abstract: The Tugen Hills sequence preserves consistently fossiliferous sediments dating from the middle Miocene to the Pleistocene. The ecology and evolution of the Old World pigs (Mammalia, Suidae) from the later part of the sequence are examined here. Over 500 suid specimens derive from the Lukeino and Chemeron Formations and the Aterir formation, which span the period from 6.5 to 1.6 Ma ago. Specimens range in preservation from fragments of tooth and bone to complete crania, mandibles and, in one case, a partial skeleton. Ten species representing four genera have been identified. In most cases, taxonomic representations are similar to those at coeval sites in eastern Africa. However one genus, *Metridiochoerus*, is represented by only a few specimens of *M. andrewsi*. At other African Pliocene sites, up to four species of metridiochoere numerically dominate the suid fauna.

Palaeoecology of the Tugen Hills suid species was studied using ecomorphological analysis of the postcranial skeleton and analysis of stable carbon isotope ratios of tooth enamel apatite. Results suggest that throughout the sequence pigs preferred habitats having relatively closed vegetation despite an emphasis on mixed C_3/C_4 to exclusive C_4 diets. The ecology of the pigs suggests that forest and woodland habitats were present throughout the Pliocene and early Pleistocene of the Tugen Hills region. This result accords with previous interpetations which reconstruct the Baringo area as having diverse vegetation during the late Neogene.

The Tugen Hills sequence documents mammalian evolution in East Africa throughout an otherwise poorly known period. Spanning the middle Miocene to the late Pleistocene, geological deposits west of Lake Baringo have produced important hominid remains as well as mammalian fossils spanning a relatively long period (Hill 1985, 1999; Hill *et al.* 1985, 1986; Hill & Ward 1988; McBrearty *et al.* 1996). This continuous sequence provides the opportunity to investigate evolutionary and ecological change over a long time period, without the confounding effects of biogeography. Here we examine the palaeoecology of the region reconstructed through studies of Suidae, the Old World pigs.

Throughout the course of palaeontological investigation in Africa, pigs have been collected preferentially. Since there are numerous suid taxa which appear, evolve and disappear relatively quickly in the geological record, they are useful in biostratigraphy for relating sites of unknown age to an overall temporal framework (Cooke 1967, 1968, 1976, 1985; Cooke & Maglio 1972; Cooke & Wilkinson 1978; Harris & White 1979; Harris 1983*a*; Bishop 1994, 1997, in press; Turner *et al.* in press).

Further investigations have yielded other uses for these fossils (Bishop 1994, in press). Pigs can be useful palaeoecological indicators which are paticularly relevant to palaeoanthropologists because, like hominids, pigs are large-bodied omnivores (Hatley & Kappelman 1980). Direct analogy with the ecology of modern suids is suspect because it is unjustified to assume that the ecology of related suids is unchanged from the Pliocene to the present. Rather than using simple analogies drawn from the ethological literature of modern pigs and transposed directly to extinct pigs, here determinations of locomotor and dietary variables are made from the fossil evidence and applied to identified specimens wherever they occur throughout the

---

*Current address: School of Biological and Earth Sciences, Liverpool John Moores University, Byron Street, Liverpool L3 3AF, UK.

Bishop, L. C., Hill, A. & Kingston, J. D. 1999. Palaeoecology of Suidae from the Tugen Hills, Baringo, Kenya. *In*: Andrews, P. & Banham, P. (eds) *Late Cenozoic Environments and Hominid Evolution: a tribute to Bill Bishop.* Geological Society, London, 99–111.

sequence. Two methods are applied: stable carbon isotope ratio analysis of tooth enamel apatite, and ecomorphological analysis of postcrania. We investigate the diets and habitat preferences of extinct pigs in the Tugen Hills sequence over the period from 6.5 to 1.6 Ma ago and use these to reconstruct the environmental context of hominid evolution within a faunal and vegetational community.

Materials

Approximately 500 suid fossils have been recovered from the later part of the Tugen Hills sequence. They are housed at the National Museums of Kenya. Two subfamilies of pigs are known from the part of the sequence encompassing the late Miocene to the late Pliocene. The older and more primitive is the Tetraconodontinae, represented here (and throughout Africa) by two genera – *Nyanzachoerus* and *Notochoerus*. Tetraconodontinae are an archaic group which possess the defining characteristic of relatively enlarged third and fourth premolars (Pickford 1986). *Nyanzachoerus* is known from the Lukeino and Chemeron Formations, and *Notochoerus* is known from the Chemeron Formation. The last documented appearance of the subfamily was approximately at 1.8 Ma, and it has no modern relatives (Harris & White 1979; Bishop 1994; Bishop & Plummer in prep; White 1995).

The other subfamily present in the latter part of the sequence, the Suinae, is the group to which all modern pig species belong. In the Tugen Hills, it is first known from sites approximately 4–4.5 Ma in the Chemeron Formation. It is represented by two genera, *Kolpochoerus* and *Metridiochoerus*. The former genus is thought to have given rise to the bushpig, *Potamochoerus*, and the forest hog, *Hylochoerus*, and the latter to the warthog, *Phacochoerus* (Harris & White 1979). No extant suid genera have been recovered from the Chemeron Formation, although they are represented in the overlying Kapthurin Formation which dates from approximately 700 to <200 ka (McBrearty 1999; McBrearty *et al.* 1996).

Ten species, from four genera, have been identified in the late Neogene part of the sequence (Table 1). In addition to the species listed here, there are a few other specimens which are perhaps incorrectly assigned to Pliocene localities in the Tugen Hills. Some allegedly Chemeron specimens of *Kolpochoerus majus* have no site numbers but have KNM-BC specimen numbers. This taxon is first reliably known from various sites in Bed I Olduvai,

Table 1. *List of suid species*

Taxon	Geological unit
Nyanzachoerus syrticus	Lukeino, Chemeron?
Nyanzachoerus devauxi	Chemeron
Nyanzachoerus kanamensis	Chemeron
Nyanzachoerus jaegeri	Chemeron, Aterir, Lukeino?
Notochoerus euilus	Chemeron
Notochoerus scotti	Chemeron
Kolpochoerus afarensis	Chemeron, Aterir
Kolpochoerus limnetes	Chemeron
Kolpochoerus majus	Chemeron?
Metridiochoerus andrewsi	Chemeron

These species have been identified on the basis of specimens from the Lukeino Formation, the Aterir formation and the Chemeron Formation.

dating to approximately 1.8 Ma (Harris & White 1979; Bishop 1994 *contra* Harris *et al.* 1988). The *K. majus* specimens attributed to the Chemeron Formation bear the notation 'KAPTH RIVER '67'. This is not an EAGRU site designation and may suggest these specimens were collected by another, completely independent expedition in 1967. Their preservation suggests they may come from the Kapthurin Formation from which numerous specimens of *K. majus* are known (Harris & White 1979; McBrearty *et al.* 1996; McBrearty 1999). This stratigraphic assignment would be more in keeping with the known age range of that taxon elsewhere in Africa (Harris & White 1979; White 1995).

A total of 56 sites in the Lukeino Formation (*c.* 6.5–5.6 Ma), the Chemeron Formation (*c.* 5.6–1.6 Ma) and the Aterir formation (*c.* 4.5–4.0 Ma) have yielded fossil pigs which are identifiable to the species level (Table 2). These 56 sites will form the focus of this study because the species is the unit of analysis. Presence/absence of taxa at a site rather than their relative numbers are used since the latter may be biased through breakage and other taphonomic factors (Behrensmeyer 1975). The purpose of this analysis is to reveal what types of habitats characterized the regional ecosystems during the time of their deposition rather than their relative proportions.

A chronological framework provides a structure for examining changes in the relative taxonomic composition and ecological strategies through time. Creating a comprehensive geochronology in the Tugen Hills succession has proven difficult because of extreme local and regional faulting and the patchiness of the exposures (Martyn 1969; Chapman 1971; Bishop *et al.* 1971; King & Chapman 1972; Pickford

Table 2. *Later Tugen Hills sites preserving suid remains*

Lukeino Formation
  BPRP# 26, BPRP# 28 (= 2/213), BPRP# 29
  (= 2/219), BPRP# 57, BPRP# 76 (= 2/225),
  BPRP# 83, BPRP# 111, BPRP# 113?, BPRP# 158,
  BPRP# 162, 1/999, 2/269, BPRP# 62 (= YK 1)

Aterir Formation
  5/1, 5/7, 5/8

Chemeron Formation
  BPRP# 1 (= JM511), BPRP# 2 (= JM85), BPRP# 8
  BPRP# 9 (= JM493), BPRP# 12 (= JM489),
  BPRP# 13 (= JM489), BPRP# 15, BPRP# 16,
  BPRP# 19, BPRP# 21, BPRP# 35 (= 2/221),
  BPRP# 75 (= 2/232), BPRP# 77, BPRP# 79,
  BPRP# 80, BPRP# 93, BPRP# 96, BPRP# 99,
  BPRP# 100, BPRP# 101, BPRP# 102, BPRP# 104,
  BPRP# 105, BPRP# 115, BPRP# 117, BPRP# 125,
  BPRP# 132, BPRP# 135, BPRP# 145, BPRP# 149,
  BPRP# 150, BPRP# 152, BPRP# 160, 2/201, 2/206,
  2/217, 2/265, 2/267, 2/271, JM509

Sites are arranged by geological unit. BPRP numbers designate Baringo Palaeontological Research Project sites. Numbers which follow in parentheses are synonymous designations used by previous projects and researchers. A question mark designates a site that at present is of unclear stratigraphic position.

1975, 1978a, b; Hill et al. 1986; Hill 1994, 1995, 1999). Many sites are dated by palaeomagnetic studies as well as geochemical analysis and radiometric dating of interbedded volcanic flows and associated volcaniclastic units (Chapman & Brook 1978; Dagley et al. 1978; Tauxe et al. 1985; Deino et al. 1990), and others have been dated relatively by a combination of biostratigraphy and stratigraphic interpolation between known dated horizons (Table 3). It can be seen that the sites are well distributed throughout the time interval represented and that there are no significant breaks in the sequence (Fig. 1).

Methods

Stable carbon isotope ratios and diet

Historically in palaeoecological studies, diet of extinct species has been extrapolated either on the basis of gross tooth morphology or with reference to diets of related modern animals. The latter approach is difficult to apply when there are no modern species which are closely related to the extinct taxon and the former relies on the relationships, such as crown height and cusp morphology, which exist between dietary preference and tooth morphology in the modern world. While useful, these methods do not

directly investigate the diets of fossils species and rely heavily on analogy at a fairly gross level. More recently, two additional methods have been used to investigate diet directly: dental microwear and chemical studies. Studies of dental microwear investigate the microscopic marks made on dental enamel by an animal's food (e.g. Walker 1981; Walker et al. 1978). Chemical studies seek to recreate various aspects of the chemical composition of diet by looking at how the elements studied have been incorporated into the tissues during life. Analysis of stable carbon isotopes in mammalian tissue is one method which has been repeatedly used to reconstruct diet and palaeoecology (DeNiro & Epstein 1978; Ericson et al. 1981; Van de Merwe 1982; Tieszen et al., 1983; Ambrose & DeNiro 1986; Lee-Thorp et al. 1989). These new approaches complement the more traditional methods, but rely on observations about tooth damage and tissue biochemistry which are more closely related to first principles and have the potential to reveal differences between the way that modern and extinct animals lived.

For the suids from the Tugen Hills, this analysis reconstructs diet using stable carbon isotope ratios of fossil dental enamel so that omnivore foraging strategies can be examined through time. Examination of changes in diet also gives information about the vegetation available in the Tugen Hills region during the time under investigation. A temporal history of vegetation in the region has been reconstructed through a study of the stable carbon isotopes in palaeosol carbonates (Kingston et al. 1994) and tooth enamel of a number of herbivorous mammalian taxa (Morgan et al 1994; Kingston 1999). The present study investigates changes in the foraging strategies of one taxon in the context of the vegetational history of the region.

Terrestrial plants assimilate carbon from the atmospheric CO_2 reservoir by one of three photosynthetic pathways. Two pathways relevant to this discussion are referred to as C_3 (Calvin–Benson) and C_4 (Hatch-Slack or Kranz) which can be clearly differentiated on the basis of the ratios of isotopes of carbon in plant tissue. While C_3 plants include almost all trees, shrubs and high latitude or high altitude grasses preferring wet, cool growing seasons, the C_4 pathway is linked almost exclusively with grasses and sedges growing in hot, arid habitats. The association between C_4 metabolism, carbon isotope ratios and tropical grasses provides a means of identifying open woodland to grassland, tropical or subtropical, ecosystems in the past.

Studies of modern herbivores have shown that the isotopic composition of carbon incorporated

Table 3. *Tugen Hills sites in this study*

Site	Alias	Formation	Age	Method	n	Ny syrticus	Ny devauxi	Ny kanamensis	Ny jaegeri	No euilus	No scotti	Ko afarensis	Ko limnetes	Ko majus	Me andrewsi
BPRP# 93	KapthR	?Chemeron	1	B	1									0	
BPRP# 160		Chemeron	2.2	B	1								0		
BPRP# 2	JM 85	Chemeron	2.4	B	1								0		
BPRP# 105		Chemeron	2.5	R	2								0		
BPRP# 99		Chemeron	2.5	B	3								0		
BPRP# 100		Chemeron	2.8	B	1					0			0		
BPRP# 104		Chemeron	2.8	B	4			0		0					
BPRP# 132		Chemeron	2.8	B	5			0							
BPRP# 135		Chemeron	2.8	B	1			0		0					
BPRP# 145		Chemeron	2.8	B	2					0					
BPRP# 150		Chemeron	2.8	B	6					0					
BPRP# 152		Chemeron	3	B	4										0
BPRP# 19		Chemeron	3.2	B	3										
BPRP# 115		Chemeron	3.2	B	2					0					
BPRP# 149		Chemeron	3.2	B	4					0					
BPRP# 8		Chemeron	3.4	B	3			0							
BPRP# 9	JM 493	Chemeron	3.4	R	15	0			0	0					
BPRP# 101		Chemeron	3.5	B	1					0					
BPRP# 102		Chemeron	3.5	B	7			0		0					
BPRP# 18		Chemeron	3.6	R	5					0	0				
BPRP# 117		Chemeron	3.8	B	1			0							
	2 / 271	Chemeron	3.8	B	5			0							
	JM 509	Chemeron	3.8	B	3			0							
BPRP# 1	JM 511	Chemeron	4	B	59			0	0						
BPRP# 12	JM 489	Chemeron	4	B	31			0	0	0			0		
BPRP# 21		Chemeron	4	B	6			0				0			
BPRP# 75	2 / 232	Chemeron	4	R	72			0	0						
BPRP# 96		Chemeron	4	B	10			0	0	0		0			
BPRP# 113		?Lukeino?	4	B	5				0			0			
BPRP# 125		Chemeron	4	B	7			0	0	0		0	0		
	5 / 1	Atenir	4	B	2				0						
	5 / 7	Atenir	4	B	1				0						
	5 / 8	Atenir	4	B	1				0						
BPRP# 13	JM 489	Chemeron	4.2	B	5			0	0						
BPRP# 35	2 / 221	Chemeron	4.2	B	17			0	0						
BPRP# 80		Chemeron	4.2	B	7			0	0						
	2 / 201	Chemeron	4.3	B	5				0						
	2 / 206	Chemeron	4.3	B	1			0	0						
	2 / 267	Chemeron	4.3	B	6			0	0						
BPRP# 15		Chemeron	4.5	B	2			0							
BPRP# 16		Chemeron	4.5	B	8			0							
BPRP# 77		Chemeron	4.5	R	25			0							
BPRP# 79		Chemeron	4.5	B	16		0		0						
	2 / 217	Chemeron	4.5	B	22				0						
	2 / 265	Chemeron	5	B	1		0								
	1 / 999	Lukeino	6.1	F	3	0									
BPRP# 28	2 / 213	Lukeino	6.1	F	6	0									
BPRP# 29	2 / 219	Lukeino	6.1	F	12	0									
	2 / 269	Lukeino	6.1	F	1	0									
BPRP# 26		Lukeino	6.1	F	2	0									
BPRP# 57		Lukeino	6.1	F	1	0									
BPRP# 76	2 / 225	Lukeino	6.1	F	38	0									
BPRP# 83		Lukeino	6.1	F	1	0			0						
BPRP# 111		Lukeino	6.1	F	4	0									
BPRP# 158		Lukeino	6.1	F	1	0									

Sites are presented in chronological order. Key: Site, BPRP site number; Alias, other designation; Age, approximate date of site; Method, method used to derive the date of the site: R = radiometric, B = biostratigraphic, F = Formational mean age (for Lukeino

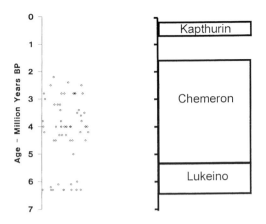

Fig. 1. Temporal distribution of Tugen Hills suid sites discussed in the text. The time scale on the y-axis represents the time interval (in millions of years before present) covered by the sediments yielding the fossils examined in this study. Each dot represents one site, placed at a position representing its geological age, determined either by radiometric dating, biostratigraphy or stratigraphic interpositioning. (see Table 3). Note that the representation of sites is relatively complete through time.

into the inorganic portion of enamel apatite is directly related to that of the diet. This biogenic signal is preserved in the fossil record and can be used to estimate relative proportions of C_3 and C_4 plants in the diet. Differences in the carbon isotopic composition of substances are expressed as $\delta^{13}C$ values which give the per mil (‰) deviation of the $^{13}C/^{12}C$ ratio of a sample relative to that of the conventional Pee Dee Belemnite carbonate standard (PDB) which has a $^{13}C/^{12}C$ value of 88.99‰. Positive values of $\delta^{13}C$ indicate an enrichment of heavy carbon (^{13}C) in the sample relative to the standard while negative readings stand for its depletion. The $\delta^{13}C$ ratio is defined by the following equation:

$$\delta^{13}C(‰) = [(^{13}C/^{12}C)sample/(^{13}C/^{12}C)std - 1]$$
$$\times 1000$$

In analyses of the stable carbon isotopic composition of suid enamel, the procedures used follow those described in detail elsewhere (Lee-Thorp et al. 1989; Kingston 1992) with a few modifications. Enamel was carefully cleaned of adhering matrix, dentine and weathering rinds with a high-speed dremel drilling tool and then pulverized in an agate mortar. A sample of 50–130 mg of powdered enamel was reacted for 24 h with 2% NaOHCl in 50 ml plastic centrifuge tubes to remove any organics and then rinsed to a pH of 7 by centrifugation with double distilled water.

Residue was treated with 0.1 M CH_3COOH for 16 h under a weak vacuum to remove surficial contaminants, rinsed to neutrality by centrifugation with double distilled water and freeze dried. Some 30–100 mg of the dried samples was reacted with 100% phosphoric acid (H_3PO_4) at 90°C in individual reaction vessels for 2 h. The liberated carbon dioxide was allowed to equilibrate with $AgPO_4$ at 25°C to remove any SO_2 or H_2S generated during the reaction. The CO_2 was further purified and isolated cryogenically into 6 mm ampoules and then analysed on a MAT-Finnegan 251 mass spectrometer in the Kline Geological Isotope facility at Yale University. Precision was 0.09‰ for $\delta^{13}C$ ratios of two replicate pairs of fossil enamel. A laboratory standard analysed with the enamel samples yielded a standard deviation of 0.07‰ ($n = 5$). Based on these data, overall analytical precision was better than 0.2‰.

Analysis of stable carbon isotope ratios has been performed on tooth enamel apatite from 14 individuals representing seven species. Specimens were taken from the Tugen Hills sequence and from the Koobi Fora Formation, east of Lake Turkana, Kenya. Results for all specimens included in this analysis are presented in Table 4 and for the specimens from the Tugen Hills sequence in Fig. 2. In order to evaluate the distribution of various dietary regimes throughout the duration of the later part of the Tugen Hills sequence, $\delta^{13}C$ results were averaged for each species and this species mean has been used to represent a dietary data point for each occurrence of the taxon at a site (Fig. 3).

Ecomorphology and habitat preference

Ecomorphology is a term used to describe the relationship between morphology and ecology. The ecomorphological analysis performed here relies on the observation that modern animal species are habitat specific, and their postcranial morphology is adapted to locomotion in their preferred habitat. This relationship has been used to reconstruct locomotor behaviour in antelopes and carnivores, as well as in pigs (Van Valkenburgh 1987; Kappelman 1988, 1991; Bishop 1994, in press; Plummer & Bishop 1994; Kappelman et al 1997; Bishop & Plummer in prep.). For the purposes of this study, habitat preferences were divided into three categories – open, intermediate and closed – which attempts to partition environments on the basis of the degree of tree cover. These categories are suggested as rough equivalents to grassland, bushland and forest respectively (Pratt et al. 1966).

Table 4. *Stable carbon isotope ratios of Suidae*

Accession number	Taxon	Description	Provenance	Age (Ma)	δ^{13}C
Tugen Hills					
KNM-BC 55	Suidae	M_3 fragment	BPRP#9 1/493	3.40	−10.61
KNM-BC 428	*Nyanzachoerus* cf *syrticus*	R M^3 fragment	BPRP#9 1/493	3.40	−6.18
KNM-BC 797	Suidae	No information			1.10
KNM-BC 992	*Notochoerus* cf *scotti*	R M^3 fragment	BPRP# 18 1/494	3.60	−0.59
KNM-BC 1310	*Nyanzachoerus*	M3 fragment	BPRP# 31 2/210	4.50	−2.71
KNM-BC 2029	*Nyanzachoerus jaegeri*	R M_3 fragment	BPRP# 31 2/210	4.50	−3.03
KNM-LU 180	*Nyanzachoerus syrticus*	Lower dentition	BPRP# 26 2/212	6.10	−7.91
KNM-LU 739	*Nyanzachoerus* cf *syrticus*	R M_3 fragment	2/269	6.10	−3.51
Koobi Fora					
KNM-ER 2795	*Nyanzachoerus kanamensis*	M^3 fragment	Area 117	3.36	−5.08
KNM-ER 3405	*Notochoerus scotti*	M3 fragment	Area 115	2.00	−0.91
KNM-ER 3696	*Metridiochoerus andrewsi*	M^3 fragment	Area 103/2	1.80	−1.19
KNM-ER 4152	*Kolpochoerus limnetes*	M_3 fragment	Area 131	1.80	−0.08
KNM-ER 4167e	*Metridiochoerus hopwoodi*	L M_3 fragment	Area 3	1.55	−0.32
KNM-ER 4182	*Metridiochoerus andrewsi*	R M_3 fragment	Area 100	2.00	−2.42

Results of stable carbon isotope analysis of suid teeth from the Pliocene and Pleistocene Koobi Fora Formation, and from the Lukeino and Chemeron Formations of the Tugen Hills.

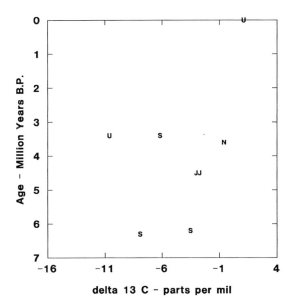

Fig. 2. Temporal distribution of carbon isotopic results for Tugen Hills Suidae discussed in the text. The time scale on the y-axis represents time in millions of years before present. Each symbol is placed at the $\delta^{13}C$ value (in parts per mil, ‰) for that specimen. Letters represent the taxon from which the enamel sample derives: S = *Nyanzachoerus syrticus*, J = *Nyanzachoerus jaegeri*, N = *Notochoerus scotti*, U = taxon/provenance unknown. Note that one specimen of *Nyanzachoerus syrticus* is attributed to a site dated outside the known range of the taxon. It is possible that the site attribution, the taxonomic identification or both are in error. However, since the $\delta^{13}C$ value was intermediate between the values obtained for the other two specimens of this taxon, the value for this specimen was included in the mean value for *Nyanzachoerus syrticus* used in further analysis.

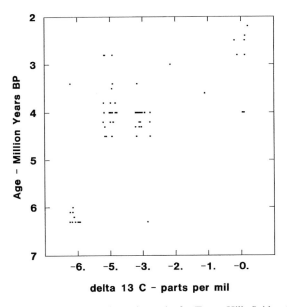

Fig. 3. Temporal distribution of taxon mean isotopic results for Tugen Hills Suidae discussed in the text. The time scale on the y-axis represents time in millions of years before present. Each dot is placed at the temporal occurrence of each specimen identified to taxon and represents the mean $\delta^{13}C$ value for the taxon as determined by this study (See Table 4).

The postcranial characteristics related to habitat preference are concentrated in the articular surfaces of the long bones. These are usually related to greater joint mobility required to allow the limb excursion necessary to move in complex substrates, such as forest, or the limitation of movement in each joint to the parasagittal plane found in animals running over more uniform substrates, such as open grasslands. Analysis is a multistage process which is documented elsewhere (Bishop 1994; Plummer & Bishop 1994). To summarize, characters which are related to habitat preference in modern animals are first determined, then quantified through measurements. These measurements are converted to dimensionless ratios which characterize certain features in joint shape. The ratios are regressed against body size, and any which correlate highly are eliminated from the analysis so as not to bias results on the basis of any modern relationship between body size and habitat preference. The remaining ratios are statistically analysed using discriminant function analysis (DFA) which characterizes specimens into previously determined, naturally occurring groups (Morrison 1976).

Identical measurements are taken on fossils, and these in turn are separated out into habitat preference groups using the DFA 'trained' by the modern specimens. The DFA analysis thus determines the affinity of each fossil limb element to

Table 5. *Habitat preferences of African Suidae*

Taxon	Habitat preference
Nyanzachoerus devauxi	Intermediate habitats
Nyanzachoerus kanamensis	Intermediate habitats
Notochoerus euilus	Closed habitats
Kolpochoerus limnetes	Closed > intermediate habitats
Kolpochoerus majus	Closed habitats
Metridiochoerus modestus	Closed habitats

These habitat preferences were determined on the basis of ecomorphological analyses of postcrania from partial skeletons attributed to taxa on the basis of associated dentition as described in the text. For more detailed methods, specimen numbers and identifications see Bishop (1994).

the morphotypes which have been delineated using the modern animals of known habitat preference. The analysis was done separately for each skeletal element. Since fossil bones are often incomplete or damaged, we sought to maximize the bones available for comparison by creating separate DFA algorithms to deal with limb bone fragments.

The usefulness of the DFA can be assessed by examining percentage correct classification for the specimens of known habitat type. A reclassification exercise showed that the DFA algorithms were between 83 and 100% correct for

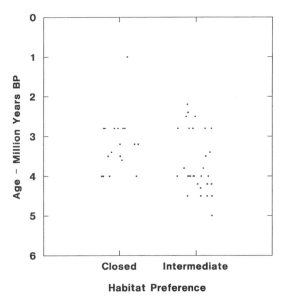

Fig. 4. Temporal distribution of habitat preference results for Tugen Hills Suidae discussed in the text. The time scale on the y-axis represents time in millions of years before present. Each dot is placed at the temporal occurrence of each specimen identified to taxon and represents the habitat preference determined for that taxon on the basis of partial skeletons (See Table 5).

complete bones and between 59 and 94% correct for partial bones (Bishop 1994). These discriminant functions were then applied to fossil postcrania in the collections of the National Museum of Kenya. Partial skeletons from several localities which are attributed to species allow us to characterize the habitat preferences of several taxa on the basis of the morphological affinities of limb elements (Table 5). Only one of these partial skeletons, KNM-TH 18934, a primitive example of *Kolpochoerus limnetes*, was recovered from the Tugen Hills sequence. The remainder derive from other localities, but examples of the same taxa are also known from the Tugen Hills. Habitat preferences are indicated on a temporal sequence each time the taxon occurs at a site in order to represent the distribution of particular habitat preferences through time (Fig. 4).

Results and discussion

Species distribution

The distribution of suid taxa throughout the Tugen Hills sequence is remarkably complete (Fig. 5). No large temporal gaps are present. Distribution of tetraconodont taxa is consistent with their known temporal ranges (Harris & White 1979; Hill *et al* 1992; Bishop 1994, in

press; White 1995). There are a few specimens of *Nyanzachoerus syrticus* and *Nyanzachoerus devauxi* which may occur outside the temporal ranges previously documented for those species (Hill *et al.* 1992). This might be due to more accurate dating for the Tugen Hills sites than has been possible at other localities where these taxa occur (Cooke & Ewer 1972; Cooke 1987).

The species distribution presents an interesting point. Although numerous sites in the Tugen Hills succession postdate the first appearance of the *Metridiochoerus* clade at approximately 4 Ma, the genus is very rare in the succession. There are four known specimens of *Metridiochoerus andrewsi* from one site in the Chemeron Formation (BPRP# 152). The other genus of Suinae, *Kolpochoerus*, known at other African sites later than 4 Ma, is more common at the later sites in the Chemeron Formation. This is a reversal of the situation in most other known late Pliocene localities, except Lower Bed I at Olduvai where *Kolpochoerus limnetes* is the most common suid at the early archaeological sites (Harris 1983*b*; Potts 1988; Bishop 1994; Bishop & Plummer in prep.). The rarity of *Metridiochoerus* in the Tugen Hills remains unexplained at present. It is possibly a result of undersampling of sediments younger than approximately 2.8 Ma at the top of the Chemeron Formation. However, the possibility exists that

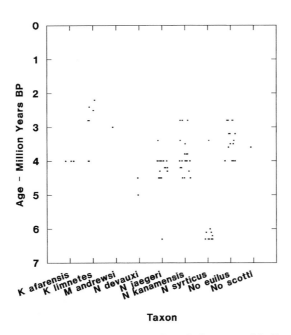

Fig. 5. Temporal distribution of identified suid remains from the later part of the Tugen Hills sequence. Each dot represents a fossil identified to the species level.

environments during Chemeron times were in some way unsuitable for the ecological requirements of the genus.

Little is known directly about the palaeoecology of the genus *Metridiochoerus*, although it is extremely widespread at all other late Pliocene and Pleistocene palaeontological sites. Assigned postcrania are rare, but ecomorphological results from a partial skeleton of *Metridiochoerus modestus* from Koobi Fora suggest a closed habitat preference for that species. The isotopic results presented here for *Metridiochoerus andrewsi* and *Metridiochoerus hopwoodi* (Table 4), suggest that at least these two species of the genus had a diet consisting almost exclusively of C_4 grasses. This supports the evidence of their hypsodont dental structure which implies that *Metridiochoerus* had a diet rich in grasses. Absence of taxa at individual Tugen Hills sites cannot, at present, be attributed to palaeoecological rather than taphonomic causes since sample sizes are small.

Stable carbon isotopes and diet

In this discussion, $\delta^{13}C$ values more positive than $-8‰$ are interpreted to suggest a component of C_4 plants in the diet. There appears to be a shift through time in dietary preferences of Suidae represented at the Baringo sites towards diets which depended more on C_4 grasses (Fig. 3). Although this is an overall trend, species with isotopic signatures indicating a more mixed diet persist through the time period examined here. None of the suid samples identified to species has isotopic values suggesting diet solely consisting of C_3 plants. One specimen of suid enamel not identified to species, KNM-BC 55 from site BPRP# 9 (EAGRU 1/493), has a $\delta^{13}C$ value of $-10.61‰$, which suggests a browse dependent diet. This site, dated to approximately 3.4 Ma, yields two specimens which have amongst the lowest $\delta^{13}C$ values in the study.

These findings are based on work in progress and potential for error comes primarily from the fact that not all the species present in the Tugen Hills sequence have been analysed at present. Isotopic analysis of only six of the 11 species reported from the sequence has been possible so far. The five species which remain unstudied at present are *Nyanzachoerus devauxi*, *Notochoerus euilus*, *Kolpochoerus afarensis*, *Kolpochoerus majus* and *Metridiochoerus compactus*. As discussed previously, the latter two species are of uncertain provenance within the sequence and probably postdate the Pliocene. *N. euilus* and *K. afarensis* are common at sites in the

Chemeron Formation. Although results are incomplete, this does not affect the conclusion that diets featuring a mix of C_3 plants and C_4 grasses were present throughout the sequence. This confirms results from studies of palaeosol carbon isotopes which, despite the fact that forest ecosystems are usually underrepresented in palaeosols, suggest that a mix of habitats was present throughout the sequence (Kingston *et al* 1994; Kingston 1999).

Results might also be altered by the use of specimens from outside the Tugen Hills in this study. For example, the single specimen of *Kolpochoerus limnetes* included in the isotopic analysis is from Area 131 at Koobi Fora and is approximately 1.8 Ma. Analysis revealed a $\delta^{13}C$ value of $-0.08‰$ for this specimen, suggesting an exclusively C_4 diet. Later specimens of *K. limnetes* tend to have far more hypsodont and elaborated third molars than do earlier examples (Harris & White 1979). Evidence from studies of postcrania suggests that this was coupled with a change in habitat preference, from closed to more intermediate or mixed vegetational environments (Bishop 1994, in press). Perhaps, then, using a specimen from sediments more recent than the Tugen Hills sample of *K. limnetes* is unjustified and misleading in this case. The earliest *K. limnetes* in the Chemeron Formation derives from sediments dated approximately 4 Ma – 2.2 Ma earlier than the proxy individual. It is possible that earlier examples of the species may have isotopic signatures suggesting a diet relying more heavily on browse. We intend to study this possibility more fully in our continuing investigations of suid palaeoecology.

Locomotor ecomorphology and habitat preference

Taxon-based investigations of habitat preference suffer from the fact that not all species are well represented by postcranial remains associated with identifiable dentitions. Even when taxa are represented by partial skeletons, there are usually only one or two individuals available. This decreases the extent to which we can know about variability in habitat preference, both intraspecifically and through geological time. Suid skeletons analysed so far fall into either intermediate or closed habitat categories (Table 5). However, partial skeletons are known for only five of the 10 species identified from the later part of the Tugen Hills sequence. From present evidence based on postcranial adaptations, it appears that intermediate and closed habitats were represented throughout the later part of the Tugen Hills sequence, at least during the Pliocene and early Pleistocene. Isolated postcrania suggest the presence of some open habitat animals ($n = 2$) (Bishop 1994).

As is the case for the dietary evidence discussed above, these results, while incomplete, contribute some details to our interpretation of the palaeoecological history of the sequence which would remain unaltered even by the addition of further evidence. The presence of intermediate and closed habitat suids throughout the sequence is well documented here. Although it is more than likely that some of the six taxa for which there is no postcranial evidence would have preferred more open habitats, the fact remains that animals preferring intermediate and closed habitats, and therefore intermediate and closed habitats themselves, would have been present throughout the latter part of the Tugen Hills sequence.

Results produced by ecomorphic analysis of postcrania contrast with previous reconstructions of habitat preferences linked to dental adaptations and level of hypsodonty (Harris 1987). The postcrania of two hypsodont taxa (*Notochoerus euilus* and *Metridiochoerus modestus*) have morphological characters associated with closed habitat preference. As mentioned previously, different postcranial adaptations for early and late specimens of *Kolpochoerus limnetes* suggest gradual change in habitat preference from closed toward more mixed-country habitats (Bishop 1994, in press). It appears that hypsodont dentition and grass-dominated diets in Pliocene suid species cannot be linked with a preference for open habitats.

Conclusions

Suids are well distributed throughout the later part of the Tugen Hills sequence and are present at numerous sites where other terrestrial vertebrate fossils have been recovered. Although the temporal representation of sites through time is quite complete, some taxa are uncommon. One of these is *Metridiochoerus*, which is rare at Chemeron Formation sites. This may be due to the local occurrence of palaeoenvironmental circumstances unfavourable to *Metridiochoerus*, which is common at the majority of African sites after the middle Pliocene. It may also be due to incomplete sampling of some Pliocene and Pleistocene horizons in the sequence. Tetracodonodont pigs and *Kolpochoerus* are well represented in the later part of the Tugen Hills sequence when they are known from elsewhere in Africa.

Later Tugen Hills pigs have diets varying from mixed C_3/C_4 to entirely dependent on C_4 grasses. There is some evidence of a shift towards more grassy diets through time, although there is no evidence for an abrupt or unidirectional shift. Evidence from the postcrania of extinct suids suggests that pigs preferring intermediate and closed habitat occurred throughout the later part of the Tugen Hills sequence. The presence of pigs preferring open habitats cannot be ruled out, but there is little evidence for this at present. In the succession, indications of closed and intermediate habitat preferences occur with diets of C_4 grasses and mixed C_3/C_4 plants. This indicates that some intermediate and closed habitat animals ate diets rich in tropical grasses. We suggest that, in order to support this unique combination of adaptations, C_4 grasses constituted a significant component in the substratum of intermediate habitats and might also have occurred in the disturbed portions of closed habitats.

Results of this study represent a first attempt to combine palaeoecological reconstructions of extinct animals from multiple lines of evidence in order to acheive a higher level of resolution in our examination of palaeobiology. In this case, we have examined evidence of adaptations for two aspects of the animals' ecology: diet and habitat preference. While ecomorphological data indicate that later Tugen Hills Suidae preferred relatively closed habitats, the stable carbon isotope ratios suggest that feeding ranged between mixed C_3/C_4 diets and exclusively C_4 grass diets. These data sets are not incongruous and when combined actually give more information about later Tugen Hills palaeohabitats. The presence of C_4 grasses, documented by both dietary and palaeosol carbon isotope studies (Kingston *et al.* 1994; Kingston 1999) suggests either seasonality, some aridity, low moisture, or a combination of these conditions. This has implications for the nature of the woodlands and forests in the region.

We thank the government of the Republic of Kenya for permission to undertake this research. This work is part of the Baringo Palaeontological Research Project based at Yale University. The staff of the National Museums of Kenya have provided excellent curatorial support. We thank them, particularly M. Muungu, A. Ibui, E. Mbua and M. Leakey. The National Museums of Kenya and M. Leakey gave permission for the export and analysis of enamel specimens. Numerous other museums have also provided access to their collections. We thank D. Rye for analytical assistance and access to the isotope facilities in the Kline Geological Laboratory at Yale University.

Funding for this research has been provided by the National Science Foundation, the Wenner Gren Foundation for Anthropological Research, The Boise Fund, Sigma Xi and, most relevant in this forum, the Bill Bishop Memorial Trust. LCB also thanks The Leverhulme Trust for their support.

References

AMBROSE, S. A. & DENIRO, M. J. 1986. Reconstruction of African human diet using bone collagen carbon and nitrogen isotope ratios. *Nature*, **319**, 321–324.

BEHRENSMEYER, A. K. 1975. The taphonomy and palaeoecology of Plio-Pleistocene vertebrate assemblages east of Lake Rudolf, Kenya. *Bulletin of the Museum of Comparative Zoology*, **146**, 473–578.

BISHOP, L. C. 1994. *Pigs and the ancestors: hominids, suids and environments during the Plio-Pleistocene of East Africa*. PhD Dissertation, Yale University.

——1997. Suidae from the Manonga Valley, Tanzania. *In*: HARRISON, T. (ed.) *Neogene Palaeontology and Geology of the Manonga Valley*. Plenum, New York 191–217.

—— (in press). Suid palaeoecology and habitat preference at African Pliocene and Pleistocene hominid localities. *In*: BROMAGE, T. G. & SCHRENCK, F. (eds) *African Biogeography, Climate Change and Early Hominid Evolution*. Oxford University.

—— & PLUMMER, T. (in preparation). Listening to the animals: what artiodactyl habitat preferences can tell us about hominid behaviour. *Journal of Human Evolution*.

BISHOP, W. W., CHAPMAN, G. R., HILL, A. & MILLER, J. A. 1971. Succession of Cainozoic vertebrate assemblages from the northern Kenya Rift Valley. *Nature*, **233**, 389–394.

CHAPMAN, G. R. 1971. *The geological evolution of the northern Kamasia Hills, Baringo District, Kenya*. PhD thesis, University of London.

—— & BROOK, M. 1978. Chronostratigraphy of the Baringo Basin, Kenya. *In*: BISHOP, W. W. (ed.) *Geological Background to Fossil Man*. Scottish Academic, London, 207–223.

COOKE, H. B. S. 1967. The Pleistocene sequence in South Africa and problems of correlation. *In*: BISHOP, W. W. & CLARK, J. D. (eds) *Background to Evolution in Africa*. University of Chicago, 175–184.

——1968. Evolution of mammals on southern continents: II. The fossil mammal fauna of Africa. *Quarterly Review of Biology*, **43**, 234–264.

——1976. Suidae from the Plio-Pleistocene strata of the Rudolf Basin. *In*: COPPENS, Y., HOWELL, F. C., ISAAC, G. LL. & LEAKEY, R. E. F. (eds) *Early Man and Environments in the Lake Rudolph Basin*. University of Chicago, 251–263.

——1985. Plio-Pleistocene Suidae in relation to African hominid deposits. *L'Environnement des Hominidés au Plio-Pleistocène*, International colloquium (June 1981). Fondation Singer-Polignac, Paris, 101–117.

——1987. Fossil Suidae from Sahabi, Libya. *In*: BOAZ, N. T., EL-ARNAUTI, A., GAZIRY, A. W., DE HEINZELIN, J. & BOAZ, D. D. (eds) *Neogene Palaeontology and Geology of Sahabi*. Liss, New York, 255–266.

—— & EWER, R. F. 1972. Fossil Suidae from Kanapoi and Lothagam, Northwestern Kenya. *Bulletin of the Museum of Comparative Zoology*, **143**, 149–296.

—— & MAGLIO, V. J. 1972. Plio-Pleistocene stratigraphy in East Africa in relation to proboscidean and suid evolution. *In*: BISHOP, W. W. & MILLER, J. A. (eds) *Calibration of Hominoid Evolution*. Scottish Academic, Edinburgh, 303–329.

—— & WILKINSON, A. F. 1978. Suidae and Tayassuidae. *In*: MAGLIO, V. J. & COOKE, H. B. S. (eds) *Evolution of African Mammals*. Harvard University, Cambridge, 435–482.

DAGLEY, P., MUSSETT, A. E. & PALMER, H. C. 1978. Preliminary observations on the palaeomagnetic stratigraphy of the area west of Lake Baringo, Kenya. *In*: BISHOP, W. W. (ed.) *Geological Background to Fossil Man*. Scottish Academic, Geological Society, London, 225–235.

DEINO, A., TAUXE, L., MONOGHAN, M. & DRAKE, R. 1990. ^{40}Ar/^{39}Ar age calibration of the litho- and palaeomagnetic stratigraphies of the Ngorora Formation, Kenya. *Journal of Geology*, **98**, 567–587.

DENIRO, M. J. & EPSTEIN, S. 1978. Influence of diet on the distribution of carbon isotopes in animals. *Geochimica Cosmochimica Acta*, **42**, 341–351.

ERICSON, J. E., SULIVAN, C. H. & BOAZ, N. T. 1981. Diets of Pliocene mammals from Omo, Ethiopia, deduced from carbon isotope ratios in tooth apatite. *Palaeogeography Palaeoclimatology Palaeoecology*, **36**, 69–73.

HARRIS, J. M. 1983*a*. Correlation of the Koobi Fora succession. *In*: HARRIS, J. M. (ed.) *Koobi Fora Research Project. Volume II*. Clarendon, Oxford, 303–317.

——1983*b*. Family Suidae. *In*: HARRIS, J. M. (ed.) *Koobi Fora Research Project. Volume II*. Clarendon, Oxford, 215–302.

——1987. Fossil Suidae from Laetoli. *In*: LEAKEY, M. D. & HARRIS, J. M. (eds) *Laetoli – A Pliocene Site in Northern Tanzania*. Clarendon, Oxford, 349–358.

—— & WHITE, T. D. 1979. Evolution of the Plio-Pleistocene African Suidae. *Transactions of the American Philosophical Society*, **69**(2), 1–128.

——, BROWN, F. H. & LEAKEY, M. G. 1988. *Stratigraphy and palaeontology of Pliocene and Pleistocene localities west of Lake Turkana, Kenya*. Natural History Museum of Los Angeles County, Contributions in Science, **399**.

HATLEY, T. & KAPPELMAN, J. 1980. Bears, pigs, and Plio-Pleistocene hominids: a case for the exploitation of belowground food resources. *Human Ecology*, **8**, 371–387.

HILL, A. 1985. Early hominid from Baringo, Kenya. *Nature*, **315**, 222–224.

——1994. Late Miocene and Early Pliocene hominoids from Africa. *In*: CORRUCCINI, R. S. & CIOCHON, R. L. (eds) *Integrative Paths to the Past*. Prentice Hall, Englewood Cliffs, 123–145.

——1995. Faunal and environmental change in the Neogene of East Africa: Evidence from the Tugen Hills Sequence, Baringo District, Kenya. *In*: VRBA, E. S., DENTON, G. H., PARTRIDGE, T. C. & BURCKLE, L. H. (eds) *Palaeoclimate and Evolution, with Emphasis on Human Origins*. Yale University, New Haven, 178–193.

——1999. The Baringo Basin, Kenya: from Bill Bishop to BPRP. *This volume*.

—— & WARD, S. 1988. Origin of the Hominidae: the record of African large hominoid evolution between 14 My and 4 My. *Yearbook of Physical Anthropology*, **31**, 49–83.

——, CURTIS, G. & DRAKE, R. 1986. Sedimentary stratigraphy of the Tugen Hills, Baringo, Kenya. *In*: FROSTICK, L. E., RENAUT, R. W., REID, I. & TIERCELIN, J.-J. (eds) *Sedimentation in the African Rifts*. Geological Society, London, Special Publications, **25**, 285–295.

——, WARD, S. & BROWN, B. 1992. Anatomy and age of the Lothagam mandible. *Journal of Human Evolution*, **22**, 439–451.

KAPPELMAN, J. 1988. Morphology and locomotor adaptations of the bovid femur in relation to habitat. *Journal of Morphology*, **198**, 119–130.

——1991. The paleoenvironment of *Kenyapithecus* at Fort Ternan. *Journal of Human Evolution*, **20**, 95–129.

——, PLUMMER, T., BISHOP, L. C., DUNCAN, A. & APPLETON, S. 1997. Bovids as indicators of Plio-Pleistocene paleoenvironments in East Africa. *Journal of Human Evolution*, **32**, 229–256.

KING, B. C. & CHAPMAN, G. R. 1972. Volcanism of the Kenya rift valley. *Philosophical Transactions of the Royal Society, London. Series A*, **271**, 185–208.

KINGSTON, J. D. 1992. *Stable isotopic evidence for hominid palaeoenvironments in East Africa*. PhD thesis, Harvard University.

——1999. Environmental determinants in early hominid evolution: issues and evidence from the Tugen Hills, Kenya. *This volume*.

——, MARINO, B. D. & HILL, A. 1994. Isotopic evidence for Neogene hominid palaeoenvironments in the Kenya Rift Valley. *Science*, **264**, 955–959.

LEE-THORP, J. A., VAN DER MERWE, N. J. & BRAIN, C. K. 1989. Isotopic evidence for dietary differences between two extinct baboon species from Swartkrans. *Journal of Human Evolution*, **18**, 183–190.

MARTYN, J. E. 1969. *The geological history of the country between Lake Baringo and the Kerio River, Baringo District, Kenya*. PhD thesis, University of London.

MCBREARTY, S. 1999. The archaeology of the Kapthurin Formation. *This volume*.

——, BISHOP, L. & KINGSTON, J. 1996. Variability in traces of Middle Pleistocene hominid behavior in the Kapthurin Formation, Baringo, Kenya. *Journal of Human Evolution*, **30**, 563–580.

MORGAN, M. E., KINGSTON, J. D. & MARINO, B. D. 1994. Carbon isotopic evidence for the emergence of C_4 plants in the Neogene from Pakistan and Kenya. *Nature*, **367**, 162–165.

MORRISON, D. F. 1976. *Multivariate Statistical Methods*. McGraw-Hill, New York.

PICKFORD, M. 1975. *Stratigraphy and palaeoecology of five late Cainozoic formations in the Kenya Rift Valley*. PhD thesis, University of London.

——1978a. Geology, palaeoenvironments and vertebrate faunas of the mid-Miocene Ngorora Formation, Kenya. *In*: BISHOP, W. W. (ed.) *Geological Background to Fossil Man*. Geological Society, Scottish Academic, London, 237–262.

——1978b. Stratigraphy and mammalian palaeontology of the late-Miocene Ludeino Formation, Kenya. *In*: BISHOP, W. W. (ed.) *Geological Background to Fossil Man*. Geological Society, Scottish Academic, London, 263–278.

——1986. *A revision of the Miocene Suidae and Tayassuidae, (Artiodactyla, Mammalia) of Africa*. Tertiary Research Special Paper, **7**, 1–83.

PLUMMER, T. & BISHOP, L. C. 1994. Hominid palaeoecology at Olduvai Gorge, Tanzania as indicated by antelope remains. *In*: OLIVER, J. S., SIKES, N. E. & STEWART, K. M. (eds) *Early Hominid Behavioural Ecology. Journal of Human Evolution*, **27**, 47–75.

POTTS, R. 1988. *Early Hominid Activities at Olduvai Gorge*. Aldine de Gruyter, Hawthorne, NY.

PRATT, D. J., GREENWAY, P. J. & GWYNNE, M. D. 1966. A classification of East African Rangeland with an appendix on terminology. *Journal of Applied Ecology*, **3**, 369–382.

TAUXE, L., MONAGHAN, M., DRAKE, R., CURTIS, G. & STAUDIGEL, H. 1985. Palaeomagnetism of Miocene East African rift sediments and the calibration of the Geomagnetic Reversal Timescale. *Journal of Geophysics Research*, **90**, 4639–4646.

TIEZSEN, L. L., BOUTTON, T. W., TESDAHL, K. G. & SLADE, N. A. 1983. Fractionation and turnover of stable carbon isotopes in animal tissues: implications for the ^{13}C analysis of diet. *Oecologia (Berlin)*, **57**, 32–37.

TURNER, A., BISHOP, L. C., DENYS, C. & MCKEE, J. (in press). A locality-based listing of African Plio-Pleistocene mammals. *In*: BROMAGE, T. G. & SCHRENCK, F. (eds) *African Biogeography, Climate Change and Early Hominid Evolution*. Oxford University.

VAN DER MERWE, N. J. 1982. Carbon isotopes, photosynthesis, and archeology. *American Scientist*, **70**, 596–606.

VAN VALKENBURGH, B. 1987. Skeletal indicators of locomotor behavior in living and extant carnivores. *Journal of Vertebrate Paleontology*, **7**, 162–182.

WALKER, A. C. 1981. Diet and teeth – dietary hypotheses and human evolution. *Philosophical Transactions. Royal Society of London*, **B 292**, 57–64.

WALKER, A., HOECK, H. N. & PEREZ, L. 1978. Microwear of mammalian teeth as an indicator of diet. *Science*, **201**, 908–910.

WHITE, T. D. 1995. African omnivores: Global climatic change and Plio-Pleistocene hominids and suids. *In*: VRBA, E. S., DENTON, G. H., PARTRIDGE, T. C. & BURCKLE, L. H. (eds) *Paleoclimate and Evolution, with Emphasis on Human Origins*. Yale University, New Haven, 369–384.

Plio-Pleistocene hominins from the Baringo Region, Kenya

BERNARD WOOD

*Department of Anthropology, George Washington University, 2110 G St NW,
Washington, DC 20052, USA
Human Origins Program, National Museum of Natural History,
Smithsonian Institution, Washington, DC 20560, USA*

Abstract: The Plio-Pleistocene hominin record of East Africa is dominated by the extensive collections from well known sites situated along the Awash River, in Ethiopia, within the Turkana basin in southern Ethiopia and northern Kenya, and on the margins of the Serengeti Plain, in Tanzania. However, important Plio-Pleistocene sediments are also exposed to the west of Lake Baringo, as part of the Tugen Hills sequence, and to the east of the lake, in the Chemoigut basin. These localities, especially the former, are proving to be particularly rich sources of information about the palaeoclimate and palaeoenvironment of East Africa, but they have also furnished a modest hominin fossil record. This paper reviews the Plio-Pleistocene hominin fossil record from the Baringo region and considers its taxonomic interpretation in the context of the synchronic hominin taxa which have been identified within the richer and more abundant fossil samples from sites to the north and to the south. It then evaluates in more detail the 'taxonomic options' for the hominins from the Kapthurin Formation, since the Baringo region is one of the few locations worldwide that samples hominins from the time range 0.1–*c*. 0.75 Ma.

Plio-Pleistocene hominins* have been recovered from four time intervals and effectively six localities in the Baringo region (Table 1). All but one of the localities are in the Tugen Hills sequence. Three of these are in the Chemeron Formation, and two are in the Kapthurin Formation. The sixth locality is at Chesowanja, which lies to the east of Lake Baringo, and is within the Chemoigut Formation (Martyn 1969).

In this contribution the Baringo region hominin remains are reviewed in a temporal sequence (Table 1), starting with the oldest, from the Chemeron Formation, and concluding with the youngest, which come from the Kapthurin Formation. The aim of this contribution is to provide researchers and students with basic contextual and bibliographic information about each of the Baringo hominin specimens. Where appropriate, the conclusions of any taxonomic, systematic or functional analyses that have included the Baringo Plio-Pleistocene hominin evidence will be summarized. Although few in number, the Baringo hominins apparently date from close to the extremes of the temporal ranges of their respective taxa, and it is perhaps for this reason

that they have received proportionally more attention than equivalent material from the sites with more comprehensive hominin fossil records. The specimens from the Kapthurin Formation are particularly important, for it is one of the few sites in Africa that has yielded hominin remains which bridge the temporal gap between the relatively well sampled Lower Pleistocene period and the Holocene evidence. Given that most of the molecular evidence points to an African origin for the modern human genotype, and given the prediction that such a genotype probably originated sometime between 100 and 750 ka before the present (e.g. Hammer 1995; Armour *et al.* 1996), the nature of any hominin evidence that dates from this period, or from the period immediately before it, is of special interest. Thus, the Kapthurin hominins are given particular emphasis.

The originals of all the fossils referred to in this report are to be found in the collections held at the National Museum of Kenya, in Nairobi. Approximate dates of the specimens are given in Table 1 and the sources of the dating information are identified.

---

* 'Hominins' is preferred to 'hominids' because there is now compelling molecular, and other evidence that *Pan, Homo, Australopithecus, Paranthropus* and *Ardipithecus* should be included within the subfamily Homininae, with *Pan* placed in the tribe Panini, and the remaining taxa in the tribe Hominini.

Hominin inventory

Tabarin

Accession no. KNM-TH 13150

WOOD, B. 1999. Plio-Pleistocene hominins from the Baringo Region, Kenya0. *In*: ANDREWS, P. & BANHAM, P. (eds) *Late Cenozoic Environments and Hominid Evolution: a tribute to Bill Bishop*. Geological Society, London, 113–122.

Table 1. *Pilo-Pleistocene hominins from the Baringo Region, Kenya*

Context	Specimen no.	Formation	Locality	Year found	Description	Dating
Surface	KNM-TH 13150	Chemeron	Tabarin (BPRP: K077)	1984	Mandibular	> 4.15 Ma* < 4.96 ± 0.03 Ma*
Surface	KNM-BC 1	Chemeron	'JM 85' (BPRP: K002)	1965	Right temporal	<c. 2.4 Ma†
Surface	KNM-BC 1745	Chemeron	'2/210'¶ (BPRP: K037)	1973	Left proximal humerus	> 4.15 Ma*
Surface	KNM-CH 1	Chemoigut	Chesowanja – GnJi2	1970	Subadult hemi-face and anterior cranial base	< 5.07 ± 0.4 Ma* > 1.42 ± 0.07 Ma‡
Surface	KNM-CH 302	Chemoigut	Chesowanja – GnJi2	1973	Molar tooth fragments	> 1.42 ± 0.07 Ma†
Surface	KNM-CH 304	Chemoigut	Chesowanja – GnJi1	1978	Cranial fragments	> 1.42 ± 0.07 Ma†
in situ	KNM-BK 63	Kapthurin	'Edward Kandini Gully'	1966	Right metatarsal	< 0.66 ± 0.01 Ma§
in situ	KNM-BK 64	Kapthurin	'Edward Kandini Gully'	1966	Hand phalanx	< 0.66 ± 0.01 Ma§
in situ	KNM-BK 65	Kapthurin	'Edward Kandini Gully'	1966	Hand phalanx	< 0.66 ± 0.01 Ma§
Surface	KNM-BK 66	Kapthurin	'Edward Kandini Gully'	1966	Right ulna	< 0.66 ± 0.01 Ma§
Surface	KNM-BK 67	Kapthurin	'Edward Kandini Gully'	1966	Mandible	< 0.66 ± 0.01 Ma§
in situ	KNM-BK 8518	Kapthurin	'MAS' – GnJh19	1982	Mandible	< 0.66 ± 0.01 Ma§
Surface	KNM-BK 114297	Kapthurin	GnJh23	1984	Upper incisor	< 0.66 ± 0.01 Ma§

* Hill & Ward (1988).

† Hill *et al.* (1992), Feibel (1992).

‡ Gowlett *et al.* (1981).

§ Wood & Van Noten (1986).

¶ Two locality numbers ('2/210' and '2/211') are used in Pickford *et al.* (1985), but Hill & Ward (1988) confirm that the correct locality is '2/210'.

Discovery and geological context. Surface find, but the nature of the adherent matrix suggests that it derives from a 'dark brown coarsely bedded ferruginous conglomerate' *c.* 50 m above the Kaparaina basalt and *c.* 20 m above a tuff unit (Hill 1985: 222).

Anatomical description. Fragment of the right side of the body (corpus) of an adult mandible. The distal fracture surface passes through the mesial part of the M_3 alveolus and the mesial fracture surface passes obliquely from the P_4 alveolus to the base of the mandible at M_2. The specimen includes the worn crowns and the embedded roots of the M_1 and M_2.

Illustrations and metrical data. Ward & Hill (1987).

Taxonomy. The initial description and assessment of this specimen was presented by Hill (1985) in which he offered the opinion that the taxon that came closest to the morphology of Tabarin was *Australopithecus afarensis*. Subsequently Ward & Hill (1987) have provided a more detailed description and assessment, which also concluded that the specimen should be attributed to *Australopithecus* cf. *afarensis*. A year later the same authors attributed the Tabarin mandible to *A. afarensis* (Hill & Ward 1988: 60–62).

The discovery, and the anticipated augmentation of the hypodigms, of other relatively primitive early hominin taxa in Africa (White *et al.* 1994; Brunet *et al.* 1995, 1996; Leakey *et al.* 1995) may enable further light to be thrown on the taxonomic status of the Tabarin mandible.

Chemeron

Accession no. KNM-BC 1

Discovery and geological context. Found on the surface of an exposure of the Upper Fish Beds. It was reported that the 'most likely source of the hominid fragment is in a very thin grit band about 8 ft. from the base of the Upper Fish Beds' (Martyn in Martyn & Tobias 1967: 478).

Anatomical description. Right adult temporal bone, including the mandibular fossa, the external acoustic meatus, part of the mastoid process and most of the petrous pyramid.

Illustrations. Diagram of details in Hill *et al.* (1992).

Metrical data. No comprehensive presentation.

Taxonomy. In his initial description of the Chemeron temporal, Tobias (in Martyn and Tobias 1967) concluded that the specimen was too incomplete to allocate to a species group and he referred to it as 'Hominidae gen. et sp. indet.'. In a subsequent assessment, Hill *et al.* (1992) concluded that the depth of the mandibular fossa and its relatively medial location, together with other features, were apomorphies of *Homo*, and thus they referred it to *Homo* sp. indet.. Wood (1992*a*) and Turner & Wood (1993) have suggested that KNM-BC 1 may belong to *Homo rudolfensis*, but Tobias (1993) and Falk & Baker (1992) argued that the case for including the specimen within *Homo* had not been made.

Strait *et al.* (1997) reported that the *Homo*-like features of KNM-BC 1 are combined 'with *Paranthropus* morphology (laterally extended tympanic, large mandibular fossa, external auditory meatus large and circular)' and suggest that 'this unique combination may be at the root of its uncertain taxonomic assignation' (*ibid*: 56), but they do not provide information about these particular characters for the taxa they include in their otherwise comprehensive phylogenetic analysis.

The Chemeron temporal fragment can be distinguished from the distinctive morphology seen in *Paranthropus*, and is not as derived as the equivalent morphology seen in *Homo ergaster*. The closest morphological 'fit' with existing taxa is probably with *H. rudolfensis*, but its morphology is probably also compatible with that of *H. habilis sensu stricto* (e.g. KNM-ER 1805) as defined in Wood (1992*b*).

Accession no. KNM-BC 1745

Discovery and geological context. Found 50 m above the 'Cheseton agglomerate' (Pickford *et al.* 1983: 343), which is also called the 'Cheseton Lapilli Tuff' (*ibid*: 339). Hill & Ward (1988: 63) refer to it as the 'Cheseton Tuff'.

Anatomical description. The proximal end of a left humerus including both the anatomical and the surgical necks, but missing part of the greater tuberosity.

Illustrations and metrical data. Senut (1983); Hill & Ward (1988).

Taxonomy. The specimen was initially described by Pickford *et al.* (1983: 267) who attributed it to Hominidae gen. et sp. indet. However, Senut (1983: 267) was not convinced about its hominid affinities and concluded that it 'cannot be clearly associated with any known Plio-Pleistocene hominid or with any modern hominoids'. Hill & Ward (1988: 63) believed it to be 'clearly hominid in its affinities', and although they suggest that 'attribution to *Australopithecus* cf. *afarensis* would seem warranted', they opt for the more conservative judgment offered by Pickford *et al.* (1983).

Until more details of *Ardipithecus ramidus* and *Australopithecus anamensis* become available it is prudent to continue to take a conservative view about the taxonomic allocation of a fragmentary and damaged specimen such as this.

Chesowanja

Accession no.   KNM-CH 1

Discovery and geological context.   Surface find that derives from 'Yellow marls' which 'overly the green silts in the west' (Carney *et al.* 1971: 511), but see Bishop *et al.* (1975: 205) where KNM-CH 1 is described as coming from 'the grey tuffaceous grit'.

Anatomical description.   The specimen consists of a partial face, part of the frontal bone and the anterior part of the base of a sub-adult hominin cranium. The preserved teeth include the crowns and the enclosed roots of the right C–M^3.

Illustrations and metrical data.   Carney *et al.* (1971); Wood (1991).

Taxonomy.   In his initial anatomical description and assessment, Walker (in Carney *et al.* 1971) referred KNM-CH 1 to cf. *A. boisei*. In a subsequent review of African hominins Howell (1978) also attributed it to *A. boisei*. Discoveries since 1970 have shown *P. boisei* to be a taxon that subsumes a range of size and shape differences which are still most economically interpreted as reflecting within-species variation (Wood *et al.* 1991). Despite hints that its morphology may be somehow aberrant, there is no reason to exclude KNM-CH 1 from the hypodigm of *P. boisei* as set out in Wood (1991).

Accession no.   KNM-CH 302

Discovery and geology context.   Surface find from 'within chocolate clays' of the Chemoigut Formation (Bishop *et al.* 1975: 205).

Anatomical description.   Fragments of upper molar tooth crown(s).

Illustrations and metrical data.   None.

Taxonomy.   In their initial, and thus far the only, description of this material, Bishop *et al.* (1975: 205) make the statement that the tooth crowns showed 'features typical of the dentition of robust australopithecines'. From this we may infer with some confidence that it was their intention to attribute the dental fragments to cf. *A. boisei*.

Accession no.   KNM-CH 304

Discovery and geological context.   Surface find, but the inference is that it came from the same 'silting-up channel' in 'clayey silts' that yielded artefacts and fauna in the excavation at GnJi 1/ 6E (Gowlett *et al.* 1981: 125).

Anatomical description.   Five cranial vault fragments (A–E) that include parts of the occipital (A), parietals (B and D) and temporal (C) bones.

Illustrations.   None.

Metrical data.   Gowlett *et al.* (1981).

Taxonomy.   Wood, in Gowlett *et al.* (1981), referred this specimen to *A. boisei*. The accumulating evidence of cranial polymorphism within *Paranthropus boisei* (Leakey & Walker 1988; Wood 1991; Suwa *et al.* 1997) has merely reinforced the likelihood that these cranial fragments belong to that taxon.

Kapthurin

Accession no.   BK 63–65

Discovery and geological context.   Excavated from a trench which was dug at the site of discovery of BK 66 (see below) 'in an attempt to recover further hominid remains and to ascertain the exact horizon from which the surface specimens had eroded' (Leakey *et al.* 1969: 54).

Anatomical description.   Solan & Day (1992: 307) describe BK 63 as a first right metatarsal, and BK 64 and 65 as proximal hand phalanges.

Illustrations and metrical data.   None.

Taxonomy.   No taxonomic assessments have been made, other than the inference that these hand and foot bones belong to the same skeleton as the mandible and the ulna (Solan & Day 1992; also see below).

Accession no.   KNM-BK 66

Discovery and geological context.   The ulna was found on the surface at the same time as the mandible BK 67, and readers should refer to the relevant information given in the next entry.

Anatomical description.   Adult right ulna which is in three main fragments. It is complete save for the distal articular surface and the immediately adjacent shaft. The shaft is relatively straight and the muscle markings are modest.

Illustrations.   Senut (1981); Solan & Day (1992).

Metrical data.   Aiello *et al.* (in press).

Taxonomy.   The initial description and taxonomic assessment of BK 66 was made by Senut (1981) who assumed that Leakey *et al.* (1969) had assigned the ulna to *Homo erectus*. However, in that paper, no specific reference was made to the discovery of an ulna; the only taxonomic assessment concerned the BK 67 mandible. Additionally, Senut (1981: 104) emphasized the *Homo*-like nature of BK 66 and proposed that it should be attributed to that genus.

Solan & Day (1992) conducted a comparative quantitative analysis in which they compared it with modern-human and Neandertal ulnae. They interpreted the results of their analysis as suggesting that BK 66 was most appropriately attributed to *H. erectus*. Churchill *et al.* (1996) included BK 66 in their sample of 'Archaic Humans' (*ibid*: 221) on the assumption that it had been attributed to '*Homo* cf. *erectus*' (*ibid*: 220). They remark on its relatively tall olecranon process, but the results of the multivariate analyses are not presented in sufficient detail to allow the identification of individual specimens. Groves (1998) has reanalysed a subset of the data used by Churchill *et al.* (1996), and the results of these analyses place BK 66 close to the Neandertal sample. They also confirm that the form of the olecranon is at least one way in which BK 66 differs from the ulnae of modern humans.

The Baringo ulna has also been included in a recent study that focused on the taxonomy and the functional interpretation of the adult ulna (OH 36) from Upper Bed II of Olduvai Gorge, Tanzania (Aiello *et al.* in press). The results of this study showed that although OH 36 and BK 66 are similar in size, the shape differences between the two fossil ulnae exceed those that are seen within any of the modern comparative samples. The authors conclude that OH 36 and BK 66 belong to two different species that

employed their forelimbs in different ways. It was also clear from the analysis that BK 66 could be distinguished from samples of modern human ulnae.

Accession no.   KNM-BK 67

Discovery and geological context.   Surface find by Edward Kandini at the locality subsequently called the 'Edward Kandini Gully' (EKG). Reported to be 'found 45 feet below the base of the tuff which caps the plateau' (Leakey *et al.* 1969: 54), but in the section of the 'Middle Silts and Gravels Member' illustrated in Wood & Van Noten (1986: 119) the stratigraphic location of 'BK 67' is given as being *c*. 12 m below the 'Bedded tuff' and immediately beneath the 'Grey tuff'. Subsequent excavations at the site resulted in the recovery of BK 63–65 (see above) from a 'sandy clay' (Leakey *et al.* 1969: 54).

Anatomical description.   An almost complete adult mandible lacking only the coronoid processes and damaged areas around the angles and the anterior part of the alveolar process. The only teeth to have their crowns preserved are the right P_4, M_{1-3} and the left M_2 and M_3 (Fig. 1).

Illustrations.   None.

Metrical data.   Leakey *et al.* (1969); Wood & Van Noten (1986); Wood (1991).

Taxonomy.   The initial description and assessment by Tobias in Leakey *et al.* (1969: 70) concluded that BK 67 'is closely related to those of the Middle Pleistocene hominids of Ternifine' and that 'it fits comfortably within the

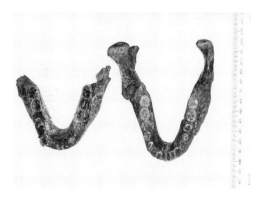

Fig. 1. Occlusal view of the Baringo hominin mandibles from the Kapthurin Formation BK 67 (right) and BK 8518 (left).

range of mandibles which have been ascribed
to *Homo erectus*'. However, because a similar-
looking mandible found at Olduvai Gorge
(OH 13) was part of a skull whose cranium was
unlike that of *Homo erectus,* and because there
may be a similar looking mandible at Swartkrans, also linked with a 'non-*Homo erectus*'
cranium, Tobias professed himself to be 'cau-
tious of assigning taxonomic identity to a hominid when the main or only evidence is based on
the mandible alone' (Leakey *et al.* 1969: 71).
Thus, he concluded that 'it would be safer,
until the post-cranial material (i.e. BK 63–66)
is studied, to assign the specimen to an East
African representative of *Homo*, with the qua-
lification that it probably but not certainly
belonged to *Homo erectus*' (Leakey *et al.* 1969:
71–72). Further discussion of the taxonomic
affinities of BK 67 are set out below (see 'Taxonomy' section of BK 8518).

Accession no.   KNM-BK 8518

Discovery and geological context.   The mandible was found effectively *in situ* 'eroding out of
sediments' some 3 m below the grey tuff at site
'MAS' (Wood & Van Noten 1986: 117).

Anatomical description.   The specimen is in four
pieces, the major part being the body (A) and a
fragment of the left ramus (B) of an adult
mandible with heavily and asymmetrically worn
teeth and a dental arcade that has suffered *post-
mortem* distortion. Separate fragments are a left
P$_4$ (C) and right lower canine (D) (Fig. 1).

Illustrations.   Wood & Van Noten (1986).

Metrical data.   Wood & Van Noten (1986);
Wood (1991).

Taxonomy.   In his initial description and taxonomic assessment of BK 8518 Wood (in Wood &
Van Noten 1986: 125) referred the mandible to
'*Homo* sp. indet. (aff. *erectus*)', which more correctly should have been expressed as '*Homo* aff.
H. erectus'. Subsequent assessments by Uytterschaut (in Cornelissen *et al.* 1990; Uytterschaut
1992) have concluded that BK 67 and BK 8518
are conspecific and that both probably belong
to an 'early *Homo erectus* or a late *Homo habilis*'
(Uytterschaut 1992: 1). Subsequently, the two
mandibles have been included in comparative
samples of *Homo erectus* on at least two
occasions (Wood 1991, 1994).
   Given their stratigraphic equivalence, there is
a strong case for the 'null hypothesis' that BK 67

and BK 8518 are conspecific, but are there
sufficient differences between the two mandibles
to cause that hypothesis to be discarded? There
is no doubt that BK 8518 is consistently the
more 'primitive' of the two mandibles, and this
is evident in both the dentition and the form of
the mandibular corpus (Wood & Van Noten
1986). The former show this most clearly in the
two-rooted posterior premolars (Wood *et al.*
1988) and in the relatively large crowns and
complex cusp morphology of the third molars
(Wood & Abbott 1983; Wood *et al.* 1983).
However, given the range of size and detailed
morphology embraced by otherwise morphologically homogeneous collections of fossil mandibles at Ternifine (Arambourg 1955a, b) and
Arago these differences are insufficient indication to abandon the null hypothesis that the two
Baringo (Kapthurin) mandibles belong to the
same taxon. Further discussion of their taxonomic attribution is presented below in the
'Taxonomic overview' section.

Accession no.   KNM-BK 114297

Discovery and geological context.   Surface find
in sediments that are 'under the grey tuff'
(Cornelissen *et al.* 1990: 65).

Anatomical description.   Upper left I^2, but it is
referred to in the hominid catalogue at the
National Museum of Kenya as an 'upper
right I^1'.

Illustrations and metrical data.   None.

Taxonomy.   None.

Taxonomic overview

The Plio-Pleistocene hominins from the Baringo
region lie within one of the four 'time bands' that
are illustrated in Fig. 2. The same diagram also
includes the species designations of the hominin
evidence known from other Plio-Pleistocene sites
in Africa. Several of these species have been
recognized since the discovery and taxonomic
attribution of the hominin evidence from the
Baringo region. The existence of this new material may affect the taxonomy of the Baringo
specimens, but do we have sufficient information
about the new taxa to merit revising the earlier
taxonomic conclusions?
   In the case of the earlier subset of specimens
from the Chemeron Formation, that is KNM-
BC 1745 and KNM-TH 13150, the relevant new

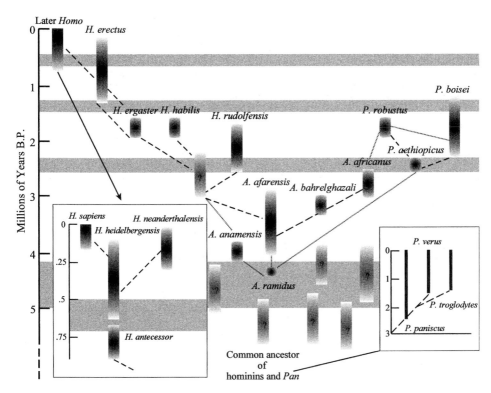

Fig. 2. Phylogram of fossil hominin species, based on a 'punctuated equilibrium' interpretation of hominin evolution. The horizontal axis groups hominin taxa with large brains and small chewing teeth to the left, and species with large chewing teeth to the right. Boxes with question marks represent speculations about taxa that are likely to be recovered as the result of future field research. The dashed lines represent probable lineages; finely dotted lines represent possible ancestor–descendant connections between taxa. The four grey horizontal bands are the approximate time ranges for the Baringo hominin fossils reviewed in the text. Thus, these hominins must either be allocated to one of the species known from that time band, or the Baringo evidence must justify the recognition of a new hominin species.

taxa are *Ardipithecus ramidus* and *Australopithecus anamensis*. There is presently insufficient information about the latter for the anatomical regions that are preserved in the Baringo specimens to come to any firm taxonomic conclusions, for the Tabarin mandible does not preserve the mandibular features (e.g. the form of the symphysis and the size of the canine roots) that are among the features listed as distinguishing *A. anamensis* from other australopithecine species (Leakey *et al.* 1995: 565). Likewise, apart from enamel thickness, there is little preserved in common between the Tabarin mandible and the published remains attributed to *Ardipithecus ramidus* (White *et al.* 1994). However, the evidence that the Tabarin mandible had 'thickened enamel' (Ward & Hill 1987: 30) would seem to rule it out from belonging to *A. ramidus*, on the grounds that one of the distinctive features of

the latter is 'absolutely and relatively thinner... molar enamel' compared to 'other hominid species' (White *et al.* 1994: 306). Temporally, at least, there is a case for KNM-TH 13150 and KNM-BC 1745 belonging to *A. anamensis*, for their temporal and geographical ranges most likely overlapped.

As far as the temporally more recent Chemeron temporal is concerned, there are two East African hominin taxa, *Homo rudolfensis* and *Paranthropus aethiopicus*, which are known from the presumed time range of KNM-BC 1 (Fig. 2). Attribution to the former taxon has already been suggested, but are there grounds for excluding the allocation of KNM-BC 1 to *P. aethiopicus*? The only specimen of *P. aethiopicus* to preserve the same anatomical regional evidence as that provided by KNM-BC 1 is KNM-WT 17000, and its morphology is sufficiently distinctive (Walker *et al.* 1986; Hill *et al.* 1992) that it is possible to be almost certain that KNM-BC 1 should not be allocated to *P. aethiopicus*.

Similarly, for the evidence from the Chemoigut Formation at Chesowanja, the distinctive features of the partial cranium (KNM-CH 1) and the cranial fragments (KNM-CH 304) virtually rule them out from allocation to any contemporary hominin taxon other than *P. boisei* (Fig. 2).

The most recent hominin evidence from the Baringo region comes from the Kapthurin Formation, and it is dated at less than 0.66 Ma. Hominin evidence from East Africa includes material from Bodo, Gombore II and Olduvai Gorge Bed IV, and fossils from these sites have been allocated to either *H. erectus,* or to archaic *Homo sapiens*. To which of these taxa (if indeed they do belong to a single hominin species) do the Kapthurin hominin remains belong?

With regard to KNM-BK 66, unfortunately there is no ulna referred to the type series of *H. erectus* with which it can be compared. There were no forelimb bones in the collection from Trinil, which is the type site for *H. erectus,* nor are there any postcranial remains from Sangiran, the type site of *Pithecanthropus robustus*. The type series of *Sinanthropus pekinensis* includes forelimb material (Weidenreich 1941), but the ulna is not represented in that collection. Turning to the evidence from Africa, part of a femoral shaft is included among the components of the fragmented skeleton KNM-ER 803, and its morphology allows that specimen to be allocated, with some confidence, to early African *Homo erectus* or *H. ergaster*. Among the limb bone fragments included in the specimen is KNM-ER 803C, which is the proximal half of the shaft of a left ulna. The shaft fragment is straight and the muscle markings are not especially prominent (Day & Leakey 1974: 369). Another associated skeleton from Koobi Fora, KNM-ER 1808, has been attributed to early African *H. erectus* on the basis of the morphology of the cranial fragments. One of the fragments, KNM-ER 803Y, is believed to be part of an ulnar shaft, but the whole of the appendicular skeleton is so severely affected by a periostitis-type lesion (Walker *et al.* 1982) that taxonomically useful interpretation of its morphology is not possible. Thus, it is only the two specimens (BP and BZ) belonging to KNM-WT 15000 that can provide any clear guide to the morphology of *H. erectus*. Their straight shafts confirm that the appearance of the KNM-ER 803 ulna was not atypical.

It is tempting to conclude from this that KNM-BK 66 should be assigned to *H. erectus*,

but if we know little about the forelimb anatomy of *H. erectus sensu stricto*, the reality is that we know even less about the forelimb of 'archaic' *Homo sapiens*, as distinct from *Homo neanderthalensis*. Thus, until we have more evidence about the upper limb morphology of Middle Pleistocene hominin taxa, the Baringo ulna cannot offer any conclusive evidence about the taxonomy of the Kapthurin hominin.

The mandibular evidence, despite the reputation the mandible has acquired for not being taxonomically discriminating, is a little more helpful. This is largely due to the relatively primitive nature of much of the morphology evident on KNM-BK 8518 (Wood & Van Noten 1986; Wood 1991). The relatively robust corpus, the complex buttressing of the symphysis, the relative size and crown complexity of the M_3s, and the form of the premolar roots (Chamberlain & Wood 1985; Wood *et al.* 1983, 1988; Wood 1991) would be unusual even as 'isolated' features in 'archaic' *H. sapiens*, let alone in combination. Thus, the mandibular evidence from the Kapthurin hominin includes a specimen that it would be difficult to reconcile with an allocation to *H. sapiens*. Therefore, it is the mandible KNM-BK 8518 which is the strongest evidence for including the Kapthurin hominin hypodigm in *Homo erectus sensu stricto*. This would be the most recent 'firm' African evidence for *H. erectus*, and it would mean that *H. erectus* and 'archaic' *H. sapiens*, in the form of the Bodo cranium (Clark *et al.*, 1994) were approximately coeval in Africa.

Research incorporated in this paper was funded by The Leverhulme Trust and The Henry Luce Foundation.

References

AIELLO, L. C., WOOD, B., KEY, C. & LEWIS, M. (in press). Morphological and taxonomic affinities of the Olduvai ulna (OH 36). *American Journal of Physical Anthropology*.

ARAMBOURG, C. 1955a. A recent discovery in human paleontology: *Atlanthropus* of Ternifine (Algeria). *American Journal of Physical Anthropology*, **13** 191–201.

——1955b. Une nouvelle mandibule 'd'*Atlanthropus*' au gisement de Ternifine. *Comtes Rendu Academie des Sciences, Paris*, **241**, 895–897.

ARMOUR, J. A. L., ANTINNEN, T., MAY, C. A., *et al.* 1996. Mini satellite diversity supports a recent African origin for modern humans. *Nature Genetics*, **13**, 154–160.

BISHOP, W. W., PICKFORD, M. & HILL, A. 1975. New evidence regarding the quaternary geology, archaeology and hominids of Chesowanja, Kenya. *Nature*, **258**, 204–208.

BRUNET, M., BEAUVILAIN, A., COPPENS, Y., HEINTZ, E., MOUNTAYE, A. H. E. & PILBEAM, D. 1995. The first australopithecine 2500 kilometers west of the Rift Valley (Chad). *Nature*, **378**, 273–275.

——, ——, ——, ——, —— & ——1996. *Australopithecus bahrelghazali*, une nouvelle espece d'hominidé ancien de la region de Koyo Toro (Tchad). *Comtes Rendu Academie des Sciences, Paris*, **322**, 907–913.

CARNEY, J., HILL, A., MILLER, J. A. & WALKER, A. 1971. Late australopithecine from Baringo district, Kenya. *Nature*, **230**, 509–514.

CHAMBERLAIN, A. T. & WOOD, B. A. 1985. A reappraisal of variation in hominid mandibular corpus dimensions. *American Journal of Physical Anthropology*, **66**, 399–405.

CHURCHILL, S. E., PEARSON, O. M., GRINE, F. E., TRINKAUS, E. & HOLLIDAY, T. W. 1996. Morphological affinities of the proximal ulna from Klasies River main site: archaic or modern? *Journal of Human Evolution*, **31**, 213–237.

CLARK, J. D., DE HEINZELIN, J., SCHICK, K. D., *et al.* 1994. African *Homo erectus*: Old radiometric ages and young Oldowan assemblages in the Middle Awash Valley, Ethiopia. *Science*, **264** 1907–1910.

CORNELISSEN, E., BOVEN, A., DABI, A., *et al.* 1990. The Kapthurin Formation Revisited. *The African Archaeological Review*, **8**, 23–75.

DAY, M. H. & LEAKEY, R. E. F. 1974. New evidence of the *genus Homo* from East Rudolf, Kenya (III). *American Journal of Physical Anthropology*, **41**, 367–380.

FALK, D. & BAKER, E. 1992. Earliest *Homo* debate. *Nature*, **358**, 289–290.

FEIBEL, C. S. 1992. Earliest *Homo* debate. *Nature*, **358**, 289.

GOWLETT, J. A. J., HARRIS, J. W. K., WALTON, D. & WOOD, B. A. 1981. Early archaeological sites, hominid remains and traces of fire from Chesowanja, Kenya. *Nature*, **294**, 125–129.

GROVES, C. P. 1998. The proximal ulna from Klasies River. *Journal of Human Evolution*, **34**, 119–121.

HAMMER, M. F. 1995. A recent common ancestry for human Y chromosomes. *Nature*, **378**, 376–378.

HILL, A. 1985. Early hominid from Baringo, Kenya. *Nature*, **315**, 222–224.

—— & WARD, S. 1988. Origin of the Hominidae: The record of African large hominoid evolution between 14 My and 4 My. *Yearbook of Physical Anthropology*, **31**, 49–83.

——, ——, DEINO, A., CURTIS, G. & DRAKE, R. 1992. Earliest *Homo*. *Nature*, **355**, 719–722.

HOWELL, F. C. 1978. Hominidae. *In*: MAGLIO, V. J. & COOKE, H. B. S. (eds) *Evolution of African Mammals*. Harvard University, Cambridge, 154–248.

LEAKEY, M., TOBIAS, P. V., MARTYN, J. E. & LEAKEY, R. E. F. 1969. An Acheulean industry with prepared core technique and the discovery of a contemporary hominid mandible at Lake Baringo, Kenya. *Proceedings of the Prehistoric Society*, **215**, 48–76.

LEAKEY, M. G., FEIBEL, C. S., MCDOUGALL, I. & WALKER, A. 1995. New four-million-year-old hominid species from Kanapoi and Allia Bay. *Nature*, **376**, 565–571.

LEAKEY, R. E. F. & WALKER, A. 1988. New *Australopithecus boisei* specimens from East and West Lake Turkana, Kenya. *American Journal of Physical Anthropology*, **76**, 1–24.

MARTYN, J. & TOBIAS, P. V. 1967. Pleistocene deposits and new fossil localities in Kenya. *Nature*, **215**, 479–480.

MARTYN, J. E. 1969. *The geological history of the country between Lake Baringo and the Kerio River, Baringo District, Kenya*. PhD thesis, University of London.

PICKFORD, M., JOHANSON, D. C., LOVEJOY, T. D., WHITE, T. D. & ARONSON, J. L. 1983. A hominoid humeral fragment from the Pliocene of Kenya. *American Journal of Physical Anthropology*, **60**, 337–346.

SENUT, B. 1981. *L'Humérus et ses Articulations chez les Hominidés Plio-Pléistocènes*. Cahiers de Paléontologie (Paléoanthropologie), Centre Nacional de la Recherche Scientifique, Paris.

——1983. Quelques remarques à propos d'un humérus d'hominoide pliocène provenant de Chemeron (bassin du lac Baringo, Kenya). *Folia Primatologica*, **41**, 267–276.

SOLAN, M. & DAY, M. H. 1992. The Baringo (Kapthurin) ulna. *Journal of Human Evolution*, **22**, 307–313.

STRAIT, D. S., GRINE, F. E. & MONIZ, M. A. 1997. A reappraisal of early hominid phylogeny. *Journal of Human Evolution*, **32**, 17–82.

SUWA, G., ASFAW, B., BEYENE, Y. *et al.* 1997. The first skull of *Australopithecus boisei*. *Nature*, **389**, 489–492.

TOBIAS, P. V. 1993. Earliest *Homo* not proven. *Nature*, **361**, 307.

TURNER, A. & WOOD, B. 1993. Comparative palaeontological context for the evolution of the early hominid masticatory system. *Journal of Human Evolution*, **24**, 301–318.

UYTTERSCHAUT, H. T. 1992. A morphological study of some old and new Pleistocene discoveries from Java. *IPPA Bulletin*, **12**, 1–9.

WALKER, A., LEAKEY, R. E., HARRIS, J. M. & BROWN, F. H. 1986. 2–5 Myr *Australopithecus boisei* from west of Lake Turkana, Kenya. *Nature*, **322**, 517–522.

——, ZIMMERMAN, M. R. & LEAKEY, R. E. F. 1982. A possible case of hypervitaminosis A in *Homo erectus*. *Nature*, **296**, 248–250.

WARD, S. & HILL, A. 1987. Pliocene hominid partial mandible from Tabarin, Baringo, Kenya. *American Journal of Physical Anthropology*, **72**, 21–37.

WEIDENREICH, F. 1941. The extremity bones of *Sinanthropus pekinensis*. *Palaeontologia Sinica, Series D*, **5**, 1–151.

WHITE, T. D., SUWA, G. & ASFAW, B. 1994. *Australopithecus ramidus*, a new species of early hominid from Aramis, Ethiopia. *Nature*, **371**, 306–312.

WOOD, B. A. 1991. *Koobi Fora Research Project, Volume 4: Hominid Cranial Remains from Koobi Fora.* Clarendon, Oxford.

——1992a. Old bones match old stones. *Nature,* **355,** 678–679.

——1992b. Origin and evolution of *Homo. Nature,* **355,** 783–790.

——1994. Taxonomy and evolutionary relationships of *Homo erectus. Courier Forschungs-Institut, Senckenberg,* **171,** 159–165.

—— & ABBOTT, S. A. 1983. Analysis of the dental morphology of Plio-Pleistocene hominids. I. Mandibular molars – crown area measurements and morphological traits. *Journal of Anatomy,* **136** 197–219.

—— & VAN NOTEN, F. L. 1986. Preliminary observations on the BK 8518 mandible from Baringo, Kenya. *American Journal of Physical Anthropology,* **69,** 117–127.

——, ABBOTT, S. A., & GRAHAM, S. H. 1983. Analysis of the dental morphology of Plio-Pleistocene hominids. II. Mandibular molars – study of cusp areas, fissure pattern and cross-sectional shape of the crown. *Journal of Anatomy,* **137,** 287–314.

——, —— & UYTTERSCHAUT, H. T. 1988. Analysis of the dental morphology of Plio-Pleistocene hominids. IV. Mandibular postcanine root morphology. *Journal of Anatomy,* **156,** 107–139.

——, YU, L. & WILLOUGHBY, C. 1991. Intraspecific variation and sexual dimorphism in cranial and dental variables among higher primates and their bearing on the hominid fossil record. *Journal of Anatomy,* **174,** 185–205.

Lower and Middle Pleistocene archaeology of the Baringo Basin

J. A. J. GOWLETT

*Department of Archaeology, The Hartley Building, University of Liverpool,
PO Box 147, Liverpool L69 3BX, UK*

Abstract: This paper gives a survey of the Pleistocene archaeology of the Baringo Basin
in Kenya, based especially on the sites and sequences at Chesowanja and Kilombe.
Chesowanja preserves sites through a span of 1.5 Ma, ranging from the Lower Pleistocene to
the Holocene. In addition to early sites of the Chemoigut Formation, one of which contains
burnt material, Chesowanja has a record of other unusual facies of archaeological material.
The paper gives a detailed account of the distribution of burnt material, and considers
alternative interpretations. In the south of the Baringo Basin is the vast Acheulean site of
Kilombe, aged about 0.8 Ma. It offers opportunities for palaeogeographical studies of biface
distributions, using a number of parameters of measurement. Multivariate allometry has
proved a powerful tool, but univariate and bivariate techniques have also demonstrated
significant differences in material across the site. Kilombe permits some comparisons with
neighbouring Acheulean sites such as Kariandusi, and with the Kapthurin Formation,
where more recent Acheulean sites show a remarkable new technology, which nevertheless
exhibits some intriguing continuities with the older material from Kilombe.

The Baringo Basin contains Pleistocene archaeological sequences which together preserve one
of the best long-term records in Africa, indeed in
the world. As a result of the scale of the basin –
50 km broad and more than 100 km long – the
sites are not closely related in terms of geological
setting: they are in different suites of sediments,
among tuffs and lavas produced by different
volcanoes. Kilombe and Chesowanja are almost
100 km apart (Fig. 1). Some of the sites present large continuous sections, but others are
fragmented even locally, and they have to be
brought together by means similar to those used
for correlating sites further apart. The sites are
linked chiefly through being found in the course
of geological prospecting, occupying the Pleistocene time range, and using similar lava raw
materials.

History of research and major sites

First archaeological work in the area was concentrated around Lake Baringo itself, especially
in the Kapthurin Formation on the western side
of the lake. The discovery of a late Acheulean
site and a hominid mandible was published by
Leakey *et al.* (1969). The next phase of work was
stimulated by the project of the East African
Geological Research Unit (EAGRU), and was
particularly inspired by the participation of Bill
Bishop. At Kapthurin, mapping by P. W. J.

Tallon (1978) gave a better context to the late
Middle Pleistocene finds. At Kilombe, near the
south end of the basin, a major Acheulean site
was discovered by W. B. Jones in the course of
mapping in 1972. At Chesowanja, on the east
side of Lake Baringo, geology and palaeontology, including hominid finds, were published by
Carney *et al.* (1971), but the presence of artefacts
was noted only later by Bill Bishop in 1973
(Bishop *et al.* 1975). Subsequent archaeological
developments are discussed below.

Recent developments in Pleistocene archaeology

Since the first discoveries in the Baringo Basin the
framework of the Palaeolithic itself has developed, expanding considerably in time-depth and
scope. The geography of early occupations has
also been extended to the Middle East and Asia,
so that we have to think of early Oldowan-like
industries being far more widespread. The first
spread out of Africa remains poorly dated, but
the balance of evidence points to it occurring by
2 Ma, suggesting that hominids, probably *Homo*,
were already adapted to a range of environments.
   The origins of the Acheulean hand-axe tradition are also confirmed to go back 1.5 Ma. Dates
of about 1.4 Ma were known previously from
Olduvai and Peninj (Leakey 1971, 1975; Isaac &
Curtis 1974), and have been substantiated again

GOWLETT, J. A. J. 1999. Lower and Middle Pleistocene archaeology of the Baringo Basin. *In*: ANDREWS, P. &
BANHAM, P. (eds) *Late Cenozoic Environments and Hominid Evolution: a tribute to Bill Bishop.* Geological Society,
London, 123–141.

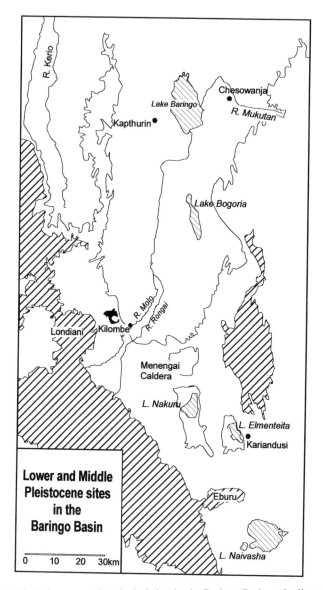

Fig. 1. Lower and Middle Pleistocene archaeological sites in the Baringo Basin and adjacent areas. Contour at 1830 m. Land over 2440 m is hatched.

at Konso-Gardula in southern Ethiopia (Asfaw *et al.* 1992). This is a further site where *Homo erectus* is found with Acheulean, and in which there are remains of a robust australopithecine at the same levels (Suwa *et al.* 1997).

Over the same period knowledge of associated hominids has improved. It has become possible to see both the long time-duration and early diversity of *Homo* (e.g. Wood 1991, 1992). Late robust australopithecines are confirmed to have survived to about 1.4 Ma (Suwa *et al.* 1997).

A modernization of *Homo erectus* in the direction of *heidelbergensis/sapiens* may be seen as early as 0.7 Ma (Rightmire 1996). In archaeological work there have been many developments of approach. Methodologies for assessing site formation processes and taphonomy have improved (e.g. Oliver *et al.* 1994). Models of subsistence and hominization have been debated and have developed. Issues of scavenging and hunting have featured strongly in the debates (Blumenschine *et al.* 1994; Pitts & Roberts 1997).

Another major change of focus has taken science away from human origins to the origins of modern humans. Recently, however, the concentration of interest has begun to move back again, towards the origins of *Homo sapiens, sensu lato*. In archaeology this has been manifested through a renewed concern with technology, especially with the variety of, and origins of, Levallois technology (Chazan 1997; Dibble & Bar-Yosef 1995; Rolland 1995). Following recent DNA studies (Krings *et al.* 1997), a position is beginning to emerge where research can come to bear on the 'deep roots' of Neanderthal divergence, perhaps more than half a million years ago. In archaeology this may create promising experimental situations for comparing the cultural branches in Europe and Africa through the Pleistocene (cf. Andresen *et al.* 1997). The archaeology of the Baringo Basin is directly relevant to all these immense changes, although it has sometimes seemed to lie between recent focuses of interest. Its importance is reinforced now as attention concentrates on the deep roots of *Homo sapiens* (cf. McBrearty *et al.* 1996; McBrearty 1999).

Outline of the Chesowanja sequence

The localities of Chesowanja lie to the east of Lake Baringo, near the foot of the Laekipia escarpment at 36°12′E, 0°39′N (Fig. 1). The sites occupy a fault-step raised towards 200 m above the level of the lake.

Chesowanja is unusual among major lower Pleistocene localities, in consisting of a set of exposures on a relatively restricted scale, and especially in having a sequence that is laid out horizontally. The sediments containing archaeology pass from older to younger from west to east, across about 1 km. The geological sequence is made up of a series of major units running through from the Lower Pleistocene to the Holocene. Description of the geological sequence has been amended with each successive phase of work in the area. The initial interpretation by Carney *et al.* (1971) interpreted the Chesowanja basalt as a dyke thrust vertically through the sediments. Bill Bishop in his surveys developed a new understanding of the structure, realizing that the Chesowanja basalt formed an integral part of the sequence, overlying the Chemoigut Formation, and underlying a series of later sediments. The basic stratigraphy given in Bishop *et al.* (1975), and especially Bishop *et al.* (1978), has thus stood the test of time, although archaeological investigations have both clarified it and also posed some new questions, through

uncovering detailed evidence of local stratigraphy and dips of sediments (Fig. 2).

In Bishop's interpretation of structure, the Chemoigut and Chesowanja Formations are folded into an anticline, with an assumed adjacent syncline on the eastern side. The axis of these trends N–S. The beds were described to have a dip of approximately 11° on the western limb, and a much steeper angle of about 60° on the eastern limb, on the basis of measurements made on the basalt. The Chemoigut Formation, underlying the Chesowanja basalt, is exposed in three 'windows' (Bill Bishop's terminology). In these areas erosion by streams has removed the covering of the basalt, which occurs residually as numerous cobbles on many surfaces. The modern drainage is created by the Losokweta River, which flows north through the area, soon joining the Mukutan, which eventually turns southwest to flow into Lake Baringo. The minor tributaries of the Losokweta river, which have exposed the sediments, possess little erosive power in the relatively shallow relief, and are not deeply incised. Bishop's section of 1975 envisaged artefacts at numerous different stratigraphic levels, exposed on a near-horizontal surface where the vault of the anticline had been uncapped (Bishop *et al.* 1975). The archaeological investigations give a revised picture, since the excavations of 1/6E and 1/5 are separated by more than 50 m are both at virtually the same absolute level, and have a similar dip of about 5°. Across a considerable area of the Chemoigut Formation, the combination of shallow relief and gentle dip thus comes close to exhuming one particular landscape, levels on the west side of Window 1 being if anything slightly younger. Further evidence for this similarity of levels is provided by the fragmentary remains of the hominid, KNM-CH 304, found in two positions almost 20 m apart, at identical levels. The 1/6E trench is on the eastern side of Window 1 close to the Chesowanja basalt, therefore presenting evidence that the consistent gentle dips to the west are maintained very close to the limb of the basalt which plunges steeply to the east.

Artefacts were found at a number of different localities in the Chemoigut Formation. The main excavations are 1/5 and 1/6 E in Window 1 and 2/8 in Window 2 but surface artefacts have been collected from a number of other positions (Harris & Gowlett 1980; Gowlett *et al.* 1981; Harris *et al.* 1983).

The Chesowanja Formation is best observed to the east of the Chemoigut Formation, and begins with the basalt dated to 1.4 ± 0.07 Ma. The Chesowanja Formation was envisaged by Bishop as including the basalt, and a thin

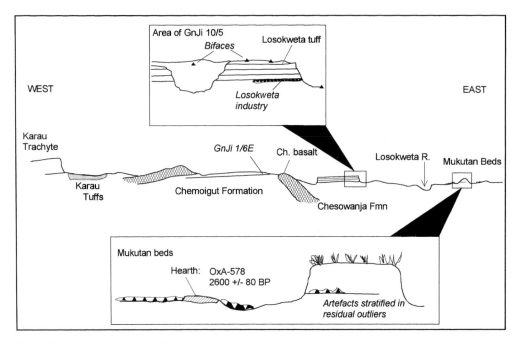

Fig. 2. Sketch section across the Chesowanja exposures, with inset boxes of the Loskweta tuff and Mukutan bed stratigraphy. Not to scale: the section has an overall length of about 2 km. The two inset sections have vertical scales of about 3 m.

covering of sediments developed upon it. The total depth of clays overlying the steeply plunging basalt remains unclear, but it has become evident that it could amount to many metres. On the east side of the exposures this local sequence is capped by a tuff, now termed the Losokweta tuff, which overlies artefact occurrences (Gowlett et al. 1981).

Along the foot of this tuff more than 20 Acheulean bifaces were found on the surface, leading Bishop to interpret these occurrences as Acheulean. Surprisingly, excavations located no hand-axes in situ among thousands of artefacts underlying the Losokweta tuff (Gowlett et al. 1981). Hand-axes were, however, found on top of the thin layers of sediment capping the tuff, and eventually one specimen was found in situ in a channel which had been cut through the tuff (Fig. 2) The archaeological sequence of the Chesowanja Formation can thus be summarized as (a) non-hand-axe industries underlying the Losokweta tuff; (b) hand-axe industries overlying the tuff, and occurring in the fill of channels which imply an erosional phase.

This sequence of finds should be emphasized, since interest in non-hand-axe industries has grown. Unfortunately, there is no solid dating evidence for these finds at present. Those above the tuff are unsealed. The Losokweta tuff was originally considered to be part of the Karau tuffs (Bishop et al. 1975). Many magnetic measurements were made on sediments of the Karau Formation, but these were not entirely consistent (Dagley et al. 1978), and it is not now plain which of them relate to the Losokweta tuffs (interpreted as distinct from the Karau tuffs by Bishop et al. (1978), and separately named by Gowlett et al. (1981)).

The dip observed in the Losokweta tuff is, however, virtually identical to that found in the various excavations in the Chemoigut Formation, although according to Bishop's hypothesis the latter should be in the anticline, and the former in the syncline. This suggests a possible alternative interpretation of the Chesowanja exposures as a fault-divided structure, with a lava-faced fault scarp mimicking the plunging limb of an anticline.

The Chesowanja sequence is completed by Later Stone Age finds made to the east of the Losokweta River. Here, along the dry former course of the Mukutan river, extensive scatters of stone artefacts are to be found (Bishop et al. 1975, 1978; Harris & Gowlett

1979, 1980). Individual patches extend to more than 10 m × 10 m of dense debris, mainly of lava flakes. The material includes some large lava picks, with butts formed by cobble cortex. In the same area, there are small numbers of obsidian flakes, pieces of pottery, and thin scatters of animal bones. Bishop *et al.* (1975, 1978) interpreted this evidence as representing two archaeological phases, one belonging to the Sangoan, the other to the Later Stone Age. More intensive survey of the area has shown that a single archaeological phase is represented, and that despite their appearance the lava artefacts are quite recent in date. The firmest evidence for this comes from sampling of a baked zone, a probable hearth, in the centre of one of the dense stone con-centrations. The hearth occurred in and among lava artefacts. A small piece of charcoal was found sealed in the baked sediment underlying the hearth, allowing sampling for AMS dating, and the following date was obtained (Gowlett *et al.* 1986): OxA-578, Charcoal sealed in baked clay of hearth, 2600 ± 80 BP. This date calibrated using the procedures of Pearson & Stuiver (1993) gives a calendrical range of *c.* 900–510 cal. BC, with an outlying range of *c.* 440–430 cal. BC. The date thus indicates a stage towards the end of the local Pastoral Neolithic/LSA. This tallies with evidence cited by Clark (1967) and Posnansky (1967) for Tunnel Rockshelter near Fort Ternan, where a radiocarbon date of 2730 ± 60 BP (Y1397) was obtained. In John Sutton's excavations pottery was associated with obsidian artefacts and animal bones believed to be of domestic bovids. Animal bones from the Mukutan site also include evidence of a bovine compatible with domesticated *Bos*, as well as a gazelle-sized antelope (identifications by F. Marshall).

Questions posed by the Chesowanja archaeology

The early industries and the 1/6E site

The industries of the Chemoigut Formation have been described as Developed Oldowan. The industry includes choppers and bifacial cores or discoids (Fig. 3). There are no finds of Karari scrapers, such as found in the Karari industry to the north at Lake Turkana (Harris & Herbich 1978; Harris & Isaac 1978), nor of any 'other bifaces' or 'proto-bifaces' as found in Developed Oldowan B and A at Olduvai (Leakey 1971), with the single exception of an apparent long pick on a cobble, which was an isolated surface find. Features of the industry, coupled with its dating, suggest that the industry may border on the Acheulean tradition. It is older than the basalt (1.4 ± 0.07 Ma), the fauna includes *Deinotherium bozasi,* and *Australopithecus boisei* is present. This evidence is consistent in suggesting a minimum age of about 1.3 Ma, but there is nothing to set a lower limit. As the Acheulean elsewhere may begin as early as 1.5 Ma, there is the possibility of a temporal overlap. What tends to blur the issue is that industries on other sites may embrace contemporary cultural and/or facies variation, as in Olduvai Bed II (Leakey 1971; Davis 1980; Stiles 1979*a, b*). Chesowanja might be seen as supporting evidence for the idea that the Acheulean developed gradually in E. Africa, but the evidence remains equivocal, here and elsewhere.

Although the only hominid remains found at Chesowanja are of *Australopithecus boisei,* Gowlett *et al.* (1981) were inclined to suggest that the maker of the stone industry was *Homo erectus.* If anything, the case for this link has strengthened, through additional finds of *H. erectus* at early dates, the frequency with which *Homo* is found on artefact sites where *A. boisei* is found, and the continued association of *Homo erectus* and bifaces following the demise of *A. boisei.* The issue is discussed further below.

The most controversial aspect of the Chesowanja evidence is the evidence of fire or burning first reported by Gowlett *et al.* (1981) (see also Harris *et al.* 1981; Clark & Harris 1985; James 1989; Bellomo 1993, 1994). The primary evidence is presented by a series of baked clay lumps found in the 1/6E excavation. This site is on the east side of Window 1. It was the largest excavation, over about 40 m^2 and yielded about 600 artefacts (Table 1). The clay clasts undoubtedly represent burnt material. Analyses by Walton gave temperatures of around 600°C (Gowlett *et al.* 1981). The initial publication did not emphasize the variety in size of the clasts, although a figure of the distribution was provided. This gave the impression that the pieces were scattered randomly along a channel floor (Fig. 4a). A size/weight distribution, however, makes clear that all the larger pieces are concentrated in a limited area 1.5 × 1 m (the 'Q zone'). There is also a concentration of larger stone finds in this area (Table 1). Further inspection of the pattern shows that the remaining pieces of baked material fall into two groups, one low, containing moderate sized pieces, the other a high lens or patch consisting largely of flecks of 1 g or less (Fig. 5). In all, 30 of the finds weigh 5 g or less.

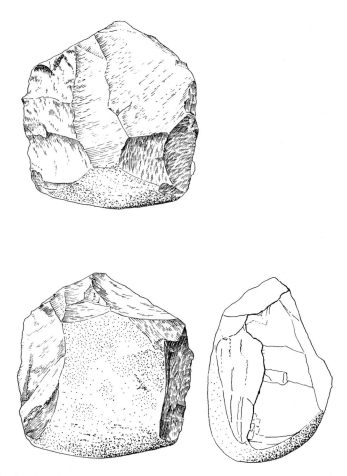

Fig. 3. Chesowanja: drawing of an Oldowan chopper from GnJi 1/6E. Reproduced ×0.6.

As a first step towards interpretation in terms of palaeocurrent and taphonomy it is necessary to remove the post-depositional dip of the sediments. Once this is done, it becomes apparent that finds at the east of the excavation were considerably lower than those in the NW corner,

suggesting a flow direction of west to east. This leads to a most parsimonious interpretation that burnt clay material was washed away from an initial limited distribution (Q zone), subsequently accumulating in the base of a nearby depression ('Lower spread'). This depression then gradually filled with sediment, through a depth of *c.* 50 cm, until it reached the level of Q: a few last flecks of burnt clay were transported as this level was approached (Fig. 5: 'Upper spread').

This interpretation is clearly compatible with the hypothesis that the Q area represents an actual hearth concentration. The question is whether any test can assess this conclusively. An alternative hypothesis is that a natural fire occurred just outside the frame of the excavation, and that baked material washed into the excavation area in two phases.

To summarize, evidence pointing towards a hearth concentration is not restricted to the clay lumps, but consists of the following:

Table 1. *Composition of finds distribution in Cheso-wanja GnJi 1/6E*

	Q zone	Rest of trench
Area (m²)	1.4	40
All finds	162	559
No. of baked clay clasts	10	41
Weight of baked clay (g)	773	136
Average weight of clast (g)	77.3	3.3
No. of bones	3	63
No. of stones >500 g	5	7
No. of stones 100–500 g	17	29

(a)

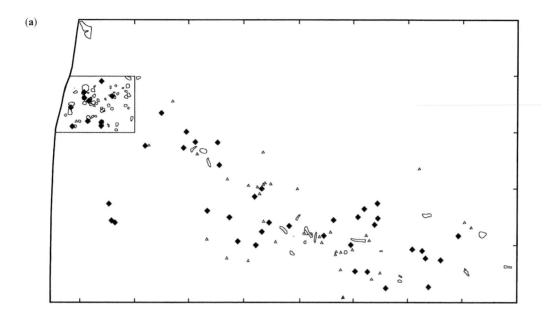

(b)

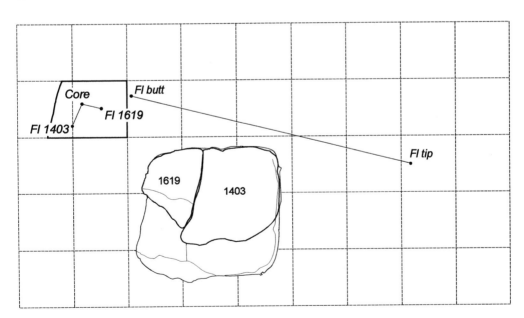

Fig. 4. Chesowanja site GnJi 1/6E. (**a**) The excavation showing the 'Q zone' with all drawn finds; and the remaining area showing bones (open triangles and shapes) and the baked clay distribution (black diamonds). The latter can be compared with Fig. 5, which shows the baked clay finds according to weight (north to top). (**b**) Refits shown against the excavation grid (in metres). Inset: the refitting cobble from the Q zone (actual size about 65 × 60 mm).

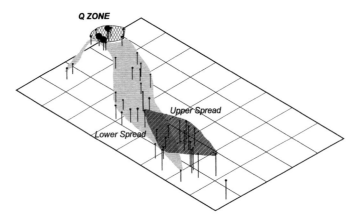

Fig. 5. Chesowanja 1/6E: reconstruction of baked clay dispersal. On this diagram the pins indicate the height of pieces, *as in the present day*. The Q zone is at a lower absolute level than other finds, but when dip is removed, it becomes higher. Relative size of the burnt clay pieces is indicated (north to top right).

(1) The distribution in the Q area, which is different in kind, and in density, from the rest of the area.

(2) The concentration in it is not limited to baked clay, but also consists of cobbles and large artefacts.

(3) The concentration does not consist preferentially of large elements. It is also a centre of smaller elements in each of the weight classes.

(4) There is a negative association with bone, except for three fragments at depth.

(5) The conjoining group of two flakes and one core (cause of fracture not known for certain) suggests very limited disturbance in this area (Fig. 4b).

(6) The temperature of burning, as pointed out in the 1981 paper, is consistent with camp fire temperatures.

Clearly the arguments of interpretation do not hang on any simple concept of disturbed/ undisturbed, primary/secondary. As with most depositional contexts, more detailed study yields a more complex picture. The analyses of Blumenschine show that the faunal assemblage may well be secondary, and have little to do with the Q area (Harris *et al.* 1983; Clark & Harris 1985). Some of the long bones appear aligned with current direction. The scatter of stone artefacts is also equivocal in its information. Few refits have been found, suggesting an incomplete assemblage. One refit of a flake body and its distal end supports the idea of movement in the same trend direction suggested by the scatter of baked clay (Fig. 4b). On the other hand, the tight group of refits in the Q area indicates that

there was minimal disturbance *in at least one phase of deposition*.

Thus the strongest support for favouring the alternative hypothesis of natural fire is given by these points:

(1) there is no single coherent baked patch;

(2) there is no overall structured pattern of bones relative to other debris;

(3) there is certain evidence of some level of disturbance to both artefacts and clay clasts.

A scenario could be envisaged in which a forest fire could burn around a dead stump, clasts could become detached in subsequent erosion, and they could then become mixed with archaeological finds and fauna.

Interpretation of the Chesowanja evidence is somewhat complicated by the presence of robust australopithecines. This provides an interesting example of the weighting of arguments. A view seeking simple parsimony would proceed along these lines: that any hominid might in principle make tools; that robust australopithecines have well developed thumbs, suggesting tool-making manipulations; and that where there are two occurrences of this hominid close to artefacts, this is suggestive of a link. Against this, however, one can take a broader view of the arguments (as does Oliver 1994).

(1) Remains of the 'more advanced' *Homo* are found elsewhere alongside robust australopithecine remains on several sites in several environments.

(2) The absence of *Homo* has no special significance, since hominids do not tend to die in their living area so as to provide markers.

(3) Chesowanja represents a Developed Old-owan, possibly including early picks as found in the Acheulean, and Acheulean industries are commonly associated with *Homo ergaster/erectus* and *Homo sapiens/ heidelbergensis*.

The Losokweta industry

Further questions of current interest are posed by the Losokweta industry, underlying the Loso-kweta tuff. There are no signs of bifaces within the industry. To what extent may non-biface industries occur as local phenomena (windows) within the Acheulean? The need for caution in assessing this is emphasized by the number of localities lacking bifaces found *within* major Acheulean complexes, and the number of cases in which rare bifaces have eventually appeared after long investigation (e.g. Barnham, Swan-scombe: Ashton *et al.* 1994; McNabb 1996). Even so, the very consistent use of very small tools in two localities of the Losokweta industry raises the possibility that it really is a distinct industrial facies local to the area.

Kilombe

The Acheulean site complex of Kilombe lies close to the southwestern margin of the Baringo Basin, on the western flank of the rift. The site was discovered by W. B. Jones in the course of geological mapping within the framework of EAGRU. Bill Bishop then organized further geological work (published in Bishop 1978), in the context of which the author began archae-ological investigations (Gowlett 1978, 1991, 1993). The features which make Kilombe espe-cially worthy of study in the Acheulean world are its areal extent, stratigraphic structure and facies variability (variety). The main horizon is far more extensive than individual localities at Olorgesailie, Olduvai or Kalambo Falls. The site also provides a rare East African case of activity on a clayey surface, as at Olduvai Bed I rather than on sands and silts – allowing comparisons of site formation processes and taphonomy. The main new aspects of study at Kilombe, however, are focused on the relation between artefact variation and site palaeogeography.

Stratigraphic and chronological framework

W. B. Jones carried out detailed mapping around Kilombe (Jones 1975; Jones & Lippard 1979). The Londiani region had been mapped by Jennings (1971), and the caldera described by McCall (1964). Bishop (1978) gives an account of the site area, and the local sequence. The western side of the Rift Valley in this area does not exhibit large fault scarps, but is dominated by two large extinct trachytic volcanoes, Londiani and Kilombe (Jennings 1971). There are, how-ever, numerous minor faults, generally trend-ing north–south. The lowest unit of the local Pleistocene sequence consists of trachyphono-lites dated to 1.7 ± 0.05 Ma by K-Ar, regarded by Jones as roughly contemporary with one of the later trachyte flows of the nearby Kilombe mountain, dated to 1.9 ± 0.15 Ma.

The main Kilombe site (GqJhl under the African site naming system) lies about 4 km southeast of Kilombe Mountain and about 10 km south of the Equator (co-ordinates 0°06'S, 35°53'E). The present-day setting of the site gives some useful general information about the past environment. The area is now drained by the Rongai and Molo rivers, which rise high on the Mau escarpment and flow NNE down to Lake Baringo, descending some 1500 m in 100 km. The highlands receive far higher rainfall than the basin, spread through several more months of the year. This situation is unlikely to have altered appreciably within the last million years. Sited on a gentle spur approximately half-way between rift valley floor and mountains, Kilombe would always have had an advanta-geous well watered position, with good access to a range of local environments (Fig. 6). The sites are at a level of around 1800 m the Rift Valley floor at c. 1500 m while Kilombe mountain rises to c. 2200 m. Although the Molo and Rongai may be modern features, it is difficult to see that the main lines of drainage from the west and southwest were ever far from the site area.

Locally the trachyphonolites are overlain by up to 30 m of sediments, derived partly from sub-aerial weathering of the lavas, partly from later volcanic eruptions. These sands, clays and tuffs are capped in places by an ash flow tuff 7 m thick (Jones 1975, 1985). The main artefact horizon extends for nearly 200 m, and is associated with an almost level surface at the top of brown clays which overlie the trachyphonolite rocks to a depth of several metres. There are some minor variations of surface topography and evidence of occasional small stream channels marked by sandy lenses 2 or 3 m wide. Mostly, however, the main artefact horizon lies on clay, overlain by a pale weathered pumice tuff which contrasts sharply in colour and composition with the underlying brown clays. These pumices have a consistency near to that of clay. In places they include signs of at least two weathering periods

Fig. 6. The setting of Kilombe on a base of 10×20 km, showing the mountains of Kilombe and Londiani (background; north to top right). The site is favourably placed to have access to several different parts of the landscape.

separating phases of deposition. In one area a scatter of small artefacts was found about 1 m above the main horizon (Gowlett 1978). As noted by Bishop (1978), the sudden increment of tuff made a sharp lithological contrast, not only sealing in the main horizon artefacts, leaving them virtually undisturbed, but also burying all other trachyphonolite outcrops and their derived clay products throughout the drainage basin.

The tuffs and palaeosols are overlain by a distinctive 'three-banded' brown lapilli tuff, around 1 m thick. The three beds exhibit graded bedding and are well laminated, leading Bishop to conclude that they were deposited in still water. Above the tuff further pumiceous sands, clays and tuffs were deposited, until the sequence was capped by the ash-flow tuff. Acheulean artefacts have been found in these upper levels at two further sites, GqJh2 and GqJh3 (1200 m ENE and 500 m NW of the main site, respectively), both appearing to be low density occurrences. Small collections of surface artefacts have been studied, but neither site has been excavated. In the main site area there is evidence of later channelling, at an unknown date, but this did not extend down to the level of the artefacts.

The archaeological sites are certainly quite considerably later in date than the lavas forming the base of the Kilombe sequence (dated by K-Ar to *c.* 1.8 Ma: Jones 1975), but no K-Ar dates have been obtained for tuffs in the neighbourhood of the site. The best dating evidence is therefore provided by palaeomagnetic measurements on the sediments. Samples taken from the three-banded tuff, overlying the main artefact horizon, show reversed magnetization, almost

certainly indicating an age in the Matuyama epoch, that is over 0.78 Ma (Dagley *et al.* 1978). A single trial sample from a higher level, processed by Dr J. Shaw, indicates that at least part of the sequence above this tuff is normal in magnetization, presumably belonging within the Brunhes. Other evidence is less direct but consistent with this dating of the site. Faunal remains are not highly diagnostic, but Dr J. Harris (pers. comm.) has indicated that pig teeth are in the range 0.4–1.0 Ma. The scanty faunal remains come exclusively from the brown clays underlying the main horizon. Apart from one bovid tooth and part of a scapula found in a deep sounding, all come from surface exposures. Accidents of preservation unfortunately prevent identification to species level in almost all cases. There is evidence, however, for a range of bovids from gazelle-size to buffalo-size, pigs, elephant, hippopotamus and crocodile (Bishop 1978; Gowlett 1985).

Site palaeogeography

The sinuous exposures at Kilombe provide us with various clues about the palaeogeography of the sites. On the main site the artefact distribution is estimated to cover up to 14 000 m² (Fig. 7a), and has been explored by excavation and by study of surface artefacts in various parts of the site. Further indications are given by comparison of sections some hundreds of metres to the west and east with those of the main site. These provide information about past topography, as the depth between the base of the

(a)

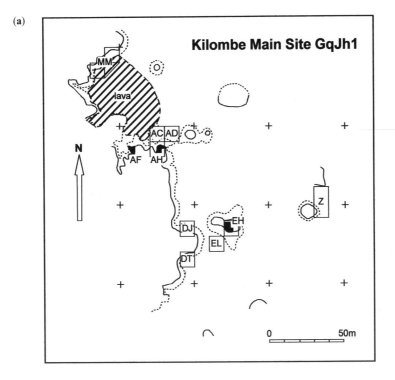

(b)

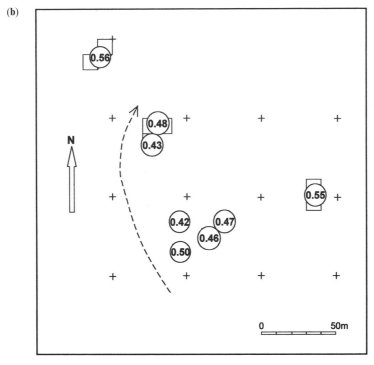

Fig. 7. Plan of the Kilombe site showing: (**a**) positions of biface samples in respect to the main scarp (surface samples deisgnated by letters; excavations in black); (**b**) mean thickness/breadth figures for the bifaces from the various areas. Dotted line shows the probable course of an ancient stream course.

three-banded tuff and the top of the brown clays varies from section to section. Following the assumption of Bishop (1978) that the base of the tuff was approximately level at the time of deposition, the site is seen to be in a broad shallow depression. On the main site, the pale weathered tuff is m or more thick, but at GqJh3 to the west and GqJh4 to the east (a small exposure found in 1985) it is of the order of 20–30 cm. Together the exposures suggest that there was a broad drainageway, some hundreds of metres across, with the surface evidently rising by about a metre at its edges. The slope of these edges has not been observed. A clue as to drainage direction may be provided by a fine powdery white deposit – a tuff not a diatomite – which crosses the site area on a north–south axis immediately below the three-banded tuff. This band, just a few metres wide, may represent a final stage in the filling of the main gully. Drainage would have been controlled to some degree by outcrops of lava rising above the brown clays. It appears that there was an outcrop of this nature to the NW of the drainage gully. One or two rounded boulders exposed here suggest the presence of a larger channel nearby.

The main artefact horizon lies on a distinctive grey-green clay, which may indicate seasonal waterlogging or gleying in the depression. Open water was evidently close to the site; it is possible that the artefacts were submerged on occasions when the level rose. Physically, their state varies from quite fresh to considerably abraded. There are signs that sometimes alteration took place *in situ*, and was partly chemical in nature, since some specimens are more abraded on the top surface than underneath.

Questions in current research:
geographic variation

Recent studies of the Acheulean offer insights into use of landscape (e.g. Potts 1989, 1994; Tuffreau *et al.* 1997). Kilombe offers a striking picture of variation *within* a single relatively continuous large complex. Excavations and surface observations in all parts of the site show that the dense concentrations of artefacts are closely associated with a single level, the junction between the brown clays and the overlying pale weathered pumice tuff. In EH and AH excavations, separated by around 60 m the surface of the clay was approximately horizontal, and assemblage composition remains very similar. A sounding in area AF, in contrast, exposed a slope of the clay surface down into a small channel or runnel. Here bifaces were almost

absent, although there were small flakes, and concentrations of cobbles.

The Kilombe site complex gives a prime example of the combination of facies variation and facies stability which seems to characterize the Acheulean. A simple hypothesis is that a large site in a favoured area is probably close to a living area, and therefore probably multi-functional. Nevertheless, it is uncertain whether the main area represents more than a particular facies: its very stability from area to area suggests the use of a particular toolkit for particular tasks (cf. the Somme sites: Tuffreau *et al.* 1997).

Even so, it has become plain that the main horizon includes components of variation which are specific to certain areas, making it unlikely that it accumulated gradually as a randomized scatter. Rather, it suggests local reoccupations by hominids over a long period. Nevertheless, it is a long-term 'favoured place'. Local variation in key parameters is discussed below. The main determinants of artefact variation can be seen as:

(1) tradition/style
(2) functional requirements (as in different activities)
(3) raw material properties
(4) individual limits and requirements (i.e. size of hominids, relation of individual to tasks performed by group).

For the Acheulean the first three were discussed by Isaac (1972), and the fourth by Gowlett (1996). Compared with other sites it can be argued that the experimental situation of Kilombe reduces the importance of (3) and enhances opportunities to investigate (4).

Issues of raw materials

Raw material has been seen increasingly as an important element in Acheulean variation (e.g. Jones 1995; White 1995).

Over 99% of the raw materials at Kilombe are lavas (there is no quartz). Over 90% is local trachyphonolite. Numbers of the bifaces preserve smooth cobble cortex. It appears that they have been made from rounded river boulders, of diameter *c.* 30–60 cm. The absence of part-worked cores of these (unless in very worked-down form) indicates that biface blanks were brought to the site. There were originally no signs as to how far these blanks were carried. Recent erosion, however, has exposed two complete rounded boulders in the fine-grained brown clays at the north end of the site, close to a rock outcrop. The position of these boulders, evidently rounded in a river, in isolation in the clays is unusual. Exotic materials occur in low proportion. Trachyte, probably from Kilombe mountain, makes up a few per cent of bifaces, but does not occur among the cobbles. Three bifaces of obsidian have been found on the surface. Thin section studies indicated that this was not the same as obsidian used at Kariandusi (Leakey 1931; Gowlett 1980). The nearest known obsidian source is on Londiani 13 km away (Merrick & Brown 1984), but it is likely that the material came from further afield.

The bifaces

Kilombe is astonishingly rich in bifaces, which occur over a large area, concentrated on the single surface represented by the main horizon. Already the site has demonstrated an almost unparalleled opportunity to examine a picture of contemporary variation across a surface. The bifaces occur at densities of up to several per square metre (AH excavation c. 2 per m^2; EH c. 4 per m^2). Through the measurement of the excavated bifaces and the photography of samples of surface material in various localities, an excellent dataset of biface material has gradually been accumulated. There is the potential to improve this greatly using stereophotographs, and digitized information. So far artefact measurements have been based on the 'traditional' schemes of Isaac (1997), similar to that of Roe (1964, 1968), but recent trends in artefact measurement show the possibilities of capturing total representations, through digitization and solid-modelling (Crompton 1997).

As is typical of many bifaces in Africa, the majority are made on large flakes. At Kilombe they have a mean of c. 15 cm in length. In many cases traces of the bulb and platform remain. The finish of individual specimens is remarkably varied. They range from those with very few flake scars, and perhaps 80% cortex remaining on one face, to others such as finely flaked ovates, with little or no cortex (Gowlett 1996). The local lavas are not easy to work well, and many bifaces drawn in section show the 'stepping out' of secondary flakes, so that lenticular sections were not generally achieved. Very few, if any, bifaces have been formed using complete cobbles as a blank.

Analyses of the Kilombe specimens in metrical terms have proceeded as new datasets have been brought into play. The basic position contrasts with that at Olorgesailie and Isimila, where assemblages which can be regarded as 'penecontemporaneous' (i.e. of approximately the same age; e.g. Isaac 1972) vary strikingly from locality to locality. At Kilombe variation on the main surface appears to be far more restrained, but it has gradually assumed some remarkable elements of geographic pattern (Fig. 7b).

The bifaces vary little from sample to sample in their basic dimensions. That is, each sample has a mean length of c. 15 cm, and there is constant presence of specimens as small as 9 cm and as large as 22 cm. Cleavers are present persistently in a minority, ranging from c. 9.5 to 27%. Thickness, however, varies greatly. For example, in Area Z the ratio T/B is 0.55 ± 0.12, compared with 0.47 ± 0.12 in EH and 0.43 ± 0.10 in AH. Some specimens from Area Z are extraordinarily thick and heavy, but they are clearly finished pieces. The extra thickness of Area Z bifaces is not a matter of chance, but is statistically significant at the $P = 0.01$ level in t-tests. Similar thickness has now been observed in the MM sample. This aspect of thickness variation at Kilombe can now be seen to have a suggestive geographic pattern (Fig. 7b), with unusually thin bifaces being found near the centre of the site, perhaps along the former watercourse. Tantalizingly, the variation remains unexplained. It has nothing to do with the sophistication of the artefacts (but demonstrates clearly the point that relative thickness cannot be used as a chronological indicator).

Overall dimensions of bifaces are very similar for each Kilombe sample, but a cluster analysis has suggested that there are distinct groups of small and large specimens within each set (Gowlett 1986, 1988). The method used was the 'Mode Analysis' of Wishart (1969, 1975). It indicates that similar 'large' and 'small' bifaces occur in assemblages at both the north and south of the site, having mean lengths of c. 15–16 cm and 9–10 cm respectively. It was argued that the two groups recognized may correspond in some way with the divisions of 'Developed Oldowan B' and 'Acheulean' made in Olduvai Bed II (Leakey 1971, 1975), although Leakey's distinction at Olduvai was based on assemblage composition as well as biface shape and size. Jones (1995) has also emphasized the importance of raw material and extent of retrimming in the distinction – factors which are not evident at Kilombe. Mary Leakey's classification of the Olduvai assemblages led to some debate about the meaning of the two variants, and whether they were made by different hominid species (e.g. Leakey 1971; Stiles 1979a, b; Davis 1980). The evidence from Kilombe gives a strong indication that similar variation occurs on other sites, and that here it belongs within a single cultural tradition (Gowlett 1988). As the two elements are not distinguished by raw materials, their presence must relate to size/shape choices made by early humans, probably in response to distinct functional needs. This need not even imply that different tasks were being performed: one possibility considered was that the two modes represent tools used in one hand and by two hands respectively.

Allometry and symmetry

The Kilombe dataset allows testing of any parameter of interest in biface variation, on this basis: 'Does short-term local variation cast light on long-term regional variation?' In this way the material has provided a useful test bench for studies of allometry, and it also has potential for studying symmetry. Crompton & Gowlett (1993) applied multivariate allometry (MVA), hoping to determine whether bifaces were made with shape adjustments according to size. The results show clear and consistent adjustments, not just for Kilombe, but for the Africa Acheulean in general (Gowlett & Crompton 1994; Crompton & Gowlett 1997). Not surprisingly, similar results are found in most areas of the Kilombe site – with the intriguing exception of Area Z. The general trend, at Kilombe and elsewhere, is for small bifaces to be

relatively squat and compact, and for large ones to be made thin and weight-saving. Area Z shows an opposite tendency for larger specimens to be thick and heavy. The only comparable dataset is one examined recently from the Sangoan at Kalambo Falls (Gowlett et al. in press). Another finding is that larger bifaces tend to be more asymmetric – a topic for further exploration (Toth 1990). The last point of general interest is that there is a very close similarity between the Kilombe allometry pattern and that seen in the bifaces from Kapthurin (Gowlett & Crompton 1994), even though the latter are about 500 000 years younger, and are technologically far more advanced (see below).

Other elements of variation

Bifaces are just one element of the assemblages. Heavy-duty tools, such as are well known from other Acheulean and Sangoan sites, are far less common than bifaces at Kilombe, although they may outnumber bifaces at some levels above the three-banded tuff. The numbers involved allow only general statements. Choppers are most common, but the sample is insufficient to suggest standardized forms, other perhaps than a 'sub-rectangular' variant.

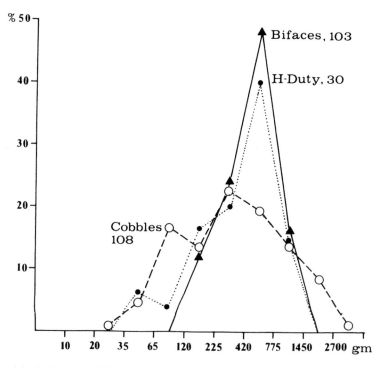

Fig. 8. The weight distribution of bifaces and cobbles from Kilombe GqJh1 EH.

Cobbles may be an important part of the picture, since their distribution, density and average weight correspond closely with those of the bifaces. Their size and weight range is, however, more extended (Fig. 8). As at Olorgesailie, only local rock is found among the cobbles. Flakes have been detached from some specimens. The presence of so many cobbles is a mystery, but cannot be ignored in considering human behaviour on the site. It seems likely that the larger specimens were used as small working surfaces: in the excavations they were commonly surrounded by small clusters of bifaces. Natural agency is unlikely to be responsible for their presence, since taphonomic experiments have shown that large objects do not move far on the clay surface on shallow slopes, even over a period of ten years or more.

Most of the flake tools are simple scrapers. As on so many sites, they are rather larger than the associated debitage. This debitage consists of a scatter of small flakes, found right across the site. These include hand-axe trimming flakes, but not in sufficient numbers to account for the primary shaping of the bifaces. The main feature of interest is illustrated by a study of the length distribution (Gowlett 1993). As at Olorgesailie, there is a bimodal distribution of length when flakes and bifaces are plotted together. The position contrasts markedly with that at Kariandusi, or STIC (Casablanca: Biberson 1961), where a substantial proportion of long flakes occurs. This observation provides a further useful working distinction between Acheulean sites, one which may not be apparent from the bifaces themselves. It seems likely that Kilombe and Olorgesailie are primarily use-sites for bifaces, and that they are sufficiently far from the factory site for other long flakes to have been winnowed out of the repertoire. Kariandusi, on the other hand, is close to a trachyte source, and STIC to quartzite raw material.

Conclusion

The importance of the Baringo archaeological sequence lies in its length and sporadic richness, but largely in its ability to provide an alternative view. It is often not quite the same record as elsewhere. Both the Oldowan and Acheulean traditions are very long-lived, and show a great deal of sameness. This can lead to the impression that they can be summarized from a few grand successions, and that they need not be sampled very intensively. In its bittiness the Baringo record provides something of a correction. Variability itself is rather a dull word. Even

so, it is at the core of Stone Age study, often – if it can be turned – the only key to hominid behaviour, and the Baringo record emphasizes that message.

In terms of site formation, the Baringo record is important because it preserves sites in clay, which is underrepresented elsewhere in East Africa, except at Olduvai Bed I. The sites are not undisturbed, but equally disturbance is limited. They allow comparisons at a taphonomic level. The Oldowan assemblages are just large enough to offer typological and technological comparisons with other sites. Chesowanja presents many puzzles over the case of fire. These are more likely to be answered by systematic long-term multisite studies than as a single investigation. As a tacit point of archaeological methodology, it may well be that archaeologists are unwilling to accept a definite answer from a single site. A more pressing need is to build up a corpus of behaviour, retaining alternative hypotheses (Potts 1994).

The Baringo Basin contributes a good deal to Acheulean studies. The Acheulean is the longest lasting of all archaeological traditions, but for its earlier part (in the lower Pleistocene, over 0.78 Ma) there is only a limited number of sites for comparison. Potassium-argon dates of c. 1.0 Ma obtained from Kariandusi, just 60 km from Kilombe, were backed up by dates of c. 1.4 Ma for Peninj and for the oldest Olduvai Acheulean (Evernden & Curtis 1965; Isaac & Curtis 1974; Leakey 1975; Gowlett & Crompton 1994). Other Acheulean sites of Lower Pleistocene age have been found in Ethiopia, at Gadeb (Clark 1980), Melka Kontouré (Chavaillon 1980; Chavaillon et al. 1979) and Konso-Gardula (Asfaw et al. 1992). The kind of material found at Kilombe would once have been placed in the 'Upper Acheulean', but other sites now provide a secure context for accepting it at about 800 000. Similarly early dating for Olorgesailie and Olduvai Bed IV reinforces this point (Bye et al. 1987; Potts 1989; Leakey 1975; Leakey and Roe 1995). No typological series of evolution in the East African Acheulean is easily recognizable. At Olduvai it is explicitly denied by Leakey (1975), and Isaac also was sceptical, finding no certain patterns within the Olorgesailie sequence (Isaac 1977). The contemporaneous variation in thickness/breadth measurements of bifaces at Kilombe particularly emphasizes the danger of arbitrary interpretations.

Nevertheless, from the beginning to the end of the Acheulean there is clearly change, and in broad terms this may be relevant to the emergence of Homo sapiens. Most of the sites just mentioned have certain general similarities in the preference for broad lanceolate bifaces, tending towards the amygdaloid shape of Bordes (1961). Sharply pointed 'Micoquian' or ficron shapes are notably absent. Generally also, hand-axes are more prevalent than cleavers. Extremely pointed bifaces occur in the region, perhaps at later dates – at Chesowanja, above the Chesowanja Formation. The same general form appears to be present at Khor Abu Anga (Arkell 1949) and the important Kenyan site of Isenya (Roche *et al*. 1988). Yet there are few dated sites through the Middle Pleistocene, until one comes to Kapthurin, where some straight-edged pointed bifaces are also found.

The most striking aspect of continuity and change comes from comparing the bifaces of Kilombe and Kapthurin, 500 000 years apart. The dramatic continuity is that of the allometry pattern, virtually identical on the two sites (Fig. 9). The remarkable point about this is

that the Kapthurin bifaces show a radical new departure in technology (McBrearty *et al*. 1996). Complete bifaces were struck off prepared cores as single flakes, accompanied also by Levallois technique for the production of flake-blades. Although large flakes were used as the basis for bifaces at Kilombe, as at Kariandusi and other early sites, these lack radial preparation of the face and a facetted platform, both commonly present at Kapthurin. Kapthurin is amongst the earliest of sites to show full Levallois technology, and it shows superb mastery of the technology – *but coupled with a far, far, older pattern of biface production.*

There is a temptation here to see a line of continuity through the Middle Pleistocene, perhaps associated with archaic *Homo sapiens*, the ancestors of modern *Homo sapiens*, except that we know the picture is more complicated. A very different late variant of the Lower

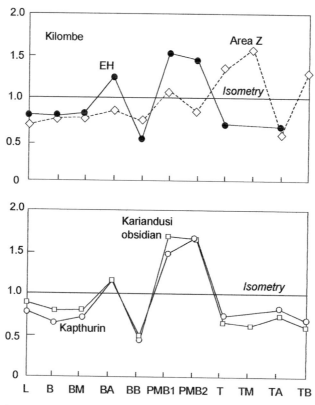

Fig. 9. The multivariate allometry of Acheulean bifaces Kilombe, Kapthurin and Kariandusi (redrawn from data in Gowlett & Crompton 1994). The variables along the base are those of the Isaac measuring scheme (e.g. Isaac 1977). At Kilombe there are two patterns: the common Acheulean pattern, and the distinctive pattern of Area Z which appears to recur at Kalambo Falls. The allometry patterns of Kariandusi obsidian (aged about 1.0 Ma) and of the Kapthurin LHR bifaces (aged about 0.25 Ma) are strikingly similar, indicating a powerful element of continuity.

Palaeolithic, the Sangoan–Lupemban, has been described from Muguruk in western Kenya (McBrearty 1988), and not so much further away is the Sangoan of Kalambo Falls itself (Clark in press). The Sangoan can perhaps be accommodated within a broader interpretation of the Acheulean (the 'Area Z' heavy-duty material at Kilombe has an allometry pattern close to that of the Kalambo Falls Sangoan), but this again would emphasize that the record is complex, even more so than has been suspected.

I am grateful to the late W. W. Bishop, M. Butler and G. Isaac for my early opportunities in Kenya; and also particularly to M. Butler, R. Leakey and P. Carter; also to K. Mulwa, P. Tallon and P. Dagley. Early work at Kilombe was supported by Cambridge University Worts and Smuts Funds; later help has been received from the Boise Fund. In respect of Chesowanja, I am especially grateful to J. W. K. Harris, G. Dawson, J. Kimengich; in more recent research to A. Field, F. Marshall, R. Mühlen-Schulpe and M. Redfern. Research at Chesowanja has received support from Wenner-Gren and Leakey Foundations, and the Boise Fund. I also thank colleagues of Oxford Radiocarbon Accelerator Unit for the Mukutan radiocarbon date.

References

ANDRESEN, S. A., BELL, D. A., HALLOS, J., PUMPHREY, T. R. J. & GOWLETT, J. A. J. 1997. Approaches to the analysis of evidence from the Acheulean site of Beeches Pit, Suffolk, England. In: SINCLAIR, A., SLATER, E. & GOWLETT, J. (eds) Archaeological Sciences 1995. Proceedings of a conference on the application of scientific techniques to the study of archaeology. Oxbow Monographs 64, Oxbow, Oxford, 389–394.

ARKELL, A. J. 1949. The Old Stone Age in the AngloEgyptian Sudan. Sudan Antiquities Service Occasional Paper, No. 1, Khartoum.

ASFAW, B., BEYENE, Y., SUWA, G., WALTER, R. C., WHITE, T. D., WOLDEGABRIEL, G. & YEMANE, T. 1992. The earliest Acheulean at Konso-Gardula. Nature, 360, 732–735.

ASHTON, N. M., BOWEN, D. Q., HOLMAN, J. A., et al. 1994. Excavations at the Lower Palaeolithic site at East Farm, Barnham, Suffolk 1989–92. Journal of the Geological Society, London, 151, 599–605.

BELLOMO, R. V. 1993. A methodological approach for identifying archaeological evidence of fire resulting from human activities. Journal of Archaeological Science, 20, 525–555.

——1994. Methods of determining early hominid behavioural activities associated with the controlled use of fire at FxJj20 Main, Koobi Fora, Kenya. Journal of Human Evolution, 27, 173–195.

BIBERSON, P. 1961. Le Paléolithique inférieur du Maroc atlantique. Publications du Service des Antiquités du Maroc, Rabat, Fascicule 17.

BISHOP, W. W. 1978. Geological framework of the Kilombe Acheulian Site, Kenya. In: BISHOP, W. W.

(ed.) Geological Background to Fossil Man. Geological Society, London, Special Publications, 6, 329–336.

——, HILL, A. & PICKFORD, M. 1978. Chesowanja: a revised geological interpretation. In: BISHOP, W. W. (ed.) Geological Background to Fossil Man. Geological Society, London, Special Publications, 6, 309–328.

——, PICKFORD, M. & HILL, A. 1975. New evidence regarding the Quaternary geology, archaeology, and hominids of Chesowanja, Kenya. Nature, 258, 204–208.

BLUMENSCHINE, R. J., CAVALLO, J. A. & CAPALDO, S. D. 1994. Competition for carcasses and early hominid behavioural ecology: a case study and conceptual framework. Journal of Human Evolution, 27, 197–213.

BORDES, F. 1961. Typologie du Paléolithique ancien et moyen. (3rd edn, 1979). CNRS, Paris.

BYE, B. A., BROWN, F. H., CERLING, T. E. & MCDOUGALL, I. 1987. Increased age estimate for the Lower Palaeolithic hominid site at Olorgesailie, Kenya. Nature, 329, 237–239.

CARNEY, J., HILL, A., MILLER, J. A. & WALKER, A. 1971. A late Australopithecine from Baringo District, Kenya. Nature, 230, 509–514.

CHAVAILLON, J. 1980. Chronologie archéologique de Melka-Kontouré. In: LEAKEY, R. E. & OGOT, B. A. (eds) Proceedings of the 8th Panafrican Congress of Prehistory and Quaternary Studies, Nairobi 1977. TILLMIAP, Nairobi, 200–201.

——, CHAVAILLON, N., HOURS, F. & PIPERNO, N. 1979. From the Oldowan to the Middle Stone Age at Melka-Kontouré, Ethiopia: understanding cultural changes. Quaternaria, 21, 87–114.

CHAZAN, M. 1997. Redefining Levallois. Journal of Human Evolution, 33, 719–735.

CLARK, J. D. 1967. The problem of Neolithic culture in subsaharan Africa. In: BISHOP, W. W. & CLARK, J. D. (eds) Background to Evolution in Africa. University of Chicago, 601–627.

——1980. The Plio-Pleistocene environmental and cultural sequence at Gadeb, northern Bale, Ethiopia. In: LEAKEY, R. E. & OGOT, B. A. (eds) Proceedings of the 8th Panafrican Congress of Prehistory and Quaternary Studies, Nairobi 1977. TILLMIAP, Nairobi, 189–193.

—— (ed.) (in press). Kalambo Falls, Vol 3. Cambridge University.

—— & HARRIS, J. W. K. 1985. Fire and its roles in early hominid lifeways. African Archaeological Review, 3, 3–27.

CROMPTON, R. H. & GOWLETT, J. A. J. 1993. Allometry and multidimensional form in Acheulean bifaces from Kilombe, Kenya. Journal of Human Evolution, 25, 175–199.

—— & —— 1997. The Acheulean and the Sahara: allometric comparisons between North and East African sites. In: SINCLAIR, A., SLATER, E. & GOWLETT, J. (eds) Archaeological Sciences 1995. Proceedings of a conference on the application of scientific techniques to the study of archaeology. Oxbow Monographs 64, Oxbow, Oxford, 400–405.

CROMPTON, S. Y. 1996. Technology and morphology: does one follow the other? *In:* SINCLAIR, A., SLATER, E. & GOWLETT, J. (eds) *Archaeological Sciences 1995. Proceedings of a conference on the application of scientific techniques to the study of archaeology.* Oxbow Monographs **64**, Oxbow, Oxford, 413–419.

DAGLEY, P., MUSSETT, A. E. & PALMER, H. C. 1978. Preliminary observations on the palaeomagnetic stratigraphy of the area west of Lake Baringo, Kenya. *In:* BISHOP, W. W. (ed.) *Geological Background to Fossil Man,* Geological Society, London, Special Publications, **6**, 225–236.

DAVIS, D. D. 1980. Further consideration of the Developed Oldowan at Olduvai Gorge. *Current Anthropology,* **21**(6), 840–843.

DIBBLE, H. L. & BAR-YOSEF, O. (eds) 1995. *The Definition and Interpretation of Levallois Technology.* Monographs in World Archaeology **23**, Prehistory, Madison.

EVERNDEN, J. F. & CURTIS, G. H. 1965. Potassium-argon dating of late Cenozoic rocks in East Africa and Italy. *Current Anthropology,* **6**, 343–385.

GOWLETT, J. A. J. 1978. Kilombe – an Acheulian site complex in Kenya. *In:* BISHOP, W. W. (ed.) *Geological Background to Fossil Man.* Geological Society, London, Special Publications, **6**, 337–360.

——1980. Acheulean sites in the Central Rift Valley, Kenya. *In:* LEAKEY, R. E. & OGOT, B. A. (eds) *Proceedings of the 8th Panafrican Congress of Prehistory and Quaternary Studies, Nairobi 1977.* TILLMIAP, Nairobi, 213–217.

——1985. Kilombe. *Nyame Akuma,* **26**, 21–22.

——1986. Culture and conceptualisation – the Oldowan-Acheulean gradient. *In:* BAILEY, G. N. & CALLOW, P. (eds), *Stone Age Prehistory: studies in memory of Charles McBurney.* Cambridge University, 243–260.

——1988. A case of Developed Oldowan in the Acheulean? *World Archaeology,* **20**, 13–26.

——1991 Kilombe – Review of an Acheulean site complex. *In:* CLARK, J. D. (ed.) *Approaches to Understanding Early Hominid life-ways in the African Savanna.* Römisch – Germanisches Zentralmuseum Forschungsinstitut für Vor- und Frühgeschichte in Verbindung mit der UISSP, 11 Kongress, Mainz, 31 August – 5 September 1987, Monographien Band **19**, Dr Rudolf Habelt, GMBH, Bonn, 129–136.

——1993. Le site Acheuléen de Kilombe: stratigraphie, géochronologie, habitat et industrie lithique. *L'Anthropologie,* **97**(1), 69–84.

——1996. Rule systems in the artefacts of *Homo erectus* and early *Homo sapiens*: constrained or chosen. *In:* MELLARS, P. & GIBSON, K. (eds) *Modelling the Early Human Mind.* McDonald Institute for Archaeological Research, Cambridge 191–215.

—— & CROMPTON, R. H. 1994. Kariandusi: Acheulean morphology and the question of allometry. *African Archaeological Review,* **12**, 3–42.

——, —— & LI YU. (in press). The Acheulean, the Sangoan, and the role of allometry. *In:* CLARK, J. D. (ed.) *Kalambo Falls, Vol 3.* Cambridge University.

——, HALL, E. T., HEDGES, R. E. M. & PERRY, C. 1986. Radiocarbon dates from the Oxford AMS system: Archaeometry Datelist 3. *Archaeometry,* **28**(1), 116–125.

——, HARRIS, J. W. K., WALTON, D. & WOOD, B. A. 1981. Early archaeological sites, hominid remains and traces of fire from Chesowanja, Kenya. *Nature,* **294**, 125–129.

HARRIS, J. W. K. & GOWLETT, J. A. J. 1979. A preliminary report on Chesowanja. *Nyame Akuma,* **14**, 22–27.

—— & ——1980. Evidence of early stone industries at Chesowanja, Kenya. *In:* LEAKEY, R. E. & OGOT, B. A. (eds) *Proceedings of the 8th Panafrican Congress of Prehistory and Quaternary Studies, Nairobi 1977.* TILLMIAP, Nairobi, 208–212.

—— & HERBICH, I. 1978. Aspects of early Pleistocene hominid behaviour east of Lake Turkana, Kenya. *In:* BISHOP, W. W. (ed.) *Geological Background to Fossil Man.* Geological Society, London, Special Publications, **6**, 529–547.

—— & ISAAC, G. LL. 1978. Archaeology. *In:* LEAKEY, M. G. & LEAKEY, R. E. (eds) *Koobi Fora Research Project, Vol. 1.* Clarendon, Oxford, 64–85.

——, GOWLETT, J. A. J., BLUMENSCHINE, R. & MAIERS, J. E. 1983. Chesowanja – a summary of the early Pleistocene Archaeology. *9th Panafrican Congress of Prehistory and Quaternary Studies, Kano.*

——, ——, WALTON, D. & WOOD, B. A. 1981. Palaeoanthropological studies at Chesowanja. *In:* CLARK, J. D. & ISAAC, G. LL. (eds) *Las industrias mas antiguas.* Union internacional de ciencias prehistoricas y protohistoricas, X Congreso, Mexico, D.F., 64–100.

ISAAC, G. LL. 1972. Early phases of human behaviour: models in Lower Palaeolithic archaeology. *In:* CLARKE, D. L. (ed.) *Models in Archaeology.* Methuen, London, 167–199.

——1977. *Olorgesailie: Archaeological studies of a Middle Pleistocene lake basin.* University of Chicago.

—— & CURTIS, G. H. 1974. Age of Early Acheulian industries from the Peninj Group, Tanzania. *Nature,* **249**, 624–627.

JAMES, S. R. 1989. Hominid use of fire in the Lower and Middle Pleistocene: a review of the evidence. *Current Anthropology,* **30**(1), 1–26.

JENNINGS, D. J. 1971. *Geology of the Molo Area.* Ministry of Natural Resources, Geological Survey of Kenya, Report No. **86**.

JONES, P. R. 1995. Results of experimental work in relation to the stone industries of Olduvai Gorge. *In:* LEAKEY, M. D. & ROE, D. A. (eds) *Olduvai Gorge, Vol. 5.* Cambridge University, 254–298.

JONES, W. B. 1975. *The geology of the Londiani area of the Kenya Rift Valley.* PhD thesis, University of London.

——1985. Discussion on the geological evolution of the trachyte caldera volcano Menegai, Kenya Rift Valley. *Journal of the Geological Society, London,* **142**, 711–712.

—— & LIPPARD, S. J. 1979. New age determinations and geology of the Kenya Rift–Kavirondo Rift junction, W. Kenya. *Journal of the Geological Society, London,* **136**, 693–704.

KRINGS, M., STONE, A., SCHMITZ, R. W., KRAIN-ITZKI, H., STONEKING, M. & PÄÄBO, S. 1997. Neandertal DNA sequences and the origin of modern humans. *Cell*, **90**, 19–30.

LEAKEY, L. S. B. 1931. *The Stone Age Cultures of Kenya Colony*. Cambridge University, reprinted 1971, Cass, London.

LEAKEY, M., TOBIAS, P. V., MARTYN, J. E. & LEAKEY, R. E. F. 1969. An Acheulian industry with prepared core technique and the discovery of a contemporary hominid at Lake Baringo, Kenya. *Proceedings of the Prehistoric Society*, **35**, 48–76.

LEAKEY, M. D. 1971. *Olduvai Gorge. Vol. 3: Excavations in Beds I and II 1960–1963*. Cambridge University.

——1975. Cultural patterns in the Olduvai sequence. *In*: BUTZER, K. W. & ISAAC, G. LL. (eds) *After the Australopithecines*. Mouton, The Hague, 477–494.

—— & ROE, D. A. (eds) 1995. *Olduvai Gorge, Vol. 5*. Cambridge University.

MCBREARTY, S. 1988. The Sangoan–Lupemban and Middle Stone Age sequence at the Muguruk site, western Kenya. *World Archaeology*, **19**, 379–420.

——1999 The archaeology of the Kapthurin Formation. *This volume*.

——, BISHOP, L. C. & KINGSTON, J. D. 1996. Variability in traces of Middle Pleistocene hominid behaviour in the Kapthurin Formation, Baringo, Kenya. *Journal of Human Evolution*, **30**, 563–580.

MCCALL, G. J. H. 1964. Kilombe caldera, Kenya. *Proceedings of the Geologists' Association*, **75**, 563–572.

MCNABB, J. 1996. More from the cutting edge: bifaces from the Clactonian. *Antiquity*, **70**, 428–436.

MERRICK, H. V. & BROWN, F. H. 1984. Obsidian sources and patterns of source utilization in Kenya and northern Tanzania: some initial findings. *African Archaeological Review*, **2**, 129–152.

OLIVER, J. S. 1994. Estimates of hominid and carnivore involvement in the FLK Zinjanthropus fossil assemblage: some socioecological implications. *Journal of Human Evolution*, **27**, 267–294.

——, SIKES, N. E. & STEWART, K. M. (eds) 1994. Early Hominid Behavioural Ecology. *Journal of Human Evolution, 27*(1–3).

PEARSON, G. W. & STUIVER, M. 1993. High-precision bidecadal calibration of the radiocarbon time scale 500–2500 BC. *Radiocarbon*, **35**, 25–33.

PITTS, M. & ROBERTS, M. 1997. *Fairweather Eden*. Century, London.

POSNANSKY, M. 1967. The Iron Age in East Africa *In*: BISHOP, W. W. & CLARK, J. D. (eds) *Background to Evolution in Africa*. University of Chicago, 629–649.

POTTS, R. 1989. Olorgesailie: new excavations and findings in Early and Middle Pleistocene contexts,

southern Kenya Rift Valley. *Journal of Human Evolution*, **18**, 477–484.

——1994. Variables versus models of early Pleistocene hominid land use. *Journal of Human Evolution*, **27**, 7–24.

RIGHTMIRE, G. P. 1996. The human cranium from Bodo, Ethiopia: evidence for speciation in the Middle Pleistocene? *Journal of Human Evolution*, **31**, 21–39.

ROCHE, H., BRUGAL, J.-P., LEFÈVRE, D., PLOUX, S. & TEXIER, P.-J. 1988. Isenya: état des recherches sur un nouveau site acheuléen d'Afrique orientale. *African Archaeological Review*, **6**, 27–55.

ROE, D. A. 1964. The British Lower and Middle Palaeolithic: some problems, methods of study, and preliminary results. *Proceedings of the Prehistoric Society*, **30**, 245–267.

——1968. British Lower and Middle Palaeolithic handaxes groups. *Proceedings of the Prehistoric Society*, **34**, 1–82.

ROLLAND, N. 1995. Levallois technique emergence: single or multiple? A review of the Euro-African record. *In*: DIBBLE, H. L. & BAR-YOSEF, O. (eds) *The Definition and Interpretation of Levallois Technology*. Monographs in World Archaeology 23, Prehistory, Madison, 333–359.

STILES, D. 1979a. Recent archaeological findings in the Sterkfontein site. *Nature*, **277**, 381–382.

——1979b. Early Acheulian and Developed Oldowan. *Current Anthropology*, **20**, 16–129.

SUWA, G., ASFAW, B., BEYENE, Y., *et al.* 1997. The first skull of *Australopithecus boisei*. *Nature*, **389**, 489–492.

TALLON, P. W. J. 1978. Geological setting of the hominid fossils and Acheulian artefacts from the Kapthurin Formation, Baringo District, Kenya. *In*: BISHOP, W. W. (ed.) *Geological Background to Fossil Man*, Geological Society, London, Special Publications, **6**, 361–374.

TOTH, N. 1990. The prehistoric roots of symmetry. *Symmetry: Culture and Science*, **1**(3), 257–281.

TUFFREAU, A., LAMOTTE, A. & MARCY, J.-L. 1997. Land-use and site function in Acheulean complexes of the Somme Valley. *World Archaeology*, **29**, 225–241.

WHITE, M. J. 1995. Raw materials and biface variability in southern Britain: a preliminary examination. *Lithics*, **15**, 1–20.

WISHART, D. 1969. Numerical classification method for deriving natural clusters. *Nature*, **221**, 97–98.

——1975. *Clustan Ic User Manual*. University College, London.

WOOD, B. A. 1991. *Koobi Fora Research Project, Vol. 4: Hominid cranial remains*. Clarendon, Oxford.

——1992. Origin and evolution of the genus *Homo*. *Nature*, **355**, 783–790.

The archaeology of the Kapthurin Formation

SALLY McBREARTY

Department of Anthropology, U-176, University of Connecticut, Storrs, CT 06269, USA

Abstract: The Kapthurin Formation is a fossiliferous sequence of fluvial, lacustrine and volcanic rocks, spanning the period from *c.* 700 ka to < 200 ka, exposed in the Rift Valley west of Lake Baringo, Kenya. Hominid fossils that have been attributed to *Homo erectus* and to archaic *Homo sapiens* have been found in the middle part of the formation. Some newly collected non-hominid fossils from this level indicate open, perhaps arid conditions; others suggest more closed habitats. These are associated with small channel features, palaeosols and rare artefacts. Penecontemporaneous sites about 1 km to the east are found with sedimentary features indicating an ancient alkaline lake shore, aquatic fauna, and a small flake-based stone artefact industry that contains no handaxes. These sites confirm the existence of a Middle Pleistocene biface-free lithic industry contemporary with Acheulian occurrences elsewhere. The Bedded Tuff (unit K4), a well defined volcanic marker bed near the top of the sequence, has been isotopically dated to > 240 ka. Acheulian artefacts at site GnJh-03, 3–4 m below K4, include handaxes and numerous refitting blades. These are the earliest reliably dated blades in Africa, and perhaps the world. The site of GnJh-15 lies on a palaeosol immediately below K4. About 600 m^2 of this site has now been exposed by excavation. The artefacts, some refitting, were produced by typical Middle Stone Age (MSA) core reduction technology, though formal tools are absent. Another site, GnJi-28, within K4 itself, contains a full array of MSA artefacts. The material from GnJh-15 and GnJi-28 represents the earliest securely dated MSA occupation yet documented in Africa.

During the Middle Pleistocene in East Africa a number of events occurred that are important to understanding human evolutionary history. The Middle Pleistocene begins at the Matuyama–Brunhes boundary at about 780 ka and persists until the beginning of the last interglacial at about 130 ka (Cande & Kent 1992; Baksi *et al.* 1992). Interpretation of the human fossil record from this period is still 'muddled,' although more than 20 years have elapsed since Isaac (1975) drew attention to the limited nature of our understanding.

The taxonomic status of Middle Pleistocene hominids is problematic. While there is no unanimity, the view of Andrews (1984) that African and Asian fossils formerly included in *Homo erectus* should be separated at the species level is gaining currency, and many accept Wood's (1991, 1992) designation of *H. ergaster* for some of the Pliocene and early Pleistocene East African fossils formerly included in *H. erectus*. Some might consider *H. erectus* a purely Asian taxon, while others, such as Wood (1992), would ascribe some early Pleistocene East African hominids, such as OH9, dating to *c.* 1.4–1.2 Ma (Hay 1976), to *H. erectus*.

Middle Pleistocene East African hominids, such as Bodo, Ndutu, Ngaloba and southern African fossils, such as Florisbad, Kabwe and Saldanha, are variously ascribed to *H. erectus* or to archaic *H. sapiens*. The latter designation does not conform to standard taxonomic practice, and the characters distinguishing the 'archaic' and 'modern' groups would seem adequate for separation at the species level (Tattersall 1992). Available names for fossils now ascribed to archaic *H. sapiens* and *H. heidelbergensis* (Stringer 1985, 1993) for the combined African and European material, excluding the Neanderthals, and *H. rhodesiensis* and *H. helmei* for the African sample alone (Stringer 1995). Inclusion of the African hominids in *H. heidelbergensis*, while rightly emphasizing the distinctness of the archaic Middle Pleistocene fossils from *H. sapiens sapiens*, risks reinstating long-discredited 'grade'-based taxonomy, in which chronology takes precedence over diagnosis. Therefore the Kapthurin material is referred here to *H. rhodesiensis*. A separate taxonomic designation for the African material recognizes autapomorphies in early European hominids such as those from Arago and Atapuerca, that suggest they are rightly placed in the Neanderthal clade (Stringer 1995). A confounding factor for the classification of African hominids is the possible survival of late populations of *H. ergaster/erectus* into the Middle Pleistocene.

African Middle Pleistocene hominid populations are interesting in their own right; they and their adaptations assume greater importance

McBrearty, S. 1999. The archaeology of the Kapthurin Formation. *In:* Andrews, P. & Banham, P. (eds) *Late Cenozoic Environments and Hominid Evolution: a tribute to Bill Bishop*. Geological Society, London, 143–156.

when it is understood that they may quite possibly have given rise to anatomically modern humans (*H. sapiens sapiens*), as both fossil and genetic evidence appears to suggest (Stringer & Andrews 1988; Aiello 1993; Stringer 1995). Fragmentary fossils from the site of Klasies River Mouth, South Africa, dating to ≥110 ka have been attributed to anatomically modern *H. sapiens* (Singer & Wymer 1982; Deacon 1989, 1993; Grün & Stringer 1991), as has a partial cranium from the Kibish Formation in the Omo region of Ethiopia, dating to *c.* 130 ka (Day *et al.* 1969; Butzer *et al.* 1969; Braüer 1984). Modern humans may well have been present in Africa prior to this date. It has been shown repeatedly for other fossil taxa that time range is a function of sample size (Strauss & Sadler 1989; Marshall 1990; Flynn *et al.* 1995). Because early modern *H. sapiens* is currently represented by a very small fossil sample, it is to be expected that future finds will enlarge its time range into the Middle Pleistocene. Thus it will not be surprising if *H. rhodesiensis/helmei*, anatomically modern *H. sapiens*, and perhaps late survivors of *H. ergaster/erectus* are found to have peopled the East African landscape contemporaneously during this period.

What do we know about the adaptations and behaviours of hominid populations of the late Middle Pleistocene? The obvious source of information is the archaeological record. It is unfortunate that our data base is so slim. The research history of Stone Age archaeology in Africa is short, and in East Africa the focus has been upon the Plio-Pleistocene. Further, it is fair to say that until the advent of the single-crystal

laser fusion (SCLF) ^{40}Ar/^{39}Ar dating method, there was no reliable technique for determining the age of Middle Pleistocene sites. Methods such as thermoluminescence (TL), electron spin resonance (ESL) and amino acid racemization (AAR), while they have their adherents (Brooks *et al.* 1990; Grün & Stringer 1991), still have problems in replicability and application (Klein 1996; Rink *et al.* 1996; El Mansoury *et al.* 1996).

The most visible archaeological event during this period is the demise of the long-lived Acheulian industry, and the beginning of the Middle Stone Age. Thus, after about 250 ka, handaxes disappear from the record, and stone tool inventories consist of flakes produced by the reduction of radial cores and other, more specialized types of prepared cores, including Levallois types. In fact, the nature of this transition is not at all well understood, and the Kapthurin Formation supplies the date of 240 ka that is often cited for the end of the Acheulian. This paper describes work performed since 1990 in the Kapthurin Formation, which provides an ideal arena to examine Middle Pleistocene hominid adaptations, as it spans over half a million years of the Middle Pleistocene, is well calibrated temporally, and contains several dozen distinct archaeological and palaeontological sites distributed throughout the sequence.

The Kapthurin Formation

The Kapthurin Formation forms the Middle Pleistocene portion of the Tugen Hills sequence west of Lake Baringo (Fig. 1). It consists of

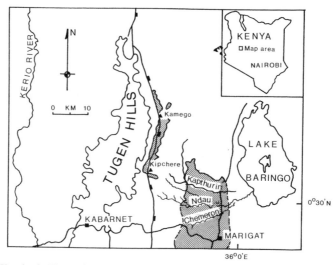

Fig. 1. Map of the Kapthurin Formation and surrounding region.

fluvial, volcanic and lacustrine sediments with a thickness of >125 m (Martyn 1969; Tallon 1976; pers. obs.). The formation covers an area in excess of 150 km² and is best exposed in the drainages of the Ndau, Chemeron and Kapthurin Rivers. It is part of the sequence termed by Gregory (1896) the Kamasia sediments, and it formed the type locality of the Kamasian pluvial of Leakey (1931). It was noted by Fuchs (1950) to be fossiliferous. Mapping by the Kenya Geological Survey established that the Kamasian sediments represent two distinct lithostratigraphical units. The lower, Pliocene unit was termed the Chemeron Formation, the upper, Middle Pleistocene unit was designated the Kapthurin Formation (McCall *et al.* 1967). The Tugen Hills sequence has been extremely well calibrated by the Baringo Palaeontological Research Project (BPRP), and it is now known that the Chemeron Formation dates to between 5.6 and 1.57 Ma (Hill *et al.* 1986).

Mapping by the East African Geological Research Unit (EAGRU) established the basic elements of the Kapthurin succession (Martyn 1969). This initial work was later refined by Tallon (1978), a research student of Bill Bishop. Martyn (1969) divided the formation into five informal units, K1 to K5 (Fig. 2). An angular unconformity separates the lowermost Kapthurin Formation from the underlying Chemeron Formation. Conventional K/Ar dates on samples from K2 range between 620 ± 6 to 890 ± 260 ka[1] (Tallon 1978; Cornelissen *et al.* 1990). However, all Kapthurin rocks are normally magnetized (Dagley *et al.* 1978), and thus postdate 780 ka. The bedded tuff (K4) near the top of the formation has been dated by Tallon (1978) to 250 ± 120 ka and 240 ± 8 ka. The latter dates are frequently cited as the age of the African terminal Acheulian. One aim of our ongoing work is to provide a more precise age estimate for this unit through SCLF ^{40}Ar/^{39}Ar dating.

For most of the area in which it is exposed, the Kapthurin Formation caps the depositional sequence, and is undergoing rapid erosion. In the downfaulted region to the east, nearer the axis of the Rift, Kapthurin Formation rocks are overlain by Holocene Loboi Silts (Farrand *et al.* 1976; Renaut 1982). Fossils and artefacts have been found throughout the Kapthurin sequence, except in the lowermost unit, K1. Three areas in K3 have been most productive, however, and they will be discussed here: the hominid level in the middle of K3, directly below the grey tuff;

---

[1] All dates cited here are corrected using new constants provided by Ness *et al.* (1980).

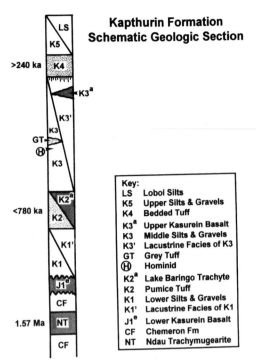

Fig. 2. Schematic stratigraphic column of the Kapthurin Formation.

the lacustrine facies, K3′; and the Acheulian and Middle Stone Age sites in upper K3, immediately below the bedded tuff (K4). One additional site within K4 itself will also be described briefly.

The hominid level

In 1965, John Martyn discovered a fragment of hominid temporal bone (KNM-BC 1) in the Chemeron Formation. This is now attributed to *Homo sp.* and dated to 2.43 Ma, rendering it the oldest known specimen of the genus *Homo* (Hill *et al.* 1992; Hill 1999). As a result of this discovery, Mary Leakey excavated at the Chemeron temporal bone site (JM-85, BPRP 2) and other members of the Leakey family became involved, with Bill Bishop, in prospecting for fossils and artefacts in the Baringo region (Leakey *et al.* 1969; Bishop *et al.* 1971). This work led to the discovery of hominid fossils in the Kapthurin Formation beneath the grey tuff in K3 (Fig. 2). The hominid remains consist of a young adult mandible (KNM-BK 67), two phalanges, a right metatarsal and a fragmentary right ulna (KNM-BK 63-66) (Leakey *et al.* 1969; Solan & Day 1992). A second, more robust adult mandible (KNM-BK 8518) was found in 1982 at the same stratigraphic position by members of a team from the Musée Royale de l'Afrique Centrale (Tervuren, Belgium) (Van Noten 1982; Van Noten & Wood 1985; Wood & Van Noten 1986). In his initial assessment of KNM-BK 67, Tobias, while noting its similarities to *H. erectus*, refrained from definitively attributing the fossil to species, stating only that it 'probably but not certainly belonged to *H. erectus*' (Leakey *et al.* 1969: 72). Wood & Van Noten (1986) likewise noted the lack of diagnostic criteria for mandibular and dental remains within the genus *Homo*, and assigned the two mandibles (KNM-BK 67 and 8518) to *H.* sp. indet. (aff. *erectus*). Subsequently Wood (1991) has included them in *H. erectus* (*sensu* Wood 1992, i.e. not *H. ergaster*). Stringer (1993), however, refers them to archaic *H. sapiens*.

The grey tuff is a discontinuous, reworked, detritally contaminated sandy ash *c.* 30 cm thick. Its age is critical to that of the Kapthurin hominids, but it has proven undatable by conventional K/Ar. Attempts by this project to date it by SCLF $^{40}Ar/^{39}Ar$ are now underway. For the moment a fair estimate of its age is about 500 ka. Faunal preservation is excellent immediately below the grey tuff, and 16 collecting localities are now known from this part of the section (McBrearty *et al.* 1996). Van Noten *et al.* (1987*b*) report but do not describe artefacts associated with a partial hippo skeleton from excavations below the grey tuff at GnJh-23. We have observed artefacts in both surface and *in situ* contexts in this part of the section, but their association with the fossil bone is ambiguous. While systematic examination has not been carried out, no cutmarks, percussion marks or carnivore tooth marks have yet been observed on faunal specimens from the hominid level. This project's future work will clarify the archaeological interpretation of these occurrences.

Fossils at the hominid level are often found associated with small palaeochannel features, which Tallon (1978) interpreted as a braided stream system. A series of calcareous palaeosols, developed upon sediments both above and below the grey tuff, suggests an aggrading landscape. The modern drainage of the Tugen Hills region approximates a grid pattern (Frostick & Reid 1989). Major channels drain the Tugen Hills to the west and empty into the main axis of the Rift to the east; secondary drainages trend north–south. During the Middle Pleistocene, drainages in the Baringo Basin probably experienced periodic increases in sediment load with movements along the Saimo fault upstream (Tallon 1976; Williams & Chapman 1986), and some of these

sediments now make up the Kapthurin Formation. Later movement along north–south trending faults farther east induced downcutting and produced the modern topography. Of the modern rivers, only the Perkerra flows throughout the year, but flow volumes for all rivers are high in the rainy season, when rainfall in the Tugen Hills may exceed 1000 mm (Renaut & Tiercelin 1994). As the rains end, the sediment-choked channels assume a braided aspect. While some Kapthurin Formation conglomerates contain boulders and cobbles, indicating perhaps intermittent torrential flow, the palaeochannels at the hominid level contain no clasts larger than cobble size, suggesting a lower energy depositional regime, and thus perhaps an ancient topography with a lower gradient than that at present.

The fauna from the hominid level includes groups with a wide variety of preferred habitats. Because most of the specimens have not been identified to species, the number of extinct taxa cannot be accurately estimated, and the following interpretation may be flawed in its reliance upon the habitat preferences of modern taxa. Catfish (*Clarias*), *Hippopotamus* and the monitor lizard (*Varanus*) reflect the presence of water, and the rodents are consistent with the riverine habitat suggested by the geology. Both the cane rat (*Thryonomys*) and the giant African pouched rat (*Cricetomys*) are good swimmers and divers, the former generally inhabiting marsh or moist savanna, the latter forest or dense thickets. The presence of the tree mouse (*Dendromus*) might be taken to reinforce the impression of a wooded habitat, but in fact, while good climbers, the members of this genus are not exclusively arboreal and can tolerate a variety of habitats (Kingdon 1974). The rufous nosed rat (*Oenomys*) generally inhabits forest clearings. Both it and the African swamp rat (*Otomys* cf. *angoniensis*) indicate moist or swampy areas with thick vegetation. Among the primates, the presence of *Colobus* confirms the presence of trees.

Among the bovids, Reduncines and Tragelaphines (*Kobus, Tragelaphus*) indicate a closed habitat, whereas Alcelaphines and Antilopines (*Alcelaphus, Damaliscus, Gazella*) suggest open grassland. The presence of both *Kolpochoerus* and *Phacochoerus* among the suids confirms the impression of habitat diversity, and the presence of the bovid *Oryx* suggests arid conditions. Another possible open habitat indicator is the porcupine (*Hystrix*). The specimen, a partial skeleton, has yet to be completely prepared, and thus the specific designation is provisional. However, the crested porcupine, *H. cristata*, while tolerating a wide variety of conditions, favours dry open rocky habitats (Kingdon 1974). While wild animals are rare in the Baringo region today, none of the fossil fauna from the hominid level in the Kapthurin Formation suggests conditions radically different from those of the present. The current ecosystem of the Baringo region may be described as a mosaic of semi-arid *Acacia* bushland and minor riverine woodland, with a significant substratum of perennial and annual grasses (Kingston *et al.* 1994). The fauna from the hominid level suggest locally dense vegetation and marshy conditions perhaps near a braided river system, and drier more open conditions away from river. However, alternative explanations, such as taphonomic mixing of remains from different habitats, or the effects of time averaging, cannot be ruled out.

The lacustrine facies

Ten sites are found within about 6 km^2 of exposures of distinctive sediments in the southeastern part of the Kapthurin Formation. These occur in an area of low relief bounded by the modern Kapthurin River to the south and east. The sediments consist of alternating fine and coarser sediments, including clays, sandstones and fine conglomerates with striking red and black colours. They seems to represent a fairly low energy environment, with few or no clasts exceeding pebble size. There are, however, sandy relict channel features with pronounced cross-bedding visible in reverse relief. These indicate fluctuating lake levels. Calcareous palaeosols and rootcasts no more than 5 mm in diameter suggest an intermittently stable landsurface supporting grassy or shrubby vegetation.

This small area has a history of conflicting interpretations regarding its stratigraphical position. Cornelissen *et al.* (1990), while not providing a detailed map or description, termed the K3′ deposits the Kwaibus Formation, and believed them to be intercalated between the Kapthurin Formation and the underlying Chemeron Formation. Our field observations have found this interpretation to be in error, and have confirmed the prior interpretations of Martyn (1969) and Tallon (1976). The sediments of K3′ are indeed underlain by the pumice tuff (K2) and overlain by the Upper Kasurein Basalt (K3^a), and thus form an integral part of the Kapthurin Formation. Archaeological and palaeontological sites are found throughout the thickness of K3′ sediments. Their age may be estimated at *c.* 700–300 ka.

Tallon (1976, 1978) considered K3′ to be the stratigraphical equivalent of the hominid level, though it is topographically lower. In his view, the braided streams of the hominid level

debouched into the lake here. Our field observations have failed definitively to resolve this point. The grey tuff cannot be traced laterally from the hominid level into the area of K3′ exposures because a northeast–southwest trending fault runs between the two areas, and modern alluvium, deposited by the Kapthurin River and its tributary, the Bartekero, obscures the intervening outcrop. Geochemical identification of the grey tuff in K3′ is rendered difficult due to chemical alteration of the sediments in what was probably a saline and alkaline lacustrine sedimentary environment.

Fossils indicating aquatic conditions are found in K3′ sediments. These include Hippo (*Hippopotamus*), catfish (*Clarias*), gastropods and turtle. *Clarias* tolerates saline and alkaline conditions, while the crocodile, conspicuous by its absence in this faunal suite, requires fresh water. The non-aquatic fauna indicate a variety of habitats. The bovids, including *Kobus* and specimens possibly attributable to *Tragelephas* and *Syncerus*, are consistent with a lake margin environment, and the presence of the cane rat (*Thryonomys*) indicates moist, marshy conditions. However, among the suids, both *Potamochoerus porcus* and *Kolpochoerus majus* are present, indicating perhaps a more diverse habitat, and the primate *Theropithecus* currently inhabits arid regions. Taken together, the sedimentary features, fossil fauna, palaeosols and rootcasts suggest the shore of an alkaline and/or saline lake, fluctuating lake levels, ephemeral nearshore fluvial channels, and a semi-arid climatic regime.

The ten sites in the lacustrine facies sediments range from tiny artefact occurrences no more than 3 m in diameter to larger scatters up to 1 ha in extent. Farrand *et al.* (1976) describe similar material from lacustrine sediments at the locality of Nyongonyek near the northern end of Lake Bogoria. In the opinion of Tallon (pers. comm. cited in Farrand *et al.* 1978: 25) these sediments are equivalent to K3′. No excavations have yet been carried out by our project in K3′ sediments, and therefore the discussion here refers to surface material only. The total number of artefacts collected is modest, consisting of a mere 368 pieces. However, they are interesting in what they reveal about hominid behaviour in the later Middle Pleistocene, a time usually thought characterized exclusively by Acheulian technology. Controlled surface collections were performed at two sites, GnJh-42 and GnJh-57, and they will be discussed in more detail here than the other eight sites.

The site of GnJh-57 is located in the easternmost area of Kapthurin Formation exposures, and is bounded to the east by a ridge of Upper Kasurein Basalt (J1^c). It is stratified 3 m above the pumice tuff (K2) and has an areal extent of roughly 7000 m^2. Faunal preservation is poor, but elephant, hippo, catfish, hyaena (*Crocuta*) and reduncine and tragelephine bovids have been identified. Artefacts from site GnJh-57 were collected from two small surface scatters, each with an area of about 50 m^2. The very small asemblage ($n = 31$) contains 23 flakes; the remainder are cores ($n = 4$) and flake fragments ($n = 4$). There are no formal tools. Pieces are fairly small; modal artefact size class is 6–7 cm. The artefacts are abraded and there are no apparent refits, so it can be safely concluded that the material is in disturbed context.

The material at GnJh-42 appears to be in more secure depositional circumstances. Here, large bone fragments were observed eroding from fine sediments over an area of *c.* 6 m^2, and stone artefacts were detected over a larger area. A 10 m × 15 m grid was laid out, and all artefacts and bone collected. Though faunal preservation is not particularly good, cranial, dental and postcranial elements were recovered. *Hippopotamus* is represented by tooth fragments, a nearly complete radioulna, and other postcranial fragments. Reduncine bovids (*cf. Redunca*) are represented by horncores, and tooth fragments indicate the presence of a buffalo-sized bovine bovid as well as the suid *Phacochoerus*. The cane rat (*Thyronomys*) is well represented, as are turtle and catfish (*Clarias*) This faunal suite is consistent with a lakeshore environment.

The artefacts from GnJh-42 are relatively fresh and unabraded; this and the fine grained nature of the sediment leads one to suggest that the material is in relatively undisturbed context. However, the artefacts are not preferentially associated with the fauna; the bones were concentrated in a relatively small area, while the artefacts were fairly evenly dispersed over the entire collecting area. No attempts were made at artefact refitting. No cutmarks were observed on the bones, though their poor preservation and adhering iron concretions may obscure or obliterate existing cutmarks. The artefacts themselves at GnJh-42 ($n = 236$) are small in size, with a modal size class of 4 cm (range: 1–9 cm). A total of 91% of the sample ($n = 215$) consists of flakes, flake fragments and angular waste. Only eight pieces can generously be considered 'tools,' but the 'retouched' items, including one notched piece, show the type of damage that might be expected on flakes as a result of postdepositional processes, such as trampling (McBrearty *et al.* 1998).

Taken as a whole, with few exceptions the stone artefacts from all sites in K3' sediments are made on small basalt cobbles (Fig. 3). Modal size class for cores is 5 cm. Only 2% of the artefacts are in raw materials other than basalt; these include andesite, chert and welded tuff. A source of raw material would have been

Fig. 3. Cores from sites GnJh- 46 and GnJh-50 in the lacustrine facies (K3') of the Kapthurin Formation: (a) single platform or 'casual' core; (b, c) multiplatform cores; (d, e) radial cores.

available very near the site at the time of occupation in the form of an outcrop of Lower Kasurein Basalt. However, fluctuating lake levels may have periodically rendered it inaccessible. While the lake would probably have been rather shallow, the outcrop may have been isolated as an island during high stands of the Middle Pleistocene lake. At present, there are outcrops of older lavas west of the site at a distance < 3 km. While some flows may have been exposed during the Middle Pleistocene, others may have been deeply buried, as faulting perhaps had not yet initiated the incision of the modern local drainage system. From the small size of the artefacts and the remaining cortex visible on cores it seems clear that the makers selected small river cobbles for artefact manufacture, rather than detaching larger slabs from outcrops themselves or selecting fallen blocks for use as cores. Currently, the modern rivers are a source of cobbles and boulders in a variety of Tugen Hills volcanic rocks, but at present the location of major riverine systems near the K3′ sites at the time they were formed is unknown. Nearby lakeshore sediments are fine grained, and the palaeochannel deposits in K3′ itself appear not to contain clasts larger than pebble size.

Flake production at K3′ sites is primarily by radial core reduction; of a total of 41 cores from the K3′ sites, 56% are radial or subradial forms (Fig. 3d, e). Other types include multi-platform (22%, Fig. 3b, c), 'casual' or single platform (10%), and opposed platform (7%); only two (5%) can be considered Levallois cores. A fairly large proportion (21%) of the cores can be considered 'exhausted'; that is, they have been flaked to the point where their obtuse edge angles present few opportunities for further flake removals. No detailed analysis of the flakes' technological features has been performed, but of an assemblage of 125 flakes, six (5%) can be classified as 'type one' flakes in the sense of Toth (1985). That is, their entire dorsal surface and platform are cortex. These flakes and some of the single platform 'casual' cores represent the initial step in core reduction, the exhausted cores, the last. Thus it appears that not only were small cobbles selected for artefact manufacture, but also that raw material was conserved. This suggests either (1) that there was no nearby contemporary source of raw material, (2) that the makers of these artefacts did not possess the ability to process large basalt blocks, or (3) that strong stylistic or functional motives dictated artefact form.

No real formal tools, such as handaxes, scrapers or points, have been observed among the Kapthurin Formation lacustrine facies material. The degree of edge modification observed on some pieces could easily have been produced by natural processes after artefact discard. Therefore inferring their makers' affinities is problematical, but in fact, no element of these assemblages would be out of place in a Middle Stone Age (MSA) industry. If they are interpreted as MSA, and because their age is probably >500 ka, they would represent by far the oldest MSA industry yet known. They are > 265 000 years older than the oldest known African MSA site at Gaddamotta, Ethiopia, dated to c. 235 ka (Wendorf et al. 1994), and exceed estimates for the earliest Middle Palaeolithic outside Africa by a similar margin. This situation points out the shortcomings of the conflation of technological and chronological entities in the three-age system currently in use in African prehistory.

The K3′ material dates to the period during which Acheulian technology is the norm throughout Africa and much of Eurasia. It is intuitively obvious that archaeological sites lacking handaxes must exist during the time span of the Acheulian. In the past, prehistorians have consigned such sites in Europe to the 'Clactonian'; in Africa they have sometimes been referred to the 'Hope Fountain.' In Europe, there is renewed interest in the Clactonian (Ashton 1992; Mithen 1996), and Mithen (1996) proposes an explanatory model for the Clactonian that invokes contrasts in habitat, and resulting variation in group size and the intensity of social learning to explain the differences between the European Acheulian and Clactonian.

In Africa, an increased emphasis on the study of lithic artefact manufacturing techniques (e.g. Toth 1985; Roche & Texier 1991; Texier 1996) now balances a former emphasis on formal tool shape (e.g. Kleindienst 1962; Gowlett 1984; Wynn & Tierson 1990), and leads perhaps to a decline in eagerness to assign such assemblages to different industrial traditions. It is conceivable that handaxe-free assemblages such as those from K3′ represent a discrete stylistic tradition maintained by hominid populations or even hominid species distinct from those responsible for the Acheulian. It is at least equally likely that they simply represent a variant of the Acheulian that is a response to task- or environment-specific demands, or simply an expedient technology adopted in the absence of raw material suitable for handaxe manufacture. It is not altogether clear why small cobbles were consistently selected for artefact manufacture at the K3′ sites, but the conservation of raw material does suggest that it may have been at a premium.

In the Kapthurin Formation, these handaxe-free assemblages are consistently associated with lacustrine environmental indicators. The arte-facts do not lack technical competence and they may well have been deliberately designed to perform activities in a lakeside environment. It is perhaps significant that similar lakeside habitats are known for flake-based industries at Olorgesailie (Potts 1989, 1994) and Olduvai (Leakey 1971; Hay 1976) while Olduvai and Olorgesailie Acheulian sites are consistently found in or near sandy channels (Leakey 1971; Isaac 1977). In the Middle Awash, sites in the same time range as those in K3′ also show a correlation between industry and depositional regime. There, however, Acheulian sites are con-sistently found in a floodplain setting, while assemblages lacking handaxes are associated with channel features (Clark et al. 1994). Taken as a group, the K3′ occupations span a period of tens if not hundreds of thousands of years when the characteristic Acheulian tech-nology was being produced not only in the Baringo–Bogoria region of the Kenya Rift Valley (Gowlett 1978, 1980, 1999), but throughout most of Africa. It is not known at present whether these industrial differences are the residues of different habitat-specific extractive activities, or whether they represent distinct lithic traditions produced by different populations, or even different species, of Middle Pleistocene hominids.

The bedded tuff level

Archaeological sites occur both below and within the bedded tuff, K4, dated by conven-tional K/Ar to c. 240 ka (Tallon 1976, 1978). One aim of our ongoing work is to provide a more precise age estimate for this unit through SCLF ^{40}Ar/^{39}Ar dating. Margaret Avery (then Margaret Leakey) and her colleagues reported stone artefacts, usually referred to the terminal Acheulian, from the 'Leakey handaxe area' (LHA or GnJh-03), a site complex lying 3–4 m below K4 (Leakey et al. 1969) Their material from GnJh-03 includes two distinctive compo-nents: first, remarkable ovate handaxes, usually unifacial or with minimal ventral trimming, made on large flakes struck from very large Levallois cores (Fig. 4); and second, a blade component (Fig. 5).

Project collaborator Pierre-Jean Texier of the Centre de Recherches Archéologiques of CNRS (Valbonne, France) has replicated the large Levallois Kapthurin 'unifaces' and blades, using five locally collected basalts. Blocks of 10–15 kg were required to produce a single biface by this method. Initial core reduction was by hard hammer, while final trimming involved the use of both hard and soft hammers. It is possible

to examine the techniques of the blade produc-tion at GnJh-03 through both artefact refitting and replication. Leakey and her collaborators were able to refit a number of objects; we have recovered and refitted further pieces. Our larg-est refitted set is made up of a core reduced from a thick cortical flake, and 11 conjoining whole blades; as some blades were snapped, the set is the product of 18 refits in all. Flaking in this instance is bidirectional; core prepara-tion makes use of hard hammer, but blade production itself was possibly done with soft hammer. The flaking method used to maintain the necessary convexity of the blade detachment surface is reminiscent of Levallois reduction techniques. The resulting blades are notable for their thinness, straightness and degree of elonga-tion (L/B = 3.4–4.2) (Fig. 5).

Kapthurin blade production techniques are not easy to replicate. Blades were successfully replicated in only one of the raw materials tested, and breakage was a recurrent problem. Again, initial core reduction was performed with hard hammer. While blades were successfully produced by means of both hard and soft hammer (wood baton), features of the archae-ological specimens are not unambiguous in revealing whether hard or soft hammers were used in their detatchment. These artefacts show definite evidence that their makers conceived of a predetermined form, planned the necessary steps, performed the process repeatedly, and had the capacity to produce a well executed end result. They therefore illustrate the existence in East Africa of a deliberate, formalized system of blade manufacture at > 240 ka.

It has been argued that blades are a techno-logical innovation indicating modern behaviour, and in Europe, the blade-based Aurignacian industry accompanies the arrival of modern humans c. 45 ka (White 1982; Mellars 1992). However, recent work shows that some Eur-opean Middle Palaeolithic industries, probably dating to between c. 90 ka and c. 115 ka, also have a blade component (Conard 1990; Révil-lion & Tuffreau 1994).

South African MSA sites have long been known to contains blades (Sampson 1974; Vol-man 1984; Thackeray 1992), though as a whole the South African MSA is poorly dated. The Amudian industry of the Levant (Garrod & Bate 1937; Jelinek 1982, 1990) likewise includes blades. There is a lack of concordance between ESR and TL age estimates at sites for the Amudian (Klein 1996), ESR at Tabun and Zuttiyeh suggesting a possible antiquity c. 170–230 ka (Grün & Stringer 1991; Klein 1996), TL as much as 300 ka (Mercier et al. 1995). The Kapthurin blades, at >240 ka,

Fig. 4. Levallois 'unifaces' from GnJh-03 and GnJh-51, *c.* 3-4 m below K4 in the Kapthurin Formation: (**a, b**) dorsal views; (**a′, b′**) ventral views. (**a, a′**) Lanceolate ovate, no ventral retouch; (**b, b′**) ovate, minimal bulbar trimming on ventral face.

are thus a minimum of 125 000 years older than the European Middle Palaeolithic blades and more than 200 000 years older than the Aurignacian; their temporal relation to the Amudian awaits resolution.

The bedded tuff (unit K4) forms a well defined volcanic marker bed near the top of the Kapthurin Formation sequence. It is particularly well exposed on the escarpment above the Bartekero River. Here, at the site of GnJh-15, stone artefacts and fossil bone lie directly on a well developed palaeosol immediately beneath the bedded tuff. Our geological mapping indicates that the deposits are overbank silts, and a

preliminary examination of palaeosol carbonates from this fossil soil at the site itself and from a 1 km E–W transect in the immediate site vicinity indicates an open, grassy, C_4-dominated landscape. Analysis of samples from sites about 2.5 km to the south, however, reveals a more closed, C_3-dominated habitat, hinting at the presence of a contemporary body of water or perhaps a large riverine system in this area (Kingston, pers. comm.)

A previous team from the Museé Royale de l'Afrique Centrale (Tervuren, Belgium) performed extensive excavation at GnJh-15 in the 1980s (Van Noten *et al.* 1987a). Our project has

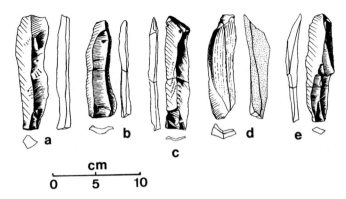

Fig. 5. Blades from GnJh-03, *c.* 3–4 m below K4 in the Kapthurin Formation.

now expanded the excavated area to $> 600 \, m^2$. Analysis of all excavated material is not yet complete, but there are now about 7000 stone artefacts and about 500 bones or bone fragments from *in situ* context at GnJh-15. Size range, vertical dispersal and conjoinability of the artefacts all indicate minimal disturbance. There are two major areas of artefact concentration at the site, one in the eastern site area, the other to the west, lying about 50 m apart. Of a random sample of the mapped artefacts, excluding material recovered in the sieve, 38% from the eastern portion of the site (n = 350) and 13% from the western portion (*n* = 479) are <2 cm in size (Cornelissen pers. comm.) Vertical dispersal rarely exceeds 20 cm, and in most areas of the excavation the material is found confined vertically within 10 cm of deposit. Therefore the

occurrence has clear stratigraphical integrity as well as good temporal control. Bone is not well preserved at GnJh-15, though we have collected large, complete, and well preserved mammalian fossils from elsewhere in the bedded tuff. None of the GnJh-15 fauna has yet been identified. There is a mean of 15 bone fragments per square metre (*n* = 407). In the eastern portion of the site, bone fragments are clustered within the artefact concentration; in the western portion the bone fragments appear to be more uniformly distributed over the excavated area. Other finds from the excavation at GnJh-15 include ostrich eggshell fragments, red ochre and the grindstones most likely used to process it.

Most of the mapped excavated lithic material from GnJh-15 consists of debitage, and a few heavy-duty items, including polyhedrons,

Fig. 6. Cores from the site of Rorop Lingop (GnJi-28). (**a, b**) Levallois cores; (**c**) radial core.

choppers and core scrapers. Basalt is the primary raw material, though chert and obsidian are also represented. A zone of coarser sediments in the centre of the excavated area has been interpreted by previous workers as a contemporary river channel from which the artefact raw material was derived. Known refits include 36 sets of 98 artefacts; mean distances between refitted artefacts are 165 cm ($r = 11$–780 cm) for the eastern site area and 210 ($r = 34$–514 cm) for the western area (Cornelissen pers. comm.). No refits were found between the western and eastern artefact concentrations, calling into question their contemporaneity. The presence of cortex on half the refitted sets indicates that early stages of core reduction are present. The artefacts, some refitting, were produced by single platform, adjacent platform, and radial core reduction technology; with the exception of a single possible biface tip from our 1996 excavations, there are no handaxes. While points are also absent, it can be argued that the material at GnJh-15 represents MSA technology, and as such appears to represent the earliest securely dated MSA occurrence yet documented in Africa.

To the north of the main Kapthurin Formation exposures, tuffaceous sediments overlie the upfaulted Lake Baringo trachyte. Tallon (1976, 1978) considers this tuff the lateral equivalent of the bedded tuff (K4), and our geochemical analyses, while provisional, support this diagnosis. At the site at Rorop Lingop (GnJi-28), about 4 km north of the Kapthurin River, numerous artefacts are found within this tuff (Fig. 6). They are thus younger than those at either GnJh-03 or GnJh-15, yet still >240 ka. A full array of MSA artefacts is present, including small bifaces, foliate points, both unifacial and bifacial, radial cores (Fig. 6c), and small, very well executed Levallois cores (Fig. 6a, b).

river. Penecontemporaneous sites in the lacustrine facies of the Kapthurin Formation (K3′) feature a stone artefact industry based upon the reduction of small basalt cobbles, and confirm the presence in Africa of a handaxe-free lithic industry contemporary with the Acheulian. If this is ascribed to the MSA, at >500 ka, it is 250 000 years older than the oldest known MSA site in Africa. Higher up in the section, sites below the bedded tuff (K4) contain both a terminal Acheulian industry (GnJh-03) characterized by blades and distinctive unifacial handaxes, and a MSA industry (GnJh-15) characterized by flakes produced by single platform, adjacent platform, and radial core reduction technology. The blades from GnJh-03 are probably the oldest in Africa, and perhaps the world. A site within K4 itself (GnJi-28) contains the full range of MSA artefacts, including points and Levallois cores. GnJh-03, GnJh-15 and GnJi-28 all date to >240 ka, and thus may be said to represent the earliest securely dated MSA occupations yet documented in Africa.

This research was carried out under a permit issued by the Office of the President of Kenya to the Baringo Palaeontological Research Project (BPRP), directed by Andrew Hill. Thanks are due to M. Isahakia director of National Museums of Kenya (NMK), to K. Munene, head of the NMK Division of Archaeology, and to M. Leakey, head of the NMK Division of Palaeontology, for facilitating the project. Many of the observations expressed in this paper would not be possible without the contributions of my collaborators in the Kapthurin project, J. Kingston, A. Deino, E. Cornelissen, and P.-J. Texier. Thanks are due to A. Hill and B. Kimeu for providing invaluable help and support in the field, both tangible and intangible. L. Bishop, A. Winkler, C. Denys, and K. Stewart kindly provided faunal identifications. This research is funded by US National Science Foundation research grants SBR-9601419, SBR-9408926 and DBS-9213775.

Summary

The Kapthurin Formation spans about 500 000 years of the Middle Pleistocene. It contains hominid fossils, dating to about 500 ka, that can be ascribed either to *H. ergaster/erectus* or to *H. rhodesiensis*. It also contains a number of stone artefact industries from a variety of sedimentary environments, that provide windows on events surrounding the latest Acheulian and earliest Middle Stone Age known in Africa. The hominid fossils are found in sediments indicating a braided river system and in association with fossil fauna suggesting locally dense vegetation, marshy conditions nearby, and perhaps drier, more open conditions away from

References

AIELLO, L. C. 1993. Fossil evidence for modern human origins in Africa: a revised view. *American Anthropologist*, **95**, 73–96

ANDREWS, P. 1984. On the characters that define *Homo erectus*. *In*: Andrews, P. & FRANZEN, J. L. (eds) *The Early Evolution of Man, with Special Emphasis on Southeast Asia and Africa*. Courier Forschungsinstitut Senckenberg, Frankfort, **69**, 167–175.

ASHTON, N. M. 1992. The High Lodge flint industries. *In*: ASHTON, N. M., COOK, J., LEWIS, S. G. & ROSE, J. (eds) *High Lodge: Excavations by G. de G. Sieveking 1962–68 and J. Cook 1988*. British Museum, London, 124–163.

BAKSI, A. K., HSU, B., WILLIAMS, M. O. & FERRAR, E. 1992. ^{40}Ar/^{39}Ar dating of the Brunhes-Matuyama geomagnetic field reversal. *Science*, **256**, 356–357.

BISHOP, W. W., CHAPMAN, G. R., HILL, A. & MILLER, J. A. 1971. Succession of Cainozoic vertebrate assemblages from the northern Kenya Rift Valley. *Nature*, **233**, 389–394.

BRAÜER, G. 1984. The Afro-European *sapiens* hypothesis and hominid evolution in Asia during the late Middle and Upper Pleistocene. *In*: ANDREWS, P. & FRANZEN, J. L., (eds) *The Early Evolution of Man with special Emphasis on Southeast Asia and Africa*. Courier Forschungsinstitut Senckenberg, Frankfort, **69**, 145–166.

BROOKS, A. S., HARE, P. E., KOKIS, J. E., MILLER, G. H., ERNST, R. D. & WENDORF, F. 1990. Dating Pleistocene archaeological sites by protein diagenesis in ostrich eggshell. *Science*, **248**, 60–64.

BUTZER, K. W., BROWN, F. B. & THURBER, D. L. 1969. Horizontal sediments of the Lower Omo Valley: the Kibish Formation. *Quaternaria*, **11**, 15–29.

CANDE, S. C. & KENT, D. V. 1992. A new geomagnetic polarity time scale for the late Cretaceous and Cenozoic. *Journal of Geophysical Research*, **97**, 13 917–13 951.

CLARKE, J. D., DE HEINZELIN, J., SCHICK, K. D. *et al.* 1994. African *Homo erectus*: old radiometric ages and young Oldowan assemblages in the Middle Awash valley, Ethiopia. *Science*, **264**, 1907–1910.

CONARD, N. J. 1990. Laminar lithic assemblages from the last interglacial complex in northwestern Europe. *Journal of Anthropological Research*, **46**, 243–262.

CORNELISSEN, E., BOVEN, A., DABI, A., *et al.* 1990. The Kapthurin Formation revisited. *African Archaeological Review*, **8**, 23–76.

DAGLEY, P., MUSSETT, A. E. & PALMER, H. C. 1978. Preliminary observations on the paleomagnetic stratigraphy of the area west of Lake Baringo, Kenya. *In*: BISHOP, W. W. (ed.) *Geological Background to Fossil Man*. Scottish Academic, Edinburgh,, 361–373.

DAY, M. H., LEAKEY, R. E. L. & BUTZER, K. W. 1969. The Omo skeletal remains. *Nature*, **222**, 1135–1138.

DEACON, H. J. 1989. Late Pleistocene palaeoecology and archaeology in the Southern Cape, South Africa. *In*: MELLARS, P. & STRINGER, C. B. (eds) *The Human Revolution: Behavioural and Biological Perspectives in the Origins of Modern Humans*. Princeton University, 547–564.

——1993. Southern Africa and modern human origins. *In*: AITKEN, M. J., STRINGER, C. B. & MELLARS, P. A. (eds) *The Origin on Modern Humans and the Impact of Chronometric Dating*. Princeton University, 104–117.

EL MANSOURY, M., EL FOUIKAR, A. & SAINT-MARTIN, B. 1996. Correlation between ^{14}C ages and aspartic acid racemization at the Upper Palaeolithic site of the Abri Pataud (Dordogne, France). *Journal of Archeological Science*, **23**, 803–810.

FARRAND, W. R., REDDING, R. W., WOLPOFFF, M. H. & WRIGHT, H. T. 1976. *An Archaeological Investigation on the Loboi Plain, Baringo District, Kenya*. Museum of Anthropology, University of Michigan, Ann Arbor, Technical Reports **4**.

FLYNN, L. J., BARRY, J. C., MORGAN, M. E., PILBEAM, D., JACOBS, L. L. & LINDSAY, E. H. 1995. Neogene Siwalik mammalian lineages: species longevities, rates of change and modes of speciation. *Paleogeography, Paleoclimatology Paleoecology*, **115**, 249–264.

FROSTICK, L. & REID, I. 1989. Is structure the main control of river drainage and sedimentation in rifts? *Journal of African Earth Sciences*, **8**, 165–182.

FUCHS, V. E. 1950. Pleistocene events in the Baringo Basin. *Geological Magazine*, **87**, 149–174.

GARROD, D. A. & BATE, D. M. A. 1937. *The Stone Age of Mount Carmel: Excavations at the Wadi-el-Mughara*. Clarendon, Oxford.

GOWLETT, J. A. J. 1978. Kilombe: an Acheulian site complex in Kenya. *In*: BISHOP, W. W. (ed.) *Geological Background to Fossil Man*. Scottish Academic, Edinburgh, 337–360.

——1980. Acheulian sites in the Central Rift Valley, Kenya. *In*: LEAKEY, R. E. L. & OGOT, B. A. (eds) *Proceedings of the 8th Panafrican Congress of Prehistory and Quaternary Studies, Nairobi, Setermber 1977*. The International Louis Leakey Institute for African Prehistory, Nairobi, 213–217.

——1984. Mental abilities of early man. *In*: FOLEY, R. (ed.) *Hominid Evolution and Community Ecology*. Academic, London, 167–192.

——1999. Lower and Middle Pleistocene archaeology of the Baringo Basin. *This volume*.

GREGORY, J. W. 1896. *The Great Rift Valley*. Murray, London.

GRÜN, R. & STRINGER, C. B. 1991. Electron spin resonance dating and the evolution of modern humans. *Archaeometry*, **33**, 153–199.

HAY, R. L. 1976. *Geology of the Olduvai Gorge*. University of California, Berkeley.

HILL, A. 1999. The Baringo Basin, Kenya: from Bill Bishop to BPRP. *This volume*.

HILL, A. P., CURTIS, G. & DRAKE, R. 1986. Sedimentary stratigraphy of the Tugen Hills, Baringo District, Kenya. *In*: FROSTICK, L. E., RENAUT, R. & TIERCELIN, J.-J. (eds) *Sedimentation in the African Rifts*. Geological Society, Special Publications, **25**, Blackwell, Oxford, 285–295.

——, WARD, S., CURTIS, G. & DRAKE, R. 1992. Earliest *Homo*. *Nature*, **335**, 719–722.

ISAAC, G. LL. 1975. Sorting out the muddle in the middle: an anthropologist's post-conference appraisal. *In*: BUTZER, K. W. & ISSAC, G. LL. (eds) *After the Australopithecines: Stratigraphy, Ecology, and Culture Change in the Middle Pleistocene*. Mouton, The Hague, 875–887.

——1977. *Olorgesailie: Archaeological Studies of a Middle Pleistocene Lake Basin in Kenya*. Chicago University Press.

JELINEK, A. 1982. The Tabun Cave and Paleolithic man in the Levant. *Science*, **216**, 1369–1375.

——1990. The Amudian in the context of the Mugharan traditions at the Tabun Cave, Mount Carmel, Israel. *In*: MELLARS, P. (ed.) *The Emergence of Modern Humans*. Cornell University, Ithaca, 81–90.

KINGDON, J. 1974. *East African Mammals. An Atlas of Evolution in Africa*. Academic, London.

KINGSTON, J. D., MARINO, B. D. & HILL, A. 1994. Isotopic evidence for Neogene hominid paleoenvironments in the Kenya Rift Valley. *Science*, **264**, 955–959.

KLEIN, R. G. 1996. Neanderthals and modern humans in West Asia: a conference summary. *Evolutionary Anthropology*, **4**, 187–193.

KLEINDIENST, M. R. 1962. Components of the East African Acheulian assemblage: an analytical approach. *In*: MORTELMANS, G. & NENQUIN, J. (eds) *Actes du IVᵉ Congrès Panafricain de Préhistoire et de l'Etude du Quaternaire*. Musée Royale de l'Afrique Centrale, Tervuren, Sciences Humaines **40**, 81–104.

LEAKEY, L. S. B. 1931. *The Stone Age Cultures of Kenya Colony*. Cambridge University.

LEAKEY, M., TOBIAS, P. V., MARTYN, J. E. & LEAKEY, R. E. F. 1969. An Acheulian industry with prepared core technique and the discovery of a con-temporary hominid mandible at lake Baringo, Kenya. *Proceedings of the Prehistoric Society*, **3**, 48–76.

LEAKEY, M. D. 1971. *Olduvai Gorge, Vol. 3: Excavations in Beds I and II 1960–1963*. Cambridge University.

MARSHALL, C. R. 1990. Confidence intervals on stratigraphic ranges. *Paleobiology*, **16**, 1–10.

MARTYN, J. 1969. *Geology of the Country Between Lake Baringo and the Kerio River, Baringo District, Kenya*. PhD thesis, University of London.

MCBREARTY, S., BISHOP, L. C., & KINGSTON, J. D. 1996. Variability in traces of Middle Pleistocene hominid behavior in the Kapthurin Formation, Baringo, Kenya. *Journal of Human Evolution*, **30**, 563–580.

——, ——, PLUMMER, T. DEWAR, R. & CONARD, N. 1998. Tools underfoot: Human trampling as an agent of lithic artefact modification. *American Antiquity*, **63**, 108–129.

MCCALL, G. J. H., BAKER, B. H. & WALSH, J. 1967. Late Tertiary and Quaternary sediments of the Kenya Rift Valley. *In*: BISHOP, W. W. & CLARK, J. D. (eds) *Background to Evolution in Africa*. Chicago University, 191–220.

MELLARS, P. A. 1992. Archaeology and the population-dispersal hypothesis of modern human origins. *In*: AITKEN, M. J., STRINGER, C. B. & MELLARS, P. A. (eds) *The Origin of Modern Humans and the Impact of Chronometric Dating*. Princeton University, 196–216.

MERCIER, N., VALLADAS, H., VALLADAS, G. & REYSS, J.-L. 1995. TL dates of burnt flints from Jelinek's excavations at Tabun and their implications. *Journal of Archaeological Science*, **22**, 495–509.

MITHEN, S. 1996. Social learning and cultural tradition. *In*: STEELE, J., & SHENNON, S. (eds) *The Archaeology of Human Ancestry: Power, Sex, and Tradition*. Routledge, London, 207–229

NESS, G., LEVI, S. & CROUCH, R. 1980. Marine magnetic anomaly time scales for the Cenozoic and late Cretaceous: a précis, critique, and synthesis. *Reviews of Geophysical and Space Physics*, **18**, 753–770.

POTTS, R. 1989. Olorgesailie: new excavations and findings in Early and Middle Pleistocene contexts, southern Kenya rift valley. *Journal of Human Evolution*, **18**, 477–484.

——1994. Variables versus models of early Pleistocene hominid land use. *In*: OLIVER, J. S., SIKES, N. E. & STEWART, K. M. (eds) *Early Hominid Behavioural Ecology. Journal of Human Evolution*, **27**, 7–24.

RENAUT, R. W. 1982. *Late Quaternary Geology of the Lake Bogoria Fault Trough, Kenya Rift Valley*. PhD dissertation, University of London.

—— & TIERCELIN, J.-J. 1994. Lake Bogoria, Kenya Rift Valley: a sedimentological overview. *In*: RENAUT, R. W. & LAST, W. M. (eds) *Sedimentology and Geochemistry of Modern and Ancient Saline Lakes*. Society for Sedimentary Geology, Special Publication **50**, 101–123.

RÉVILLION, S. & TUFFREAU, A. (eds) 1994. *Les Industries Laminaires au Paléolithique Moyen*. Dossier de Documentation Archéologique **18**, CNRS, Paris.

RINK, W. J., SCHWARCZ, H. P., LEE, H. K., CABRERA VALDÉS, V., BERNALDO DE QUIRÓS, F. & HOYOS, M. 1996. ESR dating of tooth enamel: comparison with AMS ¹⁴C at El Castillo Cave, Spain. *Journal of Archeological Science*, **23**, 945–952.

ROCHE, H. & TEXIER, P.-J. 1991. La notion de complexité dans un ensemble lithique. Application aux séries achueléenes d'Isenya (Kenya). *25 Ans d'Études Technologiques en Préhistoire: Bilan et Perspectives*. Xiᵉ Rencontres Internationales d'Archéologie et d'Histoire d'Antibes. Éditions APDCA, Juan-les-Pins, 99–108.

SAMPSON, C. G. 1974. *The Stone Age Archaeology of Southern Africa*. Academic, New York.

SINGER, R. & WYMER, J. 1982. *The Middle Stone Age at Klasies River Mouth in South Africa*. Chicago University.

SOLAN, M. & DAY, M. H. 1992. The Baringo (Kapthurin) ulna. *Journal of Human Evolution*, **22**, 307–314.

STRAUSS, D. & SADLER, P. M. 1989. Classical confidence intervals and Bayesian probability estimates for ends of local taxon ranges. *Mathematical Geology*, **21**, 411–427.

STRINGER, C. B. 1985. Middle Pleistocene hominid variability and the origin of late Pleistocene humans. *In*: DELSON, E. (ed.) *Ancestors: the Hard Evidence*. Liss, New York, 289–295.

——1993. New views on modern human origins. *In*: RASMUSSEN, D. T. (ed.) *The Origin and Evolution of Humans and Humanness*. Jones & Bartlett, Boston, 75–94.

——1995. The evolution and distribution of later Pleistocene human populations. *In*: VRBA, E. S. & DENTON, G. H. (eds) *Paleoclimate and Evolution, with Emphasis on Human Origins*. Yale University, London, 521–531.

—— & ANDREWS, P. 1988. Genetic and fossil evidence for the origin of modern humans. *Science*, **239**, 1263–1268.

TALLON, P. W. J. 1976. *The Stratigraphy, Palaeoenvironments and Geomorphology of the Pleistocene Kapthurin Formation, Kenya*. PhD dissertation, Queen Mary College, London.

——1978. Geological setting of the hominid fossils and Acheulian artefacts from the Kapthurin Formation, Baringo District, Kenya. *In*: BISHOP, W. W. (ed.) *Geological Background to Fossil Man.* Scottish Academic, Edinburgh, 361–373.

TATTERSALL, I. 1992. Species concepts and species identification in human evolution. *Journal of Human Evoution*, **22**, 341–349.

TEXIER, P.-J. 1996. L'Acheuléen d'Isenya (Kenya). *La Vie Préhistoire.* Société Préhistorique Française, Faton, Dijon, 58–63.

THACKERAY, A. I. 1992. The Middle Stone Age south of the Limpopo River. *Journal of World Prehistory* **4**, 385–440.

TOTH, N. 1985. The Odowan reassessed: a close look at early stone artefacts. *Journal of Archaeological Science*, **12**, 101–120.

VAN NOTEN, F. 1982. Excavations in the Kapthurin Formation. *Nyame Akuma*, **20**, 17–19.

—— & WOOD, B. 1985. Un nouvel hominide à Baringo, Kenya. *L'Anthropologie*, **89**, 141–143.

——, CORNELISSEN, E., GYSELS, J., MOEYERSONS, J., NIJS, K. & UYTTERSCHAUT, H. 1987a. The Kapthurin Project, Baringo: the 1984 season. *Nyame Akuma*, **28**, 20–27.

——, ——, ——, —— & UYTTERSCHAUT, H. 1987b. The Kapthurin Project, Baringo: the 1985 season. *Nyame Akuma*, **29**, 36–41.

VOLMAN, T. P. 1984. Early prehistory of southern Africa. *In*: KLEIN, R. G (ed.) *Southern African Prehistory and Palaeoenvironments.* Balkema, Rotterdam, 169–220.

WENDORF, F., CLOSE, A. E. & SCHILD, R. 1994. Africa in the period of *Homo sapiens neanderthalensis* and contemporaries. *In*: DE LAET, S. J., DANI, A. H., LORENZO, J. L. & NUNDO, R. B. (eds) *History of Humanity, Vol. 1: Prehistory and the Beginnings of Civilization.* Routledge & UNESCO, New York, 117–135.

WHITE, R. 1982. Rethinking the Middle/Upper Paleolithic transition. *Current Anthropology*, **23**, 169–192.

WILLIAMS, L. A. J. & CHAPMAN, G. R. 1986. Relationships between major structures, salic volcanism and sedimentation in the Kenya Rift from the equator northwards to Lake Turkana. *In*: FROSTICK, L. E., RENAUT, R. & TIERCELIN, J.-J. (eds) *Sedimentation in the African Rifts.* Geological Society, Special Publications, **25**, Blackwell, Oxford, 59–74.

WOOD, B. 1991. *Koobi Fora Research Project, Volume 4: Human Cranial Remains.* Oxford University.

——1992. Origin and evolution of the genus *Homo*. *Nature*, **355**, 783–790.

—— & VAN NOTEN, F. 1986. Preliminary observations on the BK 8518 mandible from Baringo, Kenya. *American Journal of Physical Anthropology*, **69**, 117–127.

WYNN, T. & TIERSON, F. 1990. Regional comparison of the shapes of later Acheulian handaxes. *American Anthropologist*, **92**, 73–84.

Part III. Quaternary Environments

The first two chapters in this section are concerned with the Middle Pleistocene of the English Midlands, where Bill Bishop began his researches under the supervision of Professor Fred Shotton. Bill's success in applying both stratigraphy and geomorphology to the problems of relating the Midlands story to the Thames story was recognized by publication in the Philosophical Transactions of the Royal Society for 1958. As Bill would have been the first to expect, the game has moved on since then, although in the first chapter David Keen acknowledges that Bill's stratigraphical conclusions, in particular, give a foretaste of developments to the present day. Keen first summarizes the history of the construction and de-construction of the concept of a Wolstonian glaciation and then moves on to report on recent work with the potential to produce a new model for the Middle Pleistocene stratigraphy of the Midlands. Emphasizing important new floral, faunal and amino-stratigraphical evidence from the Waverley Wood and Frog Hall sites, and taking into account the glacial sequence in East Anglia and the Avon terrace sequence, Keen reveals that as many as six climatic stages may be represented. The type-Wolstonian glacial sequence turns out as no older than Oxygen Isotope Stage 14 and no younger than Stage 10. That Stage 12 (Anglian) is not excluded will reassure many.

In the next chapter, Darrel Maddy focuses further on the terraces of the West Midlands with a report of the results of recent sedimentological studies of the Middle Pleistocene deposits of the Baginton River. Having established the pattern of drainage and current flow, and finding no contribution of clasts from the west at the appropriate horizons, he is obliged to take the unorthodox and re-stimulating view that there was no connection between the Severn and Thames before the Anglian glaciation.

In her chapter, Jane Hart surveys not only middle England, but the whole of glaciated Britain in her re-assessment of well-known, Middle and Upper Pleistocene sites in the light of the model of the deforming (glacier) bed. This is a concept which has arisen largely from recent observations below present-day ice sheets and glaciers. As Hart argues, the deforming bed model has major implications for the interpretations of Pleistocene glacial sequences, especially in connection with their stratigraphy and morphology.

A broad view of a different sort is taken by Chris Gleed-Owen in his detailed review of the British Quaternary herpetofauna, that is, the remains of all amphibians and reptiles. After painstakingly re-confirming identifications, these species turn out to be remarkably sensitive, not only to the degree of wetness, but also to variations in temperature. Thus, fine stratigraphical distinctions are made possible between well-known sites in the early Middle Pleistocene. Further, Ipswichian, Devensian and Holocene climates are refined; particularly, a mean July temperature of 15°C during the Lateglacial interstadial and 2°C warmer than at present during the mid-Holocene thermal optimum. Gleed-Owen's comprehensive tables and bibliography are bound to be quarried for years to come.

For the next two chapters we move to the Holocene of Scotland. During his time at the Hunterian Museum in Glasgow, Bill worked on the peat-bearing, Holocene sequence at Brighouse Bay on the Solway Firth. The latest work on that same site is very fittingly presented here by James Wells and his associates. They conclude from pollen, charcoal and radiocarbon dating that human impacts in that area began possibly as early as 6000 years ago in the Mesolithic and culminated in permanent woodland clearance during the Bronze and Iron Ages. Two major phases of dune accumulation are indicated, one just before 6000 BP and another during the thirteenth and fourteenth centuries. David Anderson's many pronged work on sites in the peatlands of Wester Ross demonstrates that climatic conditions were characteristically unstable during the Holocene in this coastal area. Regional transitions to wetter and/or cooler conditions are inferred at approximately 5.1, 3.8 and 0.8 ka cal. BP, with transitions to drier and/or warmer proposed at 4.2 and 1.4 ka cal. BP. Linking with Wells's concerns, Anderson also finds markedly increased human impact around 3.3 ka cal. BP.

For the final chapter we return to Africa for an account of Devensian and Holocene climatic events in the Mega Kalahari. During cold stages especially, dunes had a much wider distribution than at present, stretching from Cape Town to the Victoria Falls. Stephen Stokes and his colleagues have used optically stimulated luminescence(OSL) techniques to establish a chronology for the dune systems. Also, the weather records for the last century have been analysed for presentation in the context of global circulation models. By this means, remarkably clear indications of shifts in the pattern of rainfall and of the consequent formation of widespread dune systems have been found at 115–195, 46–41, 26–20 and 16–10 ka BP. In this wide-ranging contribution, links are made with sea surface temperatures and climates in the adjacent Atlantic and Indian Oceans, including a possible correlation with monsoons.

Peter Banham

The chronology of Middle Pleistocene ('Wolstonian') events in the English Midlands

DAVID H. KEEN

Centre for Quaternary Science, Coventry University, Priory Street,
Coventry, CV1 5FB, UK

Abstract: Recent data from interglacial sequences in the Midlands permit a new and more detailed understanding of the age and status of the so-called 'Wolstonian' Stage. By 1970, work by Tomlinson, Shotton, Bishop, Rice and others led to the recognition of a single major Middle Pleistocene glaciation in the Midlands, the Wolstonian. The till-bearing sequences of this glaciation were known to be overlain by a complicated sequence of terrace deposits associated with rivers such as the Warwickshire–Worcestershire Avon, Nene, Great Ouse and Welland. In total, no more than two Middle–Late Pleistocene glacial–interglacial cycles were thought to be represented. Since 1980, interpretations based on correlations with the East Anglian till succession, and on studies of the Avon and other river terrace sequences, have modified the lithostratigraphy, while extending the timescale of deposition to as many as six cold/temperate climatic stages. Recent geochronometric and biostratigraphic evidence from interglacial sediments at Waverley Wood and Frog Hall in the type area of the Wolstonian have constrained these interpretations, so that the type-Wolstonian glacial sediments must now be regarded as no older than Oxygen Isotope Stage 14, and no younger than Isotope Stage 10. These results allow improvements in the correlations of Pleistocene events both in the English Midlands and other areas.

Although the Pleistocene of the Midlands attracted the attention of geologists from the earliest days of the 19th century (Strickland 1835; Murchison 1836; Lucy 1872), an integrated stratigraphic sequence for the area of the Avon catchment and the region to the east was developed only in the 20th century, by Tomlinson (1925) and Shotton (1953). These workers examined the sediments of the area and arranged them into a fluvial, glacial, glacio-lacustrine and glacio-fluvial sequence named by Shotton the Wolston Series. This was found to be followed by a younger fluvial succession of five terraces numbered in descending altitudinal order (5–1), but with an age sequence of the terrace deposits below the surfaces in the order 5–3–4–2–1 (Fig. 1). Shotton established his succession in the area between Coventry, Rugby and Leamington. In the late 1950s and 1960s, work to the south of this area by Bishop (1958), at Fenny Compton and along the Jurassic escarpment south to the Thames catchment, and by Rice (1968, 1981) in Leicestershire, tended to confirm the model of Shotton and Tomlinson, and this became the general interpretation of the Middle Pleistocene record of the West Midlands. The perceived strength of the model also encouraged its application to the catchments draining to The Wash, so that the major glaciation of the East Mid-

lands was also regarded as equating to the Wolstonian, especially as it appeared to be followed by a similar river terrace sequence to that of the Avon (Horton 1970).

The early model

The sequence of deposits proposed for this original model can be seen in Table 1. The earliest widespread formation recognized was the Baginton Sand and Gravel deposited by a NW flowing river, Shotton's proto-Soar. This river occupied a broad valley, the line of which is now followed by the M69 motorway from Coventry to Leicester, the engineering geological data for which provided Rice (1981) with much of the evidence for his work on the tills of that area. The deposits of this river can be found at least as far SW as Snitterfield, NW of Stratford-upon-Avon (Lister *et al.* 1990; Maddy & Lewis 1991), and Rose (1987) has reconstructed a course for the lower reaches beyond Leicester, eastwards into East Anglia and the North Sea (see Fig. 2). The river was overwhelmed by a glaciation which built ice sheets to both the NW and NE of the Midlands and the interplay of this ice, advancing and retreating at least twice, was responsible for the deposition of the two major till units: the Thrussington Till, deposited

KEEN, D. H. 1999. The chronology of Middle Pleistocene ('Wolstonian') events in the English Midlands. *In:* ANDREWS, P. & BANHAM, P. (eds) *Late Cenozoic Environments and Hominid Evolution: a tribute to Bill Bishop.* Geological Society, London, 159–168.

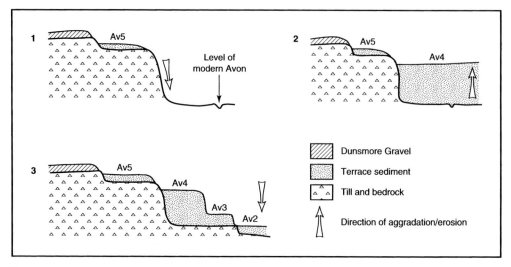

Fig. 1. The Avon terrace sequence according to Tomlinson (1925) and Shotton (1953). (**1**) Deposition of the Dunsmore Gravel, Terrace 5 and the incision of the bedrock. (**2**) Deposition of the gravel fill. (**3**) Cutting of the terrace surfaces.

by the earlier ice advance and with a predominantly NW origin, and the Oadby Till with its chalky component attesting to an ice sheet advance from the NE. Between these two glacial stages were deposited the glacio-lacustrine Wolston Clay (Bosworth Silt of Rice (1981)) and the glacio-fluvial and deltaic Wolston Sand and Gravel. The final retreat of this ice sheet

Table 1. *Lithostratigraphic terminology for the Wolstonian of the Midlands and age relationships of the Avon terraces*

Unit	Stage
Avon Terrace 1 Avon Terrace 2	Devensian
Avon Terrace 3 (surface) Avon Terrace 4 (surface) Avon Terrace 4 (deposits) Avon Terrace 3 (deposits)	Ipswichian
Avon Terrace 5	Undated
Dunsmore Gravel	Late Wolstonian
Oadby Till Wolston Sand and Gravel Lower Wolston Clay (Bosworth Silt) Thrussington Till Baginton Sand and Gravel	Wolstonian

After Tomlinson (1925), Shotton (1953, 1976) and Rice (1981).

was accompanied by the deposition of a further glacio-fluvial deposit, the Dunsmore Gravel (Table 1).

As a result of this glaciation the pre-glacial drainage of the Midlands was totally disrupted (Fig. 2). In place of the NE flowing trunk stream, now represented only by a buried valley trending from Stratford to Leicester, was the newly developed Avon drainage flowing to the SW, dissecting the Wolstonian glacial deposits and soon cutting into underlying bedrock. The evidence for the pre-glacial drainage to the south and east of this main drainage line is scanty (Fig. 2) owing to the burial beneath the till sheet of the earlier landscape and its deposits and the lack of well defined geomorphological features, but the major catchments in the south of the East Midlands were also replaced by new rivers (Nene, Great Ouse and Welland) aligned on the current Wash embayment (Fig. 2). The terraces along these 'new' rivers are best known from the Avon where an early terrace, Terrace 5 in Tomlinson's scheme and occurring only below Stratford, contains in its lower levels interglacial molluscan and mammalian remains (Whitehead 1989). Below the Terrace 5 level Tomlinson (1925) and Shotton (1953) described a complicated sequence of cut-and-fill (Fig. 1). This began with the deposition of a '50 ft' (15.5 m) sequence of sediment with warm faunas, which was later incised by the river and sculpted into Terrace 4 with younger deposits (but an older terrace surface), and Terrace 3 with its older deposits (but cut by a younger terrace flat). Both

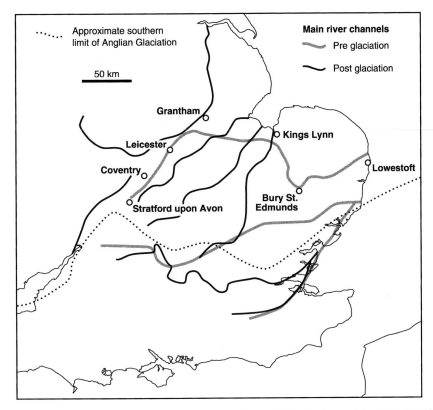

Fig. 2. The limit of the Anglian Glaciation and the pre- and post-Anglian drainage of the English Midlands.

of these terrace sediments produced warm climate Mollusca and Mammalia and were dated
to the same interglacial phase. Altitudinally
below Terraces 3 and 4 were Terraces 2 and 1
which yielded abundant faunas of mammals and
insects of cold stage aspect from sites such as
Fladbury, near Evesham (Coope 1962).

The dating of the glaciation and succeeding
terraces was at first uncertain (Shotton 1953),
but the application of pollen biostratigraphy in
other areas of Britain, especially East Anglia
(see West 1956, 1957) allowed the definition of a
timescale for the Middle and Upper Pleistocene.
Because of the identification of only one certain
temperate stage after the Wolstonian glaciation in the Tomlinson and Shotton model, the
Terrace 5 temperate deposits not being found
until later, the timescale occupied by the Wolston Series and the overlying terraces was suggested to be a short one with two major cold
stages, the Wolstonian and Last Glaciation
(later named the Devensian), separated by a
single temperate stage. Terraces 3 and 4 were
cut in this temperate episode, and because of
their contained temperate fossils and perceived

date immediately prior to the Last Glaciation,
they and their deposits were equated with the
Ipswichian of East Anglia (Mitchell *et al.* 1973;
see also Table 1). Therefore the glaciation of
the Midlands, now formally named the Wolstonian, was given the status of the immediately
pre-Ipswichian cold stage.

Thus the timescale occupied by the sequence in
the West Midlands, and by extrapolation the
whole East Midlands hinterland of The Wash,
was restricted to a short period of perhaps two
glacial/interglacial cycles occupying as little as
200 ka of late Middle and Late Pleistocene time.
The apparent strength of this model attracted
widespread interest in southern Britain so that
deposits assigned to the Wolstonian glaciation
were identified in Lincolnshire (Straw 1979,
1983), and places as far from the Midlands as
the Scillies (Mitchell & Orme 1967). However,
even while the model was still being developed,
doubts were expressed about its strength. In particular the short timespan allowed for the glaciation did not seem adequate to some authors,
and the complicated sequence of erosion and
terrace development was unique on British

rivers. From his studies of the late Wolstonian sediments around Long Itchington and Fenny Compton it is interesting to note Bishop's (1958) view that 'erosion of the Wolston series occupied an immense space of time'. Thus, while Bishop adopted Shotton's dating scheme, he perhaps had doubts about the length of time required for deposition of the succession of Shotton's model.

Revision of the model: the glacial sequence

The chalky till

The uppermost glacial unit of the Wolston Series as identified by Shotton (1976) and Rice (1981) is the Oadby Till. This is an overwhelmingly chalky till in the area to the NE of Coventry (Rice 1968; Rice & Douglas 1991), although the chalk content decreases to the south as it becomes diluted by local, mostly Mercia Mudstone, components. Discrete chalk lenses together with tabular flints up to 40 cm in their longest dimension occur as far south as Warwick where such deposits occur in the M40 motorway cuttings (D. H. Keen, unpublished data), and a chalk component can still be seen at the limit of the till sheet at Moreton-in-Marsh.

The major glacial succession in East Anglia, the Anglian, is also made up predominantly of chalky till and the uniformity of the clast content (Bristow & Cox 1973), the mineralogy (Perrin et al. 1973, 1979; Rose 1987) and the essential continuity of the deposit (Bristow & Cox 1973; Cox 1981; Sumbler 1983a) led these authors to conclude that the chalky till formed one mappable unit from Cromer to Stratford-upon-Avon. Initially this was dated to the Wolstonian of Shotton with a 'young' age immediately prior to the Ipswichian Interglacial (Bristow & Cox 1973), but most subsequent authors have equated the Midlands succession with the type Anglian, and thus an earlier Middle Pleistocene date (Sumbler 1983a, b; Rose 1987). However, it should be emphasized that the internal stratigraphic consistency of the Wolston Series of Shotton (1953) with its glacial, glacio-lacustrine and glacio-fluvial units (Tables 1 and 2) has not been significantly modified by later authors, the suggested revisions being of their age and stratigraphic position in the Pleistocene.

The terrace sequence

The second major component of the Middle Pleistocene record in the Midlands is the fluvial

Table 2. *Revised ages for major lithostratigraphic units in the Midlands and their possible Oxygen Isotope (OI) Stage equivalents*

Unit	OI stage	Stage
Avon Terrace 1 (gravels and surface)	2	
Avon Terrace 2 (gravels and surface)	3	Devensian
Avon Terrace 3 (gravels and surface)	5d–4	
Avon Terrace 3 (basal deposits)	5e	Ipswichian
Avon Terrace 4 (gravels and surface)	6	Cold stage, unnamed
Avon Terrace 4 (basal deposits)	7	Interglacial, unnamed
Avon Terrace 5 (gravels and surface)	8	Cold stage, unnamed
Avon Terrace 5 (basal deposits)	9?	? Hoxnian
Frog Hall Channel deposits	9?; 11?	? Hoxnian
Dunsmore Gravel	Late 10?; Late 12?	
Oadby Till	10?; 12?	
Wolston Sand and Gravel	10?; 12?	Anglian
Lower Wolston Clay	10?; 12?	
Thrussington Till	10?; 12?	
Baginton Sand and Gravel	10?; 12? or older, unnamed cold stage	
Waverley Wood Channel deposits	13?; 15?	Late Cromer Complex
Brandon Channel deposits	13?; 15?	

After Maddy et al. (1991, 1993), Shotton et al. (1993) and Keen et al. (1997).

terrace sequence which post-dates the glacial Wolston Series. As with almost all river terrace sequences in southern England (see Bridgland 1994), these deposits are now known to consist of basal levels of fine-grained, sometimes fossiliferous sediments of temperate origin, overlain by cold stage sands and gravels which bear the geomorphological terrace surface. The original stratigraphic model developed by Tomlinson (1925) was constructed around the complicated cut-and-fill succession described above and illustrated in Fig. 1. This sequence of events was accepted by Shotton and later authors and became a cornerstone of the short chronology outlined above.

However, recent re-examination of these terraces in boreholes and test pits at critical sites (Maddy 1989; Maddy et al. 1991) has confirmed neither a single, thick fluvial sequence nor a complex pattern of deep incisions (Fig. 3). Instead, a series of thin fluvial deposits are separated by discrete rock steps. All terraces can be distinguished by altitude and Terraces 3 and 4 are also biostratigraphically distinct. The bivalve *Corbicula fluminalis* is restricted to the base of

Terrace 4 and the southern European gastropod *Belgrandia marginata* is found only in the lower part of Terrace 3. Amino acid geochronology (Maddy et al. 1991) has confirmed that these two terraces contain deposits from Oxygen Isotope Stages 7 and 5. The lower portion of the younger Terrace 3 has been correlated with the Ipswichian Interglacial because it contains *Hippopotamus amphibius* at a number of sites (Keen & Bridgland 1986; Jones & Keen 1993). From this it follows that the higher Terrace 4 is older and represents an earlier temperate stage (Maddy et al. 1991; d'Ruffignac et al. 1995), with Terrace 5 and its fragmentary temperate fauna being older still (Whitehead 1989).

Dating of the Wolstonian by biostratigraphy

Shotton's concept of the Wolston Series had little underpinning by biostratigraphy. Few temperate sites were known associated with the Wolston Series (Shotton 1953), although scattered, mainly 19th century, records of mammalian material were used by Shotton (1953, 1983) to

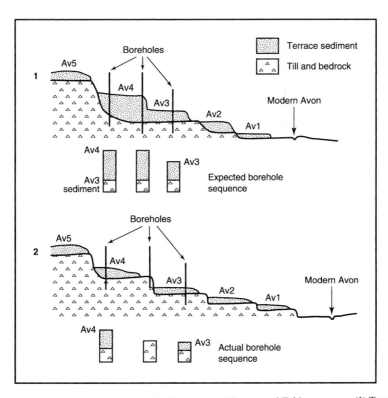

Fig. 3. The sequence of the Avon terraces in the Cropthorne, Ailstone and Eckington area. (**1**) Terraces, deposits and the expected succession from the work of Tomlinson (1925). (**2**) Actual succession shown in boreholes (after Maddy et al. 1991).

propose a late Middle Pleistocene age for the Baginton Sands and Gravel. The uncertain provenance of virtually all these finds led Sumbler (1983a, b) to doubt their use as biostratigraphic indicators. Apart from these equivocal records from the Baginton Sands and Gravels, other sites that were recorded were not directly linked with the glacial deposits (e.g. Nechells and Quinton, in the Birmingham area: Kelly 1964; Horton 1989), or such organic material as was recovered was not deemed stratigraphically significant, such as the molluscan content of the Avon terraces.

Recent work has reported organic deposits in close association with the Wolstonian in its type area. Two sites are especially significant: Waverley Wood Pit at Bubbenhall, 7 km SW of Coventry, was described by Shotton et al. (1993). At this site organic muds and sands with pollen, plant macrofossils, molluscs, mammalian bones, ostracods and insects together with a few human-made stone artefacts, occur in channels cut into the Mercia Mudstone bedrock, but also range up into the basal levels of the Wolston series in the Baginton Sands and Gravels. The Thrussington Till caps this sequence. The biostratigraphic indicators are not conclusive as to age, but some aspects of the molluscan fauna such as the occurrence of the bivalve *Unio crassus* and the presence of *Bithynia troscheli* as the only species of *Bithynia,* compares most closely with the fauna of some of the Cromerian sites of East Anglia. The occurrence in the channels of teeth of the water vole *Arvicola cantiana* also suggests an age similar to, or younger than, the most recent parts of the Cromer Forest Bed Series (Stuart 1996). As the type-Cromerian at West Runton shows no sign of human activity, it is probable that the age of the Waverley Wood channels is closest to the latter part of the 'Cromer Complex' (Turner 1996) and younger than the Cromerian of the Norfolk coast. Amino-acid geochronology on shell from Waverley Wood suggests an age in Oxygen Isotope Stage 15 (Bowen et al. 1989), and indicates that the two mollusc-bearing channels found below the Baginton Sands and Gravels were formed during the same temperate stage. A review of the Waverley Wood evidence by Meijer & Preece (1996) proposes a more complicated sequence with the channels containing *two* temperate stages, possibly dated to Stages 15 and 13.

The effect of these geochemically and biostratigraphically determined ages is to constrain the lowest part of the Wolston Series to an early Middle Pleistocene date in Oxygen Isotope Stages 14 or 12. Waverley Wood was the first major organic-bearing sequence to be found under the Wolston series, although sequences at Brandon, 2 km NW of Wolston, produced indeterminate cool climate fossils in the 1960s (Kelly 1968; Osborne & Shotton 1968), and excavations in the 1980s of an organic-filled channel with pollen, plant macrofossils and insects at Pools Farm, Brandon, confirmed the Waverley Wood pattern and suggested age for the Baginton Sands and Gravels (Maddy et al. 1993).

The dating of events after the deposition of the till is even more difficult. The terrace sequences give evidence for at least two temperate stages after the deposition of the glacial deposits, dated most plausibly on their molluscan content and amino acid ratios to Oxygen Isotope Stages 5e and 7 (Maddy et al. 1991). Although a limited temperate molluscan fauna has been found in the deposits of Terrace 5 there is no species in this which is diagnostic as to age, so dating the end of the glaciation from the terrace deposits is not precise.

Only one post-till but pre-Stage 7 site, Frog Hall, Stretton, has been described outside of the main band of river terrace deposits. This channel-fill sequence occupies a hill-top some 1.5 km S of Shotton's Wolston stratotype and rests on Wolston Clay (Sumbler 1989; Keen et al. 1997). The age of this channel fill is thus unequivocally post-Wolstonian. Although the pollen, plant macrofossils, Mollusca, Coleoptera and Ostracoda from this deposit do not readily allow correlation with any formally defined interglacial, the most likely correlation through pollen biostratigraphy is with the Hoxnian of East Anglia and, via amino acid geochronology on molluscan shell, with Oxygen Isotope Stage 9.

Discussion

The establishment of a longer chronology for the post-Wolstonian events in the Midlands has the effect of pushing the Wolstonian back in time, close to the Anglian as was suggested first by Bristow & Cox (1973) and later by Perrin et al. (1979), Sumbler (1983a, b) and Rose (1987). These authors equated the Wolstonian and Anglian glacial deposits on the grounds of the similarity of the characteristics of the tills and, in the case of Rose, because of the similar appearance and petrology of the underlying fluvial successions of the Baginton Sand and Gravel and the Bytham Sand and Gravel. The identification of the longer timescale for post-Wolstonian events from the number and succession of the river terraces that post-date the glaciation, confirms that the equation of the

Wolstonian and the Anglian can also be accomplished on time grounds.

However, problems still remain in the exact chronology for these deposits (Table 2). River terraces of Ipswichian (Sub-stage 5e) age can be found along all the major 'new' rivers of the Midlands: Terrace 3 of the Avon (Keen & Bridgland 1986; Maddy et al. 1991), the 'low' terrace of the Welland at Maxey (Davey et al. 1991) and other sites around Peterborough such as Deeping St James (Keen et al. 1999) and St Ives (Preece & Ventris 1983). However, the dating of earlier terraces is more problematical. From the geochronometrical and biostratigraphical evidence it has become clear since 1990 that fossiliferous sediments in the basal levels of Avon Terrace 4 can be dated to the interglacial which precedes the Ipswichian, the unnamed interglacial in Stage 7 (Maddy et al. 1991; de Ruffignac et al. 1995). The characteristic molluscan faunas in the basal layers of this terrace, with the abundance at most sites of the exotic bivalve *Corbicula fluminalis,* and the distinctive insect fauna with such elements as *Oxytelus gibbulus* always prominent, serve to allow correlation from the Avon into the Great Ouse valley at Stoke Goldington (de Ruffignac et al. 1995; Green et al. 1996) and help confirm the existence of this earlier interglacial. Older temperate deposits are rare. The fauna associated with Avon Terrace 5 described by Whitehead (1989) is undiagnostic as to age and undated geochronometrically, although the terrace is at a higher level than Terrace 4 and thus probably older. If the deposits of Terrace 4 are of Stage 7 age, those of Terrace 5 are likely to be of Stage 9 age.

The deposits at Frog Hall (Keen et al. 1997) are dated by amino acid geochronology to Stage 9 but are outside the immediate band of the Avon terraces and are overlain by gravels apparently graded to Terrace 4 of the River Leam, a tributary equivalent of Terrace 4 of the main valley (Sumbler 1989). However, the channel deposits at the site are incised deeply below the base of the Dunsmore Gravel and it is possible either that the incision took place in Stage 11, assuming an Anglian Glaciation in Stage 12, and that the fill of gravel, organics and gravel occurred during Stages 10 and 9 or that the whole process of channel erosion and infill was accomplished in Stages 10 and 9 alone. An episode of weathering and decalcification of the channel-fill deposits took place, probably in Stage 7 before deposition of the Stage 6 gravels immediately beneath the Terrace 4 surface from the shifting, cold stage channels of the Leam.

Elsewhere in the Midlands, few sites are known with organic remains in higher terraces than those dated to Stage 7. At Biddenham in the Great Ouse valley, W of Bedford, pits described in the 19th century (Prestwich 1861) which were excavated through the deposits of a higher terrace than the Stage 7 Stoke Goldington deposits, and which have yielded a temperate molluscan fauna (Harding et al. 1992), are also probably of Stage 9 age, although undated by any geochronometrical means. In the lower reaches of the Nene at Peterborough the Woodston Beds have been dated to the Hoxnian by pollen biostratigraphy and on mammalian evidence, and probably to Stage 9 by amino acid geochronology (Horton et al. 1992). The Woodston Beds are partly estuarine and are overlain by the Third Terrace of the Nene, the oldest generally distributed terrace in this catchment, but which from its stratigraphic position can be no older than Stage 8 in age.

Terraces higher and thus older than these have not been found along any of the Midland rivers and neither have any older temperate organic deposits been found resting on the till sheet in the region. This lack of post-Anglian temperate deposits older than Stage 9 allows the possibility that the Anglian Glaciation may be of Stage 10 age, although the general consensus is that it is dated to Stage 12, as that is the most extreme glacial phase in the Middle Pleistocene (see Bowen 1991; Raymo 1997). The deep dissection at the Frog Hall site plus the weathering of elements of the Dunsmore Gravel could be thought to take up both Stages 11 and 10, but this is not conclusive evidence. It is also possible, as Bowen (1992) has pointed out, that basins in the Anglian till sheet did not begin to infill immediately at the end of the glaciation, so that the channel at Frog Hall, and basins on the Anglian till sheet in East Anglia as at Hoxne, could have been formed at the end of the Anglian in Stage 12, but only began to be filled later.

It is possible that isostatic rebound after the Anglian deglaciation provided a stimulus to accelerated erosion and thus to the destruction of immediately post-Anglian terrace sediments. Against this, however, is the wide existence of the Dunsmore Gravel, outwash from the Anglian ice, in the core area of Anglian sediments in the Midlands. This latest Anglian sediment would have been eroded first before any terrace deposits. The only temperate deposits associated with river terraces in southern England thought to be of Stage 11 age occur along rivers outside the Anglian limit, the Thames Orsett Heath Formation which contains the classic Swanscombe site in north Kent (Bridgland 1994) being typical. However, these Stage 11 deposits are also very close to the Anglian limit, even overlying the Anglian till itself at Hornchurch in Essex, yet the spread of terrace sediment is extensive and not intensely dissected (Bridgland 1994), again suggesting little isostatic uplift and erosion.

One possible solution to this problem of the lack of fluvial deposits of Stage 11 age except outside the Anglian limit has been proposed by Sumbler (1995) from observations in the Thame and Thames valleys. Because of perceived discrepancies between the heights and distribution of the glacio-fluvial outwash terraces in the Thame and Middle Thames valleys and the Anglian tills in the Vale of St Albans, Sumbler proposed that separate ice advances had occurred in Stages 12 and 10. A somewhat similar argument has been advanced for events in the Upper Thames by Bridgland (1994). Here the input of glacially derived material into the Wolvercote Terrace appears to equate with Stage 10 rather than Stage 12 on grounds of the terrace stratigraphy. The lack of any fluvial deposits dated to Stage 11 within the area affected by Anglian ice would perhaps indicate the possibility that Sumbler's suggestion of a 'double Anglian', or Bridgland's idea of a Stage 10 glaciation of the Cotswolds and, by extension, of the Midlands, is correct. In the Wolstonian type-area in the West Midlands, the occurrence of the Thrussington and Oadby Tills might be thought to provide *prima facie* evidence for the two advances proposed. However, as Shotton (1976) realized, there is no evidence for an interlude between deposition of these two tills which might be interpreted as being of interglacial rank. Certainly no temperate deposits have been found between the tills in this area or anywhere else in southern Britain, and the work on the petrology and mineralogy of the chalky tills from East Anglia to the Midlands by Perrin *et al.* (1973, 1979) seems to establish that these tills are uniform wherever they occur and gives no support to two separate till sheets of different ages.

Neither is biostratigraphy of much help in distinguishing between phases, especially in the absence of long and detailed records form the Midlands. Pollen sequences are fragmentary and few in number and in any case pollen biostratigraphy is of limited use in separating temperate stages close together in time. Other biostratigraphical schemes using molluscs or mammals are similarly undeveloped, although the different characters of the molluscan faunas from sites such as Swanscombe (Stage 11), with a number of central European species similar to those of pre-Anglian sites, and Woodston (Stage 9), with an almost wholly modern fauna, may point to their separation by a significant extinction event which might be a glaciation in Stage 10.

Conclusions

The combination of work on the lithology of the tills and the chronology and biostratigraphy of the overlying river terraces strongly suggests that the Wolstonian and the Anglian type sequences represent a single event. However, the age of this event is not yet certain. In the type area of the Wolstonian in the West Midlands, the recent discovery of temperate deposits above and below the till allows an age bracket for the glaciation in either Stage 10 or 12, with a possibility also of Stage 14 if the amino acid ratios from Waverley Wood indicating a Stage 15 age for the channels are accurate. The puzzling absence of temperate Stage 11 deposits postdating the tills has yet to be explained, but the possibility that the major Middle Pleistocene glaciation which is represented by the Anglian and the Wolstonian may be spread over two cold Oxygen Isotope Stages must be considered as a possibility. The use of the name Wolstonian for a timespan of the Middle Pleistocene should be discontinued as it is clear that the age of the stratotype is close in time to that of the Anglian and does not succeed it.

I am grateful to D. R. Bridgland and C. P. Green for their comments which have allowed valuable modifications to be made on an early draft of this paper. The extensive referees' report by M. G. Sumbler has allowed many improvements in the paper.

References

BISHOP, W. W. 1958. The Pleistocene geology and geomorphology of three gaps in the Midlands Jurassic escarpment. *Philosophical Transactions of the Royal Society of London*, **B241**, 255–306.

BOWEN, D. Q. 1991. Time and space in the glacial sediment systems of the British Isles. *In:* EHLERS, J., GIBBARD, P. L. & ROSE, J. (eds) *Glacial Deposits in Great Britain and Ireland.* Balkema, Rotterdam.

——1992. Aminostratigraphy of non-marine Pleistocene Mollusca in Southern Britain. *Severiges Geologiska Undersökning*, **81**, 65–67.

——, HUGHES, S., SYKES, G. A. & MILLER, G. H. 1989. Land–sea correlations in the Pleistocene based on isoleucine epimerization in non-marine molluscs. *Nature*, **340**, 49–51.

BRIDGLAND, D. R. 1994. *Quaternary of the Thames.* Chapman & Hall, London, for the Joint Nature Conservation Committee.

BRISTOW, C. R. & COX, F. C. 1973. The Gipping Till: a reappraisal of East Anglian glacial stratigraphy. *Journal of the Geological Society of London*, **129**, 1–37.

COOPE, G. R. 1962. A Pleistocene coleopterous fauna with arctic affinities from Fladbury, Worcestershire. *Quarterly Journal of the Geological Society of London*, **118**, 103–123.

COX, F. C. 1981. The 'Gipping Till' revisited. *In*: NEALE, J. & FLENLEY, J. (eds) *The Quaternary in Britain: essays, reviews and original work on the Quaternary published in honour of Lewis Penny on his retirement*. Pergamon, Oxford.

DAVEY, N. D. W., BRIDGLAND, D. R. & KEEN, D. H. 1991. Maxey Gravel Pit near Peterborough. *In*: LEWIS, S. G., WHITEMAN, C. A. & BRIDGLAND, D. R. (eds) *Central East Anglia & the Fen Basin: Field Guide*. Quaternary Research Association, London.

DE RUFFIGNAC, C., BOWEN, D. Q., COOPE, G. R. *et al.* 1995. Late Middle Pleistocene interglacial deposits at Upper Strensham, Worcestershire, England. *Journal of Quaternary Science*, **10**(1), 15–31.

GREEN, C. P., COOPE, G. R., JONES, R. L. *et al.* 1996. Pleistocene deposits at Stoke Goldington, in the valley of the Great Ouse. *Journal of Quaternary Science*, **11**(1), 59–87.

HARDING, P., BRIDGLAND, D. R., KEEN, D. H. & ROGERSON, R. J. 1992 A Palaeolithic site rediscovered at Biddenham, Bedfordshire. *Bedfordshire Archaeology*, **19**, 87–90.

HORTON, A. 1970. *The drift sequence and sub-glacial topography in parts of the Ouse and Nene basin*. Institute of Geological Sciences Report **70/9**.

——1989. Quinton. *In*: KEEN, D. H. (ed.) *West Midlands Field Guide*. Quaternary Research Association, Cambridge.

——, KEEN, D. H., FIELD, M. H. *et al.* 1992. The Hoxnian Interglacial deposits at Woodston, Peterborough. *Philosophical Transactions of the Royal Society of London*, **B338**, 131–164.

JONES, R. L. & KEEN, D. H. 1993. *Pleistocene Environments in the British Isles*. Chapman & Hall, London.

KEEN, D. H. & BRIDGLAND, D. R. 1986. An interglacial fauna from Avon No 3 Terrace at Eckington, Worcestershire. *Proceedings of the Geologists' Association*, **97**, 303–307.

——, BATEMAN, M. D., COOPE, G. R., FIELD, M. H., LANGFORD, H., MERRY, J. S. & MIGHALL, T. M. 1999. Sedimentology, palaeoecology and geochronology of Last Interglacial deposits from Deeping St. James, Lincolnshire, U.K. *Journal of Quaternary Science*, **14**(4).

——, COOPE, G. R., JONES, R. L., FIELD, M. H., GRIFFITHS, H. I., LEWIS, S. G. & BOWEN, D. Q. 1997. Middle Pleistocene deposits at Frog Hall Pit, Stretton-on-Dunsmore, Warwickshire, English Midlands, and their implications for the age of the type Wolstonian. *Journal of Quaternary Science*, **12**(3), 183–208.

KELLY, M. R. 1964. The Middle Pleistocene of North Birmingham. *Philosophical Transactions of the Royal Society of London*, **B247**, 401–415.

——1968. Floras of Middle and Upper Pleistocene age from Brandon, Warwickshire. *Philosophical Transactions of the Royal Society of London*, **B254**, 401–415.

LISTER, A. M., KEEN, D. H. & CROSSLING, J. 1990. Elephant and molluscan remains from the basal levels of the Baginton-Lillington Gravels at Snitterfield, Warwickshire. *Proceedings of the Geologists' Association*, **101**(3), 203–212.

LUCY, W. C. 1872. The gravels of the Severn, Avon and Evenlode and their extension over the Cotteswold Hills. *Proceedings of the Cotteswold Naturalists Field Club*, **5**, 71–142.

MADDY, D. 1989. *The Middle Pleistocene development of the rivers Severn and Avon*. PhD thesis, University of London.

—— & LEWIS, S. G. 1991. The Pleistocene deposits at Snitterfield, Warwickshire. *Proceedings of the Geologists' Association*, **102**(4), 289–300.

——, GIBBARD, P. L., COOPE, G. R., GREEN, C. P. & LEWIS, S. G. 1993. Reappraisal of the Middle Pleistocene fluvial deposits near Brandon, Warwickshire and their significance for the Wolstonian glacial sequence. *Journal of the Geological Society of London*, **151**(2), 221–235.

——, KEEN, D. H., BRIDGLAND, D. R. & GREEN, C. P. 1991. A revised model for the Pleistocene development of the River Avon, Warwickshire. *Journal of the Geological Society of London*, **148**, 473–484.

MEIJER, T. & PREECE, R. C. 1996. Malacological evidence relating to the stratigraphical position of the Cromerian. *In*: TURNER, C. (ed.) *The Early Middle Pleistocene in Europe*. Balkema, Rotterdam.

MITCHELL, G. F. & ORME, A. R. 1967. The Pleistocene deposits of the Isles of Scilly. *Quarterly Journal of the Geological Society of London*, **123**, 59–92.

——, PENNY, L. F., SHOTTON, F. W. & WEST, R. G. 1973. *A correlation of Quaternary Deposits in the British Isles*. Geological Society, London, Special Reports, **4**.

MURCHISON, R. I. 1836. *Proceedings of the Geological Society*, **2**, 230–326.

OSBORNE, P. J. & SHOTTON, F. W. 1968. The fauna of the channel deposit of early Saalian age at Brandon, Warwickshire. *Philosophical Transactions of the Royal Society of London*, **B254**, 417–424.

PERRIN, R. M. S., DAVIES, H. & FYSH, M. D. 1973. Lithology of the Chalky Boulder Clay. *Nature*, **245**, 101–104.

——, ROSE, J. & DAVIES, H. 1979. The distribution, variation and origins of pre-Devensian tills in eastern England. *Philosophical Transactions of the Royal Society of London*, **B287**, 535–570.

PREECE, R. C. & VENTRIS, P. A. 1983. An interglacial site at Galley Hill near St Ives, Cambridgeshire. *Bulletin of the Geological Society of Norfolk*, **33**, 63–72.

PRESTWICH, J. 1861. Notes on some further discoveries of flint implements in beds of post-Pliocene gravel and clay; with a few suggestions for search elsewhere. *Quarterly Journal of the Geological Society*, **17**, 362–368.

RAYMO, M. E. 1997. The timing of major climatic terminations. *Paleoceanography*, **12**, 577–585.

RICE, R. J. 1968. The Quaternary deposits of central Leicestershire. *Philosophical Transactions of the Royal Society of London*, **A262**, 459–509.

——1981. The Pleistocene deposits of the area around Croft in south Leicestershire. *Philosophical Transactions of the Royal Society of London*, **B293**, 385–418.

—— & DOUGLAS, T. D. 1991. Wolstonian glacial deposits and glaciation in Britain. *In*: EHLERS, J., GIBBARD, P. L. & ROSE, J. (eds) *Glacial Deposits in Great Britain and Ireland*. Balkema, Rotterdam.

ROSE, J. 1987. Status of the Wolstonian glaciation in the British Quaternary. *Quaternary Newsletter*, **53**, 1–9.

SHOTTON, F. W. 1953. Pleistocene deposits of the area between Coventry, Rugby and Leamington and their bearing upon the topographic development of the Midlands. *Philosophical Transactions of the Royal Society of London*, **B237**, 209–260.

——1976. Amplification of the Wolstonian Stage of the British Pleistocene. *Geological Magazine*, **113**, 241–250.

——1983. Observations on the type Wolstonian Glacial sequence. *Quaternary Newsletter*, **40**, 27–36.

——, KEEN, D. H., COOPE, G. R., CURRANT, A. P., GIBBARD, P. L., AALTO, M., PEGLAR, S. M. & ROBINSON, J. E. 1993. The Middle Pleistocene deposits of Waverley Wood Pit, Warwickshire, England. *Journal of Quaternary Science*, **8**(4), 293–325.

STRAW, A. 1979. The geomorphological significance of the Wolstonian glaciation of eastern England. *Transactions of the Institute of British Geographers*, New Series, **4**, 540–549.

——1983. Pre-Devensian glaciation of Lincolnshire (eastern England) and adjacent areas. *Quaternary Science Reviews*, **2**, 239–260.

STRICKLAND, H. E. 1835. An account of the land and freshwater shells found associated with the bones of land quadrupeds beneath diluvial gravels at Cropthorne in Warwickshire. *Proceedings of the Geological Society of London*, **2**, 111–112.

STUART, A. J. 1996. Vertebrate faunas from the early Middle Pleistocene of East Anglia. *In*: TURNER, C. (ed.) *The Early Middle Pleistocene in Europe*. Balkema, Rotterdam.

SUMBLER, M. G. 1983a. A new look at the type Wolstonian glacial deposits of Central England. *Proceedings of the Geologists' Association*, **94**, 23–31.

——1983b. The type Wolstonian sequence – some further comments. *Quaternary Newsletter*, **40**, 36–39.

——1989. The Frog Hall sand and gravel: a post 'Wolstonian' fluvial deposit near Coventry. *Quaternary Newsletter*, **58**, 3–8.

——1995. The terraces of the rivers Thame and Thames and their bearing on the chronology of glaciation in central and eastern England. *Proceedings of the Geologists' Association*, **106**(2), 93–107.

TOMLINSON, M. E. 1925. River terraces of the lower valley of the Warwickshire Avon. *Quarterly Journal of the Geological Society of London*, **81**, 137–163.

TURNER, C. (ed.) 1996. *The Early Middle Pleistocene in Europe*. Balkema, Rotterdam.

WEST, R. G. 1956. The Quaternary deposits at Hoxne, Suffolk. *Philosophical Transactions of the Royal Society of London*, **B239**, 265–356.

——1957. Interglacial deposits at Bobbitshole, Ipswich. *Philosophical Transactions of the Royal Society of London*, **B241**, 1–31.

WHITEHEAD, P. F. 1989. The Quaternary malacofauna of the Worcestershire–Warwickshire Avon. *In*: KEEN, D. H. (ed.) *West Midlands Field Guide*. Quaternary Research Association, Cambridge.

Middle Pleistocene reconstruction of the Baginton River Basin: implications for the Thames drainage system

DARREL MADDY*

*Department of Geography and Geology,
Cheltenham and Gloucester College of Higher Education, UK*

Abstract: This paper reviews the early Middle Pleistocene deposits of the Baginton River (Baginton Formation) in the context of the development of the Thames and Severn drainage basins. An extended Thames Basin during the Cenozoic was suggested by Davis after consideration of the landform evidence and was further adapted by Buckman, who referred to this drainage line as the 'Severn–Thames'. Later, Wills argued that drainage development in the West Midlands had been tectonically guided during the Tertiary, both northwards to the Irish Sea by way of the actively sinking Cheshire Basin, and southwards to the Bristol Channel depression. More recently, Hey's re-examination of the sediments of the middle and upper Thames re-focused attention on the possibility of an extended Thames catchment, and led Whiteman & Rose to conclude that the Thames had extended beyond the Cotswolds into North Wales during the Early and early Middle Pleistocene. According to this model, the Baginton River may have later occupied part of this extended Thames Basin, with the upper part of the extended Thames Basin forming the upper reaches of the Baginton River. However, recent detailed examination of the lithological and sedimentological evidence from the Baginton Formation suggests that the upper reaches of the Baginton River Basin need not have extended west of the Birmingham area. A similar basin dimension is proposed for the extended Thames Basin.

The Baginton Formation represents the fluvial sediments deposited by the Baginton River (Maddy & Lewis 1991; Fig. 1). These sediments are of critical importance in the understanding of Middle Pleistocene events in Midland England (Shotton 1953, 1983; Rose 1987, 1989). The Baginton Formation records the existence of a pre-Anglian drainage line and its subsequent destruction by the invasion of Anglian ice, followed by the development of the present Warwickshire River Avon drainage routeway. This represents one of the most spectacular examples of drainage reversal in the British Pleistocene (Shotton 1953).

Recently the Baginton Formation has played a pivotal role in the debate concerning the status of the Wolstonian (Rose 1987; Rice 1991; Lewis 1993) glaciation. Biostratigraphical data from organic channel-fills within the Baginton Formation suggest greater antiquity than previously postulated (Shotton *et al.* 1993; Maddy *et al.* 1994), a suggestion supported by limited geochronological data (Bowen *et al.* 1989). These

observations tend to confirm the conclusion that the glaciation responsible for the destruction of the Baginton River occurred during the Anglian (Sumbler 1983). Furthermore, the Baginton Formation lies in a geographical area and stratigraphical position critical to the understanding of the evolution of the early Pleistocene Thames Basin.

The idea of an early extended Thames Basin stretching across the English Midlands was suggested by Davis (1895) and Buckman (1899) and was based upon landform evidence. However, although Wills (1948) agreed that an early drainage line may have followed this route (Fig. 2A), he argued that drainage in the West Midlands was modified as a result of early Tertiary tectonic movements associated with the Alpine orogeny. These movements resulted in the re-establishment of tectonically guided basins (Fig. 3A) and led to the development of drainage north to the Irish Sea by way of the actively sinking Cheshire Basin (Cope 1994) and south to the Bristol Channel depression via the Severn Basin.

Recent re-examination of the sediments of the middle and upper Thames (Hey 1986; Whiteman & Rose 1992) has identified a number of

*Present address: Department of Geography, University of Newcastle, Newcastle upon Tyne, NE1 7RU, UK

MADDY, D. 1999. Middle Pleistocene reconstruction of the Baginton River Basin: implications for the Thames drainage system. *In*: ANDREWS, P. & BANHAM, P. (eds) *Late Cenozoic Environments and Hominid Evolution: a tribute to Bill Bishop*. Geological Society, London, 169–182.

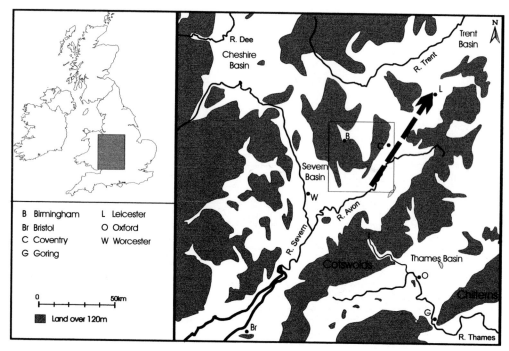

Fig. 1. General location map. Dashed arrow shows approximate position of Baginton Formation outcrop. Inset box delimits the main area of discussion in this paper.

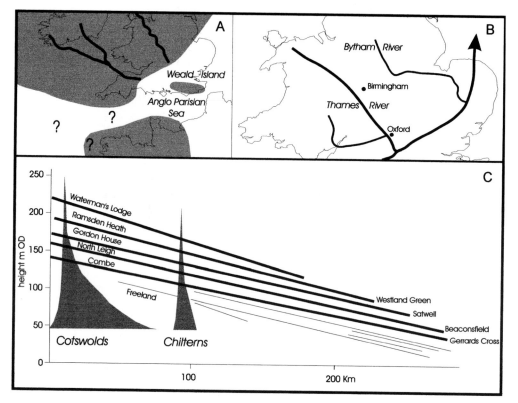

Fig. 2. (A) Early Eocene drainage (after Wills 1948). (B) The 'Great' Thames (after Rose 1994). (C) Simplified terraces of the Thames Valley (after Whiteman & Rose 1992).

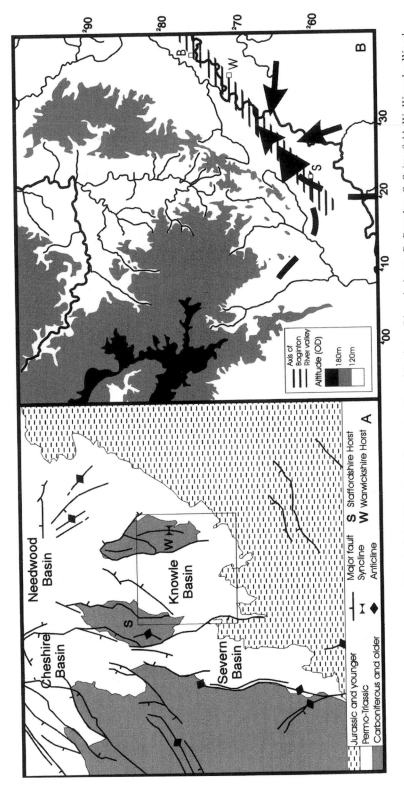

Fig. 3. (A) Major geological structures of the English Midlands. (B) Reconstruction of Baginton River drainage. B, Brandon; S, Snitterfield; W, Waverley Wood.

high-level terraces within a basin which extended beyond the present Upper Thames valley (Fig. 2C). The lithological composition of these sediments suggests an input from North Wales during the Early and early Middle Pleistocene. These observations led Rose (1994) to suggest that a 'great' Thames Basin extended into North Wales (Fig. 2B). Based upon the model of Whiteman & Rose (1992), this 'great' Thames Basin was lost after deposition of the Combe Member of the Upper Thames Formation and, bearing in mind the stratigraphy downstream, they concluded that this had occurred during the Tiglian 4c stage of the Netherlands Pleistocene sequence (itself presumed time-equivalent to Oxygen Isotope Stage 22 of the deep sea record; Funnell 1995). From that time the Baginton River is presumed to have inherited the extended Thames catchment (Rose 1994).

This paper attempts to utilize the existing database of information concerning the Baginton Formation, together with additional previously published accounts of allied deposits, firstly to describe the nature and extent of the Baginton Formation and secondly to estimate the boundaries of the Baginton River catchment. Finally, the implications of the delineation of the Baginton catchment for the limits of an early extended Thames catchment will be discussed.

Baginton Formation

This Formation consists of the fluviatile sands and gravels formally known as the Baginton–Lillington Gravel and Baginton Sand which were first described by Shotton (1953). The Formation is traceable from Snitterfield, near Stratford-upon-Avon, to Thurmaston 5 km north of Leicester (Shotton 1953; Rice 1968; Fig. 1). This outcrop has recently been confirmed by British Geological Survey (BGS) mapping (Old et al. 1987). The basal bounding surface falls from c. 87 m Ordnance Datum (OD) at Snitterfield to c. 65 m OD at Thurmaston indicating a palaeovalley falling towards the north-east. Drainage from southwest to northeast is confirmed by palaeocurrent measurements from members of the formation (Maddy et al. 1994: Lewis 1993)

Extension of this formation downstream of Thurmaston is problematical. Shotton (1953) suggested that the formation represented deposition in a tributary of the River Trent, implying continuation of the Baginton Formation along the line of the present Soar Valley towards the main Trent trunk river (Fig. 1). However, no proven correlative of the Baginton Formation

has been recorded from the Soar Valley. Alternatively, Rose (1987) suggested that lithologically similar gravels in the Wreake Valley and beyond may correlate with this formation. There are also complications with this correlation (Rice 1991), which suggest caution should be exercised. However, the downstream reconstruction of the Baginton Basin is not the subject of this paper.

In order to attempt a reconstruction of the Baginton Basin upstream of Snitterfield (Fig. 3b) it is necessary first to describe the characteristics of the Baginton Formation.

Lithostratigraphy

The Baginton Formation has its stratotype at Baginton (SP348750; Shotton 1953) where it ranges in thickness from 5 to 8 m. The formation has been subdivided into four lithostratigraphical units (Maddy 1999).

Bottom
- Thurmaston Member: type locality is at Thurmaston (SK 615101; Rice 1968) where it is c. 6 m in thickness. This member equates with the Baginton Gravel (Triassic facies) of Shotton (1953). Generally the gravels represent high-energy fluvial deposition. The detailed sedimentology suggests deposition in a multichannel (braided) system.
- Waverley Wood Beds: type locality is at Waverley Wood Pit (SP 365715; Shotton et al. 1993; Fig. 3b). These beds comprise a series of fine-grained channel-fills with a recorded thickness up to 3 m which underlie the Thurmaston Member at Waverley Wood but are intercalated with it at Brandon (Maddy et al. 1994).
- Lillington Member: type locality is at Lillington (SP 328675; Shotton 1953). This member comprises predominantly gravels with a significant Jurassic limestone component. This unit equates with the Lillington Gravel (Jurassic facies) of Shotton (1953).
- Brandon Member: type locality is at the former site of Pools Farm Pit, Brandon (SP 384763; Maddy et al. 1994; Fig. 3b). This member comprises predominant sand facies with occasional gravel and fine-grained lenses and equates with the Baginton Sand of Shotton (1953). The detailed sedimentology together with low directional variance palaeocurrent measurements suggest probable deposition in a sandy braided river (Maddy 1989; Maddy et al. 1994).

Top

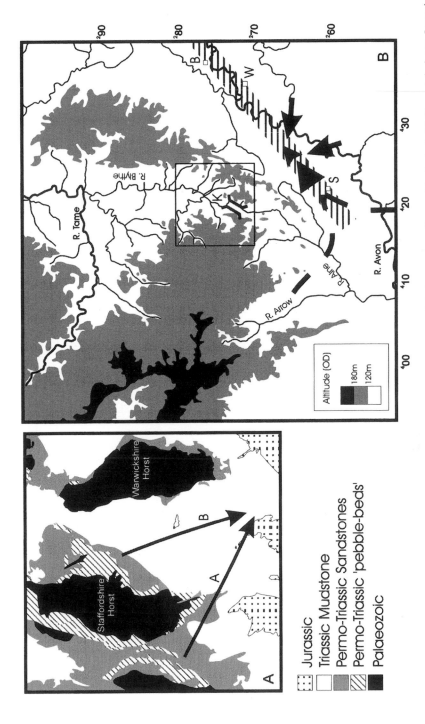

Fig. 4. (**A**) Simplified geology of the West Midlands. Arrows indicate the possible reconstructed drainage routes discussed in the text. (**B**) Current drainage. Inset delimits the area shown in Fig. 6. K, Kingswood Gap.

Nature of the lower and upper bounding surfaces

In the West Midlands, the Baginton Formation lies on an erosional lower bounding surface cut into underlying fine-grained bedrock of either Triassic Mercia Mudstone or Lower Jurassic Lias Clay (Fig. 4A). In most localities, the upper bounding surface of the formation is succeeded by members of the glacigenic Wolston Formation (Maddy 1999). The contact with the overlying Wolston Formation is often erosional, but in places is gradational. At Snitterfield (Maddy & Lewis 1991), for example, the fluvial sediments of the Baginton Formation pass upwards into a lacustrine sequence considered to be associated with damming of the Baginton River downstream by the encroaching ice lobe responsible for deposition of the Wolston Formation. Rose (1987) also recorded interdigitation between the sediments of the Baginton and Wolston Formations.

Lithology

Pebble count data from five localities are shown in Table 1. The gravels are dominated by quartzite and quartz components derived from outside the local area, the most likely source being the Triassic Kidderminster Formation (formerly Bunter Pebble Beds) which crops out extensively in an area to the west and north, stretching from Birmingham northwards across Cannock Chase (Fig. 4A). Minor components of the gravels also include chert (mainly Carboniferous from the more immediate Warwickshire Coalfield area), schorl (derived from the Kidderminster Formation) and occasional flints (most probably derived from pre-existing Pleistocene deposits, e.g. the Northern Drift: Hey 1986). Locally, as already noted, there are facies which reflect specific local inputs, e.g. the Lillington Member at Snitterfield which has a significant Jurassic limestone component indicating input from a northward flowing tributary draining the Middle Jurassic Cotswold escarpment to the east and south (Maddy & Lewis 1991).

The sand component is also most likely derived from members of the Triassic Sherwood Sandstone Group to the west, e.g. the Bromsgrove Sandstone and Wildmoor Sandstone (Permo-Triassic sandstones; Fig. 4A) (Bateman & Rose 1994).

Biostratigraphy

There is a paucity of biogenic information from the Baginton Formation. A number of localities have yielded mammalian remains which are reviewed by Lister (1989). A few localities have yielded sufficient information to allow more detailed palaeoenvironmental interpretation. The most important site is that of Waverley Wood Farm Pit (Shotton et al. 1993), where

Table 1. *Pebble count data of selected Baginton Formation localities*

	Quartz	Quartzite	Sandstone	Chert	Flint	Limestone	Igneous	Other	n
Snitterfield									
77	12.04	34.72	6.71	0.00	0.46	40.74	0.00	5.33	432
80	10.18	38.91	1.45	1.45	0.36	39.27	0.00	8.38	275
81	7.82	50.62	0.41	1.03	0.21	33.54	0.00	6.37	486
82	7.56	52.93	1.46	1.71	0.24	27.07	0.00	9.03	410
Brandon									
91	34.33	52.35	3.90	7.23	0.00	0.00	0.69	2.19	871
Ryton Plant									
96	28.54	56.22	10.30	2.36	0.86	0.00	0.00	1.72	466
97	31.05	59.52	5.91	1.85	0.00	0.00	0.92	1.67	541
98	33.03	60.40	2.19	1.82	0.00	0.00	0.91	2.56	548
Waverley Wood									
102	30.31	60.63	2.77	3.88	0.37	0.00	0.00	2.04	541
103	28.64	59.73	6.71	1.03	0.00	0.00	0.22	3.89	447
Pools Farm, Brandon									
104	36.77	55.16	1.79	1.79	0.00	0.00	0.15	4.49	669
105	33.33	57.61	2.31	2.12	0.00	0.00	0.58	4.63	519
106	32.42	58.05	2.74	3.39	0.00	0.00	1.06	3.40	472

a series of organic channel-fill sequences, the Waverley Wood Beds, underlie the coarse-grained lithofacies of the Thurmaston Member and cut directly into the Lias Clay bedrock. These sediments have yielded pollen, plant macrofossils, Coleoptera and Mollusca which suggest temperate climatic conditions. Together, these data suggest correlation with a Cromerian IV type temperate episode, thus placing these beds in a pre-Anglian context.

A comparable organic channel-fill sequence has been reported from Brandon (Shotton 1968a; Maddy et al. 1994). At Brandon, the channel-fill is both underlain and overlain by gravels of the Thurmaston Member (Maddy et al. 1994).

Geochronology

Amino acid geochronology from molluscan remains contained within the Waverley Wood Beds yielded ratios of 0.381 ± 0.027 ($n = 12$) on *Bithynia troscheli*, and 0.381 ± 0.025 ($n = 3$) on *Trichia hispida* (Bowen et al. 1989). These ratios confirm a pre-Anglian context for these deposits and suggest correlation of the Waverley Wood Beds with Oxygen Isotope Stage 15 (Bowen et al. 1989). Given that the Waverley Wood Beds lie within the Thurmaston Member, Maddy et al (1994) suggest that the Baginton Formation represents time-equivalent to Oxygen Isotope Stages 15–12. The basal Members of the Baginton Formation may, however, also relate to the preceding cold stage (Oxygen Isotope Stage 16), although no information is available to confirm their deposition under cold climatic conditions.

Reconstructing the Baginton Basin

So far only the known outcrops of the Baginton Formation have been described and thus the basin has been delimited only as far west as Snitterfield. A key remaining question concerns the extent of the Baginton catchment upstream of Snitterfield. Shotton (1953) suggested that the river basin responsible for the Baginton Formation extended westwards to the vicinity of Bredon Hill where it would have shared a watershed with the Severn Basin to the west. To the east the watershed was marked by the Cotswold escarpment with the Thames Basin to the south and east. However, the lithological composition of the Baginton Formation suggests that the bulk of the sediment input came from coarse-grained Triassic rocks to the west and north of Snitterfield.

In considering possible routes upstream of Snitterfield, several factors concerning the geomorphological viability need to be considered.

(1) *Upstream equivalent sediments must have compatible lithological characteristics.* The Pleistocene deposits to the west of Snitterfield display lithological characteristics similar to those of the Baginton Formation, i.e. they are dominated by the Triassic components. Therefore, using this criterion in isolation to correlate Pleistocene deposits is of little value. The Triassic components comprise quartzite and quartz derived ultimately from the Kidderminster Formation which crops out in the area to the northwest. However, these clasts are also present in large quantities in the older Northern Drift Formation which crops out in the Upper Thames Valley to the southeast, thus providing a possible secondary source (a possibility confirmed by the presence of flint derived most probably from the Northern Drift). The Northern Drift Gravels, however, display these components in different proportions. The dominance of quartzite over quartz within the Snitterfield and other Baginton Formation Gravels is unlike that in the Northern Drift and is more closely allied to the composition of the Kidderminster Formation, suggesting that the river was in fact predominantly fed directly from the primary outcrop.

Therefore, access to a Kidderminster Formation outcrop is of paramount importance to any reconstructed drainage route.

(2) *Upstream sediments must lie on a 'reasonable' river gradient.* At Snitterfield, the base of the Baginton Formation lies at 87 m OD; 21 km downstream at Brandon the base of the Formation lies at 68 m OD suggesting a basal gradient of c. 0.9 m/km (Fig. 5). Using the height of the base of the Brandon Member over the same distance gives a reconstruction of 0.8 m/km. However, these calculations may be misleading as these bounding surfaces are almost certainly diachronous. Furthermore, it might reasonably be expected that the river gradient would increase upstream rendering these estimates as probable minima. However, although crude, these reconstructions indicate a gradient range which could be considered 'reasonable'.

Three further criteria could be considered important.

(3) *The routeway should not ignore underlying geological structures.* It is likely that any former drainage line would be affected by the underlying horst and graben structure. Drainage was most likely concentrated within the structural basins as suggested by Wills (1948). The tectonic activity generated by the Alpine orogeny (from

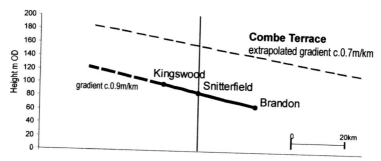

Fig. 5. Reconstructed basal profile of the Baginton River, showing a possible link with the Kingswood Gap. Extrapolated Combe Terrace gradient from Upper Thames Valley for comparison.

early movements in the Eocene though to the Oligocene/Miocene) led to 'the gentle flexuring and pronounced faulting of the Mesozoic cover . Each of the visible coalfields was uplifted as a horst with consequent anticlinal flexuring of the overlying more plastic Mesozoic cover (which has since been largely eroded away). Between the coalfields the cover was flexed downwards.' (Wills 1948: 100). The downwarping of critical areas, notably the Cheshire Basin, the Need-wood (Knowle) Basin and the Severn Basin (Fig. 3A), led to considerable modification of the early Mesozoic depositional basins. Substantial post-Oligocene tectonic movements are also supported by Cope (1994). He suggests a throw of c. 1000 m on the Wem Fault in the Cheshire Basin and concludes a similar magnitude of movement in the Severn Basin, where 'post-Oligocene movement also seems probable on the Malvern Fault, with downthrow to the east' (Cope 1994: 907).

Of paramount importance to any reconstruction of the Baginton Basin is the likely connection with either the Severn Basin to the west or the Knowle Basin to the north. Drainage directly across either the Staffordshire or Warwickshire horsts may have been possible via antecedent drainage developed on a Cretaceous cover. This scenario is rejected by Cope (1994) who states: 'Britain's present drainage clearly originated from the doming and erosion; the lost Chalk cover of western Britain can no longer be seen as a significant factor in its development' (Cope 1994: 908). This situation is further amplified by the basins being predominantly composed of more easily erodible strata. Drainage across the horsts is therefore considered unlikely.

(4) *Routes to other basins must be plausible.* Where higher bedrock is encountered, a suitable through-route must be observable, or a watershed identified.

(5) *The final reconstructed basin should be of suitable dimensions such that the expected discharge and sediment transport capabilities are compatible with the sedimentary sequence present at Snitterfield and downstream.* The Baginton Formation contains a substantial quantity of Kidderminster Formation pebbles necessitating extensive former outcrop of these strata. Much of the area upstream of Snitterfield is underlain by strata younger than the Kidderminster Formation thus rendering them unsuitable as possible supply areas. The current outcrop together with areas underlain by older strata threrefore represent the most plausible source areas.

Using the above criteria, two possible routes to the Kidderminster Formation outcrops seem the most plausible (Fig. 4A).

- *Route A to the outcrops south of the Clent Hills.* In this scenario the basin extends close to the line of the present Arrow valley progressing northwestwards to the foot of the Clent Hills where the Kidderminster Formation crops out.
- *Route B to the outcrops north of the Clent Hills.* In this scenario the river must head northwards, across the current Severn–Trent watershed and then westwards to the extensive Kidderminster Formation outcrops in the vicinity of Birmingham.

Routes A and B are assessed below.

- *Route A.* Pleistocene gravels rich in Kidderminster Formation components are widespread immediately south and west of the Clent Hills. However, these deposits are closely associated with the glacigenic sequence and tend to be interbedded with tills. No undoubted pre-Anglian fluvial sediments have been identified. This route provides ample scope for pre-Anglian drainage and utilizes the existing geological structure,

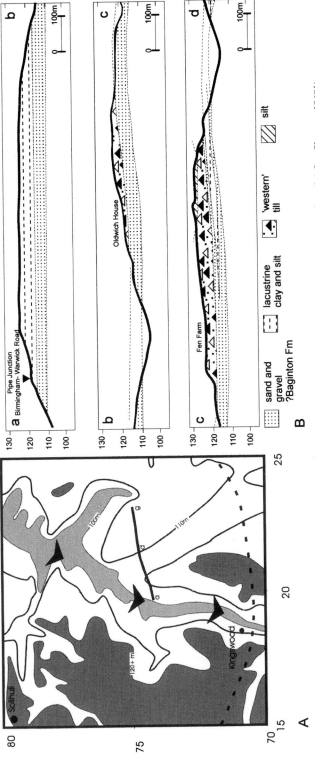

Fig. 6. (A) Subdrift contours in the Kingswood Gap area (after Old 1982). (B) Sections along the Coventry pipe-trench a–d (after Shotton 1968*b*).

i.e. the Severn Basin. There are no obvious structural obstructions as long as the route flows to the south of the Clent Hills. Outcrops of Kidderminster Formation are relatively small and the majority of the exposed strata are young, thus not allowing for previously more extensive outcrop.

- *Route B.* Pre-Anglian river gravels are known from the Blythe Valley (Shotton 1968b, 1983; Figs 4B, 6) and these gravels could lie within the range of possible correlatives with the Baginton Formation (see below). The route utilizes the pre-existing geological structure of the Knowle Basin. However, if the Baginton River extended into the area north of the Clent Hills, then it must breach the current Severn–Trent watershed in order to satisfy criterion (4) (see below). The most extensive outcrops of Kidderminster Formation lie north of the Clent Hills on this route, as do the exposures of the older strata most likely to have been previously covered by the Kidderminster Formation, thus on criterion (5) making this route the most likely.

The most likely locality for the breach of the Severn–Trent watershed is the lowest col on the present watershed which lies close to the village of Kingswood (Fig. 4B). The deposits in the area around Kingswood were extensively studied by Tomlinson (1935) and have more recently been reinvestigated by the BGS (Old 1982). The col, known as the Kingswood Gap, separates drainage which flows northwards down the Blythe Valley (which is tributary to the Tame, itself a tributary to the River Trent) from southward drainage which flows into the River Alne (a tributary of the Arrow, itself a tributary of the River Avon which forms part of the Severn drainage system) (Figs 1, 3B).

Investigation of the deposits in and around the col has demonstrated that this part of the watershed is relatively young. Fluvial deposits flowing southwards through the gap are widespread (Tomlinson 1935) and include the sands of Riley's Pit (SP201753) which display palaeocurrents indicating a southerly flow (Shotton 1953). Although these deposits may form part of a glacigenic sequence which may in part be of either Anglian age (Old 1982) or younger (Tomlinson 1935) and thus too young to be time-equivalent to the Baginton Formation, they nevertheless testify to a north–south drainage route across the col.

To the north of the Kingswood Gap, in the Blythe and Tame valleys, there is a thick sequence of glacigenic deposits. Shotton (1968b) described the sequence exposed during the cut-

ting of a major pipe-trench in the vicinity of Temple Balsall (Fig. 6B). On the grounds of their lithological composition, Shotton (1968b) suggested that the basal sands and gravels of this sequence, which underlie a till, could be correlated with the Baginton Formation, although he added that they were 'perhaps too high'. These deposits have a base at around 110 m OD. The pipe-trench exposures are c. 13 km to the north of Snitterfield, thus, assuming the 0.9 m/km gradient, lie a little too high. However, as this gradient probably represents a minimum, it is possible that these deposits could correlate in part with the Baginton Formation.

The subdrift contours of the Kingswood Gap area (Fig. 6A) suggest that a route could have existed at this level immediately prior to the Anglian, although glacigenic sands in the Kingswood Gap now fill the pre-existing valley. It is possible that older members of the Baginton Formation could have passed through this gap at higher levels.

Route B can therefore satisfy all the criteria outlined above and furthermore has tangible evidence of sediments which may correlate with the Baginton Formation. In the absence of any obvious correlatives along the line of Route A Route B is therefore chosen as the most plausible alternative.

Further inferences can be made which support this choice. The upstream extension of the valley is most likely to follow the path of the current Blythe Valley to join the Tame. A possible connection can then be suggested with the pre-Anglian Proto-Rea/ Proto-Tame valley system of Kelly (1964), Pickering (1957) and Horton (1974). Access to this valley system would give a direct route from the Kidderminster Formation to the Baginton Formation.

South of the Kingswood Gap the precise route through to Snitterfield is unclear. However, from the apparent behaviour of the Anglian ice sheets, there may be some supporting evidence for a pre-existing valley, along a line connecting the Kingswood Gap with Snitterfield. The eastern tills present around Snitterfield were deposited by an ice mass which progressed up the Baginton Valley. This ice sheet was apparently unable to surmount the high ground of the Warwickshire Coalfield, perhaps suggesting a thin, topographically controlled ice sheet. Similarly, a western ice lobe extended southeastwards from the Birmingham area coalescing with the eastern icelobe in the vicinity of Snitterfield. As the western ice lobe was unable to cross the Warwickshire Coalfield, and indeed was unable to dislodge the eastern ice lobe in the Baginton Valley, it must be concluded that it too

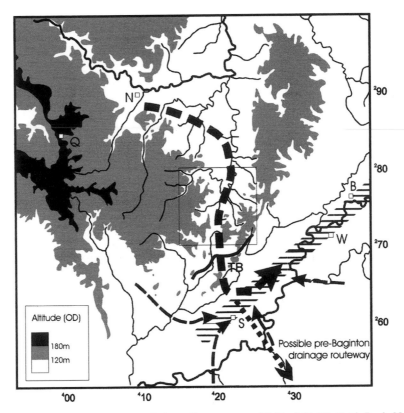

Fig. 7. Suggested reconstruction of Baginton drainage line upstream of Snitterfield. TB, Tattle Bank; N, Nechells; Q, Quinton; line marks the approximate contact between eastern and western ice sheets.

was relatively thin and probably also topographically controlled. The two ice lobes probably met immediately north of Snitterfield as deposits at Tattle Bank (Fig. 7) appear to record the interaction of the western and eastern ice sheets (Tomlinson 1935; Shotton 1983). It is possible that this line of coalescence marks the junction between the upper and lower parts of the Baginton Basin.

The suggested reconstruction of the Baginton drainage route is shown in Fig. 7.

Implications for the early extended Thames catchment

It has been suggested that the Baginton River inherited the upper reaches of an extended Thames Basin as a result of either river capture or of diversion resulting from glaciation (Rose 1994). In this regard, it is perhaps significant that the postulated Baginton drainage route (Fig. 7) appears to take a considerable turn-off line around Stratford. Having initially headed

southeast the main river turns dramatically northeast. This junction perhaps bears testament to drainage realignment consequent upon the beheading of the former extended Thames. The downstream projection of the Baginton River from Snitterfield is aligned with the modern Stour Valley, thus perhaps indicating a natural drainage towards the Thames system.

The sediments of the Baginton Formation currently known do not appear to be older than Oxygen Isotope Stage 16. However, some older remnants of this formation may have survived. The most likely candidates are the high-level 'Northern Drift' remnants of the Stour Valley (Tomlinson 1929; Hey 1986). These deposits are too low to represent a continuation of the Northern Drift terraces of the Upper Thames Basin (Hey 1986), but they bear considerable resemblance to them. Tomlinson (1929: 165) describes these deposits as 'Plateau Drift' and lists three attributes: 'Large quartzite and Bunter Pebbles in a heavy ferruginous clay; very few flints, and these – yellow and much weathered – almost resembling cherts; lack of calcareous material.' This composition is confirmed by the stone counts of Hey (1986) and field walking by the author. Important also is the low, but consistent, proportion of volcanics. Indeed Tomlinson reports 'Some boulders of a green rock, probably Welsh Volcanic Ash, also occur'. This composition not only distinguishes these deposits from the later Anglian glacigenic sediments, but also from the Baginton Formation at Snitterfield. The decalcification of these deposits suggests an age similar to that of the Northern Drift Formation.

It is unlikely that these deposits represent the upstream equivalents of Members of the Northern Drift Formation. Their altitude above 125 m is too low for the Coombe Member and indeed too low to represent a continuation of the Freeland Member of the lower Upper Thames Formation. As noted by Hey (1986), even the highest deposits (135 m) barely rise above the level of the bedrock ridge representing the current Stour–Evenlode watershed around Moreton, making correlation across the interfluve unlikely.

It is more probable that these deposits represent drainage in the opposite direction, i.e. towards the northwest in a line similar to that of the present Stour valley. Following from this, it is possible that these sediments represent

deposition in a tributary of the Baginton River at a time prior to the deposition of the Baginton Formation at Snitterfield.

If the postulated Baginton Basin is accepted, then there are obvious implications for the 'great' Thames catchment proposed by Rose (1994). In the model presented here the Baginton Basin is limited to the area around, and east of, Birmingham and shows no indication of extending beyond. This solution has the benefit of complementing the structural arguments proposed by Wills (1948) by acknowledging the development of drainage in the Knowle Basin (Fig. 3). If this upper Baginton Basin represents the extended Thames then similarly there is no evidence to support a Pleistocene extension of the early Thames Basin beyond these confines. If these limits for the early Thames Basin are accepted, this would allow for the Tertiary development of the Severn system along the Severn Basin, in parallel with an extended Thames system, thus supporting the antiquity of the Severn drainage line as suggested by Wills (1948) and Maddy (1997).

The introduction of Welsh material into the Thames system, the only tangible evidence of any Welsh connection, would require only minor ice advance into the upper basin around

Table 2. *Pre-Anglian stratigraphy of the Baginton and Upper Thames Basins*

Severn Valley	Avon Valley		Upper Thames Valley		Thames in Essex	$\delta^{18}O$ Stage
Nurseries, Wolston	**Wolston**		**Wolston**			12
? Early Severn		*Snitterfield*	**Upper Thames**	*Hanborough*		12
	Baginton	*Brandon Waverley Wood Thurmaston*				15
			Northern Drift	*Freeland*	**Colchester**	?16
		?Honnington ?Idlicote				
	?Northern Drift		**Northern Drift**	*Combe Wilcote Ramsden Heath Waterman's Lodge*	**Sudbury**	?22
						?68
Drainage to Bristol Channel Initiated	Drainage to North Sea Initiated		Unroofing of Midlands Trias			Late-Tertiary

ALPINE   MOVEMENTS

Bold: Formation Name (underlined is glacial otherwise fluvial), *italic*: Member (selected non-glacial only).

Birmingham, a location which has been frequently revisited by subsequent Middle and Upper Pleistocene Welsh ice sheets.

Conclusion

The evidence from the Baginton Formation and its reconstructed basin suggests a catchment restricted in the west to the area in the vicinity of Birmingham. The reconstructed river upstream of Snitterfield displays an anomalous course which suggests inheritance of a pre-existing drainage network. The alignment of the upstream reconstruction suggests possible earlier connection to the Stour Valley and beyond into the Upper Thames system. This evidence tends to support the existence of an early Pleistocene extended Thames catchment which was later realigned into the Baginton River system most probably as a consequence of glaciation during Oxygen Isotope Stage 22 (Whiteman & Rose 1992; Table 2).

The evidence presented above provides no support for an extended Thames catchment which lies beyond the Birmingham area and thus avoids the structural objections raised by Wills (1948) to the earlier ideas concerning an extended Thames catchment. No evidence is available to support extension of the early Thames Basin into the North Wales region and there is no evidence for a connection in the Pleistocene between the Severn drainage system and that of the early Thames. It remains possible, however, that such a route did exist prior to the alpine tectonic movements of the early Tertiary.

The author would like to acknowledge S. Lewis for helpful discussions and comments concerning an earlier version of this paper and the constructive criticism of A. Horton and a further anonymous referee.

References

BATEMAN, R. M. & ROSE, J. 1994. Fine sand mineralogy of the Early and Middle Pleistocene Bytham sands and gravels of Midland England and East Anglia. *Proceedings of the Geologists' Association*, **105**, 33–39.

BOWEN, D. Q., HUGHES, S., SYKES, G. A. & MILLER, G. H. 1989. Land–sea correlations in the Pleistocene based on isoleucine epimerization in non-marine molluscs. *Nature*, **340**, 49–51.

BUCKMAN, S. S. 1899. The development of rivers, and particularly the genesis of the Severn. *Natural Science*, **14**, 273–289.

COPE, J. C. W. 1994. A latest Cretaceous hotspot and the southeasterly tilt of Britain. *Journal of the Geological Society of London*, **151**, 905–908.

DAVIS, W. M. 1895. The development of certain English rivers. *Geographical Journal*, **5**, 127–146.

FUNNELL, B. M. 1995. Global sea-level and Island Britain. *In*: PREECE, R. C. (ed.) *Island Britain: a Quaternary Perspective*. Geological Society, London, Special Publications, **96**, 3–14.

HEY, R. W. 1986. A re-examination of the Northern Drift of Oxfordshire. *Proceedings of the Geologists' Association*, **97**, 291–302.

HORTON, A. 1974. *The sequence of Pleistocene deposits proved during the construction of the Birmingham motorways*. Institute of Geological Sciences, Report **74/22**, HMSO.

KELLY, M. R. 1964. The Middle Pleistocene of North Birmingham. *Philosophical Transactions of the Royal Society of London*, **B247**, 533–592

LEWIS, S. G. 1993. *The Status of the Wolstonian glaciation in the English Midlands and East Anglia*. PhD thesis, University of London.

LISTER, A. M. 1989. Mammallian faunas and the Wolstonian debate. *In*: KEEN, D. H. (ed.) *The Pleistocene of the West Midlands: Field Guide*. Quaternary Research Association, Cambridge, 5–11

MADDY, D. 1989. *The Middle Pleistocene development of the rivers Severn and Avon*. PhD thesis, University of London.

——1997. Midlands drainage development. *In*: LEWIS, S. G. & MADDY, D. (eds) *The Quaternary of the South Midlands & the Welsh Marches: Field Guide*. Quaternary Research Association, London, 7–18.

——1999. English Midlands. *In*: BOWEN, D. Q. (ed.) *A Revised Correlation of Quaternary Deposits in The Briitsh Isles*. Geological Society, Special Report, **23**, 28–44.

—— & LEWIS, S. G. 1991. A revised stratigraphic model and regional correlation for the Pleistocene deposits at Snitterfield, Warwickshire. *Proceedings of the Geologists' Association*, **102**, 289–300.

——, GIBBARD, P. L., COOPE, G. R, GREEN, C. P. & LEWIS, S. G. 1994. Reappraisal of Middle Pleistocene fluvial deposits near Brandon, Warwickshire and their significance for the Wolston glacial sequence. *Journal of the Geological Society of London*, 151, 221–233.

OLD, R. A. 1982. *Quaternary deposits of sheets SP17 and SP27 Solihull and Balsall Common*. Institute of Geological Sciences, Keyworth 32.

——, SUMBLER, M. G. & AMBROSE, K. 1987. *Geology of the country around Warwick*. Memoir of the British Geological Survey, Sheet **184** (England and Wales), NERC, Keyworth.

PICKERING, R. 1957. The Pleistocene geology of the South Birmingham area. *Quarterly Journal of the Geological Society of London*, **113**, 223–237.

RICE, R. J. 1968. The Quaternary deposits of central Leicestershire. *Philosophical Transactions of the Royal Society of London*, **A262**, 459–509.

——1991. Distribution and provenance of the Baginton Sand and Gravel in the Wreake Valley, northern Leicestershire, England: implications for inter-regional correlation. *Journal of Quaternary Science*, **6**, 39–54.

Rose, J. 1987. Status of the Wolstonian Glaciation in the British Quaternary. *Quaternary Newsletter*, **53**, 1–9.

——1989. Tracing the Baginton – Lillington Sands and Gravels from the West Midlands to East Anglia. *In*: Keen, D. H. (ed.) *The Pleistocene of the West Midlands: Field Guide*. Quaternary Research Association, Cambridge, 102–110.

——1994. Major river systems of central and southern Britain during the Early and Middle Pleistocene. *Terra Nova*, **6**, 435–443.

Shotton, F. W. 1953. The Pleistocene deposits of the area between Coventry, Rugby and Leamington, and their bearing upon the topographic development of the Midlands. *Philosophical Transactions of the Royal Society of London*, **B254**, 387–400.

——1968a. The Pleistocene succession around Brandon, Warwickshire. *Philosophical Transactions of the Royal Society of London*, **B254**, 387–400

Shotton, F. W. 1968b. The Pleistocene sequence in a pipe trench between Chadwick End and Gibbet Hill, South of Coventry, Warwickshire. *Proceedings of the Coventry and District Natural History and Science Society*, **4**(2), 53–59.

——1983. The Wolstonian Stage of the British Pleistocene in and around its type area of the English Midlands. *Quaternary Science Reviews*, **2**, 261–280.

——, Keen, D. H., Coope, G. R., Currant, A. P., Gibbard, P. L., Aalto, M., Peglar, S. M. & Robinson, J. E. 1993. The Middle Pleistocene deposits at Waverley Wood Pit, Warwickshire, England. *Journal of Quaternary Science*, **8**, 293–325.

Sumbler, M. G. 1983. A new look at the type Wolstonian glacial deposits of central England. *Proceedings of the Geologists' Association*, **94**, 23–31

Tomlinson, M. E. 1929. The drifts of the Stour–Evenlode watershed and their extension into the valleys of the Warwickshire Stour and Upper Evenlode. *Proceedings of the Birmingham Natural History Society*, **15**, 157–196.

——1935. The superficial deposits of the country north of Stratford-upon-Avon. *Quarterly Journal of the Geological Society of London*, **91**, 423–462.

Whiteman, C. A. & Rose, J. 1992. Thames river sediments of the British early and Middle Pleistocene. *Quaternary Science Reviews*, **11**, 363–375.

Wills, L. J. 1948. *The Palaeogeography of the Midlands*. Hodder & Stoughton, London.

The impact of the deforming bed model on the reconstruction of British Quaternary ice sheets

JANE K. HART

Department of Geography, University of Southampton, Southampton, SO17 1BJ, UK

Abstract: Traditional studies of the British Quaternary glaciations have concentrated on glacial stratigraphy, rather than interpretations of till genesis. However, recent advances in glaciology have important implications for the nature of Quaternary glaciations, which need to be considered when interpreting Quaternary landforms and sediments. In particular, since the 1980s the model of the deforming bed has been developed. In this model it is shown that when glaciers advance over an unconsolidated bedrock (the majority of the British Lowlands) there is a coupling between the glacier and the bed. This leads to an increase in velocity in the glacier and deformation in the underlying sediments. New models of glacial deformation, deposition and erosion have been developed to assist the reinterpretation of glacial sedimentology within both hard and soft bed environments. This paper highlights the importance of these new ideas in the context of British Quaternary glacial environments. An attempt is made to classify the current glaciotectonic data into a form which is useful for ice sheet reconstruction and the implications for stratigraphy are considered.

The reconstruction of past ice sheets has always been an essential part of British Quaternary science. One of the pioneers of the 19th century 'Glacial Theory', Louis Agassiz, visited Britain in 1840 to demonstrate the evidence for past ice sheets (Agassiz 1840) and convinced British geologists of these ideas (Buckland 1840; Lyell 1840). By the 1850s it was suggested that two glaciations had affected Britain and by 1877 James Geikie described evidence for four glaciations in East Anglia. Much of this research was stimulated by the visits of geologists to polar and alpine environments (e.g. Forbes 1843; Conway 1898), which were used as modern analogues for interpreting British Quaternary landforms and sediments.

However, during much of the 20th century, most glacial Quaternary research in Britain was concerned with glacial stratigraphy, rather than with interpreting till genesis and thus reconstructing glacial processes. This led to a series of problems, since the glacial history of an area cannot be reconstructed without an understanding of the glacial processes that lead to the final depositional product. Although some researchers interpreted the origin of tills (e.g. Carruthers 1953), most workers produced stratigraphies based on the following assumptions:

(a) the majority of tills were thought to be subglacial 'lodgement' tills and thus each till was thought to represent a glacial advance;

(b) deformation of the whole sequence or individual till units was thought to be unusual and to represent special conditions;

(c) discontinuous till units were correlated on lithology alone.

These assumptions will be evaluated in detail below. Criticism of the 'one till equals one glacial advance' model began in the 1970s with a renaissance in glacial process studies. In particular, the research of Boulton on supraglacial melt-out and flow tills in Spitsbergen (Boulton 1970, 1972) led to the reintrepretation of the Quaternary sediments at Glanllynnau in North Wales (Boulton 1977). This work, combined with the general increase in quantitative research in geomorphology and the study of glacial processes, has led to a re-evaluation of many British till sites.

Since the late 1980s there has been a new development in glacial geomorphology which has major implications for the study of glacial Quaternary research. This is the model of the deforming bed discussed in detail below. This paper will highlight the importance of these new ideas within the context of British Quaternary glacial environments and will investigate the following themes: (a) glaciotectonic deformation and the theory of the deforming bed; (b) the reconstruction of British ice sheets based on glaciotectonic data; and (c) implications for stratigraphy.

HART, J. K. 1999. The impact of the deforming bed model on the reconstruction of British Quaternary ice sheets. *In*: ANDREWS, P. & BANHAM, P. (eds) *Late Cenozoic Environments and Hominid Evolution: a tribute to Bill Bishop.* Geological Society, London, 183–200.

Glaciotectonic deformation and the theory of the deforming bed

Deformation is ubiquitous within the glacial environment and was described by early researchers from modern glaciated environments (e.g. Chamberlain 1895; Lamplugh 1911). Deformation of glacial sediments is known as glaciotectonic deformation, and one of the earliest workers to apply these modern analogues to the Quaternary sedimentary record was Slater (1926) in his research on the northeast Norfolk glacial sediments, which was further developed by Banham (1975, 1977, 1988a). These researchers realized that glaciotectonic deformation could have a dramatic effect on stratigraphy, which Berthelsen (1978) described as

kineto-stratigraphy and which will be discussed in more detail below.

In 1979 Boulton & Jones demonstrated from the study of the displacement of markers in the till beneath Breijðamerkurjökull, Iceland, that up to 88% of the motion of the glacier occurred, not in the ice, but in a deforming layer beneath the ice. They suggested that this occurred because meltwater from the base of the glacier became trapped in this subglacial layer leading to a reduction in sediment strength and thus deformation in the underlying sediment. An additional consequence of the weakened bed was that the glacier profile was reduced. These initial results were substantiated by the discovery of a 6 m thick saturated layer beneath one of the major ice streams discharging from the West

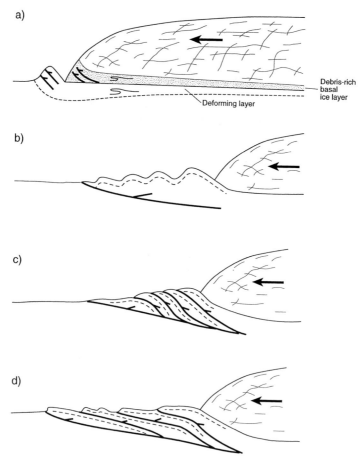

Fig. 1. Schematic diagrams to show (**a**) a glacier overlying a potentially deformable bed showing the proglacial and subglacial (shear zone) deformation in both the subglacial deforming layer and debris-rich basal ice; (**b**) a push moraine composed of folding (low longitudinal strain); (**c**) a push moraine composed of thrust-faulted slices (medium longitudinal strain); (**d**) a push moraine composed of thrust nappes (high longitudinal strain).

Antarctic Ice Sheet (Alley *et al.* 1986). Glaciologists then began to base models of glacier flow on a deforming bed rather than a passive rigid substrate (e.g. Boulton & Hindmarsh 1987; Clarke 1987; MacAyeal, 1989; Engelhardt *et al.* 1990).

These models showed that glaciotectonic deformation was an integral part of the glacial environment, and not an unusual occurrence. Glaciotectonic deformation could be related to the glacier by dividing structures into two distinct types (Fig. 1): proglacial deformation, which takes place at the glacier margin and is characterized by longitudinal compression, forming push moraines; and subglacial deformation which takes place beneath the glacier and is characterized by simple shear (subglacial shear zone). It was subsequently shown that similar deformation styles can occur within the ice itself (Hart 1995*a*) and also within permafrost (Astakhov *et al.* 1996).

Proglacial deformation

Push moraines are very common in both modern and Quaternary glacial environments, and current interest in this topic is highlighted by the four recent collections of papers on the subject (van der Meer 1987; Croot 1988*a*; Aber 1993; Warren and Croot 1994). They can occur on scales ranging in height from 0.5 m to 50 m and in length from 1 m to several kilometres. Modern examples of push moraines include: Spitsbergen; (Boulton 1986; Etzelmüller *et al.* 1996; Hambrey & Huddart 1995; Hart & Watts 1997); Canadian Arctic (Kalin 1971; Evans 1989); Iceland (Croot 1988*b*); Switzerland (Eybergen 1987); Alaska (Hart 1995*a*); and Antarctica (Fitzsimmons 1996). Push moraines have also been recorded at numerous Quaternary sites, for example North America (Aber *et al.* 1989; Bluemle & Clayton 1984); Scandinavia (Klint & Pedersen 1995); Germany (van Gijssel 1987; Kluiving 1994); Poland (Ber 1987; Aber & Ruszczynska-Szenajch 1997); UK (Thomas 1984; Hart 1990); New Zealand (Hart 1996*a*); and Argentina (van der Meer *et al.* 1992). (A full list of references on glaciotectonics can be found on the internet at page *http://www.emporia.edu/s/www/earthsci/biblio/biblio.htm* published by the INQUA Glacial Tectonics Work Group.)

Proglacial deformation can take place in sediments or rocks and the deformational styles depend on the nature of the proglacial sediments. Very often a basin is formed, upglacier from the push moraine, where material has been removed to build the moraine, e.g. 'hill-depression forms' in North America (Clayton &

Moran 1974; Bluemle & Clayton 1984). Deformational forms (Fig. 1) range from folding and fold nappes (e.g. Holmstrømbreen, Svalbard: Boulton *et al.* in press), through to thrust faults (e.g. Lamstedt, Germany: van Gijssel 1987) and thrust nappes (e.g. Damme Berge, Germany: van der Wateren 1995). These styles of deformation reflect increasing longitudinal compression from simple folding to more complex nappe structures. Deformation structures are also found at the base of thrust faults and nappes, with tectonic breccias associated with brittle deformation (e.g. Trimingham, UK: Hart 1990) and shear zones formed associated with ductile deformation (e.g. Damme Berge, Germany: van der Wateren 1995).

It has been argued by numerous workers (e.g. Croot 1987; van der Wateren 1985; Banham 1988*b*), that proglacial deformation can be modelled as thin-skin thrust tectonics and that the processes involved in the formation of push moraines are similar to mountain building in hard rock tectonic terrains. (For a review of thrust and nappe tectonics see McClay & Price 1981.) Most researchers have argued that push moraines result from frontal compression ('bulldozing'), or a combination of frontal compression and stresses transmitted through the deforming layer, the latter being a direct result of the gravity spreading of the ice sheet. This model is often known as the gravity spreading model (e.g. van der Wateren 1985; Aber *et al.* 1989). For both types to form, a basal decollement is needed as well as an advancing glacier; for the second type, a deforming bed is probably also required (van der Wateren 1995).

Deformational style is dependent on the nature of the proglacial (and subglacial) sediment. Van der Wateren (1995) has shown that push moraines consisting largely of coarse-grained sediments are characterized mainly by brittle structures, whilst fine-grained materials show dominantly ductile fold and fold nappes. A similar concept was illustrated by Hart & Watts (1997), who showed that in two adjacent surging glaciers in Svalbard, proglacial deformation of a gravel-rich foreland produced a short moraine, whilst proglacial deformation of a finer-grained foreland produced a longitudinally extensive push moraine.

Subglacial deformation

Modern examples of subglacial deformation have been described from both *in situ* instrumented sites and investigations of glacier forelands. The *in situ* measurement of the subglacial environment is a new and exciting technique that has been applied to a small but growing number of glaciers, e.g. Ice Stream B Antarctica (Engelhardt & Kamb in press); Arolla, Switzerland (Hubbard *et al.* 1995); Trapridge Glacier, Canada (Clarke & Blake 1991); Columbia Glacier, Alaska (Humphrey *et al.* 1993); Black Rapids Glacier, Alaska (Truffer 1997); Worthington Glacier, Alaska (Harper & Humphrey 1995); Storglaciären, Sweden (Iverson *et al.* 1994*a*); and Bakaninbreen, Svalbard (Porter *et al.* 1997). The technique consists of using a hot water drill to bore down to the glacier base to investigate both the ice (thickness, structure debris content and temperature) and the underlying sediment (thickness, presence of deformation, strength, sediment and glacier/sediment interface velocity). In particular, tiltmeters are used to investigate whether the till is actively shearing (Blake *et al.* 1992; Iverson *et al.* 1994*b*); a drag spool can be used to measure sliding velocity (Blake *et al.* 1994; Porter & Murray 1995); and to measure sediment strength, a ploughmeter (Fischer & Clarke 1997) or dragometer (Iverson *et al.* 1994*b*) is used. The results from these *in situ* measurements, many of which are summarized in Murray (1997) and Table 1 show that subglacial deformation occurs beneath most of the glaciers monitored, but is far more complex than previously thought, with dramatic changes in time and magnitude in subglacial strain rate and sediment strength.

Investigations have also been made of the glacier foreland, immediately after ice retreat. Typical features associated with a deforming bed glacier include lineations, flutes, drumlins and crevasse diapirs, e.g. Iceland (Sharp 1984; Hart 1995*b*; Benn 1995); and Alaska (Hart & Smith 1997). A typical landform association consists of a fluted surface immediately proximal to a push moraine formed from the compressive margin of the subglacial shear zone. The flutes represent the erosional remnants of the deforming bed, formed by the movement of subglacial material into the lee side of obstacles within the deforming layer (Boulton 1976; Benn 1995), whilst the inter-flute areas represent the faster moving material which moved out into the foreland to form push moraines (Hart 1995*b*).

Subglacial deformation has also been studied from Quaternary sequences where access is easier, but has a greater interpretative element. Most researchers have argued that the subglacial deforming layer behaves as a shear zone (e.g. Hart & Boulton 1991; van der Wateren 1995). Features typical of shear zones include tectonic laminations, boudins, augens and rotated clasts, although at very high shear strains these features can become homogenized. Some examples of Quaternary subglacial shear zones include: UK (Hart & Boulton 1991; Evans *et al.* 1995); Germany (Hart *et al.* 1996); Netherlands (Kluiving *et al.* 1991); North America (Hicock & Dreimanis 1992; Dredge & Grant 1987); and Tasmania (Fitzsimons 1992).

Implications for glacial sedimentology

Research from modern and Quaternary environments has shown that glaciotectonic deformation is very common, and thus any model for till sedimentology needs to include deformational

Table 1. *The thickness of the deforming layer recorded from in situ glacier monitoring*

In situ measuring site	Measuring techniques used	Thickness of deforming layer (m)
Breiðamerkurjökull, Iceland (Boulton 1979)	Strain markers	~0.5
Trapridge, Yukon, Canada (Clarke *et al.* 1984)	Tilt-cells, sliding sensor, ploughmeter	0.1–1
Storglaciären, Sweden (Iversen *et al.* 1994*b*)	Tilt-cells, dragometer	0.33
Columbia Glacier, Alaska (Humphrey *et al.* 1993)	Immobilized drill stem	0.65
Black Rapids Glacier, Alaska (Truffer 1997)	Tilt-cells	No deformation
Bakaninbreen, Svalbard (Porter *et al.* 1997)	Tilt-cells, sliding sensor, ploughmeter	0.3–0.5

processes. Hart & Boulton (1991) recognized that subglacial till associated with a deforming bed would have three sediment sources: (a) direct melt-out from the ice; (b) sediment from the deforming layer; (c) sediment incorporated from beneath the deforming layer. Hart *et al.* (1990) were able to predict the thickness of the deforming layer associated with different basal shear stresses for different bedrocks. This work built on the ideas of dynamic till-forming processes also suggested by Alley (1991), Hicock & Dreimanis (1992) and the till prism model of Hicock (1990).

Hart & Boulton (1991) argued that deforming bed till was deposited by simultaneous and dynamic deposition and deformation, and probably reflected the majority of subglacial tills. They concluded that subglacial conditions (e.g. pore water pressures, effective pressures, basal shear stresses, sediment type) change in time and space, with lodgement/ploughing occurring when subglacial porewater pressures and/or sediment supply are reduced, and the 'homogenization' of subglacial sediments occurring when pore water pressures and shear stress are

high. It was also suggested that melt-out is an integral component of deforming bed till.

A number of researchers (Boulton 1987; Hart & Boulton 1991; Alley 1991) have argued that since deforming bed conditions are potentially very commonly associated with lowland glaciated environments, then deforming bed till is the most likely till to be deposited. By contrast, lodgement till is thought to be a less likely deposit since it results from a frictional process whereby clasts are deposited by 'lodging' against a rigid substrate.

Research from both modern and Quaternary sites has led to the development of criteria to recognize deforming bed till (Hart & Boulton 1991; Hicock & Dreimanis 1992; Hart & Roberts 1994; van der Meer 1993; Hart 1994; Benn 1995; Benn & Evans 1996). These include (a) structures typical of a shear zone on both the macro- (i.e. field) and micromorphological scale; and (b) low till fabric strength in a thick, unconstrained shear zone, but high fabric strength in a thin, constrained shear zone (e.g. a flute). However, it is very difficult to isolate undisputed modern examples of lodgement and melt-out

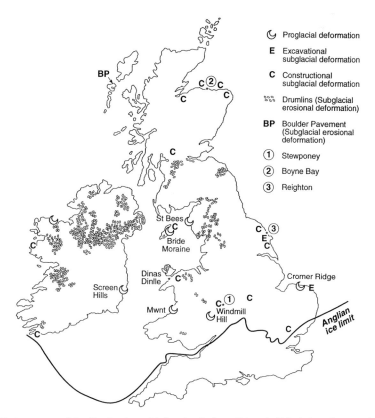

Fig. 2. A preliminary map of the distribution of deforming bed conditions in Britain based on results from Table 1.

tills. The most unequivocal locations are the stoss-side (for lodgement till) and lee-side (for melt-out till) cavities associated with rigid bedded glaciers (Boulton 1975). Moreover, lodgement is not ubiquitous in rigid bed environments, as recent studies have revealed the presence of thin (approximately 10 cm in thickness) saturated layers of debris at the base of some glaciers (e.g. Glacier Haut d'Arolla: Hubbard *et al.* 1995). Similarly, modern undisturbed melt-out till is particularly difficult to study, apart from the cavity locations, because of the very high level of mobilization and resedimentation during melting (Paul & Eyles 1990; Hart 1995a).

The reconstruction of British ice sheets from glaciotectonic data

The glaciations of mainland Britain were dominated by glaciers growing in the rigid bed mountains and then flowing outwards onto the potentially deformable bedrock of the lowlands.

In the highlands, the action of glacial erosion leads to the deposition of till, which itself is deformable; recent workers have shown the presence of deforming bed till in the Scottish Highlands (Benn 1992; Hart 1997; Rea *et al.* 1997). In the lowlands, deforming bed tills are thicker and more common (e.g. Hart & Boulton 1991; Evans *et al.* 1995).

Since the deforming bed model is relatively recent, only papers in the last decade have specifically evaluated glacial sediments within the deforming bed model. However, many previous papers mention glaciotectonic features. Figure 2 and Table 2 represent a preliminary summary of possible evidence for deforming bed conditions associated with the British ice sheets.

Glaciotectonic features have been divided into five classes and for simplicity the map (Fig. 2) shows only the last deformational event. The classes are shown in Table 3 (after Hart 1997) and are described below. In addition, it is shown how the subglacial landscape can affect some of these predicted patterns of deformation.

Table 2. *Evidence from recent publications for deforming bed conditions in Britain*

Site	Type of deformation	Author	Age
North Norfolk Coast	Proglacial Subglacial *excavational*	Hart (1990) Hart & Boulton (1991) Hart *et al.* (1990)	Anglian
Southern East Anglia	Subglacial *constructional*	Hart *et al.* (1990)	
East Yorkshire	Subglacial	Boulton & Dobbie (1993) Eyles *et al.* (1994) Evans *et al.* (1995)	Devensian
Midlands	Subglacial Subglacial Proglacial	Goodwin *et al.* (1997) Rice (1981) Richards (1997)	? Anglian ?
Isle of Man	Proglacial	Thomas (1984)	Devensian
St Bees	Proglacial	Huddart (1991)	Devensian
Dumbeg	Subglacial *constructional*	Benn & Evans (1996)	Devensian
Quinoch	Subglacial hard bed erosion	Rea *et al.* (1997)	Devensian
South Wales	Subglacial	Harris & Donnelly (1991)	Devensian
Dinas Dinlle	Proglacial or Subglacial erosional (drumlins)	Harris *et al.* (1995) Hart (1995c)	Devensian
Wylfa Head	Subglacial	Harris (1991)	Devensian
Aberdaron	Subglacial *constructional* and erosional (drumlins)	Hart (1996b)	Devensian
Uist	Subglacial erosional (drumlins and boulder pavements)	Peacock (1991) Hart (1997)	Devensian
Skye	Subglacial erosional (drumlins)	Benn (1992)	Devensian
Peak District	Subglacial erosional (drumlins)	Mitchell (1991)	Devensian
Glasgow	Subglacial erosional (drumlins)	Menzies (1996)	Devensian

Table 3. *The different glaciotectonic classes shown in Fig. 2*

Proglacial			
Subglacial	Depositional	Constructional deformation	
		Excavational deformation	
	Erosional	Drumlins	
		Boulder pavements	

After Hart (1997).

Proglacial deformation

Britain has a series of large push moraines (shown on Fig. 2). These are not necessarily associated with a deforming bed, and more research is needed on many of these. Banham (1988*a*) and Hart (1990) have shown that the Cromer Ridge in Norfolk is composed of a series of thrust fault slices of both till and rafts of chalk that have moved over a lake clay decollement surface. These structures are thought to have been formed as a result of a combination of both frontal compression and stresses transmitted through the deforming layer. Other morainic features are more controversial, e.g. Dinas Dinlle

has been interpreted by Harris *et al.* (1995) as a push moraine, whilst Hart (1995*c*) suggested that it is a drumlin.

Subglacial deformation

Constructional deformation. Three distinct zones are common (Fig. 3a; Banham 1977; Hart *et al.* 1990): (i) deformed bedrock; (ii) deformed till and bedrock; and (iii) homogeneous deforming bed till. This glaciotectonic sequence displays an increase in both deformation and the number of far-travelled clasts, upwards though the sequence. This style of deformation is formed at the ice margin, where basal shear stresses are low and thus the deforming layer thin. High subglacial sediment input then results in the deforming layer moving upwards through the sequence and subsequent deformational stages being preserved. Sites reported in the literature include Great Blakenham, in Suffolk (Hart *et al.* 1990), Drumbeg, near Glasgow (Benn & Evans 1996) and Stewponey (Goodwin *et al.* 1997) (Fig. 4).

Excavational deformation. Here, one deforming bed till unit is often found overlying a basal

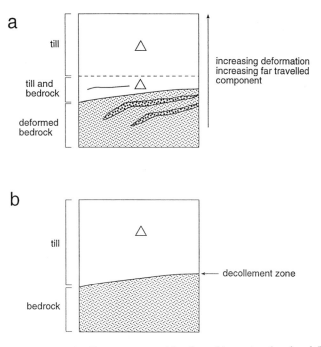

Fig. 3. Schematic diagram to show the till sequences resulting from (**a**) constructional and (**b**) excavational deformation.

(a)

(b)

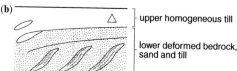

upper homogeneous till

lower deformed bedrock, sand and till

Fig 4. An illustration of constructional deformation at Stewponey, West Midlands: (**a**) a section illustrating the general pattern of deformation up through the sequence, with high angled boudins of sand (average orientation perpendicular to strike = 317°, dip = 22°) within the deformed bedrock sand and till matrix at the base (becoming more horizontally inclined upwards through the sequence), and homogeneous till at the top; (**b**) schematic diagram illustrating this general sequence.

decollement surface (Fig. 3b). This is usually found up-glacier from the margin, where basal shear stresses are high and so the base of the deforming layer cuts down (i.e. erodes) into underlying material and any earlier deformational sequences are incorporated into the deforming layer. Where the till overlies a variety of different bedrocks then there can be spectacular evidence for deformation (e.g. West Runton, Norfolk: Banham 1988a). However, if the bedrock is homogeneous and/or the till has undergone high deformation, then the resultant till will also be homogeneous. In this case, till fabric and micromorphological evidence are needed to confirm its deforming bed origins.

Drumlins. Many authors have argued that drumlins form as a result of till moving around

obstacles in the deforming bed (Smalley & Unwin 1968; Menzies 1979; Boulton 1987). However, this is a ubiquitous process within the deforming layer and so Hart (1997) has argued that drumlins reflect this process associated with net subglacial erosion, owing to either an increase in velocity or a decrease in sediment supply. There are numerous examples of drumlins throughout Britain (shown on Fig. 2); it is beyond the scope of this paper to investigate them in detail, although their locations will be discussed briefly below.

Boulder pavements. Similarly, a number of workers have suggested that boulder pavements are indicative of deforming bed conditions (Hicock 1991; Clark 1991). However, Hart (1997) has suggested they represent an erosional lag within the deforming layer, and are thus indicative of deforming bed erosion. Boulder pavements are very rare in Britain, and only one example is shown in Fig. 2.

The effect of the landscape on these basic deformation classes

The effect of the subglacial topography on the resulting style of deformation is very important, but has not been studied in any detail. Some examples are discussed below which show how topography can affect predicted deformation patterns.

Reighton, East Yorkshire (TA 147758). This site is located at the southern end of Filey Bay, just to the north of the high chalk cliffs which compose Flamborough Head. Edwards (1987) described the section as follows: (i) a basal bedrock of Speeton Clay (Lower Cretaceous); (ii) an angular chalk gravel (0.6 m); (iii) the Speeton Shell Bed (3 m; a pre-Devensian estuarine deposit); (iv) a further bed of angular chalk gravel (0.6 m); and (e) a complex Devensian till unit (25 m).

The Speeton Clay Beds, chalk gravel and Speeton Shell Beds have been tightly folded and Edwards (1987) deduced that this deformation had resulted from 2:1 compression as an ice sheet advanced from the north. He also concluded that the shell bed has been uplifted by 28 m. The till varies in texture from dark grey sandy/silt at the base to reddish brown clay-rich at the top. Both the lower grey and upper red tills contain many small sand boudins and thin ungraded laminations. Additionally, within the till there is a series of sand beds, lenses and boudins, together with large (10 m long) deformed rafts of Speeton Clay (Fig. 5).

Fig. 5. The folding of an organic layer within the till at Reighton, East Yorkshire, indicating local compressive deformation.

The till complex at this site shows extensive signs of glaciotectonic deformation; the deformation in the till (e.g. ungraded laminations and boudins) is very typical of subglacial deformation and this interpretation fits with the results of other recent research in East Yorkshire (Evans *et al.* 1995; Eyles *et al.* 1994). Apart from the evidence for deformation within a subglacial shear zone, there is compressive deformation within both the pre-glacial deposits and the till (Fig. 5). Owing to slumping at the base of the exposure it is not known whether all compressive deformation was simultaneous, and so only the compressive deformation in the till will be discussed below.

Castle Hill, Banffshire (NJ7932 6438). This site has been described by Peacock & Merritt (1997) and is composed of the Whitehills Glaciogenic Formation (dark grey clay and till with shells and Jurassic fossils: Read 1923) which is part of the Banffshire Coastal Drift Group (Fig. 2). An initial advance from the northwest produced thin para-autochthonous units (rafts) of diamicton, sand and clay bounded by horizontal shears. Peacock & Merritt concluded that the rafts formed as the glacier passed from the deformable clays of the Moray Firth onto the high coastline and interior valleys of

Banffshire. They further suggested that these sediments, previously interpreted as representing multiple glaciations, could instead be formed by 'the alternation of phases of constructional and excavational deformation within a single glacial event [which] is generally applicable to the glacial deposits of northern Banffshire and probably more widely in north-west Scotland'.

Boyne Bay, Banffshire (NJ 7932 6438). The glaciogenic sequence stratigraphy at the nearby site of the Boyne Bay limestone quarry is very similar. These glaciogenic sediments rest on limestone, and in nearby locations rest on other Dalradian hard rocks, or basic igneous rocks and granite. Figure 6 shows exposure within the quarry and details from two locations. Additionally, between these two sites a raft of bluegrey laminated silty clay has been reported (Read 1923; Peacock 1971) but at present its limits are poorly defined. The till at Site 2 can be interpreted as a deformation till, typical of a ductile subglacial shear zone, with isoclinal folds and deformed sand boudins. However, the pattern of deformation at Site 1 is more complex. It is suggested that the brown sandy diamicton reflects a subglacial till formed as the glacier first advanced over these sandy sediments, probably from the NW. Over time, the

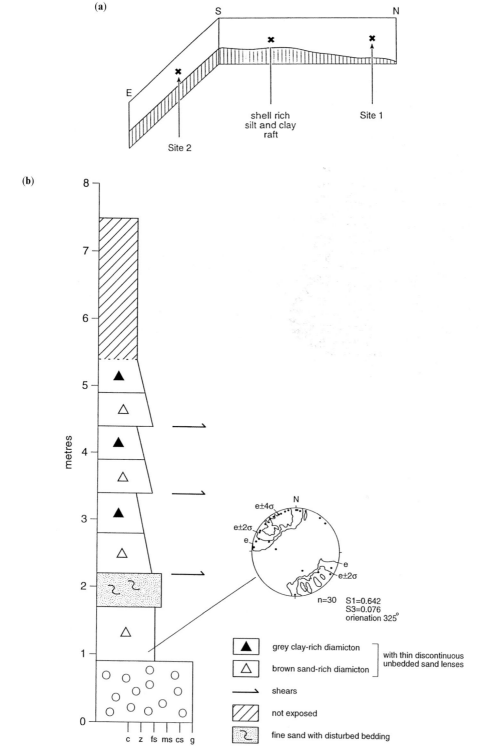

Fig. 6. Boyne Bay: (a) overview of the quarry and the location of the sites discussed; (b) the northern end of the site (Site 1) consists of a basal semi-stratified coarse gravel, which is overlain by a brown sandy diamicton. Above this is a thin sand unit showing some evidence of disturbed bedding. This is overlain by three repeated units of a lower sandy diamicton grading up into a grey clay-rich diamicton. These diamictons are mostly

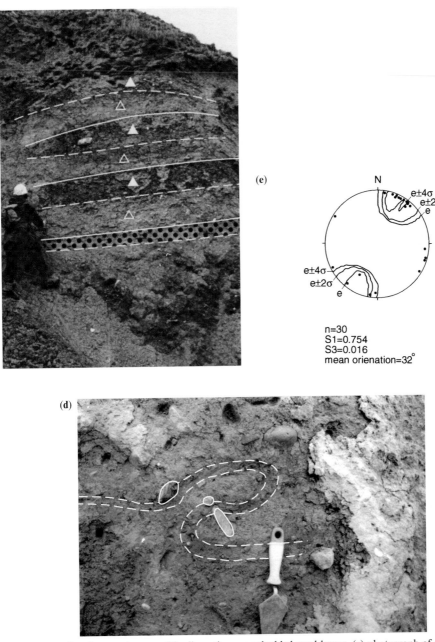

(c)

(e)

n=30
S1=0.754
S3=0.016
mean orienation=32°

(d)

homogeneous but do contain some thin discontinuous unbedded sand lenses. (c) photograph of site 1;
(d) deformation structures from Site 2 showing that the till at this site consists of a mixture of grey diamicton,
brown diamicton and stratified sand lenses, deformed into a series of folds. Measurements from a highly
isoclinal fold also suggest an ice flow direction of 268; (e) till fabric results from Site 2.

glacier incorporated more far-travelled elements into the till and it became gradually more grey in colour. This till is probably a deforming bed till since it contains discontinuous stratified lenses, which could be interpreted as tectonic laminations (Hart & Boulton 1991), and has a low fabric strength (Hart 1994; Benn 1995).

The repetitive sequence of till units (i.e. brown diamicton grading upwards into grey diamicton) is thought to reflect one till unit that was subsequently compressed into a series of thrust slices. Thus the top of the sand layer would represent a basal thrust, and each till couplet would represent a thrust slice. The grey clay raft could also be a thrust slice.

Compressive deformation within the tills. Although compressive deformation is usually indicative of proglacial deformation, the style of deformation is more complex at the three sites just described. The compressive deformation within the till at Reighton consists of

open folding. This ductile style of deformation presumably reflects a local compression zone formed on the stoss side of Flamborough Head (Fig. 7a).

The stacked till sheets at Castle Head and Boyne Bay are unusual as they do not show the large-scale folding which is very commonly associated with push moraines. Instead, the low-angled thrust sheets there could represent subglacial compression within a vertically constrained shear zone: that is, a specific type of constructional deformation, associated with a relatively thin deforming layer, well drained sediment and a subglacial obstacle to flow (compressive brittle constructional deformation). In situations where the lower part of the deforming layer becomes well drained, rafting may occur in areas of local compression (Fig. 7b). As the glacier continues to move over such a site, deforming bed till may still be being deposited in the upper part of the layer, but, because the deforming layer is moving up through the

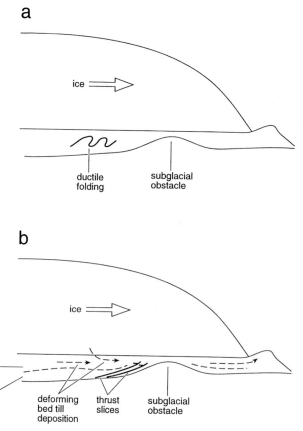

Fig. 7. Schematic diagram to show local compressive deformation within till: (**a**) ductile deformation; (**b**) brittle compressive constructional deformation.

sediments, the lower thrust slices are preserved. In this example, the local compressive zone would have been due to the presence of the Banffshire coastal cliffs.

Drumlins and the subglacial landscape. It should be noted from the map (Fig. 2) that almost all the drumlins in mainland Britain are found in hardrock valleys floored with unconsolidated sediments and that most of the individual drumlins are oriented in parallel both with the valley walls and the ice flow direction. These areas may reflect the faster moving parts of the ice streams (Clark 1994; Mitchell 1994) analogous to the modern ice streams of the Antarctic Sipple Coast (e.g. Alley *et al.* 1986).

Summary

The collation of data concerning glaciotectonic deformation in Britain has shown that deforming bed conditions were very common, being associated with lowland glaciations of a range of ages and in both hard and soft bed environments. The pattern of deformation is relatively predictable (i.e. constructional deformation at the margin and excavational deformation upglacier, with its concomitant effect on till lithology), but is modified by variations in bedrock, the subglacial environment and topographic changes.

Implications for stratigraphic correlation

Although some glaciers simply advance and retreat over a landscape and produce a 'layer-cake' stratigraphy, e.g. the glacial deposits of Wisconsin, USA (Mickelson *et al.* 1977, 1984), this is not always the case. In many areas, including Britain, glacial sequences consist of a series of discontinuous units and the widespread occurrence of glaciotectonic deformation must be taken into account in any stratigraphic

reconstruction. Berthelsen and co-workers (e.g. Berthelsen 1978; Aber 1979; Rasmussen 1975) developed the concept of kineto-stratigraphy to interpret the complex glacial sequences of Denmark. These ideas were also used by Banham (1975, 1988*b*) in his interpretations of the Norfolk coastal sections. The technique is to divide a glaciogenic section into kineto-stratigraphic units related to one specfic event. Houmark-Nielsen and Berthelsen (1981) formalized this into a chart (Table 4) that includes sedimentological and deformational data.

Kineto-stratigraphy is excellent for the stratigraphic analysis of compressive deformation, but when considering the stratigraphic analysis of shear zone deformation the following factors need to be taken into consideration:

1. The style of deformation is an important element of till stratigraphy. For example, constructional deformation results in a sequence which is rich in local lithologies at the base, and contains more far-travelled lithologies at the top, e.g. Stewponey (Figs 3a and 4); excavational deformation results in a more homogeneous sequence, e.g. Site 2 Boyne Bay (Figs 3b and 6d).

2. The resultant till lithology is also dependent on the number of non-glacial lithologies present and the amount of subglacial deformation. For example, a glacier moving over an unconsolidated bedrock composed of different lithologies combined with medium to low shear strain will produce a very spatially variable till, whilst a glacier moving over a homogeneous bedrock and/or associated with high shear strain will produce a spatially homogeneous till.

3. The resultant till lithology is also dependent on the strength of the bedrock, apart from the overall ability of the glacier to deform the sediment. Hart *et al.* (1990) were able to show that the thickness of the deforming layer changes according to the bedrock, as well as the style of deformation. An example of this can also be seen in Fig. 8. The glacier advances over two sites. During retreat it

Table 4. *Glacial stratigraphic data required for kineto-stratigraphy*

Kineto-stratigraphic unit					
I	II	III			IV
Facies log	Deformation structures	Till			Stratified drift
		Fabric	Structure	Lithology	Palaeocurrents	Lithology

After Houmark-Nielsen & Berthelsen (1981).

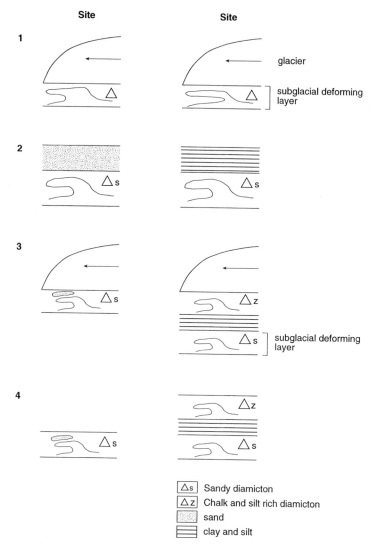

Fig. 8. Formation of different sequences based on different inter-till lithologies: Stage 1, subglacial deformation at Sites A and 2B; Stage 2, outwash sand is deposited at Site A and lake sediments deposited at Site B; Stage 3, readvance over the two sites and subglacial deformation, the outwash sand at Site B acts as a decollement surface; Stage 4, on ice retreat, there is one till at Site A and two tills at Site B.

deposits outwash sand in one location and lake clay in another. During the readvance, at Site A the outwash sand is incorporated into the deformation resulting in one till, whilst at Site B the clay acts as a zone of decollement, preventing the deforming layer from moving down any further into the till, resulting in two tills.

Thus, both compressive and shear zone processes can contribute to the production of a spatially variable and complex till stratigraphy.

In addition, the glacier may readvance over one or more glacial cycle, producing an even more complex stratigraphy.

Conclusions

The rapid expansion of *in situ* glacier monitoring, combined with modern glacier sedimentological investigations, has led to the development of the deforming bed model. This model suggests that deformation is ubiquitous in the proglacial and subglacial environment, and that subglacial deformation and deposition are interlinked. The deforming bed model further suggests that deformational (and depositional) patterns change in a relatively predictable way (e.g. proglacial/subglacial, excavational/constructional, till deposition/drumlins), which can be used in the development of a kineto-stratigraphy which takes into account both vertical and lateral changes in lithology.

The result of this is the inevitable re-evaluation of many British Quaternary sequences and concomitant changes to British Quaternary glacial stratigraphy. This represents a new opportunity to produce better reconstructions of both past glacier dynamics and Quaternary glacial histories.

I would like to thank K. Martinez for photography and field assistance at Boyne Bay; D. Maddy and M. Goodwin for introducing me to the Stewponey site; T. Aspden and his colleagues in the Cartographic Unit, University of Southampton, for their figure reproduction; and A. Jones for her manuscript editing.

References

ABER, J. S. 1979. Kineto-stratigraphy at Hvideklint, Møn, Denmark and its regional significance. *Geological Society Denmark, Bulletin*, **28**, 81–93.

——1993. *Glaciotectonics and mapping glacial deposits.* Canadian Plains Research Center, University of Regina, Canadian Plains Proceedings 25, vol. 1.

—— & RUSZCZYNSKA-SZENAJCH, H. 1997. Origin of Elblag Upland, northern Poland, and glaciotectonism in the southern Baltic region. *Sedimentary Geology*, **111**, 119–134.

——, CROOT, D. G. & FENTON, M. M. 1989. *Glaciotectonic Landforms and Structures.* Glaciology and Quaternary Geology Series, Kluwer, Dordrecht.

AGASSIZ, L. 1840. Glaciers and the evidence of their having once existed in Scotland, Ireland and England. *Proceedings of the Geological Society of London*, **3**, 327–348.

ALLEY, R. B. 1991. Deforming-bed origin for southern Laurentide till sheets? *Journal of Glaciology*, **37**, 67–76.

——, BLANKENSHIP, D. D., BENTLEY, C. R. & ROONEY, S. T. 1986. Deformation of till beneath ice stream B West Antarctica. *Nature*, **322**, 57–59.

ASTAKHOV, V. I., KAPLYANSKAYA, F. A. & TARNOGRADSKY, V. D. 1996. Pleistocene permafrost of West Siberia as a deformable glacier bed. *Permafrost and Periglacial Processes*, **7**, 165–191.

BANHAM, P. H. 1975. Glaciotectonic structures: a general discussion with particular reference to the Contorted Drift of Norfolk. *In*: WRIGHT, A. E. & MOSELEY, F. (eds) *Ice Ages, Ancient and Modern.* Seel House, Liverpool, 69–94.

——1977. Glaciotectonics in till stratigraphy. *Boreas*, **6**, 101–105.

——1988a. Polyphase glaciotectonic deformation in the Contorted Drift of Norfolk. *In*: CROOT, D. G. (ed.) *Glaciotectonic Forms and Processes.* Balkema, Rotterdam, 27–32.

——1988b. Thin-skinned glaciotectonic structures. *In*: CROOT, D. G. (ed.) *Glaciotectonic Forms and Processes.* Balkema, Rotterdam, 21–25.

BENN, D. I. 1992. The genesis and significance of 'Hummocky Moraine': Evidence from the Isle of Skye, Scotland. *Quaternary Science Reviews*, **11**, 781–800.

——1995. Fabric signature of subglacial till deformation, Breidamerkurjökull, Iceland. *Sedimentology*, **42**, 735–747.

—— & EVANS, D. J. A. 1996. The interpretation and classification of subglacially-deformed materials. *Quaternary Science Reviews*, **15**, 23–53.

BER, A. 1987. Glaciotectonic deformation of glacial landforms and deposits in the Suwalki Lakeland (NE Poland). *In*: VAN DER MEER, J. J. M. (ed.) *Tills and Glaciotectonics.* Balkema, Rotterdam, 135–143.

BERTHELSEN, A. 1978. The methodology of kineto-stratigraphy as applied to glacial geology. *Geological Society Denmark, Bulletin*, **27**, 25–38.

BLAKE, E. W., CLARKE, G. K. C. & GÉRIN, M. C. 1992. Tools for examining subglacial bed deformation. *Journal of Glaciology*, **38**, 388–396.

——, FISCHER, U. H. & CLARKE, G. K. C. 1994. Direct measurements of sliding at the glacier bed. *Journal of Glaciology*, **40**, 595–599.

BLUEMLE, J. P. & CLAYTON, L. 1984. Large-scale glacial thrusting and related processes in North Dakota. *Boreas*, **13**, 279–299.

BOULTON, G. S. 1970. The deposition of subglacial and melt-out tills at the margins of certain Svalbard glaciers. *Journal of Glaciology*, **9**, 231–245.

——1972. Modern arctic glaciers as depositional models for former ice sheets. *Journal of the Geological Society of London*, **128**, 361–393.

——1975. Processes and patterns of subglacial sedimentation, a theoretical approach. *In*: WRIGHT, A. E. & MOSELEY, F. (eds) *Ice Ages: Ancient and Modern.* Seel House, Liverpool, 7–42.

——1976. The origin of glacially fluted surfaces: Observations and theory. *Journal of Glaciology*, **17**, 287–309.

——1977. A multiple till sequence formed by a Late Devensian Welsh ice-cap, Glanllynau, Gwynedd. *Cambia*, **1**, 10–31.

——1986. Push-moraines and glacier-contact fans in marine and terrestrial environments. *Sedimentology*, **33**, 677–698.

——1987. A theory of drumlin formation by subglacial deformation. *In*: MENZIES, J. & ROSE, J. (eds) *Drumlin Symposium.* Balkema, Rotterdam, 25–80.

—— & DOBBIE, K. E. 1993. Consolidation of sediments by glaciers: relations between sediment geotechnics, soft-bed glacier dynamics and subglacial ground-water flow. *Journal of Glaciology*, **39**, 26–44.

—— & HINDMARSH, R. C. A. 1987. Sediment deformation beneath glaciers: Rheology and geological consequences. *Journal of Geophysical Research*, **92**(B9), 9059–9082.

—— & JONES, A. S. 1979. Stability of temperate ice caps and ice sheets resting on beds of deformable sediment. *Journal of Glaciology*, **24**, 29–44.

——, VAN DER MEER, J. J. M., HART, J. K., BEETS, D., RUEGG, G. H. J. & VAN DER WATEREN, F. M. (in press). The sedimentary and structural evolution of a recent push moraine complex – Holmstrømbreen, Spitsbergen. *Quaternary Science Reviews*.

BUCKLAND, W. 1840. Memoir on the evidence of glaciers in Scotland and the north of England. *Proceedings of the Geological Society of London*, **3**, 332–337, 345–348.

CARRUTHERS, R. G. 1953. *Glacial Drifts and the Undermelt Theory*. Harold Hill, Newcastle.

CHAMBERLAIN, T. C. 1895. Recent glacial studies in Greenland. *Bulletin of the Geological Society of America*, **6**, 199–220.

CLARK, C. D. 1994. Large-scale ice moulding: a discussion of genesis and glaciological significance. *Sedimentary Geology*, **91**, 253–268.

CLARK, P. 1991. Striated clast pavements: Products of deforming subglacial sediment? *Geology*, **19**, 530–533.

CLARKE, G. K. C. 1987. Subglacial till: A physical framework for its properties and processes. *Journal of Geophysical Research*, **92**, (B9), 8942–8984.

—— & BLAKE, E. W. 1991. Geometric and thermal evolution of a surge-type glacier in its quiescent state – Trapridge Glacier, Yukon-Territory, Canada 1969–89. *Journal of Glaciology*, **37**, 158–169.

CLAYTON, L. & MORAN, S. R. 1974. A glacial process-form model. *In*: COATES, D. R. (ed.) *Glacial Geomorphology*. Binghamton, New York, 89–119.

CONWAY, M., SIR 1898. An exploration in 1897 of some of the Glaciers of Spitsbergen. *Geographical Journal*, **64**, 1–42.

CROOT, D. G. 1987. Glaciotectonic structures: A mesoscale model of thin-skinned thrust sheets? *Journal of Structural Geology*, **9**, 797–808.

—— (ed.) 1988a. *Glaciotectonics: Forms and Processes*. Balkema, Rotterdam.

——1988ba. Morphological, structural and mechanical analysis of neoglacial ice-pushed ridges in Iceland. *In*: CROOT, D. (ed.) *Glaciotectonics: Forms and Processes*. Balkema, Rotterdam, 33–48.

DREDGE, L. A. & GRANT, D. R. 1987. Glacial deformation of bedrock and sediment, Magdalen Islands and Nova Scotia, Canada: Evidence for a regional grounded ice sheet. *In*: VAN DER MEER, J. J. M. (ed.) *Tills and Glaciotectonics*, Balkema, Rotterdam, 183–195.

EDWARDS, C. A. 1987. The Quaternary deposits of Filey Bay. *In*: ELLIS, S. (ed.) *East Yorkshire, Field Guide*. Quaternary Research Association, Cambridge, 15–35.

ENGELHARDT, H. F. & KAMB, B. 1998. Sliding velocity at Ice Stream B. *Journal of Glaciology*, **44**, 223–230.

——, HUMPHREY, N., KAMB, B. & FAHNESTOCK, M. 1990. Physical conditions at the base of a fast moving Antarctic ice stream. *Science*, **248**, 57–59.

ETZELMÜLLER, B., HAGEN, J. O., VATNE, G., ØDEGÅRD, R. S. & SOLLID, J. L. 1996. Glacier debris accumulation and sediment deformation influenced by permafrost: examples from Svalbard. *Annals of Glaciology*, **22**, 53–62.

EVANS, D. 1989. The nature of glacitectonic structures and sediments at subpolar glacier margins, northwest Ellesmere Island. *Geografiska Annaler*, **71**, 113–123.

EVANS, D. J. A., OWEN, L. A. & ROBERTS, D. 1995. Stratigraphy and sedimentology of Dimlington stadial glacial deposits, East Yorkshire. *Journal of Quaternary Science*, **10**, 241–265.

EYBERGEN, F. A. 1987. Glacier snout dynamics and contemporary push moraine formation at the Turtmannglacier, Wallis, Switzerland. *In*: VAN DER MEER, J. J. M. (ed.) *Tills and Glaciotectonics*. Balkema, Rotterdam, 217–234.

EYLES, N., MCCABE, A. M. & BOWEN, D. Q. 1994. The stratigraphic and sedimentological significance of Late Devensian ice sheet surging in Holderness, Yorkshire, UK. *Quaternary Science Reviews*, **13**, 727–759.

FISCHER, U. H. & CLARK, G. K. C. 1997. Ploughing of subglacial sediment. *Journal of Glaciology*, **37**, 158–169.

FITZSIMONS, S. J. 1992. Sedimentology and depositional model for glaciolacustrine deposits in an ice-dammed tributary valley, western Tasmania, Australia. *Sedimentology*, **39**, 393–410.

——1996. Formation of thrust-block moraines at the margins of dry-based glaciers, south Victoria land, Antarctica. *Annals of Glaciology*, **22**, 68–74.

FORBES, J. D. 1843. *Travels through the Alps of Savoy*. Edinburgh.

GOODWIN, M., MADDY, D. & LEWIS, S. G. 1997. Pleistocene deposits at Gibbet Hill (Stewponey Pit), Stourbridge, Staffordshire. *In*: LEWIS, S. G. & MADDY, D. (eds) *The Quaternary of the South Midlands and the Welsh Marches: Field Guide*. Quaternary Research Association, London, 91–94.

HAMBREY, M. J. & HUDDART, D. 1995. Englacial and proglacial glaciotectonic processes at the snout of a thermally complex glacier in Svalbard. *Journal of Quaternary Science*, **10**, 313–327.

HARPER, J. T. & HUMPHREY, N. F. 1995. Borehole video analysis of a temperate glaciers englacial and subglacial structure – implications for glacier flow models. *Geology*, **23**, 901–904.

HARRIS, C. 1991. Glacial deposits at Wylfa Head, Anglesey, North Wales: evidence for Late Devensian deposition in a non-marine environment. *Journal of Quaternary Science*, **6**, 67–77.

—— & DONNELLY, R. 1991. The glacial deposits of South Wales. *In*: EHLERS, J., GIBBARD, P. L. & ROSE, J. (eds) *Glacial Deposits in Great Britain and Ireland*. Balkema, Rotterdam, 279–290.

——, BRABHAM, P. J. & WILLIAMS, G. D. 1995. Glaciotectonic structures and their relation to topography at Dinas Dinlle, Arvon, north west Wales. *Journal of Quaternary Science*, **10**, 398.

HART, J. K. 1990. Proglacial glaciotectonic deformation and the origin of the Cromer Ridge push moraine complex, North Norfolk, UK. *Boreas*, **19**, 165–180.

—— 1994. Till fabric associated with deformable beds. *Earth Surface Processes and Landforms*, **19**, 15–32.

—— 1995a. An investigation of the deforming layer/ debris-rich ice continuum, illustrated from three Alaskan glaciers. *Journal of Glaciology*, **41**, 619–633.

—— 1995b. Drumlins, flutes and lineations at Vestari-Hagafellsjökull, Iceland. *Journal of Glaciology*, **41**, 596–606.

—— 1995c. Drumlin formation in southern Anglesey and Arvon, north west Wales. *Journal of Quaternary Science*, **10**, 3–14.

—— 1996a. Proglacial glaciotectonic deformation associated with glaciolacustrine sedimentation, Lake Pukaki, New Zealand. *Journal of Quaternary Research*, **11**, 149–160.

—— 1996b. Subglacial deformation associated with a rigid bed environment, Aberdaron, North Wales. *Journal of Glacial Geology and Geomorphology*, **1**, 1–18.

—— 1997. The relationship between drumlins and other forms of subglacial deformation. *Quaternary Science Reviews*, **16**, 93–108.

—— & BOULTON, G. S. 1991. The interrelationship between glaciotectonic deformation and glaciodeposition. *Quaternary Science Reviews*, **10**, 335–350.

—— & ROBERTS, D. H. 1994. Criteria to distinguish between subglacial glaciotectonic and glaciomarine sedimentation: I – Deformational styles and sedimentology. *Sedimentary Geology*, **91**, 191–214.

—— & SMITH, B. 1997. Subglacial deformation associated with fast ice flow, from Columbia glacier, Alaska. *Sedimentary Geology*, **111**, 177–197.

—— & WATTS, R. 1997. A comparison of the styles of deformation associated with two recent push moraines, south Van Keulenfjorden, Svalbard. *Earth Surface Processes and Landforms*, **22**, 1089–1107.

——, GANE, F. & WATTS, R. 1996. Evidence for deforming bed conditions on the Dänischer Wohld peninsula, northern Germany. *Boreas*, **25**, 101–113.

——, HINDMARSH, R. C. A. & BOULTON, G. S. 1990. Different styles of subglacial glaciotectonic deformation in the context of the Anglian ice sheet. *Earth Surface Processes and Landforms*, **15**, 227–242.

HICOCK, S. R. 1990. Genetic till prism. *Geology*, **18**, 517–519.

—— 1991. On subglacial stone pavements in till. *Journal of Geology*, **99**, 607–619.

—— & DREIMANIS, A. 1992. Deformation till in the Great Lakes region: implications for rapid flow along the south-central margin of the Laurentide Ice Sheet. *Canadian Journal of Earth Sciences*, **29**, 1565–1579.

HOUMARK-NIELSEN, M. & BERTHELSEN, A. 1981. Kineto-stratigraphic evaluation and presentation of glacial-stratigraphic data, with examples from northern Samsø, Denmark. *Boreas*, **10**, 411–422.

HUBBARD, B. P., SHARP, M. J., WILLIS, I. C., NIELSEN, M. K. & SMART, C. C. 1995. Borehole water level variation and the structure of the subglacial hydrological system of Haut Glacier d'Arolla, Valais, Switzerland. *Journal of Glaciology*, **41**, 572–583.

HUDDART, D. 1991. The glacial history and glacial deposits of the north and west Cumberland Lowlands. *In*: EHLERS, J., GIBBARD, P. L. & ROSE, J. (eds) *Glacial Deposits in Great Britain and Ireland*. Balkema, Rotterdam, 151–168.

HUMPHREY, N, KAMB, B., FAHNESTOCK, M. & ENGELHARDT, H. 1993. Characteristics of the bed of the lower Columbia Glacier, Alaska. *Journal of Geophysical Research*, **98**(B1), 837–846.

IVERSON, N. R., HANSON, B., HOOKE, R. LeB. & JANSSON, P. 1994a. Flow mechanism of glaciers on soft beds. *Science*, **267**, 80–81.

IVERSON, N. R., JANSSON, P. & HOOKE, R. LeB. 1994b. In-situ measurement of the strength of deforming subglacial till. *Journal of Glaciology*, **40**, 497–503.

KÄLIN, M. 1971. *The active push moraine of the Thompson glacier*. Axel Heiberg Island Research Reports, **4**, McGill University, Montreal.

KLINT, K. E. S. & PEDERSEN, S. A. S. 1995. The Hanklit glaciotectonic thrust fault complex, Mors, Denmark. *Geological Survey Denmark*, Series A, **35**.

KLUIVING, S. J. 1994. Glaciotectonics of the Itterbeck-Uelsen push moraines, Germany. *Journal of Quaternary Science*, **9**, 235–244.

——, RAPPOL, M. & VAN DER WATEREN, F. M. 1991. Till stratigraphy and ice movements in eastern Overijssel, the Netherlands. *Boreas*, **20**, 193–205.

LAMPLUGH, G. W. 1911. On the shelly moraine of the Sefström glacier and other Spitsbergen phenomena illustrative of British glacial conditions. *Proceedings of the Yorkshire Geological Society*, **17**, 216–241.

LYELL, C. 1840. On the geological evidence for the former existence of glaciers in Forfarshire. *Proceedings of the Geological Society of London*, **3**, 337–343.

MACAYEAL, D. R. 1989. Large-scale flow over a viscous basal sediment: Theory and application to ice stream B Antarctica. *Journal of Geophysical Research*, **94**, 4071–4087.

MCCLAY, K. R. & PRICE, N. J. (eds) 1981. *Thrust and Nappe Tectonics*. Geological Society Special Publication, **9**, Blackwell, Oxford.

MENZIES, J. 1979. Mechanics of drumlin formation. *Journal of Glaciology*, **27**, 372–384.

—— 1996. Glasgow's drumlins. *Scottish Geographical Magazine*, **112**, 188–193.

MICKELSON, D. M., ACOMB, L. J., BROUWER, N. et al. 1977. *Shoreline erosion and bluff stability along Lake Michigan and Lake Superior shorelines of Wisconsin*. Shore Erosion Study Technical Report, Wisconsin Coastal Management, Office of State Planning and Energy.

——, CLAYTON, L., BAKER, R. W., MODE, W. N. & SCHNEIDER, A. F. 1984. *Pleistocene stratigraphic units of Wisconsin*. Wisconsin Geological and Natural History Survey, Miscellaneous Papers, **84-1**.

MITCHELL, W. A. 1991. Dimlington Stadial Ice Sheet in the Western Pennines. *In*: MITCHELL, W. A. (ed.) *Western Pennines: Field Guide*. Quaternary Research Association, Cambridge, 24–43.

——1994. Drumlins in ice-sheet reconstructions, with reference to the western Pennines, northern England. *Sedimentary Geology*, **91**, 313–331.

MURRAY, T. 1997. Assessing the paradigm shift: deformable glacier beds. *Quaternary Science Reviews*, **16**, 995–1016.

PAUL, M. A. & EYLES, N. 1990. Constraints on the preservation of diamict facies (melt-out tills) at the margins of stagnant glaciers. *Quaternary Science Reviews*, **9**, 51–71.

PEACOCK, J. D. 1971. A re-interpretation of the Coastal Deposits of Banffshire and their place in the late-Glacial history of N.E. Scotland. *Bulletin of the Geological Survey of Great Britain*, **37**, 81–89.

——1991. Glacial deposits of the Hebridean region. *In*: ROSE, J., GIBBARD, P. L. & ELHERS, J. (eds) *The Glacial Deposits of Britain*. Balkema, Rotterdam, 109–120.

—— & MERRITT, J. W. 1997. Glaciogenic rafting at Castle Hill, Gardenstown, and its significance for the glacial history of northern Banffshire, Scotland. *Journal of Quaternary Science*, **12**, 283–294.

PORTER, P. R. & MURRAY, T. 1995. *Borehole instruments to measure glacier basal motion*. School of Geography, University of Leeds, Working Paper, **95/21**.

——, —— & DOWDESWELL, J. A. 1997. Sediment properties beneath a glacier-surge front: Bakanbreen, Svalbard. *EOS*, **78**(46), 253.

RASMUSSEN, L. A. 1975. Kineto-stratigraphic glacial drift units on Hindsholm, Denmark. *Boreas*, **4**, 209–217.

REA, B. R., EVANS, D. J. A., & BENN, D. I. 1997. Bedrock quarrying beneath deforming bed glaciers. *Supplementi di Geografia Fisica e Dinamica Quaternaria*, **3**, 324.

READ, H. H. 1923. *The Geology of the County around Banff, Huntly and Turriff*. Memoirs of the Geological Survey, Scotland, HMSO, Edinburgh.

RICE, R. J. 1981. Dunton Bassett sand and gravel pit and Croft quarry. *In*: DOUGLAS, T. D. (ed.) *Field Guide to the East Midlands Region*. Quaternary Research Association, Cambridge, 16–22.

RICHARDS, A. E. 1997. Middle Pleistocene deposits in North East Herefordshire. *In*: LEWIS, S. G. & MADDY, D. (eds) *The Quaternary of the South Midlands and the Welsh Marches: Field Guide*. Quaternary Research Association, London, 75–88.

SMALLEY, I. J. & UNWIN, D. J. 1968. The formation and shapes of drumlins and their distribution and orientation in drumlin fields. *Journal of Glaciology*, **7**, 377–390.

SHARP, M. 1984. Annual moraine ridges at Skalafellsjökull, south-east Iceland. *Journal of Glaciology*, **30**, 82–93.

SLATER, G. 1926. Glacial tectonics as reflected in disturbed drift deposits. *Geologist's Association Proceedings*, **37**, 392- 400.

THOMAS, G. S. P. 1984. The origin of the glaciodynamic structure of the Bride Moraine, Isle of Man. *Boreas*, **13**, 355–364.

TRUFFER, M., HARRISON, W., ECHELMEYER, K. & MOTYKA, R. 1997. Sampling of basal material on surge type Black Rapids Glacier, Alaska: Preliminary results. *EOS*, **78**(46), F253.

VAN DER MEER, J. J. M. (ed.) 1987. *Tills and Glaciotectonics*. Balkema, Rotterdam.

——1993. Microscopic evidence of subglacial deformation. *Quaternary Science Reviews*, **12**, 553–587.

——, RABASSA, J. O. & EVENSON, E. B. 1992. Micromorphological aspects of glaciolacustrine sediments in northern Patagonia, Argentina. *Journal of Quaternary Science*, **7**, 31–44.

VAN GIJSSEL, K. 1987. A lithostratigraphic and glaciotectonic reconstruction of the Lamstedt Moraine, Lower Saxony (FRG). *In*: VAN DER MEER, J. J. M. (ed.) *Tills and Glaciotectonics*. Balkema, Rotterdam, 145–155.

VAN DER WATEREN, F. M. 1985. A model of glacial tectonics, applied to the ice-pushed ridges in the Central Netherlands. *Geological Society Denmark, Bulletin*, **34**, 55–74.

——1995. Processes of glaciotectonism. *In*: MENZIES, J. (ed.) *Glacial Environments: Processes, Sediments and Landforms*. Pergamon, Oxford, 309–335.

WARREN, W. P. & CROOT, D. G. (eds.) 1994. *Formation and Deformation of Glacial Deposits*. Balkema, Rotterdam.

The palaeoclimatic and biostratigraphic significance of herpetofaunal remains from the British Quaternary

C. P. GLEED-OWEN

Centre for Quaternary Science, Coventry University, Priory Street, Coventry, CV1 5FB, UK

Abstract: Herpetofaunal (amphibian and reptile) assemblages from British Quaternary sites are considered here in order to extract palaeoclimatic inferences and to determine their biostratigraphic value. In the early Middle Pleistocene, thermophilous taxa distinguish Westbury-sub-Mendip lower units and Little Oakley from West Runton and Sugworth, and from the faunally distinct Boxgrove and upper Westbury herpetofaunas. Thermophilous herpetofaunas from Barnham, West Stow and Cudmore Grove include the southern European aesculapian snake *Elaphe longissima*, and three out of the seven exotic taxa at Cudmore Grove indicate a summer temperature at least 2–3°C warmer than today's. Oxygen Isotope Stage 9 appears to have been more continental than Stage 11. The Stage 7 interglacial had pond terrapin *Emys orbicularis* and tree frog *Hyla*. The Ipswichian (Substage 5e) had *E. orbicularis* and a south European natricine snake *Natrix maura* or *Natrix tessellata*. Interstadial faunas from later parts of Stage 5 and from Stage 3 include relatively thermophilous elements such as natterjack toad *Bufo calamita* and grass snake *Natrix natrix* which are consistent with summer temperatures as warm as today's. A number of Devensian Late-glacial Interstadial and early Holocene sites have also yielded *B. calamita*, indicating a mean July temperature of 15°C. Remains of *E. orbicularis* from East Wretham testify to a climate of 2°C warmer than today's during the mid-Holocene thermal optimum. Moor frog *Rana arvalis* and pool frog *Rana lessonae*, from late Holocene Fenland sites, confirm that the Holocene herpetofauna was formerly more diverse than at present.

Fossil herpetofaunal (amphibian and reptile) assemblages can be used as accurate palaeo-climatic and palaeoenvironmental indicators. Though they collectively occupy a wide range of terrestrial and aquatic environments, individual species often have specific tolerances for temperature, vegetation cover, water quality and other factors which control their distribution. Furthermore, all of the species recorded from the Pleistocene in Britain are living today, and very few from continental Europe have become extinct during the Pleistocene. Herpetofaunal remains from British Quaternary sites are little studied and much of their potential remains untapped. These remains are undoubtedly recovered from virtually all sites which produce other small vertebrate remains, but are infrequently identi-fied. Furthermore, the data available so far have not been used to their full potential as a proxy from which inferences can be drawn. From the herpetofaunas which have been described to date, useful palaeoclimatic and biostratigra-phic inferences have begun to emerge. Periglacial cold stage sites typically produce only the cold-tolerant common frog *Rana temporaria* which is

of no real palaeoclimatic or biostratigraphic value, except that it cannot tolerate permafrost. Interglacial herpetofaunas, on the other hand, often include exotic taxa which can offer useful information on palaeoclimate and for biostratigraphic correlations. The herpetofaunal evidence known so far from temperate stages is discussed below and should provide a useful basis for comparison with, and testing against, other lines of evidence. This evidence is dealt with in detail in the author's PhD thesis (Gleed-Owen 1998a), and references to this are clearly stated. Locations of fossil herpetofaunal sites are given in Tables 1 and 2.

Early Middle Pleistocene

To date, only a few early Middle Pleistocene (EMP) herpetofaunas have been described. A herpetofauna from the West Runton Fresh-water Bed, Norfolk (Substages Cr Ib–IIb) com-prised smooth newt *Triturus vulgaris*, common toad *Bufo bufo*, moor frog *Rana arvalis,* green frog *Rana esculenta* or *ridibunda*, common frog

GLEED-OWEN, C. P. 1999. The palaeoclimatic and biostratigraphic significance of herpetofaunal remains from the British Quaternary. *In*: ANDREWS, P. & BANHAM, P. (eds) *Late Cenozoic Environments and Hominid Evolution: a tribute to Bill Bishop.* Geological Society, London, 201–215.

Table 1. Fossil occurrences of amphibian and reptile taxa from Quaternary sites in the British Isles. Dots represent presence of a taxon at a site. Brackets surrounding the dot mean the record is 'cf'. Non-specific records (e.g. *Rana sp.*) are only given in the absence of a more specific record for that genus (e.g. *Rana sp.* (brown frog) or *Rana temporaria*)

Taxa (left axis):

+ = native to British Isles today

- *Triturus cristatus*, crested newt +
- *Triturus vulgaris*, smooth newt +
- *Triturus helveticus*, palmate newt +
- *Triturus vulgaris/helveticus*
- *Triturus alpestris*, alpine newt
- *Triturus sp.*
- Salamandridae indet.
- *Pelobates fuscus*, common spadefoot toad
- *Pelodytes punctatus*, parsley frog
- *Bufo bufo*, common toad +
- *Bufo calamita*, natterjack toad +
- *Bufo sp.*
- *Hyla arborea*, common tree frog
- *Hyla meridionalis*, stripeless tree frog
- *Hyla sp.*
- *Rana temporaria*, common frog +
- *Rana arvalis*, moor frog
- *Rana arvalis/dalmatina*, moor/agile frog
- *Rana sp.* (brown frog)
- *Rana lessonae*, pool frog
- *Rana ridibunda/esculenta*, marsh/edible frog
- *Rana sp.* (green frog)
- *Rana sp.*
- *Emys orbicularis*, European pond terrapin
- *Lacerta vivipara*, common or viviparous lizard +
- Lacertidae indet.
- *Anguis fragilis*, slow-worm +
- *Elaphe longissima*, aesculapian snake
- *Natrix natrix*, grass snake +
- *Natrix maura/tessellata*, viperine/dice snake
- *Natrix sp.*
- *Coronella austriaca*, smooth snake +
- *Vipera berus*, adder +

Column groupings (top): EARLY MIDDLE PLEISTOCENE · LATE MIDDLE PLEISTOCENE · LATE PLEISTOCENE · HOLOCENE

Oxygen Isotope Stage (row): 17 or 21? · 15 · 13 · 12 · 11? · 9? · 8? · 7 · 6 or 5e? · 5e · 5c/a · 3 · 2 · 1

Sites (columns, left to right):

- West Runton (freshwater Bed), Norfolk
- Sugworth, Oxfordshire
- Little Oakley, Essex
- Westbury Cave (Unit 8), Westbury-sub-Mendip, Somerset
- Westbury Cave (Units 11–15), Westbury-sub-Mendip, Somerset
- Boxgrove, West Sussex
- Half's Pit, nr. Benson, Oxfordshire
- Barnham, Norfolk
- Beeches Pit, West Stow, Suffolk
- Hoxne, Suffolk
- Barnfield Pit, Swanscombe, Kent
- Ingress Vale, Swanscombe, Kent
- Cudmore Grove, Mersea Island, Essex
- Grenlands Pit, Purfleet, Essex
- Baker's Hole Pit, Northfleet, Kent
- Itteringham, Norfolk
- Harkstead, Suffolk
- Stoke Tunnel, Ipswich, Suffolk
- Selsey, West Sussex
- Stanton Harcourt, Oxfordshire
- Marsworth (lower channel), Buckinghamshire
- Tornewton Cave (Otter Stratum), Devon
- Tornewton Cave (Glutton/Bear Stratum), Devon
- Swanton Morley, Norfolk
- Shropham, Norfolk
- Deeping St James, Norfolk
- Mundesley, Norfolk
- Bobbitshole, Ipswich, Suffolk
- Tornewton Cave (Hyaena Stratum), Devon
- Sutton Courtenay, Oxfordshire
- Cassington, Oxfordshire
- Shropham (Pocket 2), Norfolk
- Sutton Courtenay, Oxfordshire
- Wookey Hole (Hyaena Den), Wells, Somerset
- Upton Warren, Worcestershire
- Nazeing, Essex
- Broken Cavern, Torbryan, Devon
- Three Holes Cave, Torbryan, Devon
- Tornewton Six Cave, Torbryan, Devon
- Denny's Hole, Compton Bishop, Somerset
- Rogers Cave, Symond's Yat, Wye Valley, Herefordshire
- Hoyle's Mouth Cave, nr. Tenby, Dyfed
- Little Hoyle Cave, nr. Tenby, Dyfed
- Potter's Cave, Caldey Island, Dyfed
- Cow Cave, Chudleigh, Devon
- Kent's Cavern (Wolf Den), Torquay, Devon
- Broken Cavern, Torbryan, Devon
- Three Holes Cave, Torbryan, Devon
- Happaway Cave, Torquay?, Devon
- Levaton Fissure, nr. Newton Abbot, Devon
- Milton Hill Cave, nr. Wells, Somerset
- Lower Cave, Bristol, Avon
- Bratford, nr. Bath, Avon
- Rogers Cave, Symond's Yat, Wye Valley, Herefordshire
- Tiddington, Warwickshire
- Cassington, Oxfordshire
- Netteswell, Essex
- Ightham Fissure, nr. Sevenoaks, Kent
- Madawg Rockshelter, Wye Valley, Gwent
- Cathole, Gower, West Glamorgan
- Pontnewydd Cave, nr. St. Asaph, Clwyd
- Bartoddau y Cawres, Anglesey, Gwynedd
- Whitemor Channel, nr. Bosley, Cheshire
- Steeley Cave, Creswell, Derbyshire
- Pin-hole Cave, Creswell, Derbyshire
- Robin Hood's Cave, Creswell, Derbyshire
- Region, Derbyshire
- Dog Holes, Warton, Lancashire
- Badger Cave, Creag nan Uamh, Sutherland, Highland Region
- Bone Cave, Creag nan Uamh, Sutherland, Highland Region
- Smoo Cave, Durness, Sutherland, Highland Region
- Coveny (Wardey Hill), Cambridgeshire
- Deeping St Nicholas (Deeping Fen Barrow), Lincolnshire
- Market Deeping (Outgang Lane), Lincolnshire
- Gosberton (Chopdike Drove), Lincolnshire
- Gosberton (Morningtun House), Lincolnshire
- Gosberton (Third Drove), Lincolnshire
- Pinchbeck (Leaves Lake Drove), Lincolnshire
- Terrington St. Clement (Hay Green), Norfolk
- West Walton (Ingleborough Farm), Norfolk
- Walpole St. Andrew (Rose Hall Farm), Norfolk
- East Wretham, Norfolk
- Carrowmore, Co. Sligo
- Plunket Cave, Keishcorran, Co. Sligo
- Dermot and Grania's Bed Cave, Brickleve Mountains, Co. Sligo
- Pig Cave, Brickleve Mountains, Co. Sligo

Table 2. *Index of fossil herpetofaunal sites in Table 1 with sources of data used*

Badger Cave, Creag nan Uamh, Sutherland (Gleed-Owen 1998*a*)

Baker's Hole Pit, Northfleet, Kent (Holman 1995*a*)

Barclodiad y Gawres, Anglesey, Gwynedd (Pumphrey 1956)

Barnfield Pit, Swanscombe, Kent (Holman 1987*b*)

Barnham, Norfolk (Ashton *et al.* 1994)

Bathford, nr. Bath, Avon (Holman 1987*b*)

Beeches Pit, West Stow, Suffolk (Holman 1994)

Bobbitshole, Ipswich, Suffolk (Stuart 1979)

Bone Cave, Creag nan Uamh, Sutherland (Gleed-Owen 1998*a*)

Boxgrove, West Sussex (Holman 1992*a*; Gleed-Owen 1998*a*)

Broken Cavern, Torbryan, Devon (Gleed-Owen 1996, 1997*a*, 1998*a*)

Carrowmore, Co. Sligo (Ove & Persson 1980)

Cassington, Oxfordshire (Gleed-Owen 1998*a, b*; Parfitt in Maddy *et al.* 1998)

Cathole, Gower, West Glamorgan (Gleed-Owen 1998*a*)

Coveney, Cambridgeshire (Gleed-Owen 1998*a*)

Cow Cave, Chudleigh, Devon (Holman 1985)

Cudmore Grove, Mersea Island, Essex (Holman *et al.* 1990)

Deeping St. James, Norfolk (Gleed-Owen 1998*a*)

Deeping St. Nicholas, Lincolnshire (Gleed-Owen 1998*a*)

Denny's Hole, Compton Bishop, Somerset (Gleed-Owen 1998*a*)

Dermot and Grania's Bed, Bricklieve Mountains, Co. Sligo (Gleed-Owen 1998*a*)

Dog Holes, Warton, Lancashire (Holman 1987*b*)

East Wretham, Norfolk (Newton 1862; Stuart 1979)

Gosberton, Lincolnshire (Gleed-Owen 1998*a*)

Greenlands Pit, Purfleet, Essex (Holman & Clayden 1988; Holman 1995*b*)

Hall's Pit, nr. Benson, Oxfordshire (Stuart 1982)

Happaway Cave, Torquay, Devon (Holman 1987*b*, 1991)

Harkstead, Suffolk (Stuart 1979)

Hoxne, Suffolk (Holman 1993*b*; Stuart *et al.* 1993)

Hoyle's Mouth Cave, Tenby, Dyfed (Gleed-Owen 1997*b*, 1998*a*)

Ightham Fissure, nr. Sevenoaks, Kent (Holman 1985, 1987*b*).

Ingress Vale, Swanscombe, Kent (Stuart 1979; Holman 1987*b*)

Itteringham, Norfolk (Hallock *et al.* 1990; Holman 1992*b*)

Kent's Cavern, Torquay, Devon (Gleed-Owen 1998*a*)

Levaton Fissure, nr. Newton Abbot, Devon (Carreck 1957)

Little Hoyle Cave, Tenby, Dyfed (Gleed-Owen 1997*b*, 1998*a*)

Little Oakley, Essex (Lister *et al.* 1990; Holman 1992*e*)

Lower Cave, Bristol, Avon (Gleed-Owen 1998*a*)

Madawg Cave, Wye Valley, Gwent (Gleed-Owen 1998*a*)

Market Deeping, Lincolnshire (Gleed-Owen 1998*a*)

Marsworth, Buckinghamshire (Gleed-Owen 1998*a*)

Milton Hill Cave, nr. Wells, Somerset (Gleed-Owen 1998*a*)

Mundesley, Norfolk (Newton 1879; Stuart 1979)

Nazeing, Essex (Allison *et al.* 1952)

Netteswell, Essex (Holman 1987*b*)

Pig Cave, Bricklieve Mountains, Co. Sligo (Gleed-Owen 1998*a*)

Pinchbeck, Lincolnshire (Gleed-Owen 1998*a*)

Pin-hole Cave, Creswell, Derbyshire (Gleed-Owen 1998*a*)

Plunkett Cave, Keishcorran, Co. Sligo (Gleed-Owen 1998*a*)

Pontnewydd Cave, St. Asaph, Clwyd (Gleed-Owen 1998*a*)

Potter's Cave, Caldy, Dyfed (Gleed-Owen 1997*b*, 1998*a*)

Repton, Derbyshire (Raxworthy *et al.* 1990)

Robin Hood's Cave, Creswell, Derbyshire (Gleed-Owen 1998*a*)

Rogers' Cave, Symond's Yat, Herefordshire (Gleed-Owen 1998*a*)

Selsey, West Sussex (Stuart 1979; Holman 1992*d*)

Shropham, Norfolk (Holman & Clayden 1990; Holman 1992*d*; 1996)

Smoo Cave, Durness, Sutherland (Gleed-Owen 1998*a*)

Stanton Harcourt, Oxfordshire (Gleed-Owen 1998*a*)

Stoke Tunnel, Ipswich, Suffolk (Stuart 1979)

Sugworth, Oxfordshire (Stuart 1980; Holman 1987*a*, 1992*e*)

Sutton Courtenay, Oxfordshire (Gleed-Owen 1998*a*)

Swanton Morley, Norfolk (Stuart 1979; Holman 1987*c*)

Terrington St. Clement, Norfolk (Gleed-Owen 1998*a*)

Three Holes Cave, Torbryan, Devon (Gleed-Owen 1996, 1998*a*)

Tiddington, Warwickshire (Holman 1992*e*)

Torbryan Six Cave, Torbryan, Devon (Gleed-Owen 1998a)

Tornewton Cave, Devon (Holman 1990; Gleed-Owen 1996, 1998*a*)

Upton Warren, Worcestershire (Stuart 1982)

Walpole St. Andrew, Norfolk (Gleed-Owen 1998*a*)

Westbury Cave, Westbury-sub-Mendip, Somerset (Holman 1993*a*)

West Runton Freshwater Bed, Norfolk (Newton 1882*a, b*; Holman *et al.* 1988; Holman 1989)

West Walton, Norfolk (Gleed-Owen 1998*a*)

Whitemoor Channel, Bosley, Cheshire (Johnson *et al.* 1970; Holman & Stuart 1991; Gleed-Owen 1997*a*, 1998*a*)

Wookey Hole, nr. Wells, Somerset (Gleed-Owen 1998*a*)

Rana temporaria, slow-worm *Anguis fragilis*, grass snake *Natrix natrix* and adder *Vipera berus* (Newton 1882a, b; Holman et al. 1988; Holman 1989). Newton's (1882a, b) identification of great crested newt *Triturus cristatus* is very probably incorrect, and the identification of *V. berus* is less than certain as the original material cannot be traced (Holman et al. 1988). Sparse small vertebrate material from Sugworth, Oxfordshire, included *R. arvalis* and an indeterminite salamandrid (Holman 1987a), and grass snake 'cf. *N. natrix*' (Stuart 1980). Lister et al. (1990) described a herpetofauna from deposits at Little Oakley, Essex, with *R. arvalis, Rana* sp./*Bufo* sp., *Emys orbicularis* and *N. natrix*. Stuart (1979) recorded a carapacial fragment of *E. orbicularis* from Westbury Cave, Somerset, and a full herpetofaunal assemblage was later given by Holman (1993a), with parsley frog *Pelodytes punctatus, R. temporaria, E. orbicularis, A. fragilis*, smooth snake *Coronella austriaca, N. natrix* and *V. berus*. The complex stratigraphical scheme adopted by Bishop (1982) was re-evaluated by Stringer et al. (1996), but there are no changes to units containing herpetofaunal remains. The assemblage described by Holman (1993a) from Westbury actually comes from two distinct levels. The first, which I shall call the 'lower herpetofaun', is from Bed 8 of Bishop (1982), i.e. his 'Fauna 2'; this consists only of *C. austriaca* and *E. orbicularis*. The second 'upper herpetofauna' from Beds 11–15 contains the remaining species, with no species common to both assemblages. Both herpetofaunas are from the Calcareous Group and, on mammalian biostratigraphical grounds, must post-date the West Runton Freshwater Bed (Bishop 1982; Stringer et al. 1996). Stringer et al. (1996) referred to Bishop's (1982) 'Beds' as 'Units' and this scheme will be adopted here.

Holman (1992a) described a diverse herpetofauna from Boxgrove, West Sussex, with smooth newt *T. vulgaris, T. helveticus* or *T. vulgaris*, spadefoot toad *Pelobates fuscus, B. bufo, Bufo calamita, R. arvalis, R. temporaria, A. fragilis*, common lizard *L.* cf. *vivipara* and *N. natrix*. All of the material came from Units 4–6 and mostly from Unit 4c (Slindon Silts), a terrestrial phase overlying the marine Slindon Sands (Roberts et al. 1986; Holman 1992a). Recent re-examination of this material has shown some of Holman's identifications to be incorrect (Gleed-Owen 1998a). It is intended that full systematic descriptions will be published elsewhere as soon as possible, but the taxonomic changes are briefly listed here. The record of *T. vulgaris* from marine Unit 4b (Holman 1992a) is in fact *Triturus alpestris*, the first British fossil

record for this species (Gleed-Owen 1998a). One of the *T. vulgaris/helveticus* vertebrae is *T.* cf. *alpestris*, but the others are best regarded as *Triturus* sp. *P. fuscus* is probably correctly reported from Unit 4c, but the bone reported from Unit 6a is *B. calamita*. A vertebra described as *L.* cf. *vivipara* is a misidentified caudal vertebra of *A. fragilis*, and this lizard should be removed from the species list. None of the fragmentary snake remains assigned to *N. natrix* by Holman (1992a) belong to this species. Those which are identifiable belong to *V. berus* or *Vipera* cf. *berus*. The others ought to be classed as Ophidia indet. These are significant changes and the revised herpetofaunal list from Boxgrove should be as follows: *T. alpestris, P. fuscus, B. bufo, B. calamita, R. temporaria, R. arvalis, A. fragilis* and *V. berus* (Gleed-Owen 1998a).

Biostratigraphy and palaeoclimate

The herpetofaunas from West Runton and Sugworth indicate a well vegetated, fully interglacial environment, with no evidence that summer temperatures were any warmer than today in southern Britain. Six of the eight taxa are native to Britain today, though *R. arvalis* and edible or marsh frog *R. esculenta* or *ridibunda* are not. The Sugworth fish fauna is consistent with that of West Runton (Stuart 1982), and strong molluscan and mammalian evidence suggests correlation of these two sites (Meijer & Preece 1996; Stuart et al. 1993). The small mammal fauna at Sugworth is more indicative of a forested environment than at West Runton, but this could reflect regional biogeographical differences (Stuart 1982) and would help to explain the impoverished herpetofauna at Sugworth. The presence of *Mimomys savini* at both sites suggests an age early in the 'Cromerian Complex' (Meijer & Preece 1996). These herpetofaunas cannot be firmly correlated with each other but they certainly differ from other EMP herpetofaunas.

Westbury-sub-Mendip, Little Oakley and Boxgrove are largely distinct in herpetofaunal character from the West Runton and Sugworth faunas. Both Little Oakley and the Westbury lower herpetofauna have *E. orbicularis* and Westbury also has *C. austriaca*. Neither species is present at West Runton or Sugworth and both are notable thermophiles. *E. orbicularis* indicates summer temperatures of at least 18°C, and probably as high as 20°C for breeding to be successful (Degerbøl & Krog 1951). *C. austriaca* is Britain's rarest reptile today, being restricted to a small area of southern England. *E. orbicularis* is found only in continental Europe where its range represents a great reduction from its greatest extent during the Holocene thermal maximum. The absence of frogs or any amphibians from these herpetofaunas, and the lack of other species such as *A. fragilis* and *N. natrix* which are typical of fully interglacial assemblages, is remarkable. This is particularly so for the Westbury lower herpetofauna as anuran remains normally make up the bulk of herpetofaunal assemblages from caves. Their absence could be taphonomic, but given that this is the only Pleistocene record of *C. austriaca*, such an explanation would require special pleading. The reptile faunas reflect warm interglacial conditions for Westbury Bed 8 and Little Oakley and these sites could justifiably be considered correlatives.

The upper herpetofauna at Westbury (Units 11–15) is separated stratigraphically from the lower one by deposits which produced no herpetofaunal remains and were interpreted as representing the onset of cold conditions (Bishop 1982). This upper herpetofauna must represent a subsequent interglacial, and might be of the same age as Boxgrove Unit 4c (Bishop 1982; Stringer *et al.* 1996). Moreover, Currant (1989) grouped the mammal fauna of the Westbury 'pink breccia' (Unit 11) with that of Boxgrove Unit 4c in his 'Group 4 assemblages'. Most of the herpetofaunal species from the Westbury upper and Boxgrove herpetofaunas are distributed throughout southern Britain today. However, the records of *Pelodytes punctatus* (Westbury) and *Pelobates fuscus* (Boxgrove) are unique in the British Pleistocene, and neither species is present in Britain today. Furthermore, the Boxgrove and Westbury upper herpetofaunas are distinct from the subsequent Barnham-type assemblages by their lack of *Hyla* and *E. longissima*.

P. punctatus has a western continental European range, reaching north to the English Channel and eastwards no further than the French-Belgian border, the Swiss border and coastal northwest Italy (Gasc *et al.* 1997). *P. punctatus* is only found in Units 11 and 13 at Westbury and is absent from Units 14 and 15 when other temperate species were still present. *P. fuscus* from Boxgrove, on the other hand, has an eastern distribution and does not overlap with the range of *P. punctatus*. *R. arvalis* has an identical western limit to *P. fuscus*, in Belgium and at the French-German border, and is associated with increasingly continental climates in the south of its range. All three species almost meet around the border of France with Belgium, Luxembourg and Germany (Gasc *et al.* 1997), and a climatic analogy with this region is most

appropriate for Westbury (upper) and Boxgrove. The geographical divide between Somerset and West Sussex during the EMP could represent the gap between the range of *P. punctatus* and the ranges of *P. fuscus* and *R. arvalis* today. This could be used to give accurate regional climatic reconstructions of northeasternmost France for Westbury and northern Belgium for Boxgrove. However, although *T. alpestris*, *P. fuscus* and *R. arvalis* are exotic to Britain today, this is largely due to our separation from the continent. Certainly, if the southern North Sea floor were exposed today, these three species would be expected to live there, and an exact terrestrial analogy for the Boxgrove fauna may not exist today. It is also interesting to note that Meijer & Preece (1996) recorded the humid woodland obligate land-snail *Spermodea lamellata* from Unit 4c at Boxgrove. It is restricted to the northern and western British Isles and southern Scandinavia, with a few relict enclaves in coastal parts of Germany and The Netherlands (Kerney & Cameron 1979). Woodland clearance has perhaps reduced it to relict populations in the south, but it is clearly also intolerant to excessive warmth. Its presence at Boxgrove therefore confirms an oceanic climate for Unit 4c, fitting well with the north Belgian herpetofaunal analogy, but perhaps even with a summer climate no warmer than southeast England today, and maybe even a degree or so lower.

The earliest herpetofaunal indications of temperate conditions at Boxgrove are given by *A. fragilis* (Unit 4a) and *T. alpestris* (Unit 4b) in the regressive marine phase (Upper Slindon Sand), preceding deposition of Unit 4c. If Unit 11 at Westbury is believed to represent the climatic optimum of an interglacial (Stringer *et al.* 1996), and Boxgrove Unit 4c is of the same age, then it also represents optimum conditions. The subsequent absence of *P. punctatus* from Units 14 and 15 at Westbury, whilst other temperate indicators persisted, may reflect increased continentality during a post-optimum stage. The same picture would also be expected at Boxgrove, from units laid down after the thermal optimum of Unit 4c. Indeed, *B. calamita* (Unit 6a) and *A. fragilis* (Units 5a, 5b and 6) indicate at least phases of continued temperate conditions throughout the terrestrial sequence, though both species could tolerate marked continentality. *B. calamita* is a thermophile, with its distribution in Britain and Sweden closely matching the 15°C July isotherm, and reaching as far east as Belorus and northern Ukraine. *A. fragilis* has its northern limit very similar to the sinuous 13°C isotherm in northern Europe and reaches eastwards into central Asia.

Late Middle Pleistocene

Pre-Oxygen Isotope Stage 7 sites

Cudmore Grove, Essex, has produced the largest herpetofauna yet recorded from Britain: *T. cristatus, T. vulgaris, B. bufo, Hyla* sp., *R. arvalis, R. ridibunda* or *R. esculenta, R. lessonae, E. orbicularis, Lacerta* sp., *A. fragilis, E. longissima, N. natrix, N. maura* or *N. tessellata* and *V. berus*. The assemblage came from the largely freshwater Bed 3 of Bridgland *et al.* (1988). Seven of the 14 species are exotic to Britain today. Ashton *et al.* (1994) gave a similarly diverse herpetofaunal list from Barnham, Suffolk: *T. cristatus, T. vulgaris, T. helveticus, B. bufo, B. calamita, H. arborea, R. temporaria, R. arvalis, E. orbicularis, A. fragilis, E. longissima* and *N. natrix*. Holman (1994) identified a small herpetofauna from Beeches Pit, West Stow, Suffolk, with *Triturus* sp., *Rana* sp., *A. fragilis* and most notably *E. longissima*. Some herpetofaunal remains were also recovered from Dierden's Pit, Ingress Vale (close to Barnfield Pit, Swanscombe), Kent. These consist of *E. orbicularis* (Stuart 1979), undetermined frog or toad remains (Stuart 1982) and *N. natrix* (Holman 1987*b*). The amphibian remains from Ingress Vale are as yet unidentified and further examination would be useful. The herpetofaunas from these sites have obvious affinities which are discussed below. Hoxne, Suffolk, has produced only a small herpetofauna with *B. bufo* and *N. natrix* (Holman 1993*b*; Stuart *et al.* 1993). From Purfleet (Essex), Holman & Clayden (1988) and Holman (1995*b*) listed *T. cristatus, B. bufo, R. arvalis, R. temporaria, A. fragilis* and *N.* cf. *natrix*. Holman (1987*b*) identified *B. bufo* from an unspecified location at Barnfield Pit, Swanscombe, but no other taxa are known from this site at present.

Biostratigraphy and palaeoclimate

The Late Middle Pleistocene (LMP) herpetofaunal assemblages found so far from pre-Stage 7 sites could arguably be separated into two groups, although these are not incompatible with one another. Admittedly, the validity of the second group rests upon an absence of evidence, and highlights the need for more material from these and similar sites to be studied.

The first group is represented by Cudmore Grove, Barnham, West Stow and Ingress Vale. The herpetofaunas from these sites contain several particularly thermophilous southern European species as well as more northerly exotics. The most notable aspect of these herpetofaunas is the inclusion of *E. longissima* which is found at Cudmore Grove, Barnham and West Stow. These are the only records of this species from Britain to date, perhaps implying correlation of these sites and certainly allowing their distinction from older sites such as Boxgrove and Westbury, and from Stage 7 sites. Ingress Vale has no *E. longissima*, but it does have *E. orbicularis*. Since *E. orbicularis* is found at Cudmore Grove, but not at Barnham and West Stow, this allows a tentative correlation of Ingress Vale with Cudmore Grove. Also of note, *Hyla* is found at Barnham and Cudmore Grove, yet its only other British record is from Stage 7 deposits at Itteringham, Norfolk (Hallock *et al.* 1990; Holman 1992*b*).

The second group is represented only by Hoxne and Purfleet. The herpetofaunas recovered from these sites are less diverse, with only one exotic species (*R. arvalis*) and no southern thermophiles. However, as all of the species from Hoxne and Purfleet are also found at Barnham, and only *R. temporaria* is missing from Cudmore Grove, it is difficult to draw too many conclusions. There may well be taphonomic or zoogeographic reasons for the absence of the major thermophiles from Hoxne and Purfleet, especially as the material recovered so far is relatively sparse. Consequently, the separation of Hoxne and Purfleet from Barnham, Cudmore Grove, West Stow and Ingress Vale on herpetological grounds could be invalid. Nevertheless, the Hoxne and Purfleet herpetofaunas ostensibly imply a climate no different to that of northern England today. None of the recorded species is particularly thermophilous, although the presence of *T. cristatus, A. fragilis* and *N. natrix* indicates a well vegetated temperate environment.

Despite various attempts at chronostratigraphic schemes, the problem of allocating relative age(s) and position(s) in the deep sea Oxygen Isotope record for these sites has remained unresolved. The traditional placing of sites attributed to the Hoxnian in one interglacial at Stage 9 has been widely rejected, and the inability of palynology to separate temperate stages in this part of the Pleistocene is now widely recognized. Schreve (1998) has constructed a chronostratigraphic scheme, based upon mammalian biostratigraphy, which contradicts the herpetofaunal scheme suggested above. She firmly places Barnham, West Stow, Ingress Vale, Hoxne, Swanscombe and Clacton at Stage 11, with Purfleet and Cudmore Grove at Stage 9. Currant (1989) had already tentatively grouped the Hoxne and Swanscombe mammal faunas in his 'Group 3 assemblages', and Stuart *et al.* (1993) proposed the same correlation. Furthermore, the aminostratigraphies of Bowen *et al.* (1989) and Bowen (1992) appear to provide a framework which is both consistent with the oceanic record and in agreement with Schreve's (1998) scheme. Amino acid ratios on non-marine molluscs from Barnham gave values comparable to those at Swanscombe, suggesting that the deposits dated to Stage 11, around 400 000 years ago (Bowen *et al.* 1989; Ashton *et al.* 1994). Bridgland *et al.* (1995) believed that correlation of Purfleet with the Barnham group was stratigraphically unlikely. Furthermore, they noted that water vole *Arvicola terrestris cantiana* teeth from Purfleet were intermediate between those from Swanscombe and Hoxne, and those from Ipswichian sites.

Thus, it is possible that the two herpetofaunal groupings suggested above are incorrect, and Schreve's (1998) scheme will be accepted for the purposes of this paper. The Stage 11 herpetofaunas (Barnham, West Stow, Ingress Vale, Swanscombe and Hoxne) and the Stage 9 herpetofaunas (Cudmore Grove and Purfleet) are certainly compatible, but demonstrate some notable differences. The diversity of species at Cudmore Grove is outstanding, with three southern thermophiles (compared to one at Barnham, Ingress Vale and West Stow), although this does not suggest a difference in July temperature. This appears to be in contrast with Schreve's (1998) assertion that Stage 9 mammal faunas are somewhat less diverse than Stage 11 mammal faunas.

Palaeotemperature

By comparison with modern range characteristics, some palaeoclimatic reconstructions can be postulated. According to the most thermophilous species (*E. orbicularis, E. longissima* and *N. maura* or *N. tessellata*), July temperatures during both Stages 9 and 11 must have been greater than in southern Britain today, probably by 2 or 3°C. This is in keeping with the presence of particularly thermophilous elements such as the mollusc *Corbicula fluminalis* and barbary macaque *Macaca sylvanus* at Cudmore Grove and Purfleet (Bridgland *et al.* 1988; D. H. Keen pers. comm. 1998; Schreve, 1998).

Oceanicity vs continentality

By comparing modern areas of sympatry between species, suggestions for the most suitable modern analogues might also be sug-

gested. This is clearly a deterministic approach which assumes constancy of environmental tolerances since the LMP. Also, these ideas may well change as more material becomes available in the future.

The Stage 11 herpetofaunas imply a climate which is not oceanic, continental or Mediterranean, but an average of all three. According to modern distribution maps (Gasc *et al.* 1997), the Barnham assemblage does not appear to have an exact modern analogue. The northwestern *T. helveticus*, the eastern *R. arvalis* and the southern *E. longissima* almost meet in the region of the Swiss-Austrian-Italian borders, but it is uncertain if they are sympatric anywhere in that region today. The topographic effects of the Alps are probably important in determining distributions (*R. arvalis* appears to be restricted to lower altitudes in the Alps and *E. longissima* does not penetrate north farther than the lower Italian Alps). Nevertheless, the modern climate of that region ought to be a fair approximation of the Stage 11 palaeoclimate, as indicated by the Barnham herpetofauna. The herpetofaunas from West Stow, Swanscombe, Ingress Vale and Hoxne are compatible with this reconstruction.

Stage 9 herpetofaunas imply a more continental climatic analogue, mainly through the absence of the western *T. helveticus*. Holman *et al.* (1990) postulated that the exotic snake species from Cudmore Grove imply 'mild winter temperatures as well as high summer temperatures'. This is not necessarily so, as *E. longissima* and *N. tessellata* are distributed throughout most of eastern Europe where they experience fully continental winters. Furthermore, the presence of *R. arvalis* in association with the thermophilous taxa at Cudmore Grove implies a more continental climate than if it was absent from the fauna. Therefore it is most likely that the eastern-ranging *N. tessellata* is present at Cudmore Grove, rather than the western *N. maura*. Holman *et al.* (1990) concluded that the herpetofaunal evidence mostly supported an oceanic interpretation of climate, yet suggested a modern analogue of central or southern France. Holman (1993*c*) later suggested that the nearest modern analogue for the Cudmore Grove herpetofauna would be Trieste in northern Italy. In fact, based on the modern ranges of the species identified (Gasc *et al.* 1997), the nearest analogue would be around the southeast German border with northeast Austria and western Czech Republic. West (1980) argued that, palynologically, the Hoxnian in East Anglia showed 'greater oceanicity' than the subsequent (Ipswichian) interglacial. Therefore, as H. Roe (pers. comm. to Holman *et al.* 1990) reported

that Cudmore Grove is palynologically 'Hoxnian', Holman *et al.* perhaps were influenced in
their interpretation by West's view. The herpetofauna from Cudmore Grove does not indicate
an oceanic or Mediterranean climate; in fact it is
distinctly continental. The most appropriate
modern climatic analogue would be eastern
central Europe, for example the Czech Republic,
with warmer summer temperatures than in
southern Britain today, but quite likely with
colder winters. If Schreve's (1998) placing of
Cudmore Grove at Stage 9 is correct, then the
above is a fair palaeoclimatic reconstruction for
this episode.

Oxygen Isotope Stage 7 sites

Stuart (1979) recorded *E. orbicularis* from Selsey,
West Sussex. From the same site, Holman
(1992c) listed *B. bufo, B. calamita, Rana* sp. and
N. natrix. Stoke Tunnel, Ipswich, and Harkstead, both in Suffolk, have also produced
E. orbicularis (Stuart 1979). Itteringham in Norfolk has produced the largest Stage 7 herpetofauna with *B. bufo,* stripeless tree frog *Hyla
meridionalis,* marsh or edible frog *R. ridibunda* or
R. esculenta, R. temporaria, E. orbicularis and
N. natrix (Hallock *et al.* 1990; Holman 1992b).
Stanton Harcourt, Oxfordshire, has produced
sparse herpetofaunal remains of *T. vulgaris*
or *T. helveticus, R. temporaria* and *R. arvalis* or
dalmatina. The lower channel at Marsworth in
Buckinghamshire has so far produced only
fragmentary remains of a brown frog *Rana* sp.
(Gleed-Owen 1998a) and the Otter Stratum of
Tornewton Cave, Devon, has yielded a few
indeterminate toad *Bufo* sp. and frog *Rana* sp.
(Gleed-Owen 1996).

There is some contention over the age of the
Itteringham deposit. Hallock *et al.* (1990)
tentatively assigned it on stratigraphic grounds
to an Ipswichian age, but Currant (1989, 1996) is
convinced that its mammalian biostratigraphy
places it firmly in Stage 7. Lithostratigraphic,
mammalian and molluscan biostratigraphic evidence also convincingly suggests that Harkstead,
Stoke Tunnel, Selsey and Stanton Harcourt
belong to a Stage 7 interglacial (Wymer 1985;
Allen *et al.* 1996; Buckingham *et al.* 1996).

The occurrence of *H. meridionalis* at Itteringham is the only record of this species from
Britain. It has a disjunct southwest European
range, reaching somewhere between the Gironde
and the Loire, though its northern limit is
uncertain (García París 1997). Its presence at
Itteringham demands a summer temperature
2–3°C higher than today and an oceanic climate.

Unfortunately, the difficulty of identifying *Hyla*
remains specifically means that this record
should be regarded as provisional. Nevertheless,
the notable absence of *R. arvalis* from Itterng-
ham supports an oceanic climatic interpretation.
Harkstead, Stoke Tunnel, Selsey and Itteringham all have *E. orbicularis* which ranges across
Iberia and southern France and is in keeping
with a warm oceanic reconstruction. Herpetofaunal remains other than *Emys* were not recovered from Harkstead or Stoke Tunnel. The
thermophilous nature of these herpetofaunas is
in contrast with the impoverished and sparse
material recovered from some Stage 7 sites.
For example, Stanton Harcourt has *R. temporaria* and moor frog or agile frog *R. arvalis*
or *R. dalmatina,* but no notable thermophiles
(Gleed-Owen 1998a). Likewise, Marsworth and
Tornewton Cave Otter Stratum lack thermophiles though this could be taphonomic. It is
possible that the Itteringham-type thermophilous herpetofaunas date to a warmer (earlier?)
part of Stage 7 (as suggested by Schreve 1998),
and that the Stanton Harcourt-type sites represent a less warm (later?) phase.

Ipswichian Interglacial (Substage 5e)

Four sites with herpetofaunal remains of this age
have been published. Holman (1996) claimed
that eight Ipswichian herpetofaunas had been
described, but included several sites which are
actually Stage 7 (Selsey, Itteringham, Stoke
Tunnel and Harkstead; see above). *E. orbicularis* was recorded from Mundesley in Norfolk
(Newton 1879; Stuart 1979) and Bobbitshole,
Ipswich in Suffolk (Stuart 1979). Holman (1987c)
identified *B. bufo, R. temporaria, R. arvalis,
E. orbicularis* and *N. natrix* from Swanton
Morley, Norfolk. Palynological evidence from
Swanton Morley and Mundesley places these
faunas in Ipswichian subzones Ip Ib–IIb (Stuart
1979; Coxon *et al.* 1980). At Shropham in
Norfolk, Holman & Clayden (1990) recorded
T. vulgaris, B. bufo, R. temporaria, R. arvalis,
indeterminate green frog *R. ridibunda, R. lessonae* or *R. esculenta, E. orbicularis,* cf. *L. vivipara*
and *N. maura* or *N. tessellata.* Holman (1996)
added *B. bufo* and *B. calamita* to the list, but
the current author has some doubts about the
latter record.

All of these herpetofaunas have *E. orbicularis*
and are compatible with each other. *N. maura*
or *N. tessellata* has also been identified from
Ipswichian deposits at Deeping St James, Norfolk, alongside *B. bufo* and *Rana* sp. (Gleed-
Owen 1998a).

As is true of the Barnham-type faunas, the sympatry of *R. arvalis* with thermophiles such as *N. maura* or *N. tessellata* infers continentality. Hence, the most suitable palaeoclimatic reconstruction for the last interglacial would be a fairly continental climate with summers at least 2–3°C warmer than southern Britain today but possibly with colder winters. A modern analogue of southern Germany or the Czech Republic might be appropriate. Alternatively, a more southerly Mediterranean climate than this (as suggested by palynological, molluscan and mammalian evidence from Ipswichian sites) would still be in keeping with the herpetofaunal reconstruction, but the presence of *R. arvalis* would shift the modern analogue still further eastwards. In biostratigraphic terms, the presence of *N. maura* or *N. tessellata* may be of value in distinguishing Substage 5e sites from Stage 7 sites.

Post-Ipswichian Oxygen Isotope Stage 5 and Middle Devensian

The Greenland and Antarctic ice core records (Grootes *et al.* 1993; Bender *et al.* 1994) and North Atlantic deep-ocean records (Adkins *et al.* 1997) demonstrate a series of rapidly superimposed interstadials occurring for much of the period 100–40 ka BP. This makes correlation of individual events very difficult, and the importance of biostratigraphy is heightened. Though not as warm as the preceding Ipswichian, later temperate substages during Stage 5 may have been as warm as the current interglacial. Adkins *et al.* (1997) showed how the nature of terminations could be very rapid, perhaps within 400 years, thus it may be expected that thermophilous faunas and floras from post-Ipswichian interstadials would have been repeatedly wiped out. This would have meant renewed immigration of thermophiles in each interstadial, thus offering scope for biostratigraphically useful differences in faunal character.

Later Oxygen Isotope Stage 5 herpetofaunas

Herpetofaunal remains are little-known from these periods and anuran material recently identified from Cassington, Oxfordshire, and the Hyaena Stratum at Tornewton Cave, Devon, provide important new data on later Stage 5 and Middle Devensian anuran faunas. The herpetofaunal assemblage from Tornewton Cave Hyaena Stratum is the largest from a Stage 5 interstadial, with *B. bufo, B. calamita, R. temporaria,* cf. *L. vivipara, A. fragilis* and

Natrix sp. (Gleed-Owen 1996, 1998*a*). Stage 5 interstadial sediments at Cassington produced *B. bufo, R. temporaria* and indeterminate green frog *Rana ridibunda, R. lessonae* or *R. esculenta* (Gleed-Owen 1998*b*; Parfitt in Maddy *et al.* 1998). Shropham 'Pocket 2' produced *R. temporaria* and *N. natrix* (Holman 1992*d*, 1996).

Palaeoclimate and relative ages

From the present northern limits of green frogs in Scandinavia and Russia, the green frog from Cassington implies a mean July temperature of at least 16°C and probably higher. From coleopteran evidence at Cassington, Maddy *et al.* (1998) suggested a summer temperature of 17–18°C. This is in keeping with the herpetofaunal reconstruction. Both the green frog and *N. natrix* would require a long enough period of summer warmth for development of larvae and incubation of eggs respectively (longer than *B. calamita* would require). These species are also more associated with well vegetated ponds and lush meadows than with the sparse, open heath typically preferred by *B. calamita*. It is notable that whilst these herpetofaunas indicate temperatures perhaps as warm as southern Britain today, they lack the most thermophilous elements of the Ipswichian herpetofaunas. Bowen (in Maddy *et al.* 1998) obtained amino acid ratios from Cassington molluscs which indicated an age intermediate between Ipswichian (Substage 5e) and Upton Warren Interstadial ratios. Maddy *et al.* (1998) excluded correlation with the Chelford Interstadial at Substage 5c, and defined a new 'Cassington Interstadial' at Substage 5a. The Tornewton Cave assemblage is believed to date to a post-Ipswichian part of Stage 5 on stratigraphic and mammalian biostratigraphic grounds (Currant 1996; Currant & Jacobi 1997). The record of *B. calamita* from Tornewton Cave Hyaena Stratum infers a mean July temperature of at least 15°C at some time during deposition. The entire stratum was probably deposited over a considerable period of time (Currant 1996), and its herpetofauna could be placed in either Substage 5c or 5a. Correlation with Cassington, Shropham Pocket 2 or the Chelford Interstadial is possible but cannot be proved at present.

Oxygen Isotope Stage 3 (Upton Warren Interstadial) herpetofaunas

Sutton Courtenay (Oxfordshire), Wookey Hole (Somerset) and Upton Warren (Worcestershire)

have produced herpetofaunal remains of Middle Devensian age. A single bone of *B. calamita* is the only herpetofaunal evidence known from Sutton Courtenay (Gleed-Owen 1998*a*). This is taphonomically unusual as *R. temporaria* is almost always the most frequently found amphibian species in fossil assemblages. The Wookey Hole Hyaena Den also produced *B. calamita* as well as *R. temporaria* (Gleed-Owen 1998a). By their stratigraphic position and overlying mammal faunas, it is believed that these sites correlate with the Middle Devensian Upton Warren Interstadial Complex (UWIC). Herpetofaunal remains from the Upton Warren type-site have not been examined recently but Stuart (1982) recorded *R. temporaria*.

Palaeoclimate and age

The *B. calamita* finds at Wookey and Sutton Courtenay offer a reconstruction of at least 15°C for July temperatures. This ties in well with coleopteran data for the initial thermal optimum of the UWIC (Coope *et al.* 1997). Mutual climatic range (MCR) analyses produced a July temperature (TMax) of 15°C for the period 43–42 ka ^{14}C years BP, with a possible ceiling of 20°C at 43 ka ^{14}C years BP (Coope 1987). TMax before and after this period was no more than 12°C which would be inhospitable to *B. calamita*. Clearly, therefore, the occurrence of *B. calamita* at Sutton Courtenay and Wookey Hole can be tied very firmly to the short period at the beginning of the UWIC, and corroborates Coope's (1977, 1987) thermal reconstruction for this time. In Britain, *B. calamita* is today confined to coastal dunes, heaths and salt-marshes. It is a capable pioneer in newly available habitats (Boomsma & Arntzen 1985) but is soon forced out by vegetation succession and competition with *B. bufo* (T. Beebee pers. comm. 1997). This makes it an excellent and accurate marker of rapid climatic amelioration events. It also requires well drained sandy soils in which to hibernate. As Sutton Courtenay and Wookey Hole are not coastal locations, the records imply a prevalence of open grassland or heath in order for *B. calamita* to immigrate there. The absence of species such as *A. fragilis* and *N. natrix* from these faunas supports the view that stable interglacial conditions were not reached in the UWIC. Bowen *et al.* (1989) placed the UWIC at Substage 5a, but Coope *et al.* (1997) and Currant & Jacobi (1997) suggested a Stage 3 age. A sharp warm peak in the ice core curves (Jouzel *et al.* 1989), dated by annual layer counting to around 40 ka BP, could certainly accommo-

date the Upton Warren Interstadial, and would accord with traditional radiocarbon ages (e.g. Coope 1977). Even if radiocarbon ages of this magnitude are believed to be spurious, it is not easy to explain their remarkably consistent grouping around the 43–40 ka BP mark.

Devensian Lateglacial and Holocene

Rapid warmings during the Devensian Lateglacial and early Holocene are evidenced at a number of sites in southwest Britain by the presence of *B. calamita*. Its remains have been recorded in deposits at Broken Cavern, Torbryan, Devon (Gleed-Owen 1996, 1997*a*, 1998*a*), Cow Cave, Devon (Holman 1988), Kent's Cavern, Devon (Gleed-Owen, 1998*a*), Hoyle's Mouth and Potter's Cave, Pembrokeshire (Gleed-Owen 1997*b*, 1998*a*), Denny's Hole, Somerset (Gleed-Owen 1998*a*), Rogers' Cave, Herefordshire (Gleed-Owen 1998*a*) and Ightham fissure, Kent (Holman 1985). AMS radiocarbon assays demonstrate a Lateglacial presence at Broken Cavern and an early Holocene presence at Kent's Cavern and Cow Cave; none of the other sites have been dated. Recent re-examination by the current author has shown that an early Holocene record of *B. calamita* from Bosley, Cheshire (Holman & Stuart 1991) was misidentified (Gleed-Owen 1997*a*, 1998*a*). The bones actually belong to *B. bufo*, as originally identified by Stuart and reported by Johnson *et al.* (1970). A further Holocene record from Anglesey (Pumphrey 1956) cannot be checked as the remains have been lost, and a record from Carrowmore, County Sligo, Ireland (Ove & Persson 1980) is not *B. calamita* but *R. temporaria* (Gleed-Owen, unpublished notes). Newton (1917) tentatively identified *B. calamita* from the Creag nan Uamh caves of northwest Sutherland, but it is highly improbable that *B. calamita* could have reached that far north during the Holocene. Also, out of the many hundreds of toad bones seen recently from these caves, only *B. bufo* has been found and it is likely that Newton was mistaken in his identification (Gleed-Owen 1998a).

Two AMS radiocarbon assays on *B. calamita* from Broken Cavern seem to constrain the coldest part of the Younger Dryas to a period of less than 500 years (Gleed-Owen 1998*a*). One age of $10\,850 \pm 90$ ^{14}C years BP (OxA-6991) appears to fall just before the start of the Younger Dryas, though admittedly a two-sigma deviation allows a date of $11\,030$ ^{14}C years BP. Another date of $10\,420 \pm 120$ ^{14}C years BP (OxA-6993) suggests a marked amelioration in summer climate by this time, though again the true age could be as young as 10 180 ^{14}C years BP. Calibrated versions, calculated using CALIB 3.0 (Stuiver & Reimer 1993), are 12 775 cal BP and 12 323 cal BP, respectively. These data compare well with MCR beetle climates for this part of the Late-glacial (Atkinson et al. 1987), and indicate that July temperatures had returned to at least 15°C before the start of the Holocene, in the second half of the Younger Dryas. Multiproxy evidence draws the same conclusion that the second half of the Younger Dryas was significantly warmer than the first (Isarin 1997). As B. calamita could not have survived the periglacial conditions experienced during much of the Younger Dryas, it must have become extinct in Britain and then immigrated a second time. Evidently, a reasonably direct land-bridge must also have been present to enable such a fast re-immigration into southwest England. The presence of B. calamita in Britain two to four centuries before the accepted start of the Holocene suggests that summer temperatures had risen significantly by then, and it was probably only an amelioration in winter temperatures that marked the subsequent onset of the Pre-Boreal.

Remains of E. orbicularis found in Holocene peats at East Wretham in Norfolk (Newton 1862; Stuart 1979) demonstrate that whilst today's climate could not support E. orbicularis, the Holocene thermal optimum was probably 2°C warmer in East Anglia. Associated pollen spectra suggest a tentative correlation to Holocene pollen subzone VIIa, i.e. the Atlantic period (Hall in Stuart 1979). Abundant remains (several hundred individuals) have also been found in Holocene deposits in southern Sweden, the Netherlands, Denmark and northern Germany (Isberg 1929; Degerbøl & Krog 1951; Peters 1977; Podloucky 1997). Comprehensive dating shows that most E. orbicularis lived during the Boreal with some persisting into the Atlantic period (Degerbøl & Krog 1951). During the Sub-Boreal period (pollen zone VIIb), climate was rather continental with sunnier summers than today (Degerbøl & Krog 1951). The range of E. orbicularis therefore appears to have reached its maximum extent during the early and middle Holocene, and has since receded due to a worsening summer climate (Podloucky 1997). However, the youngest Danish remains are in association with Iron Age human and domestic animal skeletons dating from c. 2700 BP. Summer temperatures had declined significantly and summer rainfall had increased by this time (Frenzel 1966), factors which undoubtedly caused the final extinction of E. orbicularis in northern areas. The

modern range characteristics of some other herpetofaunal species (Gasc et al. 1997), e.g. R. dalmatina, Lacerta viridis, E. longissima and N. tessellata, imply similar reductions from maximum ranges since the Holocene climatic optimum.

Finally, it is worth mentioning that remains of R. arvalis, R. arvalis or dalmatina, and R. lessonae have recently been identified from a Middle Saxon occupation site near Gosberton, Lincolnshire (Gleed-Owen 1998a). For more than a hundred years there has been debate over whether R. lessonae might have been overlooked as a native species (evidence summarized by Snell 1994). Even if it was native (and not introduced), R. lessonae has recently become extinct. Interestingly, its last known site was less than 5 km from the E. orbicularis site at East Wretham. There are no extant R. dalmatina and/or R. arvalis in Britain today, and these frogs must have become extinct since Middle Saxon times. Clearly the Holocene herpetofauna is not as impoverished as previously thought, and although only 12 species are accepted as native today, formerly at least three additional species lived in Fenland. This is not altogether surprising considering that other southern-ranging taxa such as Dalmatian pelican Pelecanus crispus were present there in middle to late Holocene times (Forbes et al. 1958; Stuart 1974).

Conclusions

Relative to other animal groups, the volume of published knowledge on Quaternary herpetofaunas is limited, yet the proxy information which can be drawn from this is proportionately greater than has been previously realized. Fossil herpetofaunal remains can provide valuable data on the temperature and climatic character (continentality vs oceanicity) of Pleistocene temperate stages and can be of value in correlating sites and distinguishing between stages.

In the early Middle Pleistocene, the distinctly thermophilous E. orbicularis from Westbury-sub-Mendip lower units and Little Oakley distinguishes these sites from West Runton and Sugworth which have herpetofaunas which could live in southeast Britain today. The Boxgrove and upper Westbury herpetofaunas are faunally distinct from their predecessors, with the only British records of P. fuscus and P. punctatus. Thermophilous herpetofaunas from Barnham, West Stow and Cudmore Grove include the southern European E. longissima, and three of the seven exotic taxa at Cudmore Grove indicate a summer temperature at least 2–3°C warmer

than today. Based on Schreve's (1998) chronostratigraphic scheme for the late Middle Pleistocene, the herpetofaunal evidence suggests that
Stage 9 experienced a reasonably continental
climate, more so than Stage 11. The Stage 7
interglacial had *E. orbicularis* and *H. meridionalis*. The Ipswichian (Substage 5e) had *E. orbicularis* and the southern European *N. maura* or
N. tessellata. Interstadial faunas from later parts
of Stage 5 and from Stage 3 include relatively
thermophilous elements such as *B. calamita* and
N. natrix which are consistent with summer
temperatures as warm as today's. A number of
Devensian Lateglacial Interstadial and early
Holocene sites have also yielded *B. calamita*,
indicating a mean July temperature of at least
15°C. Radiocarbon assays indicate colonisation
by this cold-intolerant but open-ground species
during the Lateglacial Interstadial and apparently again in the second half of the Younger
Dryas. Remains of *E. orbicularis* from East Wretham testify to temperatures up to 2°C warmer
than today during the mid-Holocene thermal
optimum, and the remains of two other non-
native species, *R. arvalis* and *R. lessonae*, are
also known from the late Holocene. This
demonstrates that the British Holocene herpetofauna was formerly more diverse than it is
today, and was not especially different from
other interglacials. It also begs the question of
whether comparisons drawn between today's
biota ('late Holocene'?) and those of the thermal
maxima of previous interglacials are valid.

There is clearly a great deal of scope for future
work on fossil herpetofaunal remains from
Quaternary sites in the British Isles. In particular, it will be interesting to see how new data
enhance the existing picture and fill in some of
the gaps in the herpetostratigraphic sequence. It
is possible that additional species will be added
to the British Quaternary herpetofaunal list in
the future, but primarily, the study of new sites
(and further material from existing sites) will be
able to aid correlation and clarify useful
biostratigraphic indicator species. In particular
the analysis of herpetofaunal assemblages shows
a good deal of potential in the following areas:

(i)   palaeoenvironmental reconstruction and
      correlation of Middle Pleistocene intergla-
      cial sites;
(ii) the recognition and distinction of inter-
      stadials during later Stage 5 and the Early
      to Middle Devensian;
(iii) climatic changes during the Lateglacial
      and Holocene;
(iv) biogeography, land-bridges and coloniza-
      tion routes.

The author would like to thank D. H. Keen and A. P.
Currant for discussion and comments on an early draft
of this paper, and A. J. Stuart for helpful advice during
refereeing. The author's PhD studies were supported
financially by the School of Natural and Environ-
mental Sciences, Coventry University. Some of the
work was also supported by English Nature and the
Quaternary Research Association. Fossil herpetofau-
nal material was kindly made available by S. Aldhouse-
Green, C. Buckingham, S. Chapman, J. Clayden, A. P.
Currant, A. Gent, J. A. Holman, B. Irving, R. Jacobi,
P. Murphy, S. Parfitt, C. Price, C. Proctor, A. Roberts,
D. Schreve, K. Scott, A. J. Stuart, E. Walker and
M. Warren. Radiocarbon dates were funded by
NERC, and P. Pettitt at Oxford Accelerator Unit is
particularly acknowledged for his help.

References

ADKINS, J. F., BOYLE, E. A., KEIGWIN, LL. & CORTIJO,
    E. 1997. Variability of the North Atlantic thermo-
    haline circulation during the last interglacial
    period. *Nature*, **390**, 154–156.
ALLEN, L. G., GIBBARD, P. L., PETTIT, M. E., PREECE,
    R. C. & ROBINSON, E. 1996. Late Pleistocene inter-
    glacial deposits at Pennington Marshes, Lyming-
    ton, Hampshire, southern England. *Proceedings
    of the Geologists' Association*, **107**, 39–50.
ALLISON, J., GODWIN, H. & WARREN, S. H. 1952. Late-
    Glacial deposits at Nazeing in the Lea Valley,
    North London. *Philosophical Transactions of the
    Royal Society of London*, **B236**, 169–240.
ASHTON, N.M, BOWEN, D. Q., HOLMAN, J. A., HUNT,
    C. O., IRVING, B. G., KEMP, R. A., LEWIS, S. G.,
    McNABB, J., PARFITT, S. & SEDDON, M. B. 1994.
    Excavations at the Lower Palaeolithic site at East
    Farm, Barnham, Suffolk 1989–92. *Journal of the
    Geological Society of London*, **151**, 599–605.
ATKINSON, T. C., BRIFFA, K. R. & COOPE, G. R. 1987.
    Seasonal temperatures in Britain during the past
    22 000 years, reconstructed using beetle remains.
    Nature, **325**, 587–592.
BENDER, M., SOWERS, T., DICKSON, M-L., ORCH-
    ARDO, J., GROOTES, P., MAYEWSKI, P. A. &
    MEESE, D. A. 1994. Climate correlations between
    Greenland and Antarctica during the past 100,000
    years. *Nature*, **372**, 663–666.
BISHOP, M. J. 1982. *The mammal fauna of the early
    middle Pleistocene cavern infill site of Westbury-
    sub-Mendip, Somerset*. Special Papers in Palaeon-
    tology, **28**, Palaeontological Association, London,
    1–108.
BOOMSMA, J. J. & ARNTZEN, J. W. 1985. Abundance,
    growth and feeding of natterjack toads (*Bufo
    calamita*) in a 4-year-old artificial habitat. *Journal
    of Applied Ecology*, **22**, 395–405.
BOWEN, D. Q. 1992. Aminostratigraphy of non-marine
    Pleistocene mollusca in Southern Britain. *Sveriges
    Geologiska Undersökning*, **81**, 65–67.
——, HUGHES, S., SYKES, G. A. & MILLER, G. H.
    1989. Land–sea correlations in the Pleistocene
    based on isoleucine epimerization in non-marine
    molluscs. *Nature*, **340**, 49–51.

BRIDGLAND, D. R., ALLEN, P., ALLEN, P., AUSTIN, L., IRVING, B., PARFITT, S., PREECE, R. C. & TIPPING, R. M. 1995. Purfleet interglacial deposits: Bluelands and Greenlands Quarries (TQ 569786) (Part of the Purfleet Chalk Pits SSSI). Also Essex County Council temporary sections, Stonehouse Lane. *In*: BRIDGLAND, D. R., ALLEN, P. & HAGGART, B. A. (eds) *The Quaternary of the Lower Reaches of the Thames*. Field Guide, Quaternary Research Association, Durham.

——, ALLEN, P. M., CURRANT, A. C. *et al.* 1988. Report of the Geologists' Association Field Meeting in north-east Essex, May 22nd–24th 1987. *Proceedings of the Geologists' Association*, **99**(4), 315–333.

BUCKINGHAM, C. M., ROE, D. A. & SCOTT, K. 1996. A preliminary report on the Stanton Harcourt Channel Deposits (Oxfordshire, England): geological context, vertebrate remains and palaeolithic stone artefacts. *Journal of Quaternary Science*, **11**(5), 397–415.

CARRECK, J. N. 1957. A Late Pleistocene rodent and amphibian fauna from Levaton, near Newton Abbot, South Devon. *Proceedings of the Geologists' Association*, **68**, 304–308.

COOPE, G. R. 1977. Fossil coleopteran assemblages as sensitive indicators of climatic changes during the Devensian (Last) cold stage. *Philosophical Transactions of the Royal Society of London*, **B280**, 313–340.

——1987. Fossil beetle assemblages as evidence for sudden and intense climatic changes in the British Isles during the last 45,000 years. *In*: BERGER, W. H. & LABEYRIE, L. D. (eds) *Abrupt Climatic Change*. Reidel, Boston, 147–150.

——, GIBBARD, P. L., HALL, A. R., PREECE, R. C., ROBINSON, J. E. & SUTCLIFFE, A. J. 1997. Climatic and environmental reconstructions based on fossil assemblages from the Middle Devensian (Weichselian) deposits of the River Thames at South Kensington, Central London. *Quaternary Science Reviews*, **16**, 1163–1195.

COXON, P., HALL, A. R., LISTER, A. & STUART, A. J. 1980. New evidence on the vertebrate fauna, stratigraphy and palaeobotany of the interglacial deposits at Swanton Morley, Norfolk. *Geological Magazine*, **117**(6), 525–546.

CURRANT, A. P. 1989. The Quaternary origins of the modern British mammal fauna. *Biological Journal of the Linnean Society*, **38**, 23–30.

——1996. Tornewton Cave and the Palaeontological succession. *In*: CHARMAN, D. J., NEWNHAM, R. M. & CROOT, D. G. (eds) *The Quaternary of Devon and East Cornwall: Field Guide*. Quaternary Research Association, London, 174–180.

—— & JACOBI, R. 1997. Vertebrate faunas of the British Late Pleistocene and the chronology of human settlement. *Quaternary Newsletter*, **82**, 1–8.

DEGERBØL, M. & KROG, H. 1951. Den europaeiske Sumpskildpadde (*Emys orbicularis* L.) i Danmark. *Danmarks Geologiske Undersøgelse II. Raekke*, **78**, 1–130.

FORBES, C. L., JOYSEY, K. A. & WEST, R. G. 1958. On Post-Glacial Pelicans in Britain. *Geological Magazine*, **95**(2), 153–160.

FRENZEL, B. 1966. Climatic change in the Atlantic/sub-Boreal transition on the Northern Hemisphere: botanical evidence. *In*: SAWYER, J. S. (ed.) *Proceedings of the International Symposium on World Climate 8000 to 0 B.C.* Royal Meteorological Society, London, 99–123.

GARCÍA PARÍS, M. 1997. *Hyla meridionalis* Boettger, 1874. *In*: GASC *et al.* (eds) *Atlas of Amphibians and Reptiles in Europe*. Societas Europaea Herpetologica, and Museum National d'Histoire Naturelle, Paris, 126–127.

GASC, J.-P., CABELA, A., CRNOBRNJA-ISAILOVIC, J. *et al.* (eds) 1997. *Atlas of Amphibians and Reptiles in Europe*. Societas Europaea Herpetologica, and Museum National d'Histoire Naturelle, Paris.

GLEED-OWEN, C. P. 1996. Amphibian and reptile remains. *In*: ROBERTS, A. Evidence for Late Pleistocene and Early Holocene human activity and environmental change from the Torbryan Valley, South Devon. *In*: CHARMAN, D. J., NEWNHAM, R. M. & CROOT, D. G. (eds) *The Quaternary of Devon and East Cornwall: Field Guide*. Quaternary Research Association, London 191–192.

——1997a. The Devensian Lateglacial arrival of natterjack toad, *Bufo calamita*, in Britain and its implications for colonisation routes and landbridges. *Quaternary Newsletter*, **81**, 18–24.

——1997b. Investigations of microvertebrate remains in South Wales caves. *Quaternary Newsletter*, **81**, 57–58.

——1998a. *Quaternary herpetofaunas of the British Isles: taxonomic descriptions, palaeoenvironmental reconstructions, and biostratigraphic implications*. PhD thesis, Coventry University.

——1998b. Amphibian remains from Cassington. *In*: MADDY, D., LEWIS, S. G., SCAIFE, R. G. *et al.* (eds) The Upper Pleistocene Deposits at Cassington, near Oxford, UK. *Journal of Quaternary Science*, **13**(2), 230–231.

GROOTES, P. M., STUIVER, M., WHITE, J. W. C., JOHNSEN, S. & JOUZEL, J. 1993. Comparison of oxygen isotope records from the GISP2 and GRIP Greenland ice cores. *Nature*, **366**, 552–554.

HALLOCK, L. A., HOLMAN, J. A. & WARREN, M. R. 1990. Herpetofauna of the Ipswichian Interglacial Bed (Late Pleistocene) of the Itteringham Gravel Pit, Norfolk, England. *Journal of Herpetology*, **24**(1), 33–39.

HOLMAN, J. A. 1985. Herpetofauna of the Late Pleistocene fissures near Ightham, Kent. *Herpetological Journal*, **1**, 26–32.

——1987a. Middle Pleistocene Herpetological Records from Interglacial Deposits at Sugworth, Near Oxford. *British Herpetological Society Bulletin*, 21, 5–7.

——1987b. Additional records of British Pleistocene amphibians and reptiles. *British Herpetological Society Bulletin*, **19**, 18–20.

——1987c. Herpetofauna of the Swanton Morley Site (*Pleistocene: Ipswichian*), Norfolk. *Herpetological Journal*, **1**, 199–201.

——1988. Herpetofauna of the Late Devensian/Early Flandrian Cow Cave Site, Chudleigh, Devon. *Herpetological Journal*, **1**, 214–218.

——1989. Additional herpetological records from the Middle Pleistocene (Cromerian Interglacial) Freshwater Bed, West Runton, Norfolk. *British Herpetological Society Bulletin*, **27**, 9–12.

——1990. New records and comments on British Pleistocene Cold-Stage amphibians and reptiles. *British Herpetological Society Bulletin*, **34**, 39–41.

——1991. Fossil history of the Grass Snake (Natrix natrix) with emphasis on the British fossil record. *British Herpetological Society Bulletin*, **36**, 8–13.

——1992*a*. The Boxgrove, England, Middle Pleistocene herpetofauna: palaeogeographic, evolutionary, stratigraphic and palaeoecological relationships. *Historical Biology*, **6**, 263–279.

——1992*b*. Hyla meridionalis from the Late Pleistocene (Last Interglacial Age: Ipswichian) of Britain. *British Herpetological Society Bulletin*, **41**, 12–14.

——1992*c*. Herpetofauna of Pleistocene (Ipswichian) deposits at Selsey, West Sussex: The earliest British record of Bufo calamita. *Herpetological Journal*, **2**, 94–98.

——1992*d*. Additional records of Natrix natrix from the British Pleistocene, including the first record of a British Cold-Stage snake. *British Herpetological Society Bulletin*, **40**, 7–8.

——1992*e*. Amphibians from a second century Roman well at Tiddington settlement, Warwickshire. *British Herpetological Society Bulletin*, **39**, 5–7.

——1993*a*. Pleistocene Herpetofauna of Westbury-Sub-Mendip Cave, England. *Cranium*, **10**, 87–96.

——1993*b*. Herptiles from the Type Hoxnian (Middle Pleistocene Interglacial Stage) at Hoxne, Suffolk. *British Herpetological Society Bulletin*, **43**, 33–35.

——1993*c*. British Quaternary herpetofaunas: a history of adaptations to Pleistocene disruptions. *Herpetological Journal*, **3**, 1–7.

——1994. A new record of the aesculapian snake, *Elaphe longissima* (Laurenti), from the Pleistocene of Britain. *British Herpetological Society Bulletin*, **50**, 37–39.

——1995*a*. Rana temporaria from a Late Pleistocene periglacial pit in Britain. *British Herpetological Society Bulletin*, **51**, 27–29.

——1995*b*. Additional amphibians from a Pleistocene interglacial deposit at Purfleet, Essex. *British Herpetological Society Bulletin*, **52**, 38–39.

——1996. Amphibians and reptiles from Late Pleistocene Glacial and Interglacial age deposits near Shropham, Norfolk, England. *Cranium*, **13**(2), 131–138.

—— & CLAYDEN, J. D. 1988. Pleistocene Interglacial herpetofauna of the Greenlands Pit, Purfleet, Essex. *British Herpetological Society Bulletin*, **26**, 26–27.

—— & ——1990. A Late Pleistocene Interglacial herpetofauna Near Shropham, Norfolk. *British Herpetological Society Bulletin*, **31**, 31–35.

—— & STUART, A. J. 1991. Amphibians of the Whitemoor Channel Early Flandrian Site near Bosley, East Cheshire; with remarks on the fossil

distribution of *Bufo calamita* in Britain. *Herpetological Journal*, **1**, 568–573.

——, CLAYDEN, J. D. & STUART, A. J. 1988. Herpetofauna of the West Runton Freshwater Bed (Middle Pleistocene: Cromerian Interglacial), West Runton, Norfolk. *Bulletin of the Geological Society of Norfolk*, **38**, 121–136.

——, STUART, A. J. & CLAYDEN, J. D. 1990. A Middle Pleistocene herpetofauna from Cudmore Grove, Essex, England, and its paleogeographic and paleoclimatic implications. *Journal of Vertebrate Paleontology*, **10**(1), 86–94.

ISARIN, R. 1997. *The climate in north-western Europe during the Younger Dryas. A comparison of multiproxy climate reconstructions with simulation experiments*. Doctoral thesis, Vrije Universiteit, Amsterdam.

ISBERG, O. 1929. Das ehemalige Vorkommen der Sumpfschildkröte (*Emys orbicularis* L.) in Schweden und damit zusammenhängende klimatische Erscheinungen. *Arkiv für Zoologi*, **21a**(3), 1–52.

JOHNSON, R. H., FRANKS, J. W. & POLLARD, J. E. 1970. Some Holocene faunal and floral remains in the Whitemoor Channel at Bosley, East Cheshire. *Staffordshire Journal of Field Studies*, **10**, 65–74.

JOUZEL, J., RAISBECK, G., BENOIST, J. P. et al. 1989. A comparison of deep Antarctic ice cores and their implications for climate between 65,000 and 15,000 Years Ago. *Quaternary Research*, **31**, 135–150.

KERNEY, M. P. & CAMERON, R. A. D. 1979. *A Field Guide to the Land Snails of Britain and North-West Europe*. Collins, London.

LISTER, A. M., MCGLADE, J. M. & STUART, A. J. 1990. The Early Middle Pleistocene vertebrate fauna from Little Oakley, Essex. *Philosophical Transactions of the Royal Society of London*, **B328**, 359–385.

MADDY, D., LEWIS, S. G., SCAIFE, R. G. et al. 1998. The Upper Pleistocene deposits at Cassington, near Oxford, UK. *Journal of Quaternary Science*, **13**(2), 205–231.

MEIJER, T. & PREECE, R. C. 1996. Malacological evidence relating to the stratigraphical position of the Cromerian. *In*: TURNER, C. (ed.) *The Early Middle Pleistocene in Europe*. Balkema, Rotterdam, 53–82.

NEWTON, A. 1862. On the discovery of ancient remains of *Emys lutaria* in Norfolk. *Annual Magazine of Natural History*, **10**, 224–228.

NEWTON, E. T. 1879. Notes on some fossil remains of *Emys lutaria* from the Norfolk Coast. *Geological Magazine*, **6**, 304–306.

——1882*a*. Notes on the vertebrata of the Pre-Glacial Forest Bed Series of the East of England. *Geological Magazine*, **9**, 7–9.

——1882*b*. *The Vertebrata of the Forest Bed series of Norfolk and Suffolk*. Memoirs of the Geological Survey of the United Kingdom, HMSO, London.

——1917. Notes on bones found in the Creag nan Uamh Cave, Inchnadamff, Assynt, Sutherland. *Proceedings of the Royal Society of Edinburgh*, **37**, 327–349.

OVE, P. & PERSSON, E. 1980. Appendix 1: The osteo-logical analysis of the cremated and unburned bone material at the megalithic cemetery at Carrowmore, Co. Sligo, Ireland. *In*: BURENHULT, G. *The Archaeological Excavation at Carrowmore, Co. Sligo, Ireland. Excavation Sessions 1977–1979*. Burenhult, Sweden, 117–128.

PETERS, G. 1977. Die Reptilien aus dem fossilen Tierbautensystem von Pisede bei Malchin. Part I: and Part I: Analyse des Fundgutes. *Wissenschaftliche Zeitschrift der Humboldt-Universität zu Berlin, Math.-Nat.*, **26**(3), 307–320.

PODLOUCKY, R. 1997. *Emys orbicularis* (Linnaeus, 1758). *In*: Gasc *et al.* (eds) *Atlas of Amphibians and Reptiles in Europe*. Societas Europaea Herpetologica, and Museum National d'Histoire Naturelle, Paris, 170–171.

PUMPHREY, J. R. 1956. Contents of the hearth sample. *In*: POWELL, T. G. E. & DANIEL, G. E. (eds) *Barclodiad y Gawres. The excavation of a Megalithic chamber tomb in Anglesey*. Liverpool University Press, Liverpool, 16–17.

RAXWORTHY, C. J., KJØLBYE-BIDDLE, B. & BIDDLE, M. 1990. An archaeological study of frogs and toads from the eighth to sixteenth century at Repton, Derbyshire. *Herpetological Journal*, **1**, 504–509.

ROBERTS, M. B., BATES, M. R., BERGMAN, C. *et al.* 1986. Excavations of the Lower Palaeolithic site at Amey's Eartham Pit, Boxgrove, West Sussex: A preliminary report. *Proceedings of the Prehistoric Society*, **52**, 215–245.

SCHREVE, D. C. 1998. *Mammalian biostratigraphy of the later Middle Pleistocene in Britain*. PhD thesis, University College, London.

SNELL, C. 1994. The Pool Frog – a neglected native? *British Wildlife*, **6**(1), 1–4.

STRINGER, C. B., ANDREWS, P. & CURRANT, A. P. 1996. Palaeoclimatic significance of mammalian faunas from Westbury Cave, Somerset, England. *In*: TURNER, C. (ed.) *The Early Middle Pleistocene in Europe*. Balkema, Rotterdam, 133–143.

STUART, A. J. 1974. Pleistocene History of the British Vertebrate Fauna. *Biological Review*, **49**, 225–266.

——1979. Pleistocene occurrences of the European pond tortoise (*Emys orbicularis* L.) in Britain. *Boreas*, **8**, 359–371.

——1980. The vertebrate fauna from the interglacial deposits at Sugworth, near Oxford. *Philosophical Transactions of the Royal Society of London*, **B289**, 87–97.

——1982. *Pleistocene vertebrates in the British Isles*. Longman, London.

——, WOLFF, R. G., LISTER, A. M., SINGER, R. & EGGINTON, J. M. 1993. Fossil vertebrates. *In*: SINGER, R., GLADFELTER, B. G. & WYMER, J. J. (eds) *The Lower Paleolithic Site at Hoxne, England*. University of Chicago, 163–206.

STUIVER, M. & REIMER, P. J. 1993. Extended 14C data base and revised CALIB 3.0 14C Age Calibration Program. *Radiocarbon*, **35**, 215–230.

WEST, R. G. 1980. Pleistocene forest history in East Anglia. *New Phytologist*, **85**, 571–622.

WYMER, J. 1985. *The Palaeolithic Sites of East Anglia*. Geo Books, Norwich.

Brighouse Bay, southwest Scotland: Holocene vegetational history and human impact at a small coastal valley mire

J. M. WELLS,* T. M. MIGHALL, D. E. SMITH & A. G. DAWSON

Centre for Quaternary Science, Coventry University, Priory Street, Coventry, CV1 5FB UK

Abstract: Litho- and biostratigraphical investigations at the small coastal embayment, Brighouse Bay, southwest Scotland, have provided some details of coastal evolution and vegetational changes during the Holocene. Pollen and charcoal analyses in combination with radiocarbon dating have provided circumstantial evidence of human impact on the vegetation at this site over the last 6000 years, commencing with possible Mesolithic environmental impacts and culminating in permanent woodland clearance during the Bronze and Iron Ages. The presence of six silty clay layers in the stratigraphy coincides with pollen evidence for woodland clearance and agricultural activity suggesting that a major phase of prehistoric landscape instability occurred from the time of the mid-Holocene *Ulmus* decline through to the Iron Age. Stratigraphic investigations demonstrate two phases of sand accumulation, one just before *c.* 6000 years BP and a second that may equate with a regional dune-building episode during the 13th and 14th centuries. It is concluded that these results illustrate the importance of a multidisciplinary approach in differentiating between natural and anthropogenic processes and provide insights into how each of these processes has contributed to the evolution of the coastal landscape.

Recent research on Holocene landscape evolution in southwest Scotland has focused on moss development and climate change (Tipping 1995*a*), vegetational change and human impact (Edwards *et al.* 1983; Innes & Shennan 1991; Tipping 1995*b*) and fluvial activity (Tipping 1995*c*). Hitherto, less attention has been given to reconstructing human–landscape interactions in the coastal zone of southwest Scotland. This is surprising, since the coastal zone was utilized by prehistoric communities from the Mesolithic period onwards, probably because of the presence of abundant resources and milder climate (Balaam *et al.* 1987; Bell & Walker 1992). In particular, coastal habitats have been used for agricultural activity and there is evidence of woodland clearance to exploit fertile soils (Jones 1988). Moreover, recent archaeological and palaeoecological work undertaken in the coastal zone has demonstrated the wealth of data available for interdisciplinary research (e.g. Jones 1988; Neumann & Bell 1996).

A new morphological, litho- and biostratigraphical investigation was undertaken primarily to reconstruct Holocene relative sea-level changes and the coastal evolution of Brighouse Bay. As part of this study, pollen and charcoal analyses

afforded the opportunity to reconstruct the vegetational history of the site. Pollen data can also provide circumstantial evidence of human activity and, combined with foraminifera, ostracod and mollusc data, stratigraphical evidence and morphological study, can be used to test various causal hypotheses to explain the development of a coastal landscape. This paper outlines the vegetational development of the Brighouse Bay coastal site and considers the role of human activity in that development.

Study site

Brighouse Bay (NX 630 450) is a narrow inlet at the southeastern extremity of the Wigtown Bay coastline, close (*c.* 2 km) to the smaller Kirkcudbright Bay and lying approximately 25 km SE of the carseland areas at the head of Wigtown Bay (Fig. 1). The bay is the outlet of a valley *c.* 2 km in length, *c.* 400 m broad and draining SSW with sides rising to a maximum height of *c.* 50 m OD. Geologically, the rock exposures that flank the bay are of well bedded, repeatedly folded and sheared greywackes of the Carghidown Formation (Hawick Group, Llandovery Series, Silurian: Stone 1996). In the bay a 500 m long, gently sloping, sandy intertidal zone leads up to a sand and gravel beach behind which lies a stabilized dune system that is

*Present address: English Heritage, Ancient Monuments Laboratory, 23 Savile Row, London, W1X 1AB.

WELLS, J. M., MIGHALL, T. M., SMITH, D. E. & DAWSON, A. G. 1999. Brighouse Bay, southwest Scotland: Holocene vegetational history and human impact at a small coastal valley mire. *In*: ANDREWS, P. & BANHAM, P. (eds) *Late Cenozoic Environments and Hominid Evolution: a tribute to Bill Bishop.* Geological Society, London, 217–233.

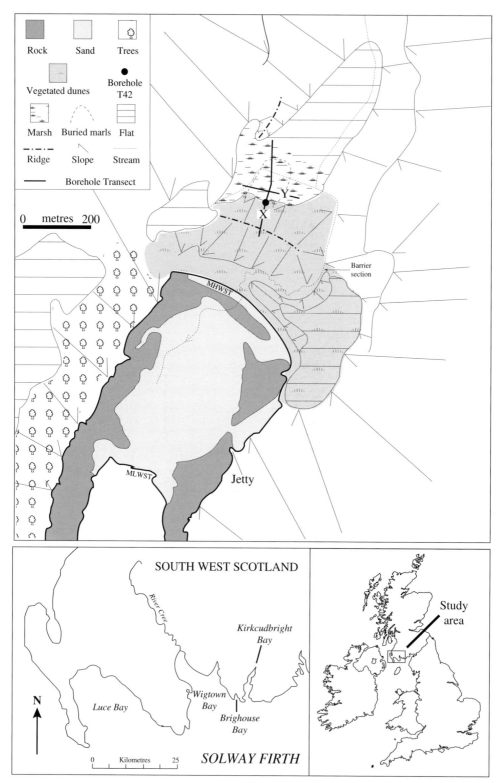

Fig. 1. Brighouse Bay: general location maps and geomorphological map showing borehole transects and the sample borehole location.

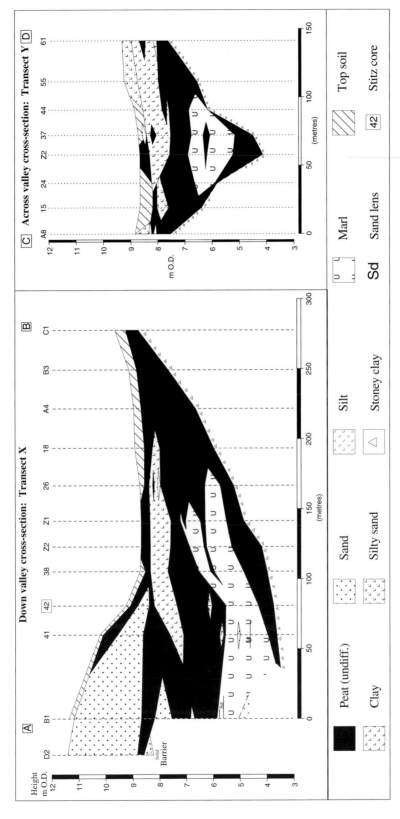

Fig. 2. Lithostratigraphical sections across the dune system and marshland in the study area adjacent to Brighouse Bay: (**a**) down-valley; (**b**) cross-valley.

intersected by a small stream. Immediately north of the dune system is a small (*c.* 100 m²) area of freshwater marshland.

Field procedures

The area to the north of the dunes at Brighouse Bay was the focus of this investigation. Initially, a morphological map was prepared at a scale of 1:10 000. Next, since the area was small, boreholes were sunk at close intervals on a *c.* 20 m grid, using an Eijkelkamp gouge sampler. In total, 80 boreholes, ranging in depth from *c.* 40 to 700 cm, were made and all were levelled in to OD with a closing error not greater than 0.05 m. Two representative borehole transects are presented as stratigraphical cross-sections in Figs 2a and b. One core (T42) was sampled for palaeoecological analysis and radiometric dating using a Stitz percussion borer.

Laboratory methods: pollen and charred particle analyses

The sample core T42 was subsampled (2 g wet weight) for pollen and charred particle analyses from 105 levels at varying intervals of 1 to 8 cm. The chemical preparation procedure followed that outlined by Barber (1976). Hydrofluoric acid was used only on those sediments with a visible minerogenic content. *Lycopodium clavatum* tablets were added to the sediment prior to chemical preparation for the purposes of calculating charred particle concentrations (Stockmarr 1971). A minimum of 300 total land pollen grains (TLP) were identified at every level; taxa values are presented as percentages of TLP. All other identified species outside the pollen sum (TLP) were calculated as TLP sum + taxon. The pollen keys of Andrew (1984), Faegri & Iversen (1989) and Moore *et al.* (1991) were used in addition to Coventry University Geography Department's type slide collection. Nomenclature follows Stace (1997) and Bennett *et al.* (1994). *Corylus* and *Myrica* pollen were not separated and are referred to as Coryloid. Charcoal counts and concentration calculations were undertaken following the procedure outlined by Clark (1982).

Percentage and concentration pollen diagrams were produced using Tilia and Tilia*graph (Grimm 1991). A complete percentage diagram is presented in Fig. 3. Seven Local Pollen Assemblage Zones (LPAZs) have been determined both qualitatively and quantitatively (using the CONNISS statistical analysis in Tilia*graph). The main characteristics of each LPAZ are summarized in Table 1. An enlarged section of the pollen diagram, that across the intercalated organic silty clays and peat layers, is reproduced to show in greater detail the vegetational changes that occurred during the deposition of these sediments (Fig. 4).

Dune system and marshland stratigraphy

The base of most boreholes was in a blue/grey deposit of silts, sands and gravels. This deposit is succeeded by a brown silty peat. Seawards, however, peat development is interrupted by layers of olive green shelly marl (*c.* 4–7 m OD). In borehole D1 (NX 263756 545912), which penetrated upper dune sand layers, the marls were not only proven to be continuous beneath these dune sands, but also to overlie a lower sand deposit. Evidence of three distinct marl layers in borehole Z1 (NX 263787 546027) indicates that deposition of this type of sediment was phased. The distribution of the marls, as suggested by the borehole records, is shown in Fig. 1; they probably extend seawards as far as a buried barrier identified beneath dune sands in a previous investigation (Maynard 1994). Marl deposition eventually was succeeded by further peat development. The marl and peat layers in turn are overlain by organic silty clays that, although not uniform, appear to be related to each other in both form and composition. These organic silty clays range in height from *c.* 7.5 to 8.5 m OD and appear to taper landwards (this excludes the grey organic silty clay unit in borehole D1 whose relationship to the other deposits is unclear). Overlying the organic silty clay deposits are more organic silts that are barely distinguishable from the silty peats that occur close to the present land surface. In borehole D1 a sand layer at 7.5–8.2 m OD occurs within peat that in turn is overlain by modern dune sediments (see boreholes T41 and T42).

Boreholes D/2 and D/3 located a buried unit of gravels and rounded stones (*c.* 8.5 m OD in D/3), suggesting the existence of a buried barrier, that could not be penetrated once reached. In D/3 a 22 cm thick buried organic-rich deposit with sandy inclusions overlies the gravel/rounded stones unit. This deposit in turn is succeeded by a sand (dune?) unit that is continuous to the surface. Further support for the existence of a buried barrier is provided in a stream bank section (NX 6388 4576) where rounded clasts are easily distinguished (see Fig. 1 for location).

Radiocarbon dates

Five samples, taken from parts of the sequence in core T42 where important litho- and bio-stratigraphical changes occur, were sent to be radiocarbon dated by Beta Analytic, Miami (see Table 2).

Early to mid-Holocene
(*c.* 10 000–5500 ^{14}C years BP)

Late-glacial and early Holocene environmental changes at Brighouse Bay were investigated by Bishop & Coope (1977: 68, 83–85). An area of buried peat, 30 cm thick and now overlain by beach sand, was radiocarbon dated to 9640 ± 180 ^{14}C years BP. Pollen and coleopteran data suggest that the peat formed part of an area of marsh vegetated by *Typha*, *Phragmites* and possibly *Carex* and *Sparganium*. The presence of *Quercus*, *Pinus* and *Corylus* pollen suggests that mixed woodland had become established in the pollen catchment. The composition of the coleopteran assemblage suggests that the climate ameliorated rapidly after the Loch Lomond (Younger Dryas) Stadial so that by the time the Brighouse Bay peat deposits were forming, the climate was at least as warm as, or warmer than, in southwest Scotland today.

The pollen assemblage noted by Bishop & Coope (1977) strongly resembles the pollen assemblage for zone BB/POL/1 in borehole T42. The high values for Poaceae and Cyperaceae pollen, combined with the sporadic occurrence of non-arboreal taxa such as Caryophyllaceae, Chenopodiaceae, Asteraceae and *Filipendula*, suggest that a damp grassland/marsh existed in the pollen catchment throughout BB/POL/1. Alternatively, some of these taxa may represent relicts of a Late-glacial tundra-type vegetational community.

Arboreal pollen values suggest that mixed woodland, characterized by *Betula*, *Quercus*, *Pinus* and Corylid, existed on the slopes surrounding Brighouse Bay. *Salix* pollen percentages increase throughout the zone, suggesting that willow occupied the wetter valley bottom. Based on the similarity of the pollen data, it is possible that the basal peats at borehole T42 and the buried peat detected by Bishop & Coope (1977) form part of an area of peat extending into the foreshore area of Brighouse Bay, a suggestion that is supported by recent trenching in this area (see Maynard 1994). This hypothesis remains unproven as the sedimentary sequence beneath the dune system and buried barrier beach (now separating the foreshore area and the marsh) is unknown.

The sustained and relatively high values for *Betula*, *Quercus*, Coryloid and *Pinus* pollen suggest that all four tree taxa were well established. In particular *Betula*, Coryloid and *Quercus* pollen values exceed 5% TLP at the base of zone BB/POL/1 implying that their empirical rise predated the sampled sequence. The basal stony clay is non-polleniferous and therefore the timing of the arrival and establishment of each taxon cannot be firmly established. The pattern for *Pinus* is less clear; the increase midway through the zone may represent its rational limit (*sensu* Birks 1989).

Without a radiocarbon date for the base of BB/POL/1, the age for the initial accumulation of peat at borehole T42 is uncertain. A comparison with pollen data from other sites in southwest Scotland suggests that the base of this lower layer of peat might extend back to 9500 ^{14}C years BP (Birks 1977, 1989). Boyd & Dickson (1986) date the rise in hazel to between 9300 and 9200 ^{14}C years BP, although Birks (1989) indicates that their date may refer to a second *Corylus* rise. Huntley (1993) suggests that the character of the early Holocene climate is the most probable explanation for the establishment of hazel. Seasonal solar radiation and the likelihood of a greater incidence of natural fires, however, would have favoured hazel over its competitors. At Brighouse Bay, small but regular amounts of charcoal are recorded throughout zone BB/POL/1, suggesting that fire might have aided hazel expansion.

At Loch Dungeon (NX 525 846), a pollen sequence records the expansion of *Ulmus* and *Quercus* by 8500 ^{14}C years BP (Birks 1972). Isochrone maps for these taxa suggest they expanded after 9500 and 8500 ^{14}C years BP respectively in southwest Scotland (Birks 1989). At Brighouse Bay, *Quercus* pollen values consistently exceed 5% TLP throughout zone BB/POL/1. *Ulmus* pollen is regularly recorded in low values during this zone before rising over the boundary between BB/POL/1 and BB/POL/2, and this increase may represent its rational rise. However, the relatively high percentages of *Quercus*, Coryloid and *Betula*, suggest that zone BB/POL/1 could extend back to around 9500 ^{14}C years BP.

A shortlived peak in *Alnus* pollen prior to its main regional expansion occurs midway through zone BB/POL/1. Similar peaks have been described in southwest Scotland at Moss of Cree (Wells 1997), Aros Moss, Kintyre (Nicholls 1967), in the Galloway Hills (Birks 1972), on Machrie Moor (Robinson & Dickson 1988) and in North Knapdale (Rymer 1974) at approximately 8000–7800 ^{14}C years BP. This early

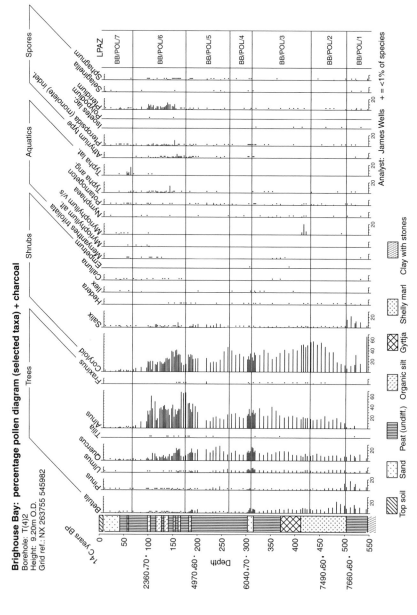

Fig. 3. Brighouse Bay: percentage pollen diagram (selected taxa) + charcoal.

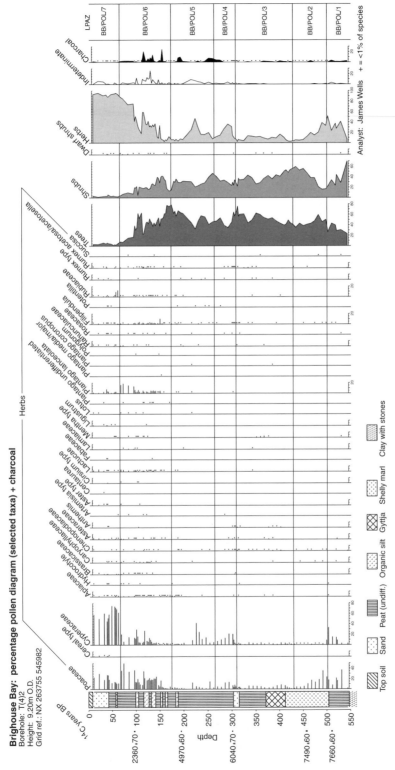

Fig. 3. (*continued*).

Table 1. *Main characteristics and ages of Local Pollen Assemblage Zones (LPAZs) in the sedimentary sequence recorded in borehole T42, near Brighouse Bay*

T42 LPAZ	Altitude, m OD (Depth, cm)	Main charcteristics of the LPAZ	Duration (^{14}C BP)
BB/POL/7	9.20–8.53 (0–67)	**Cyperaceae–Poaceae** High values for Cyperaceae and Poaceae throughout the zone. Cereals record a noticeable presence from 50–0 cm. *Plantago lanceolata* present in low numbers throughout zone. AP values are low.	Present–*c.* 1800
BB/POL/6	8.53–7.45 (67–175)	***Alnus–Quercus–Coryloid–Poaceae–Cyperaceae–P. lanceolata*** *Alnus*, *Quercus* and Coryloid initially dominate although there is a general fall of AP values throughout the zone. Poaceae, Cyperaceae, *P. lanceolata* and other herb values increase synchronously throughout to dominate by the upper limit of the zone. Pteropsida (monolete) indet. and *Pteridium* are well represented. Indeterminate grains and charcoal values fluctuate.	*c.* 1800–*c.* 4500
BB/POL/5	7.45–6.55 (175–265)	***Alnus–Quercus–Coryloid*** Stable values of AP throughout. Cyperaceae increases to a peak (*c.* 40%) in mid-zone as do Indeterminate grains. Pteropsida (monolete) indet. and *Polypodium* values are low but consistent components. Charcoal values record three noticeable peaks.	*c.* 4500–*c.* 5700
BB/POL/4	6.55–6.10 (265–310)	**Coryloid–*Alnus–Quercus*–Cyperaceae–Poaceae** Stable values of AP throughout. *Ulmus* values are consistently present in low numbers. Poaceae and Cyperaceae values increase synchronously to a peak mid-zone. Charcoal and spore values increase toward the upper limit of the zone.	*c.* 5700–*c.* 6150
BB/POL/3	6.10–4.90 (310–430)	**Coryloid–*Alnus–Quercus–Betula–Ulmus*** Moderate fall in Coryloid values throughout zone although this taxon remains dominant. Stable AP values for *Alnus*, *Betula*, *Quercus* and *Ulmus*. *Pinus*, Poaceae and Cyperaceae are all recorded at low but consistent values. *Myriophyllum verticillatum/spicatum* reach a small peak at 420 cm.	
BB/POL/2	4.90–4.18 (430–502)	**Coryloid–*Alnus–Betula–Quercus*–Poaceae–*Ulmus–Pinus*** Strong increase in Coryloid percentages. *Alnus*, *Quercus* and *Ulmus* values are stable throughout the zone. Decrease in *Betula* and *Pinus* values mid-zone. Poaceae values fall significantly from base to top of zone.	*c.* 7250–*c.* 7630
BB/POL/1	4.18–3.70 (502–550)	**Coryloid–Poaceae–*Salix–Betula–Pinus–Quercus*** Significant fall in Coryloid values synchronously with falling Poaceae and increases in *Salix* and Cyperaceae. Values of *Betula*, *Pinus* and *Quercus* are constant throughout the zone.	*c.* 7630–*c.* 9600?

expansion of alder is considered to have been caused by either a rise in sea level (Robinson & Dickson 1988) and/or an increase in the oceanity of climate (Birks 1972).

The increase in presence of *Alnus* pollen at the start of BB/POL/2 represents the early Holocene alder rise (Chambers & Elliott 1989; Bennett & Birks 1990; Tallantire 1992). The empirical limit of the *Alnus* rise is dated to 7660 ± 60 ^{14}C years BP at Brighouse Bay and is similar to the main expansion of alder elsewhere in the region,

including the Cree estuary (Wells 1997) and the Southern Uplands (Birks 1993; Jones & Stevenson 1993).

Possible reasons for the establishment of *Alnus* in early Holocene times include climatic wetness, sea-level rise, Mesolithic activity, natural fires, beaver activity or the creation of suitable habitats through hydroseral succession and floodplain development (Huntley & Birks 1983; Smith 1984; Chambers & Price 1985; Brown 1988; Chambers & Elliott 1989; Bennett

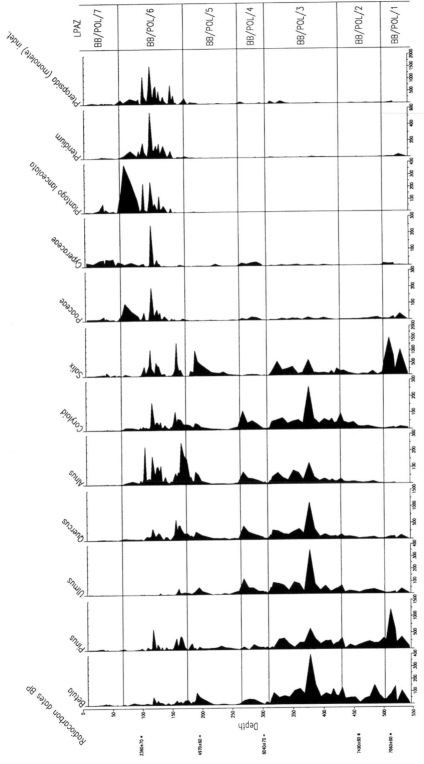

Fig. 4. Brighouse Bay: pollen concentration diagram (selected taxa).

Table 2. *Radiocarbon dates from samples obtained at five levels in boreholes T42 (i.e. BB/4/2) near Brighouse Bay*

Site/borehole	Laboratory code	^{14}C date (years BP)	Age (cal. years BP, 2 sigma)	Altitude, m OD (Depth, cm)	National Grid Ref. (NX)	Material	Environment	^{14}C Procedure
BB/4/2	Beta-83741	2360 ± 70	2710–2165*	8.33 to 8.30 (95–98)	263755 545982	Peat	Human impact clear – high herbs, low trees and shrubs	Standard
BB/4/2	Beta-83742	4970 ± 60	5890–5600*	7.34 to 7.32 (193.5–195.5)	263755 545982	Peat	Beginning of human impact. Deposition of slope wash.	Standard
BB/4/2	Beta-83743	6040 ± 70	7025–6735	6.28 to 6.30 (300–302)	263755 545982	Peat	[Sample taken from above sand layer]	Standard
BB/4/2	Beta-83744	7490 ± 60	8000–7780	4.73 to 4.69 (455–459)	263755 545982	Marine Shell	End of brackish water sedimentation (marl)	AMS
BB/4/2	Beta-83745	7660 ± 60	8510–8335	4.19 to 4.16 (509–512)	263755 545982	Peat	Alder rise. Start of brackish water sedimentation	Standard

Note that the conventional radiocarbon age of Beta-83744 has not been adjusted to account for the 'old carbon' stored in marine shells: the regional value has been calculated as being *c.* 425 years and should be subtracted from the conventional age (an adjusted calibrated age is also necessary).
*Max./min. values.

& Birks 1990; Tallantire 1992). At Brighouse Bay, the *Alnus* rise and the fall in *Pinus* and *Salix* pollen values in BB/POL/2 are concurrent with the deposition of marls. Evidence provided by foraminifera, ostracod and mollusc analyses indicates that the marls were deposited initially under brackish conditions possibly caused by the development of a barrier. Stratigraphical evidence suggests that a barrier formed at Brighouse Bay at this time during the Main Postglacial Transgression (Wells 1997). The creation of wet conditions, most probably caused by the rise in sea level, therefore seems to have facilitated the expansion of *Alnus* to form an alder carr in the valley floor at Brighouse Bay (cf. Bennett 1984; Brown 1988). Pollen analytical evidence of Mesolithic activity at this time is scant. Humans, therefore, are unlikely to have influenced the rise in alder.

Concurrent with the expansion of *Alnus* is a short-lived rise in *Betula* pollen, a sustained increase in Coryloid percentages and the suppression of *Pinus*, *Salix*, Poaceae and Cyperaceae pollen values at the start of BB/POL/2. As both *Alnus* and *Betula* are prolific pollen producers they might be over-represented in the pollen record. Alternatively hazel-dominated woodland and alder carr may have spread into open areas and displaced either pine and willow on wetter substrates and birch on drier soils. Indeed Birks (1989) noted that *Corylus* became a dominant arboreal species in early Holocene times by expanding rapidly on fertile soils of coastal areas in the absence of competition from taller, long-lived, dense-shade-producing trees. *Pinus* percentages fall from *c.* 18% TLP to below 5% and remain at low values for the duration of the Holocene at Brighouse Bay, suggesting that pine has been lost from local woodlands. Pine does not appear to have been a major component of Scottish woodlands in the southwest region as it is uncommon in most pollen diagrams after the rise of *Alnus* pollen, suggesting that alder outcompeted pine and willow in wet habitats (Bennett 1984; Robinson & Dickson 1988).

Coryloid, *Alnus*, *Quercus* and, to a lesser extent, *Betula* and *Ulmus* pollen values remain fairly stable throughout zones BB/POL/2 and BB/POL/3, suggesting that mixed woodland was prevalent in the Brighouse Bay catchment between *c.* 7500 and 6000 ^{14}C years BP. Towards the end of zone BB/POL/2, *Fraxinus* pollen is recorded for the first time and is regularly present in low values throughout zone BB/POL/3. Birks (1989) suggested that small numbers of *Fraxinus* grew on seasonally wet basic soils within deciduous forests and in the drier parts

of fen-carr woodlands in central and southern parts of England between 7000 and 6000 ^{14}C years BP; the spread of ash into southwest Scotland occurred sometime after 5000 ^{14}C years BP. The *Fraxinus* pollen curve at Brighouse Bay may represent long-distance transport although it is possible that a limited local population was present, particularly as this species is known to be a poor pollen producer (Godwin 1975). The slightly warmer conditions provided by this coastal location may also have been conducive to the establishment of an early Holocene *Fraxinus* community in this region. Nevertheless, the taxon never achieves its rational limit, suggesting that ash never fully established itself as a major component of woodland surrounding Brighouse Bay.

Immediately following the deposition of a sand layer, percentages of several of the major arboreal pollen taxa decrease in the sedimentary record. The decline in the percentage and concentration of total arboreal pollen (Figs. 3 and 4) at the start of zone BB/POL/4 occurs at approximately 6040 ± 70 ^{14}C years BP; this date also times the recommencement of peat formation following the deposition of the sand layer. Values of *Betula*, *Alnus*, *Quercus*, Coryloid and *Ulmus* fall and this marks the first substantial decrease in woodland cover at Brighouse Bay. Pteropsida (monolete) indet. and *Polypodium* spore values increase which suggests that ferns and polypody are exploiting shade-free areas at the woodland's edge. Concomitant with the decline of arboreal pollen is the rise in Poaceae and Cyperaceae values. The first occurrence of *Plantago lanceolata*, combined with the appearance of Chenopodiaceae, Asteraceae, Brassicaeae, Apiaceae and *Rumex acetosa/acetosella*, is contemporaneous with the decline in arboreal pollen. Although some of these taxa (e.g. Chenopodiaceae) occur naturally in coastal zones, collectively their occurrence may suggest some form of anthropogenic disturbance.

Mesolithic peoples are known to have occupied the seaboard of southwest Scotland from approximately 8000 ^{14}C years BP (e.g. Cormack 1970; Edwards *et al.* 1983). Coastal sites of Mesolithic age have been identified around the coastline of Luce Bay in the west and as far east as Redkirk Point (Jardine & Morrison 1976) and there is archaeological and palynological evidence for Mesolithic occupation of river valleys in the Galloway Hills (Edwards *et al.* 1983; Edwards 1989). The hunter/gathering economy of Mesolithic peoples is commonly associated with firing of the vegetation, especially in the uplands (Simmons 1996). At Brighouse Bay charcoal values remain low during the fall in arboreal pollen at the start of zone BB/POL/4, suggesting that deliberate or natural fires did not play a major role in reducing woodland cover.

Equally, however, the increased diversity of herb taxa and the slight fall in percentages of arboreal taxa may be purely a natural response related to the deposition of the sand layer. Determining the provenance of the sands has been made difficult by the absence of diatoms. Nonetheless, there is a striking similarity between this sand and the overlying dune sands. The sharpness of the lower and upper contacts of the sand layer with the underlying and overlying peats further indicated that the process which resulted in sand deposition was very rapid. It is probable that the sand deposit represents a period of local aeolian activity resulting in the patchy distribution of sand within the accumulating marsh. Inclusion of sand in coastal peats throughout the Holocene is common, but this unit is earlier than the main period of dune building identified in northwest England, northwest Scotland and Northern Ireland around 5000 ^{14}C years BP (Tooley 1990). The vegetational changes that follow the deposition of the sand possibly reflect a rapid alteration of the environment rather than any human impact (cf. Edwards 1989). Alternatively, Mesolithic people may have exploited natural gaps in woodland cover created by an incursion of blown dune sand rather than utilize woodland openings created by natural or anthropogenic fires.

Mid- and late Holocene (5500 ^{14}C years BP–present)

The decline in woodland cover at Brighouse Bay during the early part of zone BB/POL/4 was short-lived. By mid-zone *Alnus* and *Quercus* had recovered, but not to their original values, and *Ulmus* and *Betula* pollen values remain low (Figs 3 and 4). Coryloid values peak at the start of zone BB/POL/5, hazel perhaps benefiting from the reduction in shade-forming trees. Other shade-intolerant taxa, especially Pteropsida (monolete) indet. and *Polypodium*, increase in representation. However, mid-Holocene vegetational history at Brighouse Bay is characterized by a sequence of woodland disturbance and recovery leading to soil erosion. Woodland cover is reduced in two stages during the first part of zone BB/POL/5 (Fig. 3). Coryloid and *Alnus* percentages begin to decline at the start of the zone. *Alnus* quickly recovers and increases with *Quercus* pollen. The lack of anthropogenic indicators in the non-arboreal pollen record suggests that these changes were competitive;

oak expanded as hazel and elm declined whilst the decline of alder appears to have encouraged the spread of willow and sedges. However, the high charcoal values which accompany the reduction in Coryloid and *Ulmus* pollen suggest that fire, natural or anthropogenic, may have created openings in the woodland cover. By 240 cm total tree pollen percentages recover as *Quercus* and *Alnus* reach an early zone maxima and *Pinus* and *Salix* pollen increase in representation. *Quercus, Ulmus, Pinus* and *Alnus* values then decrease and tree pollen percentages fall to their lowest value for the zone at approximately 5500 ^{14}C years BP. The decline in woodland is also evident in the pollen concentration diagram as the first part of BB/POL/5 is characterized by low concentrations of Coryloid, *Betula, Alnus* and *Quercus*. However, the relatively low pollen concentrations may also be the result of rapid peat accumulation. As woodland cover diminishes, non-arboreal pollen values rise. Cyperaceae and Poaceae values peak and Ranunculaceae, Chenopodiaceae, *Plantago lanceolata, Rumex acetosa/acetosella*, Caryophyllaceae and *Pteridium* spores are all recorded, albeit sporadically and in low values, during and just after the drop in arboreal pollen. Thus, late Mesolithic human activity to open up woodland to attract game (cf. Simmons 1996) and/or early Neolithic human activity to create areas for rough pasture (cf. Edwards and Whittington 1997) may have played some part in opening up woodlands at Brighouse Bay between 6040 ± 70 and *c.* 5500 ^{14}C years BP. Woodland regenerated during the second part of zone BB/POL/5; increases in *Alnus* and Coryloid percentages and concentrations suggest that alder carr re-established itself in wet parts of the valley bottom and hazel–oak woodland dominated the drier parts of the catchment.

Multiple *Ulmus* declines have been described elsewhere in the region and further afield (e.g. Hirons & Edwards 1986). Nichols (1967) recorded several periods of decline and regeneration of *Ulmus* at around 5000 ^{14}C years BP at Racks Moss. Two declines in *Ulmus* pollen occur at Brighouse Bay in zone BB/POL/5. The first, mentioned in the previous paragraph, occurs mid-zone at approximately 5500 ^{14}C years BP and is followed by a second fall radiocarbon-dated to 4970 ± 60 ^{14}C years BP. Both occur at a time when elm populations underwent a marked decline throughout large areas of northwest Europe, commonly referred to as the mid-Holocene *Ulmus* decline (Birks 1989). The second decline broadly coincides with the deposition of an organic-rich silty clay layer, the first in a sequence of intercalated clay and peat layers. *Quercus*, Coryloid and *Betula* values also fall, suggesting a reduction in woodland cover across the zone boundary between BB/POL/5 and BB/POL/6. Values of *Alnus* rise, suggesting a short-lived expansion of alder carr close to the sampling site.

At present, the most favoured hypothesis to explain the mid-Holocene decline of *Ulmus* is a combination of human activity and disease (Girling 1988; Peglar & Birks 1993). There is evidence in the non-arboreal pollen record that implicates humans in the reduction of woodland cover and accounts for the second decline in elm. Low and sporadic values of taxa such as *Plantago lanceolata*, Apiaceae, Lactucae, Chenopodiaceae and *Rumex acetosa/acetosella*, as well as a peak in charcoal, are recorded in the second part of zone BB/POL/5. Pastoral or even arable agriculture, which involved the clearance of woodland, may have continued in the region at the time of the second *Ulmus* decline.

Soil instability, possibly the result of woodland disturbance and agricultural activity at the time of the second *Ulmus* decline at Brighouse Bay, is suggested by the deposition of the clay layer between 189 and 184 cm. There is archaeological evidence of the presence of Neolithic people in the Solway Firth region at about this time. A dug-out canoe discovered at Catherinefield Farm, Locharbriggs, has been radiocarbon-dated to 3754 ± 125 ^{14}C years BP, a chambered cairn at Lochhill yielded timber radiocarbon dated to 5070 ± 105 ^{14}C years BP (Jardine & Morrison 1976; Jardine & Masters 1977) and the occurrence of Neolithic round cairns in the Galloway Hills and pottery in the Luce Bay area attest to a Neolithic presence in the uplands and lowlands of southwest Scotland (Yates 1984) .

Marked Neolithic woodland regeneration after the mid-Holocene elm decline occurs in several Scottish pollen diagrams (e.g. Black Loch, Braeroddach Loch and Machrie moor) (Robinson & Dickson 1988; Edwards & Whittington 1997) and is observed at Brighouse Bay as *Quercus* and Coryloid values recover during the early stages of zone BB/POL/6. Their previous apparent decline may have been slightly exaggerated by the rise in *Alnus* pollen since alder is a prolific pollen producer and can be over-represented in pollen diagrams (Janssen 1959). Edwards & Whittington (1997) state that the reason for the recovery of woodland is unknown, but suggest that improved climatic conditions, the abandonment of land by people possibly owing to soil impoverishment, lowered human impact or the adoption of a forest farming economy, are all possible explanations. However, the re-establishment of woodland at Brig-

house Bay was short-lived and this phase of woodland regeneration might represent a lull in Neolithic activity recorded in other Scottish pollen diagrams (e.g. Robinson & Dickson 1988).

The recovery of *Quercus* and Coryloid pollen is temporary as they gradually decline to approximately 5% TLP throughout the remainder of zone BB/POL/6. *Betula*, *Salix*, *Ulmus* and *Pinus* pollen frequencies all decline to less than 1%, suggesting the loss of woodland cover on the Brighouse Bay slopes. An increase in Pteropsida (monolete) indet., *Polypodium* and *Pteridium* spores suggests a gradual opening of the woodland canopy that allowed ferns, polypody and bracken to occupy shade-free ground. Arable activity is suggested by the substantial increase in Poaceae at *c.* 140 cm and the regular occurrence of a suite of non-arboreal pollen taxa (Chenopodiaceae, Caryophyllaceae, Brassicaceae and *Artemisia* type), whilst the presence of *Plantago lanceolata*, *Rumex acetosa/acetosella*, Ranunculaceae, Asteraceae, Lactucae and *Pteridium* spores is indicative of rough grazing and ruderal plant communities (Edwards & Whittington 1997). An intensification of agriculture, probably by Bronze Age peoples, occurred from approximately the 4th millennium ^{14}C years BP onwards at Brighouse Bay. A succession of charcoal peaks corresponding with the decline in arboreal taxa suggests fire may have been used to clear woodland (Fig. 4).

Bronze Age round cairns, urn and cist sites, associated with metalwork and pottery, are common in the Dumfries and Galloway region. The majority of the 378 round cairns occur in lowland contexts below 300 m altitude (Yates 1984). Yates (1984) suggests that the distribution of the round cairns reflects the agricultural potential of the area, and the exploitation of the lowlands for agricultural purposes would provide a good source of stone for cairn construction. The archaeological evidence for a sizeable Bronze Age population in the lowlands of the Solway Firth is supported in the pollen record at Brighouse Bay, with permanent woodland clearance occurring between approximately *c.* 4000 and 2360 ± 70 ^{14}C years BP. Pollen evidence indicates that the removal of woodland commenced in the Late Neolithic and possibly intensified during the Bronze Age across the Galloway region and elsewhere in Scotland (Edwards & Whittington 1997). Progressively open conditions occur at Clatteringshaws (Birks 1975), Loch Dungeon and Snibe Bog (Birks 1972) and a more abrupt decline in woodlands is seen at Burnswark shortly after the mid-Holocene elm decline (Squires 1978).

Throughout zone BB/POL/6 a series of silty clay layers is recorded in the stratigraphy of T42. A comparison with the total percentage curves for tree, shrub and herb taxa, recorded in Fig. 5 reveals that deposition of each of these inorganic layers corresponds with a trough or a fall in the total tree pollen curve and a peak or rise in herb pollen values. This relationship may have been induced by human activity, for example by woodland clearance on the slopes causing the erosion of soil on to the valley floor. Simmons *et al.* (1975), Brown & Barber (1985) and Tipping (1992) have all shown that woodland clearance during prehistoric times increased soil erosion rates in valley and floodplain contexts. In the Galloway Hills minerogenic sediments occur within peat deposits at Loch Dee (NX 464 783) (Edwards *et al.* 1991). Most of these minerogenic layers seem to have been deposited at times of demonstrable vegetational impacts and during periods of human activity from *c.* 5340 ^{14}C years BP. It is interesting to note that two layers appear to have been deposited after 2600 ^{14}C years BP, close to the Bronze Age/Iron Age boundary and during a similar period of soil instability at Brighouse Bay. Thus, there is evidence for localized vegetational disturbances associated with agricultural activity coeval with minerogenic deposition in the uplands and lowlands of southwest Scotland between 5000 and 2300 ^{14}C years BP.

The possibility that a further rise in relative sea-level at this time could have been responsible for the deposition of these minerogenic layers cannot be ignored. However, no diatoms, foraminifers, ostracods nor molluscs, which could have shed light on this possibility, are present in these layers (see Wells 1997). Wells (1997) has also produced evidence from the raised estuarine sediments that flank the nearby Cree estuary which indicates that Mean High Water of Spring Tides in this area would have been at *c.* 9–10 m OD for at least some (but probably not all) of the time period that encompasses the minerogenic-rich layers at Brighouse Bay; this height for relative sea levels is somewhat above that of the layers themselves. However, Maynard (1994) has provided stratigraphical evidence that a barrier at approximately 10.3 m OD would have prevented a marine incursion into this part of the valley during the relevant time period Moreover, non-arboreal taxa associated with human activity and not normally affliated with coastal communities (e.g. *Plantago lanceolata, Rumex acetosa/ acetosella*, Lactucae, *Cirsium*-type, Brassicaceae) are present in all the minerogenic layers. Species diversity is also higher in the minerogenic layers than in the intercalated peat, suggesting that the silty clay has been derived from the deforested slopes of Brighouse Bay rather than from a

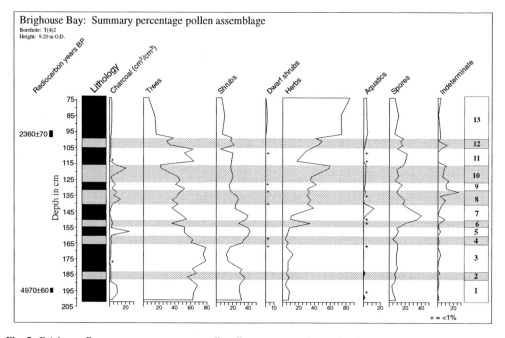

Fig. 5. Brighouse Bay: summary percentage pollen diagrams across intercalated peats and silty clay layers.

marine source. Halophytic taxa commonly found in coastal communities are also present (e.g. Chenopodiaceae, Caryophyllaceae, *Artemisia* type), especially between 130 and 85 cm, but, whilst values for Caryophyllaceae and Chenopodiaceae show slight increases in value, they do not display any discernible pattern to suggest that marine conditions significantly altered or that a halophytic-rich assemblage formed at this time.

From 2360 ± 70 ^{14}C years BP, arboreal pollen taxa remain low as Poaceae and Cyperaceae dominate the pollen record in the latter part of zone BB/POL/6 and during zone BB/POL/7. High Cyperaceae values, *c.* 20% TLP, in association with *Filipendula*, *Hydrocotyle*, *Caltha*-type, *Menyanthes* and Rubiaceae, suggest that marsh/fen-type vegetation formed in wetter areas, probably on the valley floor. The presence of open water is suggested by the continued presence of aquatic taxa including *Typha/Sparganium*, *Typha latifolia*, *Myriophyllum* and *Nymphaea*. High Poaceae values, combined with the presence of other non-arboreal taxa such as Ranunculaceae, *Rumex acetosa/acetosella* and Lactucae, reflect the contemporary vegetation characterized by grasslands and pasture. An intensification of grazing is suggested by a peak in *Plantago lanceolata* at the end of zone BB/POL/6 and the occurrence of cereal pollen suggests that both arable and pastoral agriculture was being practised in the pollen catchment in recent times.

Calluna pollen and *Sphagnum* spores are recorded in consistently low values during both zones BB/POL/6 and BB/POL/7. Given the low values, it is unlikely that heather established itself at Brighouse Bay and the pollen of this taxon probably represents a regional expansion of heather. The spread of acid heath and peat in the Scottish uplands and on the Scottish Isles commonly occurs after the removal of woodland and intensive land use from around 3500 ^{14}C years BP and/or as the result of climate change (Robinson & Dickson 1988; Edwards & Berridge 1994). The pollen record suggests that farming has continued unabated at Brighouse Bay since the permanent removal of woodlands. In contrast to upland sites, it appears that the soils were less vulnerable and/or climatic conditions were not sufficiently conducive to widespread acidification and peat development at Brighouse Bay to cause a cessation in agriculture.

Zone BB/POL/7 is also characterized by the deposition of a sand layer between 42 and 8 cm. Notwithstanding the difficulties in establishing regional chronologies of sand dune sequences (see, for example, Tooley 1990; Wilson & Braley 1997), the sand deposited at Brighouse Bay may be comparable with phases of sand deposition in Donegal, northern Ireland and elsewhere in northwest Europe. These appear to have occurred during the mid-13th to mid-14th centuries AD when there was a marked increase in the incidence of severe storms (Wilson & Braley 1997). However, Tooley (1990) and Wilson & Braley (1997) note that dune formation and the reworking of sand can be affected by a range of factors including positive and negative sea-level tendencies, climate change, anthropogenic activity, sand supply and soil development.

Conclusion

The palaeoecological and stratigraphical data presented from Brighouse Bay provide evidence of vegetational change and landscape evolution throughout most of the Holocene. The evidence presented in this paper and elsewhere (Wells 1997) suggests that both natural processes such as relative sea-level changes, aeolian deposition and anthropogenic activity contributed to these changes, which, together or individually, took place over a variety of timescales.

The complexities of reconstructing landscape and vegetational changes along a continually evolving coastline are many. Nonetheless, a multi-proxy approach at Brighouse Bay has proved to be of value in differentiating between natural processes and human impacts and in understanding how each has contributed to the shaping of the coastal landscape. Although Mesolithic impact on the vegetation could be implied from the pollen evidence, it is probable that the effect of aeolian activity and the deposition of a sand layer on the marsh surface could have produced a similar vegetational response to minor woodland disturbance. The absence of charcoal, however, should not preclude the possibility of Mesolithic occupation of the coastal zone at Brighouse Bay to exploit open areas of woodland formed by natural processes. In contrast, pollen analysis across minerogenic layers within peat has provided compelling evidence of forest clearance by humans from the Neolithic to the Iron Age, with consequent soil erosion. This evidence is consistent with the deposition of colluvium and later prehistoric activity in this region and elsewhere in the British Isles (Edwards *et al.* 1991; Macklin & Needham, 1992).

We are grateful for fieldwork assistance provided by J. Campbell, E. Bruetschy and R. Cullingford. Many thanks are also due to L. Elliott and E. Milwain

(Cartographic Unit, Coventry University) for their help in the production of the diagrams. This research was funded through the European Union contract project *Relative Sea-level Changes and Extreme Flooding Events Around European Coasts* (EV5V-CT930266) and the radiocarbon dating was funded by the Centre for Quaternary Science at Coventry University. Thanks are also due to Mr Graham for providing access to his land and to J. B. Innes and W. G. Jardine for their constructive comments on an earlier draft of this paper.

References

ANDREW, R. 1984. *A Practical Guide to the British Flora*. Technical GUIDE, 1. Cambridge: Quaternary Research Association.

BALAAM, N. D., BELL, M. G., DAVID, A. E. U., LEVITAN, B., MACPHAIL, R. I., ROBINSON, M. & SCAIFE, R. G. 1987. Prehistoric and Romano-British sites at Westward-Ho!, Devon. Archaeological and palaeoenvironmental surveys 1983–1984. *In*: BALAAM, N. D., LEVITAN, B. D. & STRAKER, V. (eds) *Studies in the Palaeoeconomy and Environment in South-west England*. British Archaeological Reports, BS, **181**, Oxford, 163–264.

BARBER, K. E. 1976. History of vegetation. *In*: CHAPMAN, S. B. (ed.) *Methods in Plant Ecology*. Blackwell, Oxford, 5–83.

BELL, M. & WALKER, M. J. C. 1992. *Late Quaternary Environmental Change*. Longman, Harlow.

BENNETT, K. D. 1984. The post-glacial history of *Pinus sylvestris* in the British Isles. *Quaternary Science Reviews*, **3**, 133–155.

—— & BIRKS, H. J. B. 1990. Postglacial history of alder (*Alnus glutinosa* (L.) Gaertn.) in the British Isles. *Journal of Quaternary Science*, **5**, 123–133.

——, WHITTINGTON, G. & EDWARDS, K. J. 1994. Recent plant nomenclatural changes and pollen morphology in the British Isles. *Quaternary Newsletter*, **73**, 1–6.

BIRKS, H. H. 1972. Studies in the vegetational history of Scotland II. Two pollen diagrams from the Galloway Hills, Kirkcudbrightshire. *Journal of Ecology*, **60**, 183–217.

——1975. Studies in the vegetational history of Scotland IV. Pine stumps in Scottish blanket peats. *Philosophical Transactions of the Royal Society London*, **270B**, 181–226.

——1977. The Flandrian forest history of Scotland: a preliminary synthesis. *In*: SHOTTON, F. W. (ed.) *British Quaternary Studies – Recent Advances*. Clarendon, Oxford, 119–135.

——1989. Holocene isochrone maps and patterns of tree-spreading in the British Isles. *Journal of Biogeography*, **16**, 503–540.

——1993. Loch Dungeon. *In*: GORDON, J. E. & SUTHERLAND, D. G. (eds) *Quaternary of Scotland*. Chapman and Hall, London, 604–609.

BISHOP, W. W. & COOPE, G. R. 1977. Stratigraphical and faunal evidence for Lateglacial and early Flandrian environments in south-west Scotland. *In*: GRAY, J. M. & LOWE, J. J. (eds) *Studies in the Scottish Late Glacial Environment*. Pergamon, Oxford, 61–88.

BOYD, W. E. & DICKSON, J. H. 1986. Patterns in the geographical distribution of the early Flandrian *Corylus* rise in southwest Scotland. *New Phytologist*, **102**, 615–623.

BROWN, A. G. 1988. The palaeoecology of *Alnus* (alder) and the postglacial history of floodplain vegetation. Pollen percentage and influx data from the West Midlands, United Kingdom. *New Phytologist*, **110**, 425–436.

—— & BARBER, K. E. 1985. Late Holocene palaeoecology and sedimentary history of a small lowland catchment in central England. *Quaternary Research*, **24**, 87–102.

CHAMBERS, F. M. & ELLIOTT, L. 1989. Spread and expansion of *Alnus* Mill. in the British Isles: timing, agencies and possible vectors. *Journal of Biogeography*, **16**, 541–550.

—— & PRICE, S-M. 1985. Palaeoecology of *Alnus* (alder) early post-glacial rise in a valley mire, northwest Wales. *New Phytologist*, **101**, 333–344.

CLARK, R. L. 1982. Point count estimation of charcoal in pollen preparations and thin sections of sediments. *Pollen et Spores*, **24**, 523–535.

CORMACK, W. F. 1970. A Mesolithic site at Barsalloch, Wigtownshire. *Transactions of the Dumfriesshire and Galloway Natural History and Antiquarian Society*, **47**, 63–80.

EDWARDS, K. J. 1989. Meso-Neolithic vegetational impacts in Scotland and beyond: palynological considerations. *In*: BONSALL, J. C. (ed.) *The Mesolithic in Europe*. Donald, Edinburgh, 143–155.

—— & BERRIDGE, J. M. A. 1994. The Late Quaternary vegetational history of Loch a'Bhogaidh, Rinns of Islay, S.S.S.I., Scotland. *New Phytologist*, **128**, 749–769.

—— & WHITTINGTON, G. 1997. Vegetation change. *In*: EDWARDS, K. J. & RALSTON, I. B. M. (eds) *Scotland: Environment and Archaeology 8000BC–AD1000*. Wiley, Chichester, 63–82.

——, ANSELL, M. & CARTER, B. A. 1983. New Mesolithic sites in south-west Scotland and their importance as indicators of inland penetration. *Transactions of the Dumfriesshire and Galloway Natural History and Antiquarian Society*, **58**, 9–15.

——, HIRONS, K. R. & NEWELL, P. J. 1991. The palaeoecological and prehistoric context of minerogenic layers in blanket peat: a study from Loch Dee, southwest Scotland. *The Holocene*, **1**, 29–39.

FAEGRI, K. & IVERSEN, J. 1989. *Textbook of Pollen Analysis* (4th edition). Wiley, Chichester.

GIRLING, M. A. 1988. The bark beetle *Scolytus scolytus* (Fabricius) and the possible role of elm disease in the early Neolithic. *In*: JONES, M. (ed.) *Archaeology and the Flora of the British Isles*. Oxford University Committee for Archaeology Monographs, **14**, 34–38.

GODWIN, H. 1975. *History of the British Flora* (2nd edition). Cambridge University.

GRIMM, E. 1991. *Tilia 1.08/Tilia?graph 1.16*. Illinois State Museum.

HIRONS, K. R. & EDWARDS, K. J. 1986. Events at and around the first and second *Ulmus* declines: palaeoecological investigations in Co. Tyrone, Northern Ireland. *New Phytologist*, **104**, 131–153.

HUNTLEY, B. 1993. Rapid early Holocene migration and high abundance of hazel (*Corylus avellana* L.): alternative hypotheses. *In*: CHAMBERS, F. M. (ed.) *Climate Change and Human Impact on the Landscape*. Chapman and Hall, London, 205–216.

—— & BIRKS, H. J. B. 1983. *An Atlas of Past and Present Pollen Maps for Europe: 0–13000 years ago*. Cambridge University.

INNES, J. B. & SHENNAN, I. G. 1991. Palynology of archaeological and mire sediments from Dod, Borders Region, Scotland. *Archaeological Journal*, **148**, 1–45.

JANSSEN, C. R. 1959. *Alnus* as a disturbing factor in pollen diagrams. *Acta Botanica Neerlandica*, **8**, 55–58.

JARDINE, W. G. & MASTERS, L. J. 1977. A dug-out canoe from Catherinefield Farm, Locharbriggs, Dumfriesshire. *Transactions of the Dumfriesshire and Galloway Natural History and Antiquarian Society*, third series, **LII**, 56–65.

—— & MORRISON, A. 1976. The archaeological significance of Holocene coastal deposits in southwestern Scotland. *In*: DAVIDSON, D. A. & SHACKLEY, M. L. (eds) *Geoarchaeology: Earth Science and the Past*. Duckworth, London, 175–195.

JONES, R. L. 1988. The impact of man on coastal plant communities in the British Isles. *In*: JONES, M. (ed.) *Archaeology and the Flora of the British Isles*. Oxford University Committee for Archaeology Monographs, **14**, 96–106.

—— & STEVENSON, A. C. 1993. Round Loch of Glenhead. *In*: GORDON, J. E. & SUTHERLAND, D. G. (eds) *Quaternary of Scotland*. Chapman and Hall, London, 609–613.

MACKLIN, M. G. & NEEDHAM, S. 1992. *Alluvial Archaeology in Britain*. Oxbow Monographs, **27**, Oxford.

MAYNARD, D. J. 1994. Archaeological discoveries in the Dune System at Brighouse Bay. *Transactions of the Dumfriesshire and Galloway Natural History and Antiquarian Society*, 3rd series, **69**, 13–34.

MOORE, P. D., WEBB, J. A. & COLLINSON, M. E. 1991. *Pollen Analysis* (2nd edition). Blackwell, Oxford.

NEUMANN, H. & BELL, M. 1996. Intertidal survey in the Welsh Severn Estuary 1996. *Archaeology in the Severn Estuary*, **7**, 3–20.

NICHOLS, H. 1967. Vegetational change, shoreline displacement and the human factor in the late Quaternary history of south-west Scotland. *Transactions of the Royal Society of Edinburgh*, **67**, 145–187.

PEGLAR, S. & BIRKS, H. J. B. 1993. The mid-Holocene *Ulmus* fall at Diss Mere, south-east England – disease and human impact? *Vegetation History and Archaeobotany*, **2**, 61–68.

ROBINSON, D. & DICKSON, J. H. 1988. Vegetational history and land use: a radiocarbon-dated pollen diagram from Machrie Moor, Arran, Scotland. *New Phytologist*, **109**, 233–236.

RYMER, L. 1974. *The palaeecology and historical ecology of the parish of North Knapdale, Argyll*. PhD thesis, University of Cambridge.

SIMMONS, I. G. 1996. *The Environmental Impact of Later Mesolithic Cultures in the Uplands*. Edinburgh University.

——, ATHERDEN, M. A., CUNDILL, P. R. & JONES, R. C. 1975. Inorganic layers in soligenous mires of the North Yorkshire Moors. *Journal of Biogeography*, **2**, 49–56.

SMITH, A. G. 1984. Newferry and the Boreal–Atlantic transition. *New Phytologist*, **98**, 35–55.

SQUIRES, R. 1978. The pollen analysis of a short core from Brunswark Hill. *Transactions of the Dumfries and Galloway Natural History and Antiquarian Society*, **53**, 99–103.

STACE, C. 1997. *New Flora of the British Isles* (2nd edition). Cambridge University.

STOCKMARR, J. 1971. Tablets with spores used in absolute pollen analysis. *Pollen et Spores*, **13**, 614–621.

STONE, P. (ed.) 1996. *Geology in South-west Scotland: an excursion guide*. British Geological Survey, Keyworth.

TALLANTIRE, P. A. 1992. The alder [*Alonus glutinosa* (L.) Gaertn.] problem in the British Isles: a third approach to its palaeohistory. *New Phytologist*, **122**, 717–731.

TIPPING, R. 1992. The determination of cause in the generation of valley fills in the Cheviot Hills, Anglo-Scottish border. *In*: NEEDHAM, S. & MACKLIN, M. G. (eds) *Alluvial Archaeology in Britain*. Oxbow, Oxford, 111–122.

——1995a. Holocene evolution of a lowland Scottish landscape: Kirkpatrick Fleming. Part I peat- and pollen-stratigraphic evidence for raised moss development and climatic change. *The Holocene*, **5**(1), 69–82.

——1995b. Holocene evolution of a lowland Scottish landscape: Kirkpatrick Fleming. Part II, regional vegetation and land-use change. *The Holocene*, **5**(1), 83–96.

——1995c. Holocene evolution of a lowland Scottish landscape: Kirkpatrick Fleming. Part III, fluvial history. *The Holocene*, **5**(2), 189–195.

TOOLEY, M. J. 1990. The chronology of coastal dune development in the United Kingdom. *In*: BAKKER, TH. W. M., JUNGERIUS, P. D. & KLIJN, J. A. (eds) *Dunes of the European Coasts. Catena* supplement **18**, 81–88.

WELLS, J. M. 1997. *Flandrian relative sea-level changes in the Cree estuary region, south west Scotland*. PhD Thesis, Coventry University.

WILSON, P. & BRALEY, S. M. 1997. Development and age structure of Holocene coastal sand dunes at Horn Head, near Dunfanaghy, Co. Donegal, Ireland. *The Holocene*, **7**(2), 187–197.

YATES, M. J. 1984. *Bronze Age Round Cairns in Dumfries and Galloway*. British Archaeological Report British Series **132**, Oxford.

The peatlands of northwest Scotland as Holocene palaeoclimatic archives

DAVID E. ANDERSON

School of Geography, University of Oxford, Mansfield Road, Oxford OX1 3TB, UK

Abstract: Analyses of peat sequences from Wester Ross, northwest Scotland, illustrate the potential of peatlands as archives of palaeoclimatic change. Measurements of humification, C : N ratios, macrofossils and microfossils in these sequences have provided time series of past changes in bog hydrology spanning much of the Holocene. These time series contain several distinct and abrupt transitions, suggesting dynamic, rather than stable, climatic conditions in this coastal area. Using radiocarbon-based chronostratigraphies, regional transitions to wetter and/or cooler conditions are inferred at approximately 5.1, 3.8 and 0.8 ka cal. BP, and transitions to drier and/or warmer conditions are inferred at approximately 4.2 and 1.4 ka cal. BP. Around 3.3 ka cal. BP, increased land-use in the surrounding area creates difficulties for interpreting the peat hydrological record. Little is known about the nature and causes of climatic change on sub-Milankovitch timescales during the Holocene, and improving and extending peat-based palaeoclimatic records could make important contributions. The usefulness of the peat archive could be improved by advances in dating and in deriving quantitative climatic information.

Studies of peat stratigraphy can reveal past changes in the surrounding landscape while also yielding palaeoclimatic information. Although rates of peat accumulation can be highly variable, peat sequences from European raised bogs average between 10 and 15 years of accumulation per centimetre (Barber 1994). Additionally, the sedimentation record in peatlands is often continuous for long periods and sometimes extends from the early Holocene to the present. This makes peatlands useful for examining climatic variability on decadal to centennial timescales, intermediate between the longer timescale of Milankovitch orbital forcing and the short timescale derived from instrumental climate records (Blackford & Chambers 1991, 1995).

This article begins with a brief review of past and present approaches to reconstructing palaeoclimates from peat stratigraphy. Specific methods are then illustrated by summarizing a high-resolution study based on peat bogs from northwest Scotland. Following a presentation of the main inferences, the third part of the article discusses some limitations of the peat-based record and makes suggestions for further research which may improve the usefulness of the peat archive.

Early palaeoclimatic reconstructions from peat deposits

Since the late 19th century, it has been known that changes in peat stratigraphy reflect past hydrological changes and that this can provide a basis for inferring past climates. Blytt (1876) studied peat deposits in Norway and inferred a pattern of post-glacial climatic changes which, when combined with the work of Sernander (1908) in Sweden, became known as the 'Blytt–Sernander' scheme. This scheme related phases of enhanced peat growth to wetter climatic periods (the Atlantic and SubAtlantic), which were preceded by periods of drier conditions (the Boreal and SubBoreal).

Before radiocarbon dating, the scheme appeared to present a useful climatic framework, and it was assumed that the Blytt–Sernander climatic shifts were broadly synchronous across northwest Europe. However, more recent radiocarbon dating studies have disproved the synchroneity of most transitions associated with the scheme (e.g. Smith & Pilcher 1973; Birks 1975), and it is now clear that the scheme was an over-generalization of the spatial and temporal complexity of Holocene climatic changes in Europe (Lowe 1993).

Present approaches to peat-based palaeoclimatic reconstruction

With the realization that the Europe-wide correlations of 'Blytt–Sernander' transitions were invalid, it became clear that peat-based palaeoclimatic inferences must be kept to a regional

ANDERSON, D. E. 1999. The peatlands of northwest Scotland as Holocene palaeoclimatic archives. *In*: ANDREWS, P. & BANHAM, P. (eds) *Late Cenozoic Environments and Hominid Evolution: a tribute to Bill Bishop.* Geological Society, London, 235–245.

scale (Blackford 1993). There has also been an increasing awareness of non-climatic factors which requires more caution when making palaeoclimatic inferences. For instance, valley mires may develop and change during the course of a hydroseral succession, and many blanket peatlands in Britain appear to have developed in response to human-induced hydrological changes within catchments over the past 5000 years (Moore 1972, 1986a, b). In addition, soil paludification can turn previously forested areas into peatlands without anthropogenic or climatic forcing (Klinger et al. 1990), although climatic shifts to more humid conditions may often play an important role in speeding up and intensifying this otherwise gradual process (Korhola 1995, 1996). Following peatland initiation, stratigraphic changes may be due to a range of autogenic and allogenic factors; however, with careful selection of sites, it is possible to maximize the allogenic signal for palaeoclimatic reconstruction (Barber 1994).

For much of the mid-20th century, belief in the 'cyclic regeneration' theory, involving an alternation between dry hummocks and wet hollows across a bog, discouraged palaeoclimatic research on peatlands (Barber 1993, 1994). Hummocks and hollows are common on present-day oligotrophic bogs, and plant species vary along the intervening moisture gradients. Barber (1981) found no evidence for cyclic regeneration in the peat sections from Bolton Fell Moss, Cumbria, and this has been supported by other stratigraphic studies in Britain (Smith 1985; Wimble 1986) and in Sweden (Svensson 1988). Furthermore, recent studies of the mechanisms of pool/hollow formation and on decomposition rates of different bog flora suggest that hummocks and hollows tend to maintain their position through time (Johnson & Damman 1991; Moore 1991); and it has been shown that peat cores extruded from a hollow, or wet Sphagnum lawn, can provide a sensitive hydrological record which is representative of the entire bog surface (Aaby 1976; Barber 1994).

Minimizing the effects of changes in drainage and/or catchment vegetation cover on the peat stratigraphic record requires careful selection of sites. Raised bogs and blanket peats, which are fed predominantly by precipitation (ombrogenous) rather than by groundwater or streamflow, are used most often for palaeoclimatic reconstruction. Topogenous bogs (formed in basins) may also be useful if hydrologically isolated, in other words, situated above and away from catchment drainage systems; and bogs formed in glacial kettle holes can fulfil this criterion as they are often isolated by circular mounds of till.

After selecting a suitable site, a range of proxy data are needed to identify palaeohydrological changes. Peat humification data (degree of decomposition) are one of the most direct forms of evidence, as this is closely related to past water table heights. The deepest water table in summer divides the unsaturated, aerated zone at the bog surface (the acrotelm) from the permanently saturated, anaerobic zone beneath (the catotelm) (Ingram 1978). As humification is primarily a function of the time organic matter spends in the acrotelm before being deposited within the catotelm, short-term changes in the humification of peat samples taken from a core are related to past hydrological changes which altered the depth of the acrotelm during the summer season. However, slow, anaerobic peat decay does occur within the catotelm which is reflected in a long-term trend to higher humification for peat samples with increased age in a sequence (Clymo 1984), and this decay trend should be removed before making palaeohydrological inferences.

While several techniques have been devised to measure peat humification (Malterer et al. 1992), the most objective is the colorimetric method. This involves extracting humic acids (produced during decomposition) from peat samples using an alkaline agent (such as NaOH) and assessing their concentration in solution with a colorimeter (Aaby & Tauber 1975; Aaby 1976, 1986; Blackford & Chambers 1993). A high percentage of light transmittance indicates weakly humified peat, whereas a lower light transmittance indicates more humified peat.

Palaeohydrological changes may also leave a signal in the floral and faunal composition of the peat matrix (Moore et al. 1986). For instance, analyses of different Sphagnum species have enabled detailed palaeohydrological inferences (e.g. Barber et al. 1994), and many non-pollen microfossils also have value as hydrological indicators (van Geel 1978, 1986). Rhizopods (testate amoebae) in particular have much potential for detailed reconstructions of palaeowater tables and moisture levels which is only beginning to be exploited fully (Tolonen 1986; Warner & Charman 1994; Hendon & Charman 1997).

Determining whether inferred palaeohydrological changes reflect climatic shifts, rather than localized factors, depends upon considering the peat record within the larger palaeoenvironmental context. This generally requires pollen analysis to develop a picture of vegetational change (either natural or human-induced). Palaeoclimatic inferences should also be based on data from more than one site, and of course, this depends upon obtaining a degree of chronological control on peat sequences for intercomparison. Chronologies are usually constructed by radiocarbon dating bulk peat samples or *in situ* macrofossils (e.g. seeds or wood) using either conventional or accelerator mass spectrometer (AMS) methods.

Contributions of a study from northwest Scotland

The Wester Ross region of northwest Scotland contains numerous oligotrophic peatlands, many of which occupy glacial kettle holes produced during the retreat of Loch Lomond Stadial ice. Results obtained by analysing sequences from three different peat bogs in this area help to illustrate some of the advantages and limitations of peat-based records.

Sites and methodology

Three peat bogs in Wester Ross were examined (Fig. 1). Criteria for site selection, specific characteristics of each bog, and details of field and laboratory methods are described in more detail in Anderson (1996). The Glen Torridon bog, 57°33.6′N 5°22.6′W (NG 983 576), occupies a glacial kettle hole west of Loch Clair in Glen

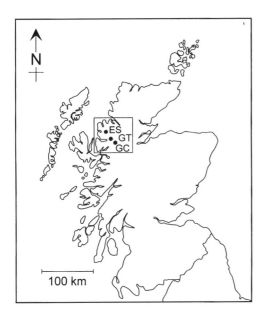

Fig. 1. Outline map showing the location of the Eilean Subhainn (ES), Glen Torridon (GT) and Glen Carron (GC) sites in Wester Ross, Scotland.

Torridon. It lies at an altitude of approximately 90 m a.s.l., and is 90 m wide. The bog is almost completely circled by a rim of till. The Glen Carron bog, 57°31.3′N 5°09.6′W (NH 113 533), also occupies a glacial kettle hole. It is located east of Loch Sgamhain in Glen Carron at an altitude of approximately 180 m a.s.l. The bog is roughly circular in shape, with a diameter of 50 m and has till ridges on its northeast and northwest flanks. The Eilean Subhainn bog, 57°41.2′N 5°28.4′W (NG 923 725), occupies a rock basin on the island of Eilean Subhainn in Loch Maree. Its altitude is approximately 20 m a.s.l., and it has a diameter of about 150 m. All three bogs feature a hummock/hollow surface topography and conform closely with the Trichophoreto–Eriophoretum–Caricetosum peatland association described by McVean & Ratcliffe (1962).

A principal core from each bog was subsampled for a variety of physical and palaeoecological properties, including bulk density, humification, C:N ratios, macrofossils, pollen and non-pollen microfossils. Wet and dry bulk density measurements followed Bengtsson & Enell (1986), and humification measurements were made using the colorimetric method described previously. Measurements of carbon (C) and nitrogen (N) content for peat samples were made on a Carlo Erba CHN Elemental Analyser.

Macrofossil analyses focused on the proportions of woody, ericaceous, herbaceous and bryophyte material within the peat matrix. This involved disaggregating peat subsamples and estimating the abundances of different components by eye with the aid of a low power microscope. Pollen analyses followed procedures described in Moore et al. (1991). During pollen counting, non-pollen microfossils and charred particles were also recorded. Nomenclature for vascular plants follows Stace (1991), and nomenclature for rhizopods, fungal remains and other non-pollen microfossils follows van Geel (1978, 1986). Pollen data are presented as a percentage of the total land pollen sum (ΣTLP), ranging between 400 and 500 pollen and spores per sample (excluding *Sphagnum* and aquatics). Non-pollen microfossils are presented as a percentage of their own sum added to ΣTLP.

Samples for radiocarbon dating were extracted from each core and sent to specialist dating laboratories for assessment.

Results

The dry bulk density and percentage C curves indicate that all three cores contain an abrupt transition from basal inorganic material to organic peat deposition (Fig. 2). In the Glen Torridon and Eilean Subhainn cores, basal layers consist of laminated limnic sediments. The basal depths of cores taken from the Glen Torridon (GT), Glen Carron (GC) and Eilean Subhainn (ES) cores are 471, 374 and 643 cm, and the organic peat sequences (containing approximately 54% C) from each bog reach depths of 407, 360 and 445 cm respectively (corresponding to ages of *c*. 9.3, 10.0 and 8.2 ka cal. BP). The peat sequences are dominated by herbaceous remains with some bryophyte remains (mainly *Sphagnum*). Wood and ericaceous material are most abundant in the lower sections of the GT and GC sequences.

Colorimetric humification data are similar between the three cores, displaying long-term trends of increasing humification with depth (Fig. 2). Superimposed on the long-term catotelm decay trends are several fluctuations in

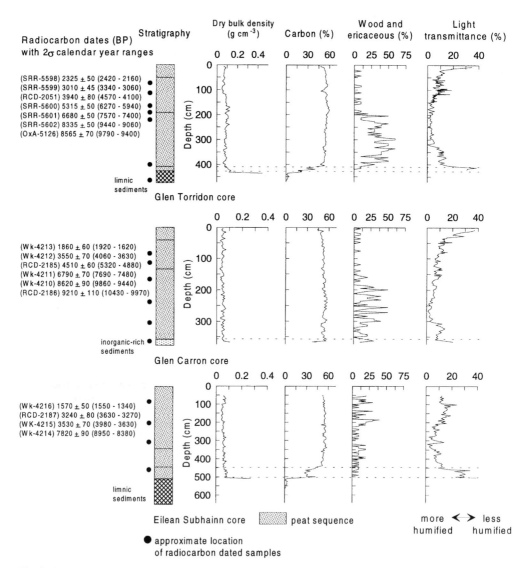

Fig. 2. Core stratigraphy, dry bulk density, carbon content, wood and ericaceous content and light transmittance from each site plotted against depth (cm). Radiocarbon determinations are presented with laboratory codes and 2σ calendar year ranges derived from CALIB (Stuiver & Reimer 1993). Percentage light transmittance (measured by colorimetry) is used as a proxy for peat humification.

humification, indicative of short-term palaeo-hydrological changes. Low humification (high light transmittance) at the base of cores reflects an increased inorganic component, whereas the abrupt decreases in humification towards the top of the GT and GC cores (not sampled at ES) reflect the transitions from the catotelm to the acrotelm.

Radiocarbon dating was applied to 17 samples from the three sequences (Fig. 2), and dates have been calibrated into calendar year age ranges using the calibration programme of Stuiver & Reimer (1993). Depths have been transformed into calendar years BP by linear interpolation between calendar year age ranges of radio-carbon-dated depths and by incorporating a humification-based correction of peat accumula-tion rates between dates (Anderson 1996). Proxy data used for palaeohydrological reconstruction include humification, C:N ratios, percentage Cyperaceae pollen and percentage Copepoda spermatophores (derived from water fleas). On the basis of these data, a number of palaeohy-drological shifts have been inferred from each peat sequence (Fig. 3a).

Regional reconstruction and palaeoclimatic inferences

To make regional inferences, the local palaeohy-drological reconstructions from each sequence have been compared. Because of the large age ranges associated with calendar year calibrations of radiocarbon dates, it is not possible to con-firm synchroneity in palaeohydrological shifts between different bogs. However, there should at least be an overlap in the confidence ranges of the timing of local shifts before any regional-scale event is inferred. If two or more sequences show similar timing between shifts to wetter or drier conditions, hypotheses can be generated concerning regional-scale factors which can be tested by analysing additional sites.

Calendar year 2σ confidence ranges for the local palaeohydrological shifts (Fig. 3a) have been derived from the maximum and mini-mum 2σ calendar year age estimates of depths marking the mid-point of the steepest changes in humification (percentage light transmittance). In some cases, these calendar year ranges were derived from direct radiocarbon dates on humi-fication shifts within the sequences, although most of the ranges are based on interpolation between calibrated radiocarbon dates. More specific information on the supporting evidence, the age estimates and the duration of each local

shift is provided (Anderson 1998). The compar-ison of age ranges for local palaeohydrological shifts shows six instances when ranges overlap between two or three sequences (Fig. 3b).

Similarities in the timing of palaeohydro-logical shifts between sites could reflect past climatic changes, although such similarities may also be coincidental, or due to natural vegeta-tional shifts or human activities within the area. Detailed pollen analyses of the GT and GC cores are presented and discussed elsewhere (Anderson 1996, 1998). However, for compar-ison with the palaeohydrological reconstruction, some selected pollen taxa are included in Fig. 3a. The initial shift to wetter conditions represented in the three sequences between $c.\,5.5$ and 4.7 ka cal. BP was not associated with any large-scale vegetational changes which might have influenced catchment hydrology. Furthermore, this initial shift predates evidence for prehistoric land-use in the area, represented by the rise of *Plantago lanceolata* in the GT and GC sequences, and it precedes the onset of a large pine pollen decline within the GT sequence.

The pine pollen declines found in the three sequences (Fig. 3a) relate to a large-scale reduction in the distribution of Scots pine in northern Scotland around 4000 years ago (Birks 1972, 1975, 1996; Bennett 1984, 1995; Gear & Huntley 1991; Anderson, 1995). As Scots pine was the woodland dominant in Wester Ross during the early and mid-Holocene (Birks 1972; Pennington *et al.* 1972; Kerslake 1982), it could be postulated that its widespread decline (and the consequent reduction in total forest cover) resulted in increased runoff from surround-ing slopes and higher water tables in catch-ments as water loss through evapotranspiration decreased. Such conditions would be expected to enhance peat growth. However, it is widely thought that the Scots pine decline itself was caused by a shift to cooler and wetter climatic conditions in which enhanced waterlogging and paludification of soils inhibited pine regeneration (e.g. Bennett 1984, 1995). Indeed, it is pos-sible that the wet shift at around 5.1 ka cal. BP inferred from the peat stratigraphy (Fig. 3b) provided the impetus for the spread of blanket peat and the subsequent pine decline within the region. A pollen diagram from Loch Maree (Birks 1972) provides the earliest estimate of the pine decline in Wester Ross at 4206 ± 55 ^{14}C years BP (Q-1005), spanning $c.\,4.9$ to 4.6 ka cal. BP at 2σ confidence.

A shift to drier conditions is inferred from $c.\,4.5$ to 3.9 ka cal. BP in the GT and ES sequences. In these sequences, the shifts to drier bog conditions occur after the main declines

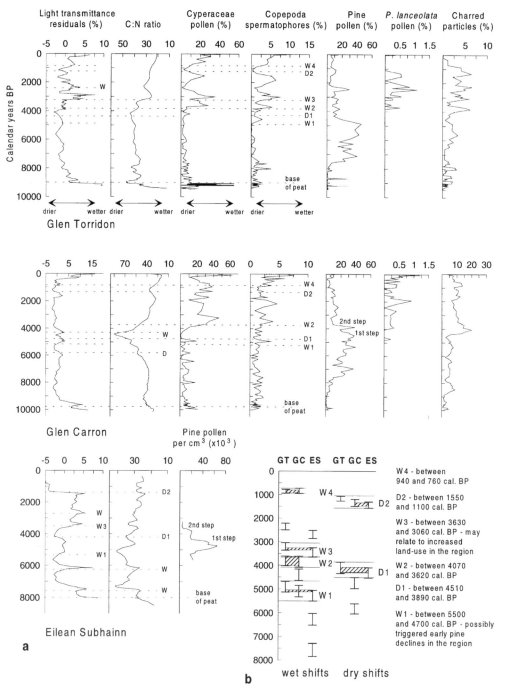

Fig. 3. (a) Palaeohydrological data, and other palaeoenvironmental data, from each site plotted against calendar years BP. Data are smoothed with a three-sample moving average (excluding percentage pollen and Copepoda data). Local wet shifts (W) and dry shifts (D) are marked, and supporting evidence is indicated by dashed lines. Local shifts used in regional inferences are also numbered for intercomparison. (b) Intersite comparison of wet and dry shifts. The estimated timing of local shifts from each sequence is plotted as a 2σ confidence range against calendar years BP. Regional shifts are inferred by grouping local shifts of similar timing. Combined age ranges of similar shifts are enclosed within solid lines, while the time spans of overlaps between age ranges are indicated by cross-hatching.

in pine pollen, contrary to expectations that reduced pine might result in wetter bog conditions. It is possible that this dry phase reflects a regional climatic shift that was associated with a brief, northerly range expansion of Scots pine estimated between 4.4 and 3.8 ^{14}C ka BP by Gear & Huntley (1991). Pollen diagrams from southeastern Skye (Birks & Williams 1983) and from central Sutherland (Charman 1994) also show evidence for a brief phase of pine afforestation prior to its decline around 4000 years ago. It is unclear why a similar re-expansion of Scots pine is not inferred from the GT, GC and ES pine pollen curves; however, there is a possibility that the Scots pine decline in the area was characterized by two steps (Fig. 3a) with early and late episodes of decline separated by this drier interval (Anderson 1996).

A shift to wetter conditions ranging between *c.* 4.1 and 3.6 ka cal. BP is supported by the GT and GC sequences. This inferred shift agrees with peat humification data from near Beinn Dearg, Wester Ross (Binney 1997) and with evidence for an increase in lake level at Achany Glen, Sutherland (Smith 1996). Comparison with these data suggests that the age range of the climatic shift may be slightly later, between *c.* 3.9 and 3.5 ka cal. BP (Anderson *et al.* 1998). Although age estimates cannot be correlated precisely, there is similar evidence for increasing wetness around 4.0 ka cal. BP in peat stratigraphic data from across the British Isles and northern Europe (Aaby & Tauber 1975; Aaby 1976; van Geel 1978; Blackford 1990; Nilssen & Vorren 1991; Barber *et al.* 1994; Korhola 1995, 1996). The shift coincides with an abrupt decline in pine pollen in the GC sequence, raising the possibility that pine reduction was associated with the hydrological change within the Glen Carron catchment. However, such a connection is not represented in the GT sequence. There is also some possibility that prehistoric land-use was influencing catchment hydrology as indicated by a contemporaneous increase in *P. lanceolata* and charred particles within both sequences (Fig. 3a), although percentages of *P. lanceolata* pollen are low (under 0.5%). Evidence for human land-use in the area increases at *c.* 3.0 ka cal. BP with the sustained presence of *P. lanceolata* within the GT sequence, and it is less clear whether the wet shift ranging from *c.* 3.6 to 3.1 ka cal. BP should be attributed to climatic change or human-induced hydrological changes.

The final two regional-scale shifts probably represent climatic changes which are known from historical records. A distinct dry shift supported by all three sequences is dated between *c.* 1.5 and 1.1 ka cal. BP; and if it is assumed that the age estimate from the GT sequence is more realistic than the relatively older estimates from GC and ES, then the shift may reflect the onset of drier and warmer conditions in northwest Europe associated with the 'Medieval Optimum' (Lamb 1982). This assumption is also likely considering the evidence for wetter and/or cooler conditions during the Dark Ages (around 500 to 700 AD) derived from blanket peats in Ireland, Wales and northern England (Blackford & Chambers 1991). The shift to wetter conditions after *c.* 0.9 ka cal. BP may reflect the onset of the 'Little Ice Age'; although again, the estimated age range for the shift is slightly early when compared with the historical evidence for climatic cooling in the British Isles during the mid-14th century (Crowley & North 1991).

Limitations of the peat-based record and potential for improvement

The Wester Ross study offers an example of how different types of proxy data preserved in peatlands can be used to infer palaeoclimatic changes. Consideration of palaeohydrological data in the light of other palaeoenvironmental evidence strongly supports an oscillation from wet, to dry, to wet bog conditions between about 5.0 and 4.0 ka cal. BP which was probably driven by climatic change, and closely associated with the dynamics of Scots pine woodlands in northern Scotland during the mid-Holocene. Human activities may have been implicated in palaeohydrological changes during the late Holocene, although the final dry and wet shifts are broadly consistent with historic records of climatic change.

While the study does help to constrain the pattern of mid- to late Holocene climatic change within the region, it has not provided precise age estimates for shifts, or quantitative information about their magnitude. At present, chronological control presents a major limitation. After calibration, radiocarbon dates generally do not enable the real age of events to be defined more precisely than a 500 year time span (Pilcher 1993). This range is considerably larger than the duration of the transitions themselves as inferred from the data.

One solution is the 'wiggle match' [14]C dating technique. The AMS method is usually required to date small, closely spaced samples across important transitions within a peat sequence, and the resultant pattern of age determinations can be compared with patterns of atmospheric

[14]C variability derived from dendrocalibration curves (van Geel & Mook 1989). The method has been applied successfully on some well studied peat sequences from The Netherlands (e.g. Kilian *et al.* 1995; van Geel *et al.* 1996), enabling age estimates within years rather than centuries. The wet shift between *c.* 4.1 and 3.6 ka cal. BP inferred from the Wester Ross peat sequences would be an ideal candidate for wiggle match dating in the future because of its strong support within the sequences and its broad agreement with peat stratigraphic data from elsewhere in Europe.

Since short-term atmospheric ^{14}C variability is related to changes in solar activity during the mid- to late Holocene (Stuiver & Braziunas 1993), wiggle match dating has the added advantage of allowing the hypothesized climatic effects of solar forcing to be tested in relation to the peat hydrological record. However, the precision of wiggle match dating itself depends upon the time interval of interest and its relationship to past changes in the atmospheric ratio of ^{14}C to ^{12}C which produce wiggles in the dendrocalibration curves. Additionally, the cost of obtaining a large number of AMS radiocarbon dates can be prohibitive, and a preliminary radiocarbon-based chronostratigraphy is often necessary before choosing which horizons to date by the wiggle match technique.

Tephrochronology provides another means of obtaining better age control on peat sequences in areas where tephras have been deposited. By analysing tephra shards found in peat it is possible to attribute shards to regional tephras which are known from historical accounts, or which have already been radiocarbon dated precisely using the wiggle match technique. Several Icelandic eruptions have deposited tephras in northern Scotland (Blackford *et al.* 1992; Dugmore *et al.* 1995) which may be preserved in many Scottish peatlands. Yet, the preservation of a tephra layer can depend on site-related conditions, and tephra layers do not always coincide with horizons of interest. Nonetheless, tephra layers can provide valuable age-equivalent marker horizons, and, when used with regional pollen horizons, they can provide some chronological control (e.g. Charman *et al.* 1995).

The usefulness of the peatland archive would also be enhanced by advances in deriving quantitative climatic information. Past attempts to produce continuous temperature records from peatlands have mainly centred around the analysis of stable isotopes. Using known relationships between temperature and the ratios of hydrogen (^{2}H/^{1}H) and oxygen (^{18}O/^{16}O) in precipitation, some climatic reconstructions

have been attempted from isotopic measurements of plant cellulose derived from raised bogs (Brenninkmeijer *et al.* 1982; Dupont 1986; Dupont & Mook 1987; Aucour *et al.* 1996). For instance, Dupont (1986) used ^{2}H/^{1}H data from a peatland in The Netherlands to infer a mean annual temperature decline of over 1°C between 4.0 and 3.0 ka cal. BP. However, using a similar approach on recent peat from Ireland, van Geel & Middeldorp (1988) found a poor relationship between ^{2}H/^{1}H data and changes in climate known from historical records, highlighting the difficulty in accounting for species-controlled variability in leaf-water enrichment and biochemical fractionation of isotopes during photosynthesis.

Efforts have also been directed at using stable carbon isotopes in peats to infer past changes in climate and/or concentrations of atmospheric CO_2. Such reconstructions based on carbon isotopes have been more successful in tropical/subtropical environments where large differences in ^{13}C/^{12}C ratios can occur due to past changes in the abundance of plants using either the C_3 or C_4 photosynthetic pathways (e.g. Aucour *et al.* 1994). By exploiting differences in the assimilation of atmospheric CO_2 between *Sphagnum* mosses and sedges, quantitative reconstructions of past atmospheric CO_2 based on stable carbon isotope data from peat have been produced (White *et al.* 1994; Figge & White 1995). However, these reconstructions have been criticized for underestimating the variability in ^{13}C/^{12}C ratios of *Sphagnum* which can occur due to localized changes in water supply and microhabitat (Rice & Giles 1994; Price *et al.* 1997). The value of stable isotope analyses ought to increase with further studies which focus on individual species within peat sequences, and which compare isotope ratios with other geochemical and palaeoecological data.

Conclusions

Peatlands have much potential as a terrestrial source of palaeoclimatic information because of the continuous and high-resolution stratigraphic records which they contain. Furthermore, deep peat deposits are widespread in temperate/oceanic and boreal regions of Eurasia and North America, yet relatively few have been studied intensively. This study, based in Wester Ross, Scotland, illustrates how an analysis of peat sequences can lead to a better understanding of regional patterns of past climatic change. The most interesting feature of the record is the oscillation between drier and wetter climatic conditions during the mid-Holocene. As investigation of Holocene climatic changes is becoming a new priority for palaeoclimatic research (Maslin & Berger 1997); improving and extending peat-based records could prove even more profitable in the future.

I am grateful to the CVCP Overseas Research Students Award Scheme, the Oxford University Overseas Bursary, the NERC (radiocarbon dating allocation number 563/1293), the Dudley Stamp Memorial Trust and the Bill Bishop Memorial Trust for funding and support while conducting doctoral research. I am also grateful to F. A. Street-Perrott and R. A. Perrott for assistance in planning the project, and I thank R. A. Perrott, A. G. Parker and H. Kalle for help in the field. Finally, I am grateful to K. E. Barber and an anonymous referee for valuable comments on an earlier manuscript.

References

AABY, B. 1976. Cyclic climatic variations in climate over the past 5500 years reflected in raised bogs. *Nature*, **263**, 281–284.

——1986. Palaeoecological studies of mires. *In*: BERGLUND, B. E. (ed.) *Handbook of Holocene Palaeoecology and Palaeohydrology*. Wiley, Chichester, 145–160.

—— & TAUBER, H. 1975. Rates of peat formation in relation to degree of humification and local environment, as shown by studies of a raised bog in Denmark. *Boreas*, **4**, 1–17.

ANDERSON, D. E. 1995. *An abrupt mid-Holocene decline of* Pinus sylvestris *in Glen Torridon, north-west Scotland, and implications for palaeoclimatic change*. Oxford School of Geography Research Papers, **52**, 1–29.

——1996. *Abrupt Holocene climatic change recorded in terrestrial peat sequences from Wester Ross, Scotland*. DPhil thesis, University of Oxford.

——1998. A reconstruction of Holocene climatic changes from peat bogs in northwest Scotland. *Boreas*, **27**, 208–229.

——, BINNEY, H. A. & SMITH, M. A. 1998. Evidence for abrupt climatic change in northern Scotland between 3900 and 3500 calendar years BP. *The Holocene*, **8**, 97–103.

AUCOUR, A.-M., HILLAIRE-MARCEL, C. & BONNEFILLE, R. 1994. Late Quaternary biomass changes from ^{13}C measurements in a highland peatbog from equatorial Africa (Burundi). *Quaternary Research*, **41**, 225–233.

——, —— & ——1996. Oxygen isotopes in cellulose from modern and Quaternary intertropical peatbogs: implications for palaeohydrology. *Chemical Geology*, **129**, 341–359.

BARBER, K. E. 1981. *Peat Stratigraphy and Climatic Change*. Balkema, Rotterdam.

——1993. Peatlands as scientific archives of past biodiversity. *Biodiversity and Conservation*, **2**, 474–489.

——1994. Deriving Holocene palaeoclimates from peat stratigraphy: some misconceptions regarding the sensitivity and continuity of the record. *Quaternary Newsletter*, **72**, 1–9.

——, CHAMBERS, F. M., MADDY, D., STONEMAN, R. & BREW, J. S. 1994. A sensitive high-resolution record of late Holocene climatic change from a raised bog in northern England. *The Holocene*, **4**, 198–205.

BENGTSSON, L. & ENELL, M. 1986. Chemical analysis. *In*: BERGLUND, B. E. (ed.) *Handbook of Holocene Palaeoecology and Palaeohydrology*. Wiley, Chichester, 423–448.

BENNETT, K. D. 1984. The post-glacial history of *Pinus sylvestris* in the British Isles. *Quaternary Science Reviews*, **3**, 133–155.

——1995. Post-glacial dynamics of pine (*Pinus sylvestris* L.) and pinewoods in Scotland. *In*: ALDHOUS, J. R. (ed.) *Our Pinewood Heritage*. Forestry Commission, RSPB, SNH, Inverness, 23–39.

BINNEY, H. A. 1997. *Holocene environmental change in the Scottish Highlands: multiproxy evidence from blanket peats*. PhD thesis, London Guildhall University.

BIRKS, H. H. 1972. Studies in the vegetational history of Scotland III: A radiocarbon dated pollen diagram from Loch Maree, Ross and Cromarty. *New Phytologist*, **71**, 731–754.

——1975. Studies in the vegetational history of Scotland IV: Pine stumps in Scottish blanket peats. *Philosophical Transactions of the Royal Society, London*, **B270**, 181–226.

BIRKS, H. J. B. 1996. Great Britain–Scotland. *In*: BERGLUND, B. E., BIRKS, H. J. B., RALSKA-JASIEWICZOWA, M. & WRIGHT, H. E. (eds) *Palaeoecological Events During the Last 15 000 Years*. Wiley, Chichester, 95–143.

—— & WILLIAMS, W. 1983. Late Quaternary vegetational history of the Inner Hebrides. *Proceedings of the Royal Society of Edinburgh*, **B83**, 269–292.

BLACKFORD, J. J. 1990. *Blanket mires and climatic change; a palaeoecological study based on peat humification and microfossil analysis*. PhD thesis, University of Keel.

——1993. Peat bogs as sources of proxy climatic data: past approaches and future research. *In*: CHAMBERS, F. M. (ed.) *Climate Change and Human Impact on the Landscape*. Chapman & Hall, London, 47–55.

—— & CHAMBERS, F. M. 1991. Proxy records of climate from blanket mires: evidence for a Dark Age (1400 BP) climatic deterioration in the British Isles. *The Holocene*, **1**, 63–67.

—— & ——1993. Determining the degree of peat decomposition for peat-based palaeoclimatic studies. *International Peat Journal*, **5**, 7–24.

—— & ——1995. Proxy climate record for the last 1000 years from Irish blanket peat and a possible link to solar variability. *Earth and Planetary Science Letters*, **133**, 145–150.

——, EDWARDS, K. J., DUGMORE, A. J., COOK, G. T. & BUCKLAND, P. C. 1992. Icelandic volcanic ash and the mid-Holocene Scots pine (*Pinus sylvestris*) pollen decline in northern Scotland. *The Holocene*, **2**, 260–265.

BLYTT, A. 1876. *Essay on the Immigration of the Norwegian Flora During Alternating Rainy and Dry Periods.* Cammermeyer, Kristiana.

BRENNINKMEIJER, C. A. M., VAN GEEL, B. & MOOK, W. G. 1982. Variations in the D/H and $^{18}O/^{16}O$ ratios in cellulose extracted from a peat bog core. *Earth and Planetary Science Letters,* **61**, 283–290.

CHARMAN, D. J. 1994. Late-glacial and Holocene vegetation history of the Flow Country, northern Scotland. *New Phytologist,* **127**, 155–168.

——, WEST, S., KELLY, A. & GRATTAN, J. 1995. Environmental change and tephra deposition: the Strath of Kildonan, Northern Scotland. *Journal of Archaeological Science,* **22**, 799–809.

CLYMO, R. S. 1984. The limits to peat bog growth. *Philosophical Transactions of the Royal Society, London,* **B303**, 605–654.

CROWLEY, T. J. & NORTH, G. R. 1991. *Paleoclimatology.* Clarendon, Oxford.

DUGMORE, A. J., COOK, G. T., SHORE, J. S., NEWTON, A. J., EDWARDS, K. J. & LARSEN, G. 1995. Radiocarbon dating tephra layers in Britain and Iceland. *Radiocarbon,* **37**, 379–388.

DUPONT, L. M. 1986. Temperature and rainfall variation in the Holocene based on comparative palaeoecology and isotope geology of a hummock and a hollow (Bourtangerveen, The Netherlands). *Review of Palaeobotany and Palynology,* **48**, 71–159.

—— & MOOK, W. G. 1987. Palaeoclimate analysis of $^{2}H/^{1}H$ ratios in peat sequences with variable plant composition. *Chemical Geology,* **66**, 323–333.

FIGGE, R. A. & WHITE, J. W. C. 1995. High-resolution Holocene and late glacial atmospheric CO_2 record: variability tied to changes in thermohaline circulation. *Global Biogeochemical Cycles,* **9**, 391–403.

GEAR, A. J. & HUNTLEY, B. 1991. Rapid changes in the range limits of Scots pine 4000 years ago. *Science,* **251**, 544–547.

HENDON, D. & CHARMAN, D. J. 1997. The preparation of testate amoebae (Protozoa: Rhizopoda) samples from peat. *The Holocene,* **7**, 199–205.

INGRAM, H. A. P. 1978. Soil layers in mires: function and terminology. *Journal of Soil Science,* **29**, 224–227.

JOHNSON, L. C. & DAMMAN, A. W. H. 1991. Species controlled *Sphagnum* decay on a south Swedish raised bog. *Oikos,* **61**, 234–242.

KERSLAKE, P. 1982. *Vegetational history of wooded Islands in Scottish lochs.* PhD thesis, University of Cambridge.

KILIAN, M. R., VAN DER PLICHT, J. & VAN GEEL, B. 1995. Dating raised bogs: New aspects of AMS ^{14}C wiggle matching, a reservoir effect and climatic change. *Quaternary Science Reviews,* **14**, 959–966.

KLINGER, L. F., ELIAS, S. A., BEHAN-PELLETIER, V. M. & WILLIAMS, N. E. 1990. The bog climax hypothesis: fossil arthropod and stratigraphic evidence in peat sections from southeast Alaska, USA. *Holarctic Ecology,* **13**, 72–80.

KORHOLA, A. 1995. Holocene climatic variations in southern Finland reconstructed from peat-initiation data. *The Holocene,* **5**, 43–58.

——1996. Initiation of a sloping mire complex in southwestern Finland: Autogenic *versus* allogenic controls. *Ecoscience,* **3**, 216–222.

LAMB, H. H. 1982. *Climate History and the Modern World.* Methuen, London.

LOWE, J. J. 1993. Isolating the climatic factors in early- and mid-Holocene palaeobotanical records from Scotland. *In*: CHAMBERS, F. M. (ed.) *Climate Change and Human Impact on the Landscape.* Chapman & Hall, London, 67–80.

MCVEAN, D. N. & RATCLIFFE, D. A. 1962. *Plant Communities of the Scottish Highlands.* HMSO, London.

MALTERER, T. J., VERRY, E. S. & ERJAVEC, J. 1992. Peat classification in relation to several methods used to determine fiber content and degree of decomposition. *In*: *Proceedings of the 9th International Peat Congress.* International Peat Society, Uppsala, Sweden, 310–318.

MASLIN, M. A. & BERGER, A. 1997. A European view of the future of palaeoclimate research. *Quaternary Science Reviews,* **16**, 501–504.

MOORE, P. D. 1972. The initiation of peat formation and the development of peat deposits in mid-Wales. *In*: *Proceedings of the 4th International Peat Congress.* International Peat Society, Otaniemi, Finland, 89–100.

——1986a. Hydrological changes in mires. *In*: BERGLUND, B. E. (ed.) *Handbook of Holocene Palaeoecology and Palaeohydrology.* Wiley, Chichester, 91–105.

——1986b. Man and Mire: a long and wet relationship. *Transactions of the Botanical Society of Edinburgh,* **45**, 77–95.

——1991. Ups and downs in peatland. *Nature,* **353**, 299–300.

——, EVANS, A. T. & CHATER, M. 1986. Palynological and stratigraphic evidence for hydrological changes in mires associated with human activity. *In*: BEHRE, K. E. (ed.) *Anthropogenic Indicators in Pollen Diagrams.* Balkema, Rotterdam, 209–220.

——, WEBB, J. A. & COLLINSON, M. E. 1991. *Pollen Analysis.* Blackwell, Oxford.

NILSSEN, E. & VORREN, K. D. 1991. Peat humification and climate history. *Norsk Geologisk Tiddskrift,* **71**, 215–217.

PENNINGTON, W., HAWORTH, E. Y., BONNY, A. P. & LISHMAN, J. P. 1972. Lake sediments in northern Scotland. *Philosophical Transactions of the Royal Society, London,* **B264**, 194–294.

PILCHER, J. R. 1993. Radiocarbon dating and the palynologist: a realistic approach to precision and accuracy. *In*: CHAMBERS, F. M. (ed.) *Climate Change and Human Impact on the Landscape.* Chapman & Hall, London, 47–55.

PRICE, G. D., MCKENZIE, J. E., PILCHER, J. R. & HOPER, S. T. 1997. Carbon-isotope variation in *Sphagnum* from hummock–hollow complexes: implications for Holocene climate reconstruction. *The Holocene,* **7**, 229–233.

RICE, S. K. & GILES, L. 1994. Climate in the Pleistocene. *Nature*, **371**, 111.

SERNANDER, R. 1908. On the evidences of Post-glacial changes of climate furnished by the peat-mosses of Northern Europe. *Geologiska Foreningens i Stockholm Forhandlingar*, **30**, 467–478.

SMITH, A. G. & PILCHER, J. R. 1973. Radiocarbon dates and vegetational history of the British Isles. *New Phytologist*, **72**, 903–914.

SMITH, B. M. 1985. *A palaeoecological study of raised mires in the Humberhead Levels*. PhD thesis, University of Wales (Cardiff).

SMITH, M. A. 1996. *The role of vegetation dynamics and human activity in landscape changes through the Holocene in the Lairg area, Sutherland, Scotland*. PhD thesis, University of London (Royal Holloway).

STACE, C. 1991. *New flora of the British Isles*. Cambridge University Press.

STUIVER, M. & BRAZIUNAS, T. F. 1993. Sun, ocean, climate and atmospheric $^{14}CO_2$: An evaluation of causal and spectral relationships. *The Holocene*, **3**, 289–305.

—— & REIMER, P. J. 1993. Extended ^{14}C base and revised CALIB 3.0 ^{14}C age calibration program. *Radiocarbon*, **35**, 215–230.

SVENSSON, G. 1988. Fossil plant communities and regeneration patterns on a raised bog in south Sweden. *Journal of Ecology*, **76**, 41–59.

TOLONEN, K. 1986. Rhizopod analysis. *In*: BERGLUND, B. E. (ed.) *Handbook of Holocene Palaeoecology and Palaeohydrology*. Wiley, Chichester, 645–660.

VAN GEEL, B. 1978. A palaeoecological study of Holocene peat bog sections in Germany and the Netherlands, based on the analysis of pollen, spores and macro- and microscopic remains of fungi, algae, cormophytes and animals. *Review of Palaeobotany and Palynology*, **25**, 1–120.

——1986. Application of fungal and algal remains and other microfossils in palynological analyses. *In*: BERGLUND, B. E. (ed.) *Handbook of Holocene Palaeoecology and Palaeohydrology*. Wiley, Chichester, 497–505.

—— & MIDDELDORP, A. A. 1988. Vegetational history of Carbury Bog (Co. Kildare, Ireland) during the last 850 years and a test of the temperature indicator value of $^2H/^1H$ measurements of peat samples in relation to historical sources and meteorological data. *New Phytologist*, **109**, 377–392.

—— & MOOK, W. G. 1989. High-resolution ^{14}C dating of organic deposits using natural atmospheric ^{14}C variations. *Radiocarbon*, **31**, 151–155.

——, BUURMAN, J. & WATERBOLK, H. T. 1996. Archaeological and palaeoecological indications of an abrupt climate change in The Netherlands, and evidence for climatological teleconnections around 2650 BP. *Journal of Quaternary Science*, **11**, 451–460.

WARNER, B. G. & CHARMAN, D. J. 1994. Holocene soil moisture changes on a peatland in north-western Ontario based on fossil testate amoebae (Protozoa) analysis. *Boreas*, **23**, 270–279.

WHITE, J. W. C., CIAIS, P., FIGGE, R. A. & MARKGRAF, V. 1994. A high-resolution record of atmospheric CO_2 content from carbon isotopes in peat. *Nature*, **367**, 153–156.

WIMBLE, G. A. 1986. *The palaeoecology of lowland coastal raised mires of south Cumbria*. PhD thesis, University of Wales (Cardiff).

Late Quaternary evolution of the central and southern Kalahari: environmental responses to changing climatic conditions

STEPHEN STOKES, RICHARD WASHINGTON & ANTHONY PRESTON

School of Geography, University of Oxford, Mansfield Road, Oxford OXI 3QJ, UK

Abstract: Hitherto, explanations of regional environmental changes within the Mega Kalahari of central Southern Africa have been based either on evidence collected from scarce cave deposits and marginal coastal sequences, or on broad-scale inferences of global low latitude responses to changing insolation parameters. Such interpretations do not properly take into account the profound effects on airmass stability and rainfall distribution of the globally unparalleled temperature contrast between the southeast Atlantic and southern Indian Oceans. Two approaches are employed here: first, optical dating is used to provide an absolute chronology for the presently inactive, linear dunes and related deposits; secondly, a deterministic Atmospheric General Circulation Model simulation for the past century is developed to reveal the controls on the contemporary Kalahari climate. The data suggest that dramatic shifts in the NE–SW rainfall gradient resulted in periods of widespread aridity and dune reactivation at *c.* 115–95, 46–41, 26–20, 16–10 ka BP. More recent periods of dune deposition have been recorded only in the southwestern desert core. Large-scale wet–dry transitions can be explained in relation to changes in sea surface temperatures in the adjacent southeast Atlantic. Explaining long-term variations in wind energy is more complex, although a low frequency mode of variability may be linked to the strength of outflow from the Asian monsoon and associated ridging anticyclones in the adjacent south Indian Ocean.

Large desert basins such as the Mega Kalahari of central Southern Africa (Fig. 1) are a potentially potent source of palaeoenvironmental information (Thomas & Shaw, 1991*b*), and many researchers have focused attention on extracting this record. Studies have integrated a wide range of data sources including terrestrial archives (e.g. Warren 1970; Street & Grove 1976; Ritchie *et al.* 1985; Lancaster 1990; Kropelin & Soulie-Marsche, 1991; Gasse 1994). Others have focused on chemical and physical characteristics of sediments in adjacent oceans (e.g. Parkin & Shackleton 1973; Sarnthein *et al.* 1981; Prell & Van Campo, 1986; de Menocal *et al.* 1993). Although limited in temporal coverage, studies of closed-lake basins of the northern hemisphere have provided perhaps the clearest picture of climatic changes which have taken place since the last glacial maximum (Petit-Maire & Riser 1981; Street-Perrott *et al.* 1989; Gasse *et al.* 1990; Petit-Maire 1993; Van Campo & Gasse 1993; Street-Perrott 1994). In relation to the Quaternary desert basins of Africa, two main models have emerged: a 'passive' African climate model which suggests that independent climate changes at high latitudes are the key determinant of Afri-

can palaeoenvironments (e.g. de Menocal *et al.* 1993); and an 'active' African climate model in which changes in the location and abundance of rainfall driven by low latitude insolation levels are the significant determinant (e.g. Blomendal & de Menocal 1989). A third model which identifies both factors playing deterministic roles during discrete climatic periods has also been described (Prell & Van Campo 1986).

Almost without exception, these models have been developed by considering a combination of proxy records and climatic boundary conditions for the Sahara Desert, with a mirroring of conditions in the Mega Kalahari to the south being assumed (e.g. Heine 1982; Van Zinderen Bakker 1982). This view has recently been questioned on the basis of radiocarbon-dated evidence from lake and cave sequences in central southern Africa (Shaw *et al.* 1988; Shaw & Thomas 1996), but is generally supported by analysis of deep-sea cores from high southern latitudes (Charles *et al.* 1996). The aeolian sequences which dominate the landscapes of both hemispheres in low latitude continental settings have not, however, been widely utilized in such reconstructions, primarily owing to

STOKES, S., WASHINGTON, R. & PRESTON, A. 1998. Late Quaternary evolution of the central and southern Kalahari: environmental responses to changing climatic conditions *In*: ANDREWS, P. & BANHAM, P. (eds) *Late Cenozoic Environments and Hominid Evolution: a tribute to Bill Bishop.* Geological Society, London, 247–268.

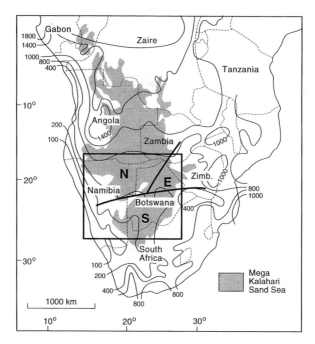

Fig 1. The extent of the Mega Kalahari (adapted from (Thomas & Shaw 1991a). Northern (N), eastern (E) and southern (S) sectors of Kalahari Desert are delineated. Annual rainfall distributions for Southern Africa (isohyets in mm) are also plotted. Area enclosed in rectangle identifies approximate area of Fig. 2.

difficulties in establishing absolute chronological controls (Shaw et al. 1988; Thomas & Shaw 1991b; Lancaster 1995).

The arid to semi-arid Mega Kalahari region of central Southern Africa (Fig. 1) covers an area in excess of 2.5 million km² and constitutes the largest continuous sand sea on Earth (Thomas & Shaw, 1991a). The preserved record of environmental changes includes palaeolake basins, ephemeral stream channels and widespread, presently inactive and in places extensively degraded, aeolian dune forms, those of the linear variety being most abundant (Thomas, 1983). Rainfall in the Mega Kalahari occurs during the austral summer period and exhibits a pronounced NE–SW gradient. This gradient is attributable to the meridional alignment of convection over Southern Africa. The large cross-continental zonal asymmetry of tropical convection relates directly to sea surface temperatures (SST) in the adjacent oceans; the inter-tropical convergence zone (ITCZ) in the SW Indian Ocean occupies the most southerly location of any ocean at 23°S, while tropical convection in the eastern Atlantic is restricted to areas north of 5°N (Stokes et al. 1997b). The SW Indian Ocean is the warmest ocean at 23°S while the SE Atlantic is the coldest (present-day January mean of

27.5 and 21.6°C, respectively). The extreme SST contrast across the subcontinent determines the Southern African rainfall gradient. Wetter conditions east of the Kalahari result from disturbances in the tropical easterlies associated with the Mascarene anticyclone. Westward propagation of easterly waves off the African subcontinent is blocked by cold stable air overlying the Benguela Current. Conditions west of the wave axis are therefore dry. Intense subsidence into subtropical anticyclones dominates the climatology of the austral winter, ensuring aridity. Additionally, the elevated southern African landmass (2000 m) cools through long-wave emission thereby providing an interhemispheric sink for Asian Monsoon outflow (Harrison 1986). Figure 2 shows the mean 200 hPa velocity potential for July averaged over a 16 year period from National Center for Environmental Prediction (NCEP) Reanalysis data (Kalnay et al. 1996). These data, which show the non-rotational component of upper tropospheric mass transport, clearly demonstrate the importance of mass outflow from the Asian Monsoon and its delivery to southern Africa.

Under the present climatic conditions the winter circulation in the region is governed by flow around the continental anticyclone which

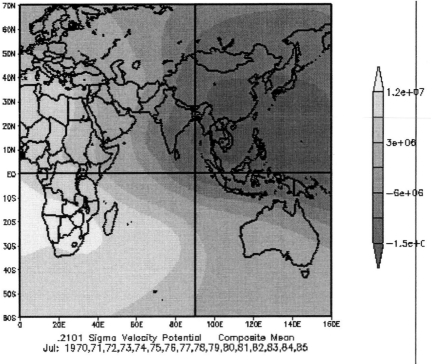

Fig. 2. July long-term mean (1979–1985) air flow near the top of the atmosphere (200 hPa) from the NCEP Reanalysis Project. The flow shown is the velocity potential (i.e. non-rotating component of flow).

results in a combination of easterly flow over the interior of the subcontinent and north to north-westerly winds in the southwestern core of the basin (Stokes *et al.* 1997*b*). Figure 3 shows the July mean near-surface 850 hPa wind vectors and contoured speeds from NCEP Reanaly-sis data, and Fig. 4 shows the June–September mean 850 hPa geopotential field. The dominance of the near-surface austral winter anticyclone circulation is clear. Contemporary aeolian activity in the Kalahari is severely limited by a combination of excessive annual rainfall and insufficient wind energy, even in the driest, southwestern area of the sand sea (Breed *et al.* 1979; Wiggs *et al.* 1995).

Linear dunes of the Kalahari have been classified into three discrete dune fields (Lan-caster 1989; Thomas & Shaw 1991*a*) (Fig. 1): The southwestern field occurs south of latitude 23°S, and is centred between 18 and 22°E. This area constitutes the driest part of the Kalahari, with the aeolian landscape dominated by well pre-served, partially vegetated, steep-sided (mean slope 13.4° (Lancaster 1988); heights ranging from 5 to 25 m), asymmetrical linear dunes that predominantly trend NW–SE, and sporadic pans with associated lunette dunes (Bullard *et al.*

1995). While the dunes of the SW portion of the Kalahari are least degraded and therefore the youngest, the wind regime at present is not sufficiently strong to induce widespread aeolian sediment transportation (Bullard *et al.* 1996). The northern dune field occurs north of latitude 23°S and consists almost exclusively of linear dune forms and is bounded by Etosha Pan to the west and the Okavango Delta to the east (Fig. 5). Linear dune trend lines form an arc which varies from WNW–ESE through to WSW–ENE. The dunes are vegetation covered, and are frequently extensively degraded, although in places dune heights may reach up to 25 m (Grove 1969; Thomas & Shaw 1991*a*). Occurring in an area where rainfall currently exceeds 400 mm per annum and increases northwards to 1200 mm per annum, these aeolian features have fre-quently been described as some of the strongest evidence for previous periods of enhanced aridity (Thomas 1983). The dunes of the eastern dune field, occupying the area north of 23°S, and west of the Okavango Delta and eastwards beyond the Gwayi River (Fig. 1), have similarly been identified as strong evidence for past periods of enhanced aridity (e.g. Bond 1948; Flint & Bond 1968; Thomas 1984). Annual present-day

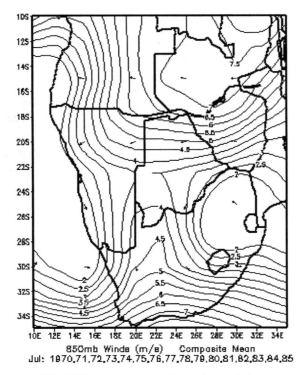

Fig. 3. July long-term mean NCEP 850 hPa vector winds (arrows) and wind speeds (contoured).

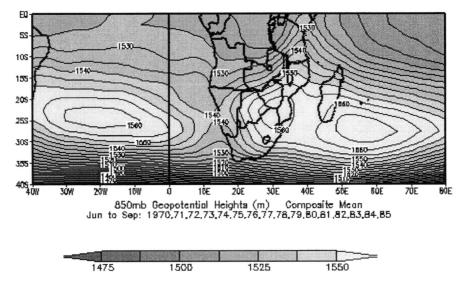

Fig. 4. Height of June–September mean 850 hPa pressure field (geopotential). This essentially shows pressure distribution at 1.5 km above the surface.

rainfall totals in this region of up to 800 mm have resulted in an extensively degraded dune landscape recognizable for the most part by contrasting dune and interdune vegetation com- munities. As an area marginal to the core of southern African aridity, which is centred on the Namib and southwest Kalahari deserts, desicca- tion during arid periods was probably late to

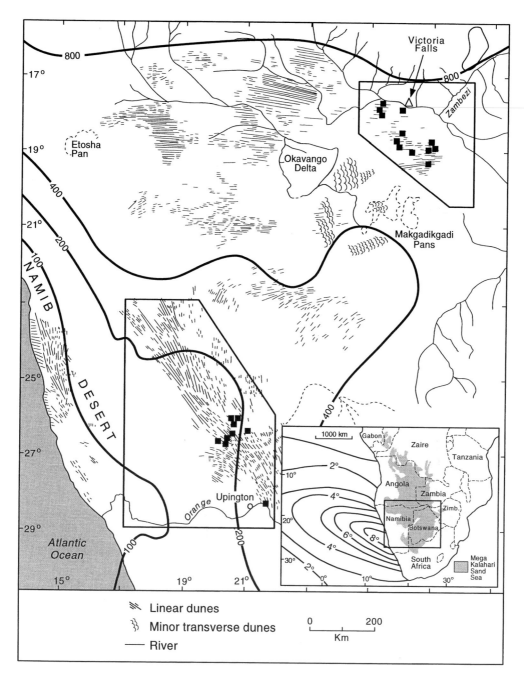

Fig. 5. Sample sites within the linear dune systems of the NE and SW Kalahari (specific localities are shown by ■). Isohyets (–100–) show present-day mean annual rainfall in the region and demonstrate the NE–SW regional rainfall gradient in the continental interior. Inset shows symmetrical Indian–Atlantic Ocean mean (1951–1980) temperature differences in °C for January period. The temperature difference contours show the cold anomaly of the Atlantic Ocean relative to the Indian Ocean.

arrive and relatively short-lived; being replaced by more humid conditions which accentuate pedogenesis, vegetation and dune stabilization.

Direct quantification of the climatic factors which most strongly influence the degree of region-wide desiccation (specifically wind regime and precipitation) is complicated by the short length (for wind regime at most two to three decades) and spatial paucity of most instrumental records. As such, analysis of the variability of the regional climate during this or previous periods and interpretations of the sensitivity of the dune systems to climatic changes have been made on a somewhat speculative basis.

This study provides a chronology of linear ridges in the northeastern and southwestern dune fields, based on optical dating of quartz sand grains, and additionally interrogates a century-long data set generated from an Atmospheric General Circulation Model (AGCM) to identify significant climatic factors which influence variations in rainfall and wind energy over the Kalahari. Some aspects of these studies have already been described in Stokes *et al.* (1997*a*), and Thomas *et al.* (1997*a, b*). We first present summary findings of the optical dating programme, and then consider possible factors affecting regional moisture availability and windiness for the past century.

Study areas

Two study areas were selected from opposite ends of the NE–SW rainfall gradient which effectively represent basin marginal (NE) and basin core (SW) localities. Some details of each locality are provided below.

Dunes of eastern system

The extent of Kalahari sediments and linear dune ridges of the northeastern dune field is depicted in Fig. 5. Dune topography is most clearly reflected in contrasting dune ridge and interdune trough vegetation patterns (Bond 1948). Previous descriptions of these features have been provided (Bond 1948; Flint & Bond 1968; Thomas 1983; Thomas & Shaw 1991*a*; Lancaster 1995). The dune ridges are generally broader and more widely spaced than the linear dunes of the southwest Kalahari. Dune spacing ranges from 1500–2500 m and individual ridge widths range from 500 to 2500 m (Thomas & Shaw, 1991*a*). Heights of the ridges above the interdune troughs are typically low (<10 m), especially given the considerable width of the

features, although some have been recorded up to a maximum height of 22.5 m (Thomas 1984). Dune ridge orientation varies in a systematic arc-like pattern across the dune field from an orientation WNW–ESE in the east and north of the field, to ENE–WSW to the west where the ridges intersect the Botswana border (Fig. 5).

While rainfall levels in the region are presently relatively high, they are highly seasonal with 80% of the total rains falling during the summer (October–April) season. Low relative humidity and high year-round temperatures result in annual potential evapotranspiration that exceeds 2000 mm (Thomas & Shaw 1991*a*). Definitive statements on the wind regime are problematic owing to the paucity of data (for discussion, see Thomas 1984). A complex wind regime is, however, apparent, exhibiting net resultant sand drift directions from ESE to WNW, a direction close but not identical to the trend of the linear dunes. Total drift potential of the current wind field is low (Fryberger & Dean 1979) and incapable of significant aeolian sand transportation (Heine 1982; Thomas 1984).

All previous studies have inferred extensive degradation of the initial linear dunes to generate the subdued ridges that are present today. Within the dune ridges primary sedimentary structures have been destroyed. Active agents in this degradation process include sheet-wash erosion (Flint & Bond 1968) and bioturbation (Thomas 1984). Internally, the dune sediment appears as largely structureless red sand interrupted only by scarce, laterally continuous zones of charcoal, and at depth in some pits, by post-depositional wavy non-parallel laminations that in part mimic former primary sedimentary structures. Post-depositional reddening of the sand has also occurred, the degree of reddening varying systematically from the south (7.5 YR–10 YR) to the north (2.5 YR–5 YR) within the study area. This has previously been used to infer a north–south (older–younger) relative dune chronosequence (Thomas 1984).

Dunes of the southwestern system

The southwestern Kalahari desert is presently the driest part of the Mega Kalahari. It is centred on the Northern Cape Province, South Africa, but also encompasses portions of eastern Namibia and Western Botswana (Fig. 1). The area is presently semi-arid (annual rainfall 150–200 mm) and vegetation consists of perennial and annual grasses and sparse shrubs (Stokes *et al.* 1997*b*). As with the eastern dune system, linear dunes, varying in height from 3 to

20 m dominate the aeolian landscape. In the southwest, however, the linear dunes exhibit a more varied range of depositional styles which Bullard et al. (1995) subdivided into five classes based on ridge continuity and degree of intersection. In addition to linear dunes, lunette dunes associated with pans, and patches of hummocky dunes in localized areas are key morphological components of the southwestern dune system (Stokes et al. 1997a). Dominant wind flow in this area is north to northwesterly, and although linear dunes generally trend approximately in this direction detailed analysis of wind records available over the past two decades indicate that the calculated resultant drift directions for many sites are not consistent with average dune orientations (Bullard et al. 1996). The most detailed contemporary aerodynamic studies of the region have been undertaken by Bullard et al. (1996) who generally found the wind directions to be variable, and the wind regime incapable of transporting large amounts of aeolian sediment.

Internally, the dune sediments are largely structureless red sand with poorly developed soils and little evidence of depositional hiatuses or primary sedimentary structures. Postdepositional reddening in this area has resulted in 2.5 YR through to 5 YR dune coloration.

Optical dating

Samples were collected for optical dating during three field seasons (1992, 1993 and 1995). The distribution of sampling localities is shown in Fig. 5. Summary locality and stratigraphic data are also provided in Table 1. Samples were collected by hammering light-proof PVC cylinders of known volume (c. 500 cm) horizontally into the vertical walls of freshly cleaned exposures prepared at each site. The ends of the cylinders were sealed with black tape and placed in black polythene bags for transportation to the dating laboratory in Oxford. In the laboratory, samples were processed under subdued red light.

Details of the optical dating method and related phenomenon are provided elsewhere (Aitken 1985, 1989, 1992; Huntley et al. 1985; Smith et al. 1990; Stokes 1994). A portion of each sample was wet-sieved to separate the 90–150 μm size fraction and immersed for two days in HCl to remove carbonate, followed by immersion for two days in H_2O_2 to remove organic matter. Heavy minerals (density $2.72 \, g \, cm^{-3}$) were removed from the treated sample fraction by magnetic and heavy liquid (sodium polytungstate) separations. The samples were then treated

with 48% HF for 60 min, and H_2SiF_6 for four days in order to concentrate quartz grains further. The quartz separates were then mounted as monolayers (approximately 5 mg per disc) onto 10 mm diameter stainless steel discs using a silicone spray adhesive (Silkospray).

Palaeodoses were calculated using the multiple aliquot dose method (Aitken 1992). The aliquots were exposed to an argon laser (Coherent 2W), operated at an emission wavelength of 514.5 nm and at a power output level at the sample of $40 \, mW \, cm^{-2}$. The resulting sample optically stimulated luminescence (OSL) emissions were detected using a photomultiplier filtered by BG-39 and Corning 7-51 glass filters. Prior to OSL measurements, aliquots were preheated to remove geologically unstable charge populations created during laboratory irradiation procedures. The preheat procedure involved heating the discs at 160°C for 16 h, or 220°C for 5 min. More detailed accounts of experimental conditions may be found in Stokes et al. (1997a, b).

Dose rate estimation was undertaken both in the field via portable gamma spectrometry and in the laboratory via instrumental neutron activation analysis. Sample splits for laboratory-based dose rate determinations were crushed and homogenized by ring milling for 1 h. Conversion from concentrations to dose rate followed the procedures outlined in (Aitken 1985). The optical dates calculated incorporate both random and systematic errors (Aitken & Alldred 1972) and are quoted to ±one standard deviation.

Dune system chronologies

The resulting age estimates of dune sediment deposition range from c. 157 to 1 ka BP and exhibit considerable contrasts between the two dune fields (Table 1). When observed independent of location or sampling depth the data set is suggestive of a virtual continuum of dune activity spanning much of the latter half of the last glacial period (c. 10–50 ka BP), with evidence of less frequent and spatially restricted activity during the middle and later Holocene, and also between 100 and 50 ka BP. Examination of the chronology of the dune deposits within a stratigraphic framework provides a clearer picture of dune age (Fig. 6).

The four types of aeolian deposit sampled in the southwest Kalahari yielded contrasting age assessments spanning the last c. 30 ka BP (Fig. 6; Table 1). Samples from basal sediments within linear dunes consistently yielded ages exceeding 20 ka BP, while analyses on sands from the body of dunes describing the main linear forms of the

Table 1. *Summary of optical dating samples and results*

Sample	Lat.	Long.	Locality/description	Sample depth (m)	Radioactivity data K₂O (%)	Th (ppm)	U (ppm)	D_cosmic (Gy ka⁻¹)	Dose rate (Gy ka⁻¹)	Palaeodose (Gy)	Age (ka)
889/1	18°55′S	26°25′E	Nehimba Pan, Hwange, Zimbabwe	1.4	0.05 ± 0.01	1.60 ± 0.10	0.50 ± 0.06	0.18	0.46 ± 0.06	13.4 ± 0.08	29.44 ± 3.58
890/1	18°45′S	25°45′E	Shabi Shabi, Hwange, Zimbabwe (abandoned channel)	3.0	0.04 ± 0.01	0.50 ± 0.10	0.30 ± 0.05	0.14	0.28 ± 0.03	22.8 ± 3.80	82.12 ± 17.00
890/2	18°45′S	25°45′E	Shabi Shabi, Hwange, Zimbabwe (at campsite on dune)	2.0	0.08 ± 0.01	1.40 ± 0.10	0.70 ± 0.06	0.14	0.48 ± 0.05	10.5 ± 1.10	22.07 ± 3.23
891/1	18°50′S	25°50′E	Border security road (Botswana/Zimbabwe), Hwange, Zimbabwe	1.75	0.17 ± 0.02	1.30 ± 0.10	0.50 ± 0.06	0.18	0.53 ± 0.05	13.1 ± 1.50	24.75 ± 3.54
891/2	18°50′S	25°50′E	Border security road (Botswana/Zimbabwe), Hwange, Zimbabwe	0.9	0.17 ± 0.02	1.20 ± 0.10	0.50 ± 0.06	0.17	0.51 ± 0.05	12.6 ± 1.20	24.62 ± 3.24
892/1	19°15′S	26°22′E	south of Mitswiri, Hwange, Zimbabwe	1.2	0.07 ± 0.03	1.70 ± 0.10	0.60 ± 0.07	0.18	0.51 ± 0.09	11.0 ± 1.40	21.70 ± 4.61
892/2	19°15′S	26°22′E	south of Mitswiri, Hwange, Zimbabwe	0.7	0.07 ± 0.02	1.60 ± 0.10	0.60 ± 0.07	0.18	0.50 ± 0.08	7.0 ± 1.40	14.01 ± 3.61
893/1	18°35′S	26°30′E	Dopi Pan, Hwange, Zimbabwe	2.0	0.05 ± 0.02	1.30 ± 0.10	0.60 ± 0.07	0.18	0.46 ± 0.10		
894/1	18°55′S	26°41′E	Giraffe Springs, Hwange, Zimbabwe	1.2	0.07 ± 0.03	2.50 ± 0.10	1.00 ± 0.08	0.19	0.67 ± 0.16	7.1 ± 0.40	10.60 ± 2.54
895/1	18°43′S	26°57′E	Hwange Maincamp, Hwange, Zimbabwe	1.0	0.10 ± 0.03	1.50 ± 0.10	2.30 ± 0.10	0.18	0.91 ± 0.17	13.3 ± 3.00	14.60 ± 4.31
896/1	18°00′S	25°50′E	Victoria Falls rubbish dump, Victoria Falls, Zimbabwe	1.6	0.27 ± 0.05	2.60 ± 0.10	0.70 ± 0.08	0.18	0.75 ± 0.09	15.7 ± 5.60	21.01 ± 7.89
942/1	28°24′S	21°30′E	30 km E of Uppington on R27, near Orange River	3.5	0.56 ± 0.02	1.70 ± 0.18	0.40 ± 0.12	0.13	0.79 ± 0.15	11.0 ± 1.00	13.98 ± 3.03
942/2	28°24′S	21°30′E	30 km E of Uppington on R27, near Orange River	2.5	0.58 ± 0.02	2.00 ± 0.20	0.50 ± 0.13	0.14	0.86 ± 0.15	12.9 ± 0.70	15.03 ± 2.71
942/3	28°24′S	21°30′E	30 km E of Uppington on R27, near Orange River	1.5	0.66 ± 0.03	2.50 ± 0.20	0.50 ± 0.14	0.16	0.98 ± 0.18	11.2 ± 0.90	11.46 ± 2.25
943/1	26°33′S	20°35′E	Behind Schneider Ranch settlement, S of Twee Riveren, South Africa	1.5	0.88 ± 0.04	1.00 ± 0.16	0.30 ± 0.12	0.17	1.00 ± 0.27	10.4 ± 2.10	10.38 ± 3.53
944/1	26°39′S	20°36′E	Off main Uppington–Twee Riveren Hgwy, South Africa	1.55	0.94 ± 0.04	1.50 ± 0.17	0.40 ± 0.12	0.14	1.08 ± 0.23	18.1 ± 2.60	16.77 ± 4.29
945/1	26°14′S	26°14′S	Borrow pit, Twee Riveren–Nossob Hgwy	1.75	0.78 ± 0.03	1.80 ± 0.18	0.50 ± 0.13	0.16	1.02 ± 0.18	23.5 ± 3.60	23.04 ± 5.38
945/2	26°14′S	26°14′S	Borrow pit, Twee Riveren–Nossob Hgwy	0.8					0.94 ± 0.17	5.2 ± 1.50	5.52 ± 1.88
946b/1	26°27′S	20°48′E	Kalahari-Gemsbok National Park, Botswana	1.5	0.78 ± 0.03	1.80 ± 0.17	0.40 ± 0.12	0.17	1.01 ± 0.20	26.8 ± 5.30	26.63 ± 7.41
947/1	26°07′S	20°39′E	Hummocky dune, Kalahari-Gemsbok National Park, South Africa	2.0	0.36 ± 0.01	0.90 ± 0.16	0.20 ± 0.10	0.17	0.56 ± 0.16	1.0 ± 0.30	1.77 ± 0.72
947/2	26°07′S	20°39′E	Hummocky dune, Kalahari-Gemsbok National Park, South Africa	1.0	0.51 ± 0.02	0.90 ± 0.15	0.30 ± 0.11	0.17	0.71 ± 0.16	1.0 ± 0.30	1.42 ± 0.54

Table 1. (*continued*)

Sample	Lat.	Long.	Locality/description	Sample depth (m)	Radioactivity data			D_{cosmic} (Gy ka^{-1})	Dose rate (Gy ka^{-1})	Palaeodose (Gy)	Age (ka)
					K$_2$O (%)	Th (ppm)	U (ppm)				
948/1	26°31'S	20°36'E	Basal red sands, Twee Riveren–Uppington Hgwy	1.0	1.09 ± 0.04	2.60 ± 0.23	0.60 ± 0.15	0.19	1.37 ± 0.24	37.9 ± 6.40	27.57 ± 6.64
949/2	26°41'S	20°10'E	Wit Pan lunette, near border Namibia–South Africa	1.0	1.17 ± 0.05	2.80 ± 0.31	0.80 ± 0.20	0.18	1.49 ± 0.27	2.1 ± 0.11	1.42 ± 0.27
949/3	26°41'S	20°10'E	Wit Pan lunette, near border Namibia–South Africa	1.0	1.11 ± 0.04	3.20 ± 0.23	1.00 ± 0.19	0.22	1.56 ± 0.20	2.1 ± 0.13	1.37 ± 0.20
949/4	26°41'S	20°10'E	Wit Pan lunette, near border Namibia–South Africa	1.0	1.39 ± 0.06	2.60 ± 0.23	0.70 ± 0.16	0.19	1.63 ± 0.27	1.8 ± 0.08	1.10 ± 0.19
949/5	26°41'S	20°10'E	Wit Pan lunette, near border Namibia–South Africa	1.0	1.25 ± 0.05	2.50 ± 0.24	0.80 ± 0.18	0.23	1.58 ± 0.25	1.7 ± 0.07	1.06 ± 0.17
950/1	17°58'S	25°38'E	Chamabondo Vlei, Zambesi National Park, Vic. Falls, Zimbabwe	1.25	0.03 ± 0.00	1.80 ± 0.17	0.60 ± 0.13	0.17	0.47 ± 0.05	17.5 ± 3.40	37.46 ± 8.33
951/1	18°02'S	25°41'E	Chamabondo Vlei, Zambesi National Park, Vic. Falls, Zimbabwe	1.23	0.05 ± 0.00	1.80 ± 0.17	0.70 ± 0.14	0.17	0.51 ± 0.05	16.1 ± 2.30	31.79 ± 5.65
952/1	17°55'S	25°28'E	Kazungula Road, Zambesi National Park, Vic. Falls, Zimbabwe	4.5	0.03 ± 0.00	1.80 ± 0.17	0.70 ± 0.13	0.17	0.49 ± 0.05	37.8 ± 4.60	77.03 ± 12.05
952/2	17°55'S	25°28'E	Kazunguia Road, Zambesi National Park, Vic. Falls, Zimbabwe	3.0	0.03 ± 0.00	1.90 ± 0.18	0.60 ± 0.13	0.17	0.47 ± 0.05	24.6 ± 2.90	51.83 ± 8.33
952/3	17°55'S	25°28'E	Kazungula Road, Zambesi National Park, Vic. Falls, Zimbabwe	1.8	0.03 ± 0.00	1.50 ± 0.17	0.50 ± 0.13	0.18	0.43 ± 0.05	71.0 ± 11.00	164.51 ± 32.07
1003/1	18°35'S	25°54'E	10 km N of Robins Camp, Northern Zimbabwe	1	0.41 ± 0.02	2.3 ± 0.21	0.8 ± 0.13	0.17	0.85 ± 0.09	12.74 ± 1.48	15.07 ± 2.40
1003/2	18°35'S	25°54'E	10 km N of Robins Camp, Northern Zimbabwe	2	0.41 ± 0.02	2.8 ± 0.22	1.1 ± 0.15	0.17	0.96 ± 0.09	22.00 ± 1.92	23.01 ± 2.97
1004/A	19°23'S	26°45'E	Josibamini, Hwange Game Reserve, Zimbabwe	0.5	0.17 ± 0.01	1.0 ± 0.15	0.5 ± 0.10	0.21	0.54 ± 0.06	9.64 ± 2.48	17.94 ± 5.02
1004/B	19°23'S	26°45'E	Josibamini, Hwange Game Reserve, Zimbabwe	1	0.2 ± 0.01	1.3 ± 0.18	0.6 ± 0.10	0.18	0.57 ± 0.06	13.06 ± 2.45	22.85 ± 4.94
1004/C	19°23'S	26°45'E	Josibamini, Hwange Game Reserve, Zimbabwe	1.5	0.2 ± 0.01	1.4 ± 0.24	0.7 ± 0.12	0.16	0.58 ± 0.07	16.18 ± 2.35	27.81 ± 5.37
1004/D	19°23'S	26°45'E	Josibamini, Hwange Game Reserve, Zimbabwe	2	0.17 ± 0.01	1.6 ± 0.24	0.5 ± 0.11	0.15	0.52 ± 0.07	22.23 ± 3.30	42.95 ± 8.64
1004/E	19°23'S	26°45'E	Josibamini, Hwange Game Reserve, Zimbabwe	2.5	0.17 ± 0.01	1.5 ± 0.24	0.8 ± 0.12	0.14	0.57 ± 0.07	24.33 ± 3.50	42.63 ± 7.97
1004/F	19°23'S	26°45'E	Josibamini, Hwange Game Reserve, Zimbabwe	3	0.18 ± 0.01	1.6 ± 0.22	0.7 ± 0.12	0.13	0.55 ± 0.07	25.65 ± 2.78	46.30 ± 7.54

(*continued*)

Table 1. (*continued*)

Sample	Lat.	Long.	Locality/description	Sample depth (m)	Radioactivity data			D_{cosmic} (Gy ka^{-1})	Dose rate (Gy ka^{-1})	Palaeodose (Gy)	Age (ka)
					K_2O (%)	Th (ppm)	U (ppm)				
1004/G	19°23'S	26°45'E	Josibannini, Hwange Game Reserve, Zimbabwe	3.5	0.19 ± 0.01	1.6 ± 0.16	0.7 ± 0.10	0.13	0.56 ± 0.05	21.79 ± 1.84	38.84 ± 5.02
1004/H	19°23'S	26°45'E	Josibannini, Hwange Game Reserve, Zimbabwe	4	0.16 ± 0.01	1.6 ± 0.18	0.7 ± 0.09	0.12	0.53 ± 0.05	27.98 ± 2.94	53.03 ± 7.56
1004/I	19°23'S	26°45'E	Josibannini, Hwange Game Reserve, Zimbabwe	4.5	0.29 ± 0.01	1.5 ± 0.17	0.6 ± 0.09	0.11	0.59 ± 0.07	26.68 ± 3.11	45.53 ± 7.37
1004/J	19°23'S	26°45'E	Josibannini, Hwange Game Reserve, Zimbabwe	5	0.16 ± 0.01	1.9 ± 0.22	0.6 ± 0.11	0.10	0.51 ± 0.06	52.41 ± 5.54	103.38 ± 16.96
1004/K	19°23'S	26°45'E	Josibannini, Hwange Game Reserve, Zimbabwe	5.5	0.17 ± 0.01	1.6 ± 0.17	0.6 ± 0.10	0.10	0.49 ± 0.06	54.65 ± 5.94	111.63 ± 17.58
1004/L	19°23'S	26°45'E	Josibannini, Hwange Game Reserve, Zimbabwe	6	0.21 ± 0.01	1.7 ± 0.17	0.6 ± 0.10	0.09	0.52 ± 0.06	53.39 ± 6.45	101.95 ± 17.15
1005/A	15°51'S	26°56'E	Dopi Pan, Hwange Game Reserve, Zimbabwe	0.5	0.08 ± 0.00	1.2 ± 0.11	0.5 ± 0.07	0.20	0.46 ± 0.03	4.29 ± 0.78	9.23 ± 1.80
1005/B	15°51'S	26°56'E	Dopi Pan, Hwange Game Reserve, Zimbabwe	1	0.03 ± 0.00	1.5 ± 0.15	0.7 ± 0.07	0.18	0.50 ± 0.06	14.14 ± 2.18	28.28 ± 5.53
1005/C	15°51'S	26°56'E	Dopi Pan, Hwange Game Reserve, Zimbabwe	1.5	0.08 ± 0.00	1.6 ± 0.19	0.7 ± 0.11	0.16	0.50 ± 0.05	10.11 ± 2.14	20.09 ± 4.68
1005/D	15°51'S	26°56'E	Dopi Pan, Hwange Game Reserve, Zimbabwe	2	0.08 ± 0.00	1.3 ± 0.19	0.7 ± 0.13	0.14	0.46 ± 0.05	19.35 ± 2.03	41.80 ± 6.61
1005/E	15°51'S	26°56'E	Dopi Pan, Hwange Game Reserve, Zimbabwe	2.5	0.09 ± 0.00	1.5 ± 0.18	1.0 ± 0.12	0.14	0.56 ± 0.05	16.6 ± 1.81	29.85 ± 4.26
1005/F	15°51'S	26°56'E	Dopi Pan, Hwange Game Reserve, Zimbabwe	3	0.09 ± 0.00	1.5 ± 0.16	0.7 ± 0.11	0.13	0.48 ± 0.05	18.9 ± 2.08	39.75 ± 5.90

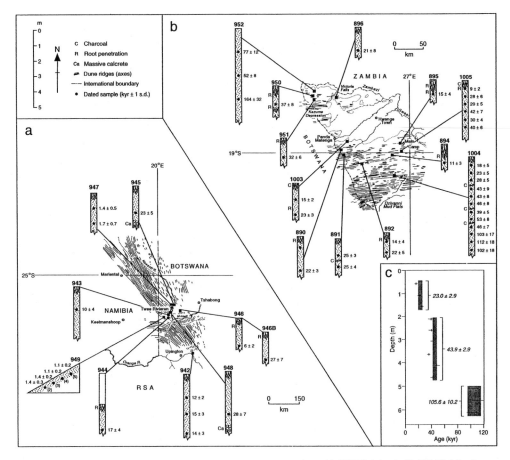

Fig. 6. Summary stratigraphic and chronological data for dune sites: (**a**) SW Kalahari; (**b**) NE Kalahari. (**c**) A summary of optical dates and inferred aeolian depositional phases for site 1004 from the NE Kalahari (weighted average and standard deviations for grouped samples are provided). Note different scales in (a) and (b).

area generally indicate depositional ages in the range 20–10 ka BP. Samples 945/1 and 948/1 from the basal sands at the contact of non-aeolian strata demonstrate that aeolian activity from 22 to 28 ka BP operated to the full depth of the sand sea, precluding the preservation of older dunes. The maximum extent of the Kalahari to the SW is constrained by three optical dates from a dune which invaded the Orange River valley at c. 13.2 ± 1.5 ka BP. Palaeoecological evidence from nearby sites suggests periods of enhanced moisture in the periods 22–16 and 10–6 ka BP (Thackeray & Lee Thorpe 1992) and we thus infer either reduction or cessation of dune activity during these times.

Dune construction during the Holocene appears to have been less intensive, resulting only in localized dune deposits. Mid-Holocene (c. 6 ka BP) aridity is demonstrated from super-

ficial reticulate dunes (site 946) and late Holocene aridity (c. <2 ka BP) from lunette deposition (site 949) and localized disturbance patches (site 947). The timing of the three post-Late Glacial Maximum periods of aridity accord well with gaps in the northern Cape humid chronologies (Partridge *et al.* 1990).

The eastern dune field was extensively sampled in both the number and depths to which the dunes were excavated (Fig. 6). Age estimates are generally in sensible stratigraphic order and sampling pits on dunes within 1 or 2 m of the present land surface indicated two phases of dune activity at c. 30–20 ka BP and c. 15–12 ka BP which are in most cases statistically distinct. The small number of age estimates from the Victoria Falls area suggest that they were formed during the former of these two phases and during earlier periods.

When the dates from sites 1004 and 1005 are grouped into statistically distinct sets, three discrete phases of Pleistocene aeolian activity are recognized at 115–95, 42–38 and 26–20 ka BP, the last phase also being well represented in the linear dunes to the southwest (Fig. 6). The ages demonstrate that dune construction in this area has taken place episodically, with relatively short-lived (5–20 ka) periods of dune development interspersed with extended (20–40 ka) periods of non-deposition. Each depositional phase resulted in the accumulation of between 1 and 2.5 m of sediment. These 'active' depositional phases were presumably punctuated by more humid times during which rainfall was greater, stabilizing dune activity via changing soil and plant ecosystems, and/or wind speed were reduced, prohibiting active sediment transportation. The present period of inactivity appears to have commenced at or near to the Pleistocene–Holocene boundary and only two samples yielded (early) Holocene ages.

In both the NE and SW Kalahari there is evidence of extensive linear dune field construction during the later Quaternary, which was succeeded in the SW by episodes of minor, spatially confined dune emplacement. The record of linear dune development in the NE, where major dune construction periods extend to the Pleistocene–Holocene boundary, is of considerably greater antiquity than that preserved in the SW, and supports our conceptual understanding of the structure of the NE–SW rainfall gradient and related atmospheric conditions.

Evaluating climatic controls on dune mobility

Knowledge of climatic controls during the Late Quaternary have been obtained by means of at least three methods. First, palaeoclimatic indicators of variables such as moisture and temperature have been used to infer, heuristically, the type of circulation that might have produced anomalous conditions in the past. This interpretation is usually based on theoretical knowledge of the sensitivity of the General Circulation to changes in climatic forcing (e.g. Van Zinderen Bakker 1982; Flohn 1984). More recently, General Circulation Models (GCMs) have been used to determine numerically the climates of the past. Such model integrations are currently possible only for static boundary conditions thereby producing snapshots of the past (e.g. Hewitt & Mitchell 1996; Hall & Valdes 1997). Such modelling studies are beset by considerable problems. If an atmosphere-only GCM is used, then sea ice boundaries, SSTs and land surface conditions have to be specified for each grid box, of which there are typically more than 7000. Such data are not available and are unlikely to become available. An alternative is to use a coupled Ocean–Atmosphere GCM whereby the model is able to compute SSTs. Land surface characteristics still have to be specified, however.

Owing to these problems, much of the progress in understanding the climates of the past, particularly in Southern Africa, have occurred through analogue techniques whereby knowledge of the current variability of the climate system is applied to the past. In the case of Southern Africa, much of this analogue work rests on the progress made over the last two decades in understanding summer rainfall variability (Tyson 1986; Mason & Jury 1997).

In the absence of a highly resolved observational record of past atmospheric and oceanic conditions over the Kalahari, we use an approach that is essentially within the analogue mould, but which uses a GCM integration over multidecadal time scales. The overall aim is to understand the large-scale controls on the Kalahari climate as it relates to dune mobilization since these cannot be gained from the very short available observational record. It must be stressed that the GCM is not forced by boundary conditions of any Late Quaternary period. It serves merely to provide a continuous record of current climatic conditions in the Kalahari so that these can be related to broad-scale controls in a mechanistically plausible way, assuming that the GCM's climate itself is physically consistent. In this sense the approach is identical to that used by Cockroft et al. (1987); Tyson & Lindesay (1992); Tyson (1993) and Cohen & Tyson (1995) in their efforts to explain past conditions in Southern Africa, except that we substitute the observational record with a GCM study in order to learn about the climate controls.

We have used the United Kingdom Meteorological Office (UKMO) HADAM2A Atmospheric GCM (resolution 2.5′ lat., 3.75′ long., 19 vertical layers) century-long integrations. These feature the integration of HADAM2A by sea ice and historical SSTs for the period 1903 to 1994. We assume that the model simulation reveals constraints on the circulation in the Kalahari, local or through teleconnections, which are real. This assumption is strengthened by the generally excellent agreement between model and observed mean fields (Gates et al. 1995; Joubert 1997). As stated earlier, present-day dune activity is restricted to localized reactivation only within the most arid core of the

SW Kalahari. Essentially both relatively high levels of precipitation and regionally low wind regimes prohibit widespread dune mobilization.

Our approach has been a two-fold one and acknowledges the importance of contrasting seasonal controls on the two climatic parameters which are critical in facilitating dune activity: We initially sought to identify patterns and factors which influence the variations in summertime rainfall over the period (Stokes *et al.* 1997*b*) and independently compared the data set of regional wind fields (for the 850 hPa surface). In both cases we have first summarized the data sets and then compared them with a zero phase lag to other parameters generated by the AGCM (including SSTs, sea level pressures

(SLPs) and regional wind fields), noting statistically significant correlations and using these to infer large-scale influences. These are summarized separately below.

Patterns of summer rainfall variability over the past century

Empirical Orthogonal Functions (EOFs) of model austral summer (January–March: JFM) rainfall were calculated for the African land area and adjoining oceans using the ensemble average of four runs. An east–west dipole of rainfall, with centres over western Southern Africa and the western Indian Ocean, captures

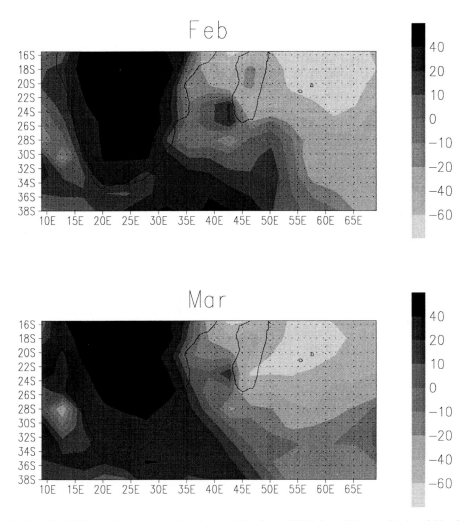

Fig. 7. Model rainfall correlation empirical orthogonal functions (EOFs) from February (top) and March (bottom). Values are correlation coefficients ×100.

260   S. STOKES, R. WASHINGTON & A. PRESTON

82% of rainfall variance of this broad region. This dipole structure has been noted in satellite imagery (Harrison 1986; Tyson 1986) and has been shown to account for about 60% of the variance of monthly rainfall anomalies on the basis of observed satellite-derived rainfall estimates (Washington & Todd 1998). The model results therefore seem to identify real structure. Examples of this dipole structure for the individual summer months of February and March are shown in Fig. 7. The time coefficients of the JFM EOF were correlated with global SSTs. The field shows a large coherent region of significant correlation in the SE Atlantic such that wet (dry) Kalahari conditions are associated with dry (wet) western Indian Ocean conditions, and positive (negative) SST anomalies in the SE Atlantic. Model circulation fields show the strengthening (weakening) of the South Atlantic anticyclone during Kalahari dry (wet) phases. When this analysis is undertaken on fields which have been filtered to exclude variability on time scales of less than eight years, the same features remain. As shown by Harrison (1986), tropical-temperate troughs which have a dipole structure in the Southern Africa region are the most important rainfall-producing system in the subcontinent. The modelling studies combined with the objective satellite analysis suggest that this is so from time scales of days to centuries.

Patterns of winter wind variability in the SW Kalahari over the past century

Using the same model ensemble, an area-averaged (i.e. regional) low-level (850 hPa) wind speed index was created for grid boxes over the SW Kalahari (Fig. 8). While it is not possible to directly translate the regional wind index into a direct record of surface wind flow above the threshold for aeolian sand entrainment, it does provide an alternative means of evaluating wind

variability over the century time scale. The spectrum of this index reveals a low frequency peak at 30.7 years along with a high frequency peak at 2.7 years (Fig. 9). Kalman filtering based on the spectral peaks of the wind speed index identifies two periods of relatively enhanced winds, 1930–1940 and 1960–1970, and minima of regional winter wind speed during the late 1970s and 1980s (Fig. 8). This pattern is not inconsistent with the observational record for the period since the late 1970s as measured at meteorological stations within and adjacent to the SW Kalahari dune field (Bullard et al. 1996). Correlations between the wind speed index and global sea level pressure (SLP) and zonal wind indexes are shown in Fig. 10. A weak but significant positive correlation with SLP over India and Kalahari winds is evident such that a weakened (strengthened) Monsoon is associated with anomalously high (low) SLP southeast of Southern Africa, suggesting the additional importance of the strength and frequency of anomalous ridging anticyclones.

Composites of 850 hPa winter (July–September) winds for calm years in the Kalahari (the five most calm years from the calm extended decade 1975–1987) are shown in Fig. 11. The structure of these anomalies indicates an anomalous cyclone situated over the Kalahari consistent with a weakened continental anticyclone. Over much of the Kalahari these are realized as anomalous southerly to southwesterly winds. The composite divergence anomalies (Fig. 12) for the calm years show a clear convergence anomaly centred on 19°S 19°E, but extending over much of the western Kalahari. In contrast, near-surface wind composites for windy years of a windy decade (five most windy years from 1934 to 1946) indicate an anticyclone anomaly with northerly to northwesterly wind anomalies over much of the Kalahari (Fig. 13). The composite divergence anomalies of these windy years (Fig. 14) show a near-surface divergence

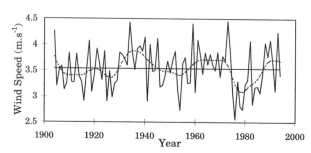

Fig. 8. Area-averaged low-level (850 hPa) wind speed index as created from AGCM data. The raw index was smoothed using an integrated walk Kalman filter (cut off = 24 years).

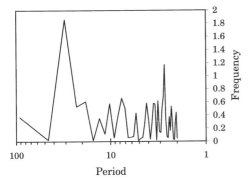

Fig. 9. Fast Fourier transform spectrum of the area-average wind speed index. See text for details.

anomaly extending in a band northwest to southeast over much of the Kalahari. What is clear from these results is that windy years in the Kalahari are associated with an enhanced continental anticyclone, and enhanced near-surface divergence.

Discussion

Our study provides a useful numerical chronology for dune construction within the extensive relict linear dune fields of the NE and SW Kalahari. Past changes in aeolian dynamism must be related both to changes, i.e. reductions, in rainfall intensity in the area, which in turn

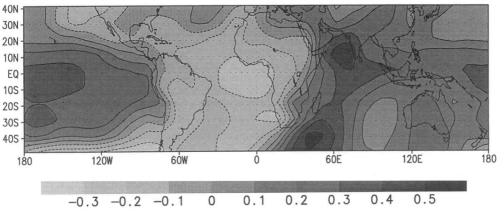

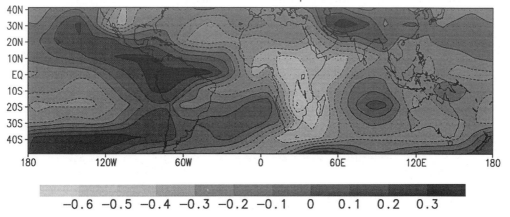

Fig. 10. Example correlation fields between area-averaged SW Kalahari austral winter wind strength and (**a**) sea level pressure, (**b**) zonal (east–west) and (**c**) vector of winds at 850 hPa.

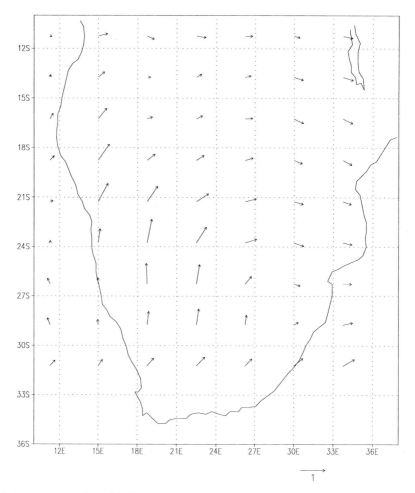

Fig. 11. Wind vector composites of 850 hPa for July–September calm years. Vectors show scale as $1\,m\,s^{-1}$.

relates to the large-scale atmospheric changes limiting summertime convection and increases in regional wind.

The novel approach adopted here, which is a variant of the widely used analogue approach to interpreting climate change, features the use of a GCM to gain insights into the mechanistic controls of both wind and rainfall over the Kalahari. Such an approach is useful in that the data fields are everywhere complete for nearly 100 years. Critical results emerging from this work are that SE Atlantic SSTs strongly influence present-day regional summertime rainfall levels, primarily through the modulation of the main mode of rainfall variability in the Southern Africa–southwest Indian Ocean region, namely a tropical-temperate trough with a dipole structure. This dipole operates on time scales ranging from days to multidecades such

that enhanced (suppressed) rainfall over the interior of Southern Africa is associated with suppressed (enhanced) rainfall over the southwest Indian Ocean. A great deal has been done from the observational record to link rainfall over Southern Africa with SSTs (Mason 1995; Mason & Jury 1997). All this research has necessarily adopted rainfall variability over the Southern African landmass owing to the data constraints of the rain gauge network. This study shows the importance of considering rainfall over both the land and the oceans if the main mode of rainfall variability over the broader region is to be considered; this is possible only with modelling or satellite data. From this it is clear that an east–west variability of rainfall, as expressed by the rainfall dipole, is critically important and yields new insights into the controls on rainfall variability. In addition to

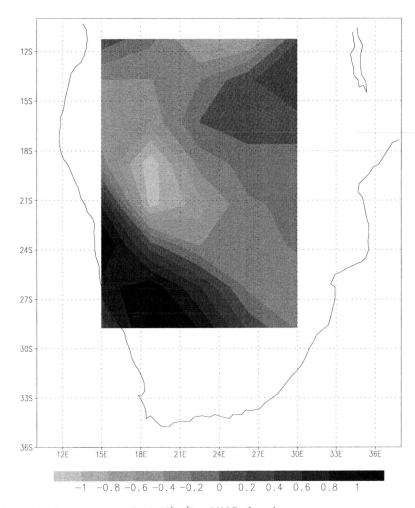

Fig. 12. Composite divergence anomalies ($\times 10^6\,\mathrm{s}^{-1}$) at 850 hPa for calm years.

the moisture balance, kinetic energy available in the winter wind field is modulated such that stronger (weaker) anticyclones over the Kalahari are associated with windier (calmer) conditions. There is some evidence to suggest that the strength of this circulation feature is modulated by the Asian Monsoon.

This approach to analysing the contemporary variability of the Kalahari climate yields useful insights into the mechanistic broad-scale controls on variables crucial to wind and rain. It provides a complete data record of nearly 400 years (four ensemble members each nearly 100 years long) over both land and ocean. In the same way that much has been learned from the analysis of rainfall variability in the observational record from which analogue models of

Late Quaternary change have been constructed for Southern Africa, this approach yields new insights. There are, nonetheless, numerous notes of caution, not least of which is that the model, however perfect, is not the real world. The insights offered can, however, be tested against the ever expanding satellite and conventional observational records.

Equipped with these mechanistic insights we may begin to consider the aeolian record. Our data indicate that widespread aridity and linear dune emplacement occurred in the eastern dune system during at least three periods since the last interglacial at c. 95–115, 38–42 and 20–26 ka BP; additionally, some localized reworking has taken place since that time. The arid phases are short-lived (5–20 ka) in comparison to

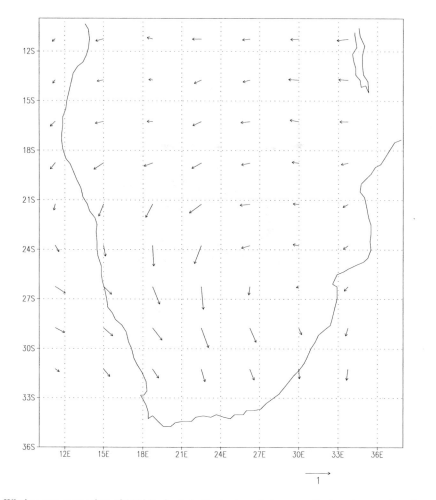

Fig. 13. Wind vector composites of 850 hPa for July–September windy years. Vectors show scale as $1\,\mathrm{m\,s^{-1}}$.

the intervening humid periods (20–40 ka) and appear to be restricted almost exclusively to pre-Holocene times.

Recent studies by (Little *et al.* 1997*a*, *b*) have provided a detailed record of palaeo-SSTs in the adjacent southeastern Atlantic Ocean over the same period which they relate to the changing position of oceanic convergence zones. They further demonstrated that such changes are tele-connected to equatorial Atlantic temperature seasonality, trade wind intensity and zonality, and high latitude palaeoclimates. We consider it likely that past changes in SE Atlantic SSTs may have likewise influenced regional aridity. Little and co-workers identified nine periods of cold SE Atlantic SSTs and enhanced upwelling during the past 140 ka in the SE Atlantic with an average spacing of 10 ka during marine iso-

tope stages (MIS) 2–4 and longer (*c.* 20 ka) spacing during MIS 5. They termed these cold periods PS events, and related them to times of enhanced trade winds and reduced rainfall across Southern Africa. These were also correlated, incorporating a 2–3 ka south–north phase lag, with Heinrich events and Dansgaard–Oeschger cycles identified respectively in the northern Atlantic Ocean and Greenland ice cap (Little *et al.* 1997*b*). Four of the five most extreme of these PS events compare closely in duration and timing to the identified periods of linear dune activity in the northeastern Kalahari.

Furthermore, it is possible to compare monsoon upwelling and other indexes of the strength (or weakness) of the Asian monsoon from Indian Ocean sediments to reconstruct a record of past regional winter wind strength. Prell &

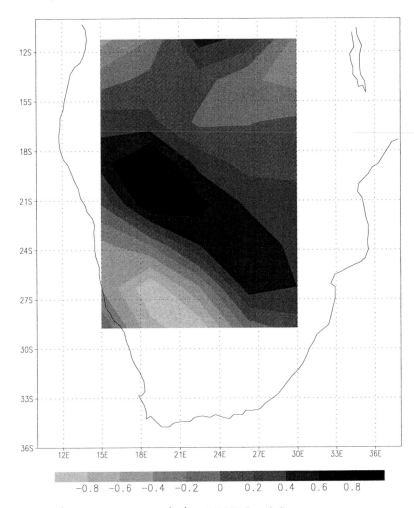

Fig. 14. Composite divergence anomalies ($\times 10^6 \, \text{s}^{-1}$) at 850 hPa for windy years.

Van Campo (1986) undertook such an exercise for a 140 ka time series and identified monsoon intensity maxima (SW Kalahari wind speed minima) primarily during interglacial periods. Their record of monsoonal minima (SW Kalahari wind speed maxima) includes events at 115, 90, 75–60 and 50–12 ka BP, which are broadly comparable to the periods of widespread aeolian reactivation identified by the optical dating studies. Coherence of both Asian monsoonal minima and low SE Atlantic SSTs would provide the required combination of desiccation and increased wind energy required to initiate dune reactivation across the Mega Kalahari.

Given the sensitivity of the current climatic regime of the Kalahari, as determined by numerical simulation, it seems reasonable that changes in aridity within the NE Kalahari are closely related to global-scale changes in glacial phase palaeoclimates which may be collectively caused by changes in equatorial and mid-latitude oceanic and atmospheric processes (Little *et al.* 1997*b*). In the case of the Kalahari, neither the 'passive Africa–high latitude forcing' nor the 'active Africa–precessional forcing' models account for the observed arid–humid transitions. Instead, a model which identifies the Southern African continental landmass playing a passive role, but in turn being strongly influenced by mid- to low latitude, southern hemisphere oceanic–atmospheric processes and Asian monsoonal outflow may be more appropriate.

While much of the upper few metres of the aeolian landscape preserved within the NE Kalahari was emplaced or reworked during the later portion of the last glacial period (*c*. 20–10 ka BP) we note that the period spanning *c*. 50–40 ka BP is more extensively preserved at depth. Conversely, latest Pleistocene dune reactivation in the SW Kalahari is superimposed on linear dune plinths emplaced at around 28–22 ka BP. Our data both support previously inferred periods of aeolian activity in the southwest Kalahari (Lancaster 1989), and identify additional older phases of activity. The three main ergs of the Kalahari have been active at different times during the later Quaternary and this activity has been preserved in a spatially variable manner. These findings in part reflect the location of the field area studied. In the case of the eastern dune system, being positioned at the NE margin of the SW–NE regional rainfall gradient, away from the core of aridity, both reduces the likelihood of long-lived aridity causing wholesale erosion and reworking of pre-existent dunes, and enhances the extent of pedogenesis and dune stabilization during humid periods. These two factors indicate that the linear dune system of the NE Kalahari is a sensitive archive of long-term changes in moisture balance. The southwestern dune system in contrast provides a more highly resolved record of subtle dune reactivations over shorter time scales which may not be reflected across the entire desert system.

Conclusions

We have described a direct chronology of the linear dunes preserved in the NE and SW Kalahari. Our chronology is based on the application of optical dating to sand-sized quartz separates from the dune bodies. At least four phases of dune activity are identified in the NE Kalahari (*c*. 115–95, 46–41, 26–20 and post-20 ka BP). In contrast, the record of aeolian deposition within the SW core of the Kalahari is shorter in duration (<30 ka). This shortness of record reflects the tendency towards total reworking of the dune system rather than preservation of a long-term record at the desert margin. Dune reactivation and/or deposition occurred in the SW Kalahari *c*. 27–20, 14–10, 6 and less than 2 ka BP, the latter phase being restricted to lunette deposition at pan marginal locations.

In order to explain the timing of dune reactivation at both the core and margins of the NE–SW transect across the Mega Kalahari, we have interrogated the output of an AGCM covering the last century. We conclude that phases of aeolian deposition and aridity may be linked to changes in SE Atlantic SSTs, which may in turn exert a strong influence on late Quaternary global climate changes, and changes

(reductions) in either the intensity of Asian monsoonal outflow and/or anticyclonic ridging in the southern Indian Ocean southeast of the Southern African landmass. Aeolian deposition during full interglacial conditions has not been identified (i.e., during Holocene or MIS 5e). Vertical accretion of the dunes during depositional periods was rapid, and punctuated by extended periods of inactivity which we correlate with humid periods. The timing of these humid episodes is in agreement with previous studies in the Mega Kalahari that have frequently focused upon direct determination of the timing of wetter episodes in the Pleistocene. Linear dune ridges provide a powerful and extended archive of aeolian activity which may be broadly correlated with regional aridity.

Financial assistance for this project was provided by the Leakey Foundation, the Royal Society, and the Trapnell Fund for Environmental Research in Africa. B. Adder, L. Thomas, P. Ngwenya, T. Tshuma and J. Klimowicz are thanked for field assistance. Professors M. S. Tite, M. J. Aitken and D. S. G. Thomas are thanked for advice and support. Images of the NCEP Reanalysis data were made available by the NOAA-CIRES Climate Diagnosis Center, Boulder, Colorado from their Web site at 'http://www.cdc.noaa.govt'.

References

AITKEN, M. J. 1985. *Thermoluminescence Dating*. Academic, London.
——1989. Luminescence dating: a guide for non-specialists. *Archaeometry*, **31**(2), 147–159.
——1992. Optical dating. *Quaternary Science Reviews*, **11**, 127–131.
—— & ALLDRED, J. C. 1972. The assessment of error limits in thermoluminescent dating. *Archaeometry*, **14**, 257–267.
BLOMENDAL, J. & DE MENOCAL, P. 1989. Evidence for a change in the periodicity of tropical climate cycles at 2.4 Myr from whole core magnetic susceptibility measurements. *Nature*, **342**, 897–900.
BOND, G. 1948. The direction of origin of the Kalahari sand of Southern Rhodesia. *Geological Magazine*, **85**(5), 305–313.
BREED, C. S., FRYBERGER, S. G., ANDREWS, S., MCCAULEY, C., LENNARTZ, F., GEBEL, D. & HORSTMAN, K. 1979. Regional studies of sand seas, using Landsat (ERTS) imagery. *In*: MCKEE, E. D. (ed.) *A Study of Global Sand Seas*, Vol. I. United States Printing Office, 305–397.
BULLARD, J. E., THOMAS, D. S. G., LIVINGSTONE, I. & WIGGS, G. F. S. 1995. Analysis of linear sand dune morphological variability, southwestern Kalahari Desert. *Geomorphology*, **11**, 189–203.
—, —, — & ——1996. Wind energy variations in the southwestern Kalahari desert and implications for linear dunefield activity. *Earth Surface Processes and Landforms*, **21**, 263–278.

CHARLES, C. D., LYNCH-STEIGLITZ, J., NINNEMANN, U. S. & FAIRBANKS, R. G. 1996. Climate connections between the hemispheres revealed by deep-sea sediment core/ice core correlations. *Earth and Planetary Science Letters*, **142**, 19–27.

COCKROFT, M. J., WILKINSON, M. J. & TYSON, P. D. 1987. The application of a present-day climatic model to the late Quaternary in southern Africa. *Climate Change*, **10**(2), 161–181.

COHEN, A. L. & TYON, P. D. 1995. Sea-surface temperature fluctuations during the Holocene off the south coast of Africa: Implications for terrestrial climate and rainfall. *The Holocene*, **5**(3), 304–312.

DE MENOCAL, P. B., RUDDIMAN, W. F. & POKRAS, E. M. 1993. Influences of high-and low-latitude processes on African terrestrial climate: Pleistocene eolian records from equatorial Atlantic ocean drilling program site 663. *Paleoceanography*, **8**(2), 209–242.

FLINT, R. F. & BOND, G. 1968. Pleistocene sand ridges and pans in Western Rhodesia. *Geological Society of America Bulletin*, **79**, 299–314.

FLOHN, H. 1984. Climate evolution in the southern hemisphere and the equatorial region during the Late Cenozoic. *In*: VOGEL, J. C. (ed.) *Late Cenozoic Palaeoclimates of the Southern Hemisphere*. Balkema, Rotterdam, 5–20.

FRYBERGER, S. G. & DEAN, G. 1979. Dune forms and wind regime. *In*: MCKEE, E. (ed.) *A Study of Global Sand Seas*, 137–169.

GASSE, F. 1994. Lacustrine diatoms for reconstructing past hydrology and climate. NATO ISI Series (Long-term Climatic Variations), **122**, 335–369.

——, TEHET, R., DURAND, A., GIBERT, E. & FONTES, J.-C. 1990. The arid–humid transition in the Sahara and the Sahel during the last deglaciaton. *Nature*, **346**, 141–146.

GATES, W. L., HENDERSON-SELLERS, A., BOER, G. J. *et al.* 1995. Climate models – evaluation. *In*: HOUGHTON, J., MEIRA FILHO, L. G., CALLANDER, B. A., HARRIS, N., KATTENBERG, A. & MASKELL, K. (eds) *Climate Change 1995 – The Science of Climate Change*. Cambridge University, 229–284.

GROVE, A. T. 1969. Landforms and climatic change in the Kalahari and Ngamiland. *Geographical Journal*, **135**(2), 91–212.

HALL, N. M. J. & VALDES, P. J. 1997. A GCM simulation of the climate 6000 years ago. *Journal of Climate*, **10**(1), 3–17.

HARRISON, M. S. J. 1986. *A synoptic climatology of South African rainfall variations*. PhD thesis, University of Witwatersrand.

HEINE, K. 1982. The main stages of the late Quaternary evolution of the Kalahari region, southern Africa. *Palaeoecology of Africa*, **15**, 53–76.

HEWITT, C. D. & MITCHELL, J. F. B. 1996. GCM simulations of the climate of 6 kyr BP: mean changes and interdecadal variability. *Journal of Climate*, **9**(12), 3505–3529.

HUNTLEY, D. J., GODFREY-SMITH, D. I. & THEWALT, M. L. W. 1985. Optical dating of sediments. *Nature*, **313**(5998), 105–107.

JOUBERT, A. 1997. Simulation by the Atmospheric Model Intercomparison Project of the atmospheric circulation over southern Africa. *International Journal of Climatology*, **17**, 1129–1154.

KALNAY, E., KANAMITSU, M., KISTLER, R. *et al.* 1996. The NCEP/NCAR 40-year Reanalysis project. *Bulletin of the American Meteorological Society*, **77**, 437–471.

KROPELIN, S. & SOULIE-MARSCHE, I. 1991. Charophyte remains from Wadi Howar as evidence for deep Mid-Holocene freshwater lakes in the eastern Sahara of northwest Sudan. *Quaternary Research*, **36**, 210–223.

LANCASTER, N. 1988. Development of linear dunes in the southwest Kalahari, southern Africa. *Journal of Arid Environments*, **14**, 233–244.

——1989. Late Quaternary palaeoenvironments of the southwestem Kalahari. *Palaeogeography, Palaeoclimatology, Palaeoecology*, **70**, 367–376.

——1990. Palaeoclimatic evidence from sand seas. *Palaeogeography, Palaeoclimatology, Palaeoecology*, **176**, 279–290.

——1995. *Geomorphology of Desert Dunes*. Routledge, London.

LITTLE, M. G., SCHNEIDER, R. R., KROON, D., PRICE, B., BICKERT, T. & WEFER, G. 1997a. Rapid palaeoceanographic changes in the Benguela Upwelling System for the last 160,000 years as indicated by abundances of planktonic foraminifera. *Palaeogeography, Palaeoclimatology, Palaeoecology*, **130**.

——, ——, PRICE, N. B., SUMMERHAYES, C. P. & SEGL, M. 1997b. Trade wind forcing of upwelling, seasonality, and Heinrich events as a response to sub-Milankovitch climate variability. *Palaeoceanography*, **12**, 568–576.

MASON, S. J. 1995. Sea surface temperature – South African rainfall associations 1910–1989. *International Journal of Climatology*, **15**, 119–135.

—— & JURY, M. R. 1997. Climate change and interannual variability over southern Africa: a reflection on underlying processes. *Progress in Physical Geography*, **21**, 24–50.

PARKIN, D. W. & SHACKLETON, N. J. 1973. Trade wind and temperature correlations down a deep sea core off the Saharan coast. *Nature*, **245**, 251–253.

PARTRIDGE, T. C., AVERY, D. M., BOTHA, G. A. *et al.* 1990. Late Pleistocene and Holocene climatic change in Southern Africa. *South African Journal of Science*, **86**, 302–306.

PETIT-MAIRE, N. 1993. Past global climatic changes and the tropical arid/semi-arid belt in the North of Africa. *Geoscientific Research in Northeast Africa*. Balkema, Rotterdam, 551–560.

—— & RISER, J. 1981. Holocene lake deposits and palaeoenvironments in Central Sahara, Northeastern Mali. *Palaeogeography, Palaeoclimatology, Palaeoecology*, **35**, 45–61.

PRELL, W. L. & VAN CAMPO, E. 1986. Coherent response of Arabian Sea upwelling and pollen transport to late Quaternary monsoonal winds. *Nature*, **323**, 526–529.

RITCHIE, J. C., EYLES, C. H., & VANCE HAYNES, C. 1985. Sediment and pollen evidence for an early

to mid-Holocene humid period in the eastern
Sahara. *Nature*, **314**, 352–355.
SARNTHEIN, M., TETZLAFF, G., KOOPMANN, B.,
    WOLTER, K. & PFLAUMANN, U. 1981. Glacial and
    inter-glacial wind regimes over the eastern sub-
    tropical Atlantic and North-West Africa. *Nature*,
    293, 193–197.
SHAW, P. A., COOKE, H. J. & THOMAS, D. S. G. 1988.
    Recent advances in the study of Quaternary
    landforms in Botswana. *Southern African Society
    for Quaternary Research*, **19**, 15–26.
——— & THOMAS, D. S. G. 1996. The Quaternary
    palaeoenvironmental history of the Kalahari,
    Southern Africa. *Journal of Arid Environments*,
    32, 9–22.
SMITH, B. W., RHODES, E. J., STOKES, S., & SPOONER,
    N. A. 1990. The optical dating of sediments using
    quartz. *Radiation Protection Dosimetry*, **34**(1/4),
    75–78.
STOKES, S. 1994. *Optical dating of selected aeolian
    sediments from the southwestern United States*.
    DPhil thesis, Oxford University.
———, THOMAS, D. S. G. & SHAW, P. A. 1997a. New
    chronological evidence for the nature and timing
    of linear dune development in the southwest
    Kalahari Desert. *Geomorphology*, **20**, 81–93.
———, ——— & WASHINGTON, R. 1997b. Multiple
    episodes of aridity in southern Africa since the
    last interglacial. *Nature*, **388**, 154–158.
STREET, F. A. & GROVE, A. T. 1976. Environmental
    and climatic implications of late Quaternary lake-
    level fluctuations in Africa. *Nature*, **261**, 385–390.
STREET-PERROTT, F. A. 1994. Palaeo-perspectives:
    changes in terrestrial ecosystems. *Ambio*, **23**(1),
    37–43.
———, MARCHAND, D. S., ROBERTS, N. & HARRISON,
    S. P. 1989. Global lake-level variations from
    18,000 to 0 years ago: a palaeoclimatic analy-
    sis. *Tropical Palaeoenvironments Research Group*,
    19–31.
THACKERAY, J. F. & LEE THORPE, J. A. 1992. Isotopic
    analysis of equid teeth from Wonderweek Cave,
    Northern Cape Province, South Africa. *Palaeo-
    geography, Palaeoclimatology, Palaeoecology*, **99**,
    141–150.
THOMAS, D. S. G. 1983. Ancient ergs of the former
    arid zones of Zimbabwe, Zambia and Angola.
    *Transactions of the Institute of British Geogra-
    phers*, **9**, 75–88.

———1984. *Late Quaternary environmental change in
    central southern Africa with particular reference to
    extensions of the arid zone*. DPhil thesis, Oxford
    University.
——— & SHAW, P. A. 1991a. *The Kalahari Environment*.
    Cambridge University.
——— & ———1991b. 'Relict' desert dune systems: inter-
    pretations and problems. *Journal of Arid Environ-
    ments*, **20**, 1–14.
———, STOKES, S. & O'CONNOR, P. W. 1997a. Late
    Quaternary aridity in the southwestern Kalahari
    Desert: New contributions from OSL dating of
    aeolian deposits: northern Cape Province, South
    Africa. *In*: GLENNIE, K. W. & AL ASHRAN, M. A.
    (eds) *Geology of Quaternary Desert Margins*.
    Balkema, Rotterdam, 245–260.
———, ——— & SHAW, P. A. 1997b. Holocene aeolian
    activity in the southwestern Kalahari Desert,
    southern Africa: Significance and relationship to
    late-Pleistocene dune-building events. *The Holo-
    cene*, **7**(3), 273–281.
TYSON, P. D. 1986. *Climate Change and Variability in
    Southern Africa*. Oxford University Press, Cape
    Town.
———1993. Recent developments in the modelling of the
    future climate of southern Africa. *South African
    Journal of Science*, **89**, 494–505.
——— & LINDESAY, J. A. 1992. The climate of the last
    2000 years in southern Africa. *The Holocene*, **2**(3),
    271–278.
VAN CAMPO, E. & GASSE, F. 1993. Pollen- and diatom-
    inferred climatic and hydrological changes in
    Sumxi Co Basin (Western Tibet) since 13,000
    yr B.P. *Quaternary Research*, **39**, 300–313.
VAN ZINDEREN BAKKER, E. M. 1982. African
    palaeoenvironments 18000 years BP. *Palaeoecol-
    ogy of Africa*, **15**, 77–99.
WARREN, A. 1970. Dune trends and their implications
    in the Central Sudan. *Zeitschrift für Geomorpho-
    logie*, **10**, 154–180.
WASHINGTON, R. & TODD, M. 1998. The structure of
    tropical-temperate troughs in daily rainfall esti-
    mates over southern Africa and the southwest
    Indian Ocean. *International Journal of Climatol-
    ogy*.
WIGGS, G. F. S., THOMAS, D. S. G., BULLARD, J. E.
    & LIVINGSTONE, I. 1995. Dune mobility and
    vegetation cover in the southwest Kalahari
    desert. *Earth Surface Processes and Landforms*,
    20, 515–529.

Index